# NUMERICAL MATHEMATICAL ANALYSIS

# NUMERICAL MATHEMATICAL ANALYSIS

BY

JAMES B. SCARBOROUGH, Ph.D.

ASSOCIATE PROFESSOR OF MATHEMATICS
AT THE U. S. NAVAL ACADEMY

BALTIMORE: THE JOHNS HOPKINS PRESS
LONDON: HUMPHREY MILFORD
OXFORD UNIVERSITY PRESS
1930

Composed, Printed and Bound by
The Collegiate Press
George Banta Publishing Company
Menasha, Wisconsin

*To the memory*
*of my son*

JAMES BLAINE SCARBOROUGH, JR.
(1919–1927)

# PREFACE

Applied mathematics comes down ultimately to numerical results, and the student of any branch of applied mathematics will do well to supplement his usual mathematical equipment with a definite knowledge of the numerical side of mathematical analysis. He should, in particular, be able to estimate the reliability of any numerical result he may arrive at. The object of this book is to set forth in a systematic manner and as clearly as possible the most important principles, methods, and processes used for obtaining numerical results; and also methods and means for estimating the accuracy of such results. The book is concerned only with fundamental principles and processes, and is not a treatise on computation. For this reason little attention is paid to computation forms, the assumption being that the reader who has much computation of a particular kind to do will be able to devise his own form.

The plan of treatment followed throughout the book may be briefly stated as follows: Each major subject or topic is introduced by a short statement of "what it is all about." Then follows a brief statement of the underlying theory of the subject under consideration. With this theory as a basis, the processes and formulas are then developed in the simplest and most direct manner. Formulas and methods for checking or estimating the accuracy of results are also worked out wherever possible. The reader is then shown just *how to use* the formulas and processes developed, by applying them to a variety of examples. Finally, the limitations of the formulas and the pitfalls connected with the processes are carefully pointed out by means of appropriate examples. Notes and remarks are also added wherever they will throw further light on the subjects under consideration.

The treatment of all topics has been made as elementary as was consistent with soundness, and in some instances the explanations may seem unnecessarily detailed. For such detailed explanations no apology is offered, as the book is meant to be understood with a minimum of effort on the part of the reader. Moreover, experience in teaching certain topics has shown that even a good student must receive considerable assistance from teacher, textbook, or some other source. I have tried everywhere to clear up the difficulties before the student meets them, so that no teacher or other source of information will be needed. In order to make the book everywhere as readable as possible I have purposely refrained from using notations peculiar to certain subjects, and from employing symbolic methods and divided differences in deriving the standard formulas of interpolation. A knowledge of calculus to the extent of the usual first course is all that is needed for the understanding of anything in the book.

The more important formulas throughout the book are numbered in heavy black type to distinguish them from those of less importance.

The worker who is to obtain numerical results with a minimum of effort must provide himself with every possible aid for lessening the labor of his task. In addition to such aids as slide rules, computing machines, and logarithmic tables, the computer will find that Barlow's tables of squares, cubes, etc., and the Smithsonian Mathematical Tables are practically indispensable. Crelle's "Calculating Tables," Jahnke and Emde's "Funktionentafeln," and Jordan's "Opus Palatinum" (tables of natural sines and cosines to seven decimal places) will also prove their worth in many instances.

In the preparation of the book I have consulted the writings of the majority of previous writers on the subjects treated, and am indebted to many of them for ideas and methods; but my greatest debt is to the writings of the late and great Carl Runge, who undoubtedly contributed more to numerical mathematical analysis than any other man since Gauss. References to the works of other writers will be found here and there in the text and in footnotes.

It is a pleasure to record my thanks to the U. S. Naval Institute for permission to use certain copyrighted material which I originally prepared for *Engineering Mathematics* (1925, 1926); to Dr. L. M. Kells, of the U. S. Naval Academy, for helpful criticism on parts of the manuscript; and to the Johns Hopkins Press and the George Banta Publishing Company for their hearty cooperation in meeting my wishes concerning the make-up and publication of the book.

J. B. SCARBOROUGH

*Annapolis, Md.*
*November, 1930*

# CONTENTS

## CHAPTER I

### THE ACCURACY OF APPROXIMATE CALCULATIONS

## CHAPTER II

### INTERPOLATION

#### DIFFERENCES.  NEWTON'S FORMULAS OF INTERPOLATION

## CHAPTER III

### INTERPOLATION

#### CENTRAL-DIFFERENCE FORMULAS

## CHAPTER IV

### INTERPOLATION
#### LAGRANGE'S FORMULA.  INVERSE INTERPOLATION

## CHAPTER V

### THE ACCURACY OF INTERPOLATION FORMULAS

## CHAPTER VI

### INTERPOLATION WITH TWO INDEPENDENT VARIABLES TRIGONOMETRIC INTERPOLATION

## CHAPTER VII

### NUMERICAL DIFFERENTIATION AND INTEGRATION
#### I.  NUMERICAL DIFFERENTIATION

# CHAPTER X

## GRAEFFE'S ROOT-SQUARING METHOD FOR SOLVING ALGEBRAIC EQUATIONS

# CHAPTER XI

## THE NUMERICAL SOLUTION OF DIFFERENTIAL EQUATIONS

### THE METHOD OF SUCCESSIVE APPROXIMATIONS

# CHAPTER XII

## CONVERGENCE AND ACCURACY OF THE ITERATION PROCESS

# CHAPTER XIII

## OTHER METHODS FOR THE NUMERICAL SOLUTION OF DIFFERENTIAL EQUATIONS

## CHAPTER XIV

### THE NORMAL LAW OF ERROR AND THE PRINCIPLE OF LEAST SQUARES

## CHAPTER XV

### THE PRECISION OF MEASUREMENTS

## CHAPTER XVI

### EMPIRICAL FORMULAS

## CHAPTER XVII

## HARMONIC ANALYSIS OF EMPIRICAL FUNCTIONS

# NUMERICAL MATHEMATICAL
## ANALYSIS

# NUMERICAL MATHEMATICAL ANALYSIS

## CHAPTER I

## THE ACCURACY OF APPROXIMATE CALCULATIONS

**1. Introduction.** The art of computation is dealt with to some extent in arithmetic, but the ordinary school arithmetics fail to give all the ideas and methods the practical computer needs. These arithmetics work only with *exact* numbers and say nothing about computation with numbers which are correct to only a few figures. The result of such teaching is that the student gets into the habit of making all computations as long as possible, or else, if the labor seems too great, cuts down some of the numbers to two or three figures and then gives his results to as many figures as possible. This habit usually stays with him throughout life and frequently causes him to get six-figure results from three-figure data.

Now, as a matter of fact, the numerical data used in solving the problems of everyday life are not exact, and the numbers expressing such data are therefore not exact numbers. They are mere approximations, true usually to two, three, or more figures.

Not only are the data of practical problems usually approximate, but sometimes the methods and processes by which the desired result is to be found are also approximate. An approximate calculation is one which involves approximate data, approximate methods, or both.

It is therefore evident that the error in a computed result may be due to one or both of two sources: errors in the data and errors of calculation. Errors of the first type cannot be remedied, but those of the second type can usually be made as small as we please. Thus, when such a number as $\pi$ is replaced by its approximate value in a computation, we can decrease the error due to the approximation by taking $\pi$ to as many figures as desired, and similarly in most other cases. We shall therefore assume in this chapter that the calculations are always carried out in such a manner as to make the errors of calculation negligible.

Nearly all numerical calculations are in some way approximate, and the aim of the computer should be to obtain results consistent with the data with a minimum of labor. The object of the present chapter is to set forth some basic ideas and methods relating to approximate calculations and to give methods for estimating the accuracy of the results obtained.

1

**2. Definitions.** An approximate number is one which differs slightly from the exact number for which it stands.* Thus, 1.4142 is an approximate number when it stands for $\sqrt{2}$. Likewise, 3.1416 is an approximate number when it is taken as the numerical value of $\pi$.

A number is approximated *by defect*† when the approximate number is *less* than the exact number; and it is approximated *by excess* when the approximate number is *greater* than the exact number.

A *significant figure* is any one of the digits 1, 2, 3, $\cdots$ 9; and 0 is a significant figure except when it is used to fix the decimal point or to fill the places of unknown or discarded digits. Thus, in the number 0.00263 the significant figures are 2, 6, 3; the zeros are used merely to fix the decimal point and are therefore not significant. In the number 3809, however, all the digits, including the zero, are significant figures. In a number like 46300 there is nothing in the number as written to show whether or not the zeros are significant figures. The ambiguity can be removed by writing the number in one of the forms $4.63 \times 10^4$, $4.630 \times 10^4$, or $4.6300 \times 10^4$, the number of significant figures being indicated by the factor at the left.

To *round off* or simply *round* a number is to retain a certain number of digits, *counted from the left*, and drop the others. Thus, to round off $\pi$ to three, four, five, and six figures, respectively, we have 3.14, 3.142, 3.1416, 3.14159. Numbers are rounded off so as to cause the least possible error. This is attained by rounding according to the following rule:

To round off a number to $n$ significant figures discard all digits to the right of the $n$th place. If the discarded number is less than half a unit in the $n$th place, leave the $n$th digit unchanged; if the discarded number is greater than half a unit in the $n$th place, add 1 to the $n$th digit. If the discarded number is *exactly* half a unit in the $n$th place, leave the $n$th digit unaltered if it is an even number, but increase it by 1 if it is an odd number; in other words, round off so as to leave the $n$th digit an *even* number in such cases.

The following numbers are rounded off according to the above rule:

$3.65 \mid 43 = 3.65, \ 0.497 \mid 81 = 0.498, \ 22.6 \mid 5 = 22.6, \ 1.73 \mid 5 = 1.74.$

The errors due to rounding are largely neutralized when the rule is followed consistently.

* Some readers may object to the term "approximate number" and insist that one should always say "approximate value" of a number. The shorter term, however, is less cumbrous, is perfectly definite as defined above, and reminds us by its very name that it stands for the approximate value of a number. It has been used in this sense by no less an authority than Jules Tannery in his *Leçons d'Arithmetique*.

† The word "defect" as here used means *deficiency*—the opposite of excess.

When a number has been rounded off according to the rule stated above, it is said to be *correct to n significant figures.*

**3. Absolute, Relative, and Percentage Errors.** The *absolute error* of a number, measurement, or calculation is the numerical difference between the true value of the quantity and its approximate value as given, or obtained by measurement or calculation. The *relative error* is the absolute error divided by the true value of the quantity. The *percentage error* is 100 times the relative error. For example, let $Q$ represent the true value of some quantity. If $\Delta Q$ is the absolute error of an approximate value of $Q$, then

$\Delta Q/Q =$ relative error of the approximate quantity.

$100\Delta Q/Q =$ percentage error of the approximate quantity.

If a number is correct to $n$ significant figures, it is evident that its absolute error can not be greater than half a unit in the $n$th place. For example, if the number 4.629 is correct to four figures, its absolute error is not greater than $0.001 \times \frac{1}{2} = 0.0005$.

*Remark.* It is to be noted that relative and percentage errors are independent of the unit of measurement, whereas absolute errors are expressed in terms of the unit used.

**4. Relation between Relative Error and the Number of Significant Figures.** The belief is widespread, even in scientific circles, that the accuracy of a measurement or of a computed result is indicated by the number of decimals required to express it. This belief is erroneous, for the accuracy if a result is indicated by the number of *significant figures* required to express it. The true index of the accuracy of a measurement or of a calculation is the relative error. For example, if the diameter of a 2-inch steel shaft is measured to the nearest thousandth of an inch the result is less accurate than the measurement of a mile of railroad track to the nearest foot. For although the absolute errors in the two measurements are 0.0005 inch and 6 inches, respectively, the relative errors are $0.0005/2 = 1/4000$ and $1/10560$. Hence in the measurement of the shaft we make an error of one part in 4000, whereas in the case of the railroad we make an error of one part in 10560. The latter measurement is clearly the more accurate, even though its absolute error is 12000 times as great.

The relation between the relative error and the number of correct figures is given by the following fundamental theorem:

*Theorem I. If the first significant figure of a number is k, and the number is correct to n significant figures, then the relative error is less than $1/(k \times 10^{n-1})$.*

Before giving a literal proof of this theorem we shall first show that it holds for several numbers picked at random.  Henceforth we shall denote absolute and relative errors of numbers by the symbols $E_a$ and $E_r$, respectively.

*Example 1.*  Let us suppose that the number 864.32 is correct to five significant figures.  Then $k=8$, $n=5$, and $E_a \leqq 0.01 \times \frac{1}{2} = 0.005$.  For the relative error we have

$$E_r \leqq \frac{0.005}{864.32 - 0.005} = \frac{5}{864320 - 5} = \frac{1}{2 \times 86432 - 1}$$

$$= \frac{1}{2(86432 - \frac{1}{2})} < \frac{1.}{2 \times 8 \times 10^4} < \frac{1}{8 \times 10^4}.$$

Hence the theorem holds here.

*Example 2.*  Next, let us consider the number 369230.  Assuming that the last digit (the zero) is written merely to fill the place of a discarded digit and is therefore not a significant figure, we have $k=3$, $n=5$, and $E_a \leqq 10 \times \frac{1}{2} = 5$.  Then

$$E_r \leqq \frac{5}{369230 - 5} = \frac{1}{2 \times 36923 - 1} = \frac{1}{2(36923 - \frac{1}{2})}$$

$$< \frac{1}{2 \times 3 \times 10^4} < \frac{1}{3 \times 10^4}.$$

*Example 3.*  Finally, suppose the number 0.0800 is correct to three significant figures.  Then $k=8$, $n=3$, $E_a \leqq 0.0001 \times \frac{1}{2} = 0.00005$, and

$$E_r \leqq \frac{0.00005}{0.0800 - 0.00005} = \frac{5}{8000 - 5} = \frac{1}{1600 - 1}$$

$$= \frac{1}{2(800 - \frac{1}{2})} < \frac{1}{8 \times 10^2}.$$

It is to be noted that in this example the relative error is not certainly less than $1/(2k \times 10^{n-1})$, as was the case in Examples 1 and 2 above.

To prove the theorem generally, let

$$N = \text{any number (exact value),}$$
$$n = \text{number of correct significant figures,}$$
$$m = \text{number of correct decimal places.}$$

Three cases must be distinguished, namely $m < n$, $m = n$, and $m > n$.

*Case 1.*  $m < n$.  Here the number of digits in the integral part of $N$ is $n - m$.  Denoting the first significant figure of $N$ by $k$, as before, we have

$$E_a \leqq \frac{1}{10^m} \times \frac{1}{2}, \quad N \geqq k \times 10^{n-m-1} - \frac{1}{10^m} \times \frac{1}{2}.$$

Hence

$$E_r \leqq \frac{\dfrac{1}{10^m} \times \dfrac{1}{2}}{k \times 10^{n-m-1} - \dfrac{1}{10^m} \times \dfrac{1}{2}} = \frac{10^{-m}}{2k \times 10^{n-1} \times 10^{-m} - 10^{-m}}$$

$$= \frac{1}{2k \times 10^{n-1} - 1} = \frac{1}{2(k \times 10^{n-1} - \frac{1}{2})}.$$

Remembering now that $n$ is a *positive integer* and that $k$ stands for any one of the digits from 1 to 9 inclusive, we readily see that $2k \times 10^{n-1} - 1 > k \times 10^{n-1}$ in all cases except $k=1$ and $n=1$. But this is the trivial case where $N=1$, 0.01, etc.; that is, where $N$ contains only one digit different from zero and this digit is 1—a case which would never occur in practice. Hence for all other cases we have $2k \times 10^{n-1} - 1 > k \times 10^{n-1}$, and therefore

$$E_r < \frac{1}{k \times 10^{n-1}}.$$

*Case 2.* $m = n$. Here $N$ is a decimal and $k$ is the first decimal figure. We then have

$$E_a \leqq \frac{1}{10^m} \times \frac{1}{2}, \quad N \geqq k \times 10^{-1} - \frac{1}{10^m} \times \frac{1}{2}.$$

$$\therefore E_r \leqq \frac{10^{-m} \times \frac{1}{2}}{k \times 10^{-1} - 10^{-m} \times \frac{1}{2}} = \frac{10^{-m}}{2k \times 10^{-1} - 10^{-m}} = \frac{1}{2k \times 10^{m-1} - 1}$$

$$= \frac{1}{2k \times 10^{n-1} - 1} < \frac{1}{k \times 10^{n-1}}.$$

*Case 3.* $m > n$. In this case $k$ occupies the $(m-n+1)$th decimal place and therefore

$$N \geqq k \times 10^{-(m-n+1)} - \frac{1}{10^m} \times \frac{1}{2}, \quad E_a \leqq \frac{1}{10^m} \times \frac{1}{2}.$$

$$\therefore E_r \leqq \frac{10^{-m} \times \frac{1}{2}}{k \times 10^{-m} \times 10^{n-1} - 10^{-m} \times \frac{1}{2}} = \frac{10^{-m}}{2k \times 10^{-m} \times 10^{n-1} - 10^{-m}}$$

$$= \frac{1}{2k \times 10^{n-1} - 1} < \frac{1}{k \times 10^{n-1}}.$$

The theorem is therefore true in all cases.

*Corollary 1.* Except in the case of approximate numbers of the form $k(1.000 \cdots) \times 10^p$, in which $k$ is the only digit different from zero, the relative error is less than $1/(2k \times 10^{n-1})$.

*Corollary 2.* If $k \geq 5$ and the given approximate number is not of the form $k(1.000 \cdots) \times 10^p$, then $E_r < 1/10^n$; for in this case $2k \geq 10$ and therefore $2k \times 10^{n-1} \geq 10^n$.

To find the number of correct figures corresponding to a given relative error we can not take the converse of the theorem stated at the beginning of this article, for the converse theorem is not true. In proving the formula for the relative error we took the lower limit for $N$ in order to obtain the upper limit for $E_r$. Thus, for the lower limit of $N$ we took its first significant figure multiplied by a power of 10. In the converse problem of finding the number of correct figures corresponding to a given relative error we must find the upper limit of the absolute error $E_a$; and since $E_a = NE_r$, we should use the upper limit for $N$. This upper limit will be $k+1$ times a power of 10, where $k$ is the first significant figure in $N$. For example, if the approximate value of $N$ is 6895, the lower limit to be used in finding the relative error is $6 \times 10^3$, whereas the upper limit to be used in finding the absolute error is $7 \times 10^3$.

To solve the converse problem we utilize Theorem II:

*Theorem II. If the relative error in an approximate number is less than $1/[(k+1) \times 10^{n-1}]$, the number is correct to $n$ significant figures, or at least is in error by less than a unit in the nth significant figure.*

To prove this theorem let

$N =$ the given number (exact value),
$n =$ number of correct significant figures in $N$,
$k =$ first significant figure in $N$,
$p =$ number of digits in the integral part of $N$.

Then

$n - p =$ number of decimals in $N$,

and $N \leq (k+1) \times 10^{p-1}$.

Let

$$E_r < \frac{1}{(k+1) \times 10^{n-1}}.$$

Then

$$E_a < (k+1) \times 10^{p-1} \times \frac{1}{(k+1) \times 10^{n-1}} = \frac{1}{10^{n-p}}.$$

Now $1/10^{n-p}$ is one unit in the $(n-p)$th decimal place, or in the $n$th significant figure. Hence the absolute error $E_a$ is less than a unit in the $n$th significant figure.

If the given number is a pure decimal, let

$p$ = number of zeros between the decimal point and first significant figure. Then $n+p$ = number of decimals in $N$, and

$$N \leqq \frac{(k+1)}{10^{p+1}}.$$

Hence if

$$E_r < \frac{1}{(k+1) \times 10^{n-1}},$$

we have

$$E_a < \frac{(k+1)}{10^{p+1}} \times \frac{1}{(k+1) \times 10^{n-1}} = \frac{1}{10^{n+p}}.$$

But $1/10^{n+p}$ is one unit in the $(n+p)$th decimal place, or in the $n$th significant figure. Hence the absolute error $E_a$ is less than a unit in the $n$th significant figure.

*Corollary 3.* If $E_r < 1/[2(k+1) \times 10^{n-1}]$, then $E_a$ is less than half a unit in the $n$th significant figure and the given number is correct to $n$ significant figures in all cases.

*Corollary 4.* Since $k$ may have any value from 1 to 9 inclusive, it is evident that $k+1$ may have any value from 2 to 10. Hence the upper and lower limits of the fraction $1/[2(k+1) \times 10^{n-1}]$ are $1/(4 \times 10^{n-1})$ and $1/(2 \times 10^n)$, respectively. We can therefore assert that

*If the relative error of any number is not greater than $1/(2 \times 10^n)$ the number is certainly correct to n significant figures.*

*Remark.* The reader can readily see from the preceding discussion that *the absolute error* is connected with the number of *decimal places,* whereas the *relative error* is connected with the number of *significant figures.*

**5. The General Formula for Errors.** Let

(5: 1)                    $N = f(u_1, u_2, u_3, \cdots u_n)$

denote any function of several independent quantities $u_1, u_2, \cdots u_n$, which are subject to the errors $\Delta u_1, \Delta u_2, \cdots \Delta u_n$, respectively. These errors in the $u$'s will cause an error $\Delta N$ in the function $N$, according to the relation

(5: 2)        $N + \Delta N = f(u_1 + \Delta u_1, u_2 + \Delta u_2, \cdots u_n + \Delta u_n).$

To find an expression for $\Delta N$ we must expand the right-hand member of (5: 2) by Taylor's theorem for a function of several variables. Hence we have

$$f(u_1 + \Delta u_1, u_2 + \Delta u_2, \cdots u_n + \Delta u_n) = f(u_1, u_2, \cdots u_n) + \Delta u_1 \frac{\partial f}{\partial u_1}$$

$$+ \Delta u_2 \frac{\partial f}{\partial u_2} + \cdots + \Delta u_n \frac{\partial f}{\partial u_n} + \frac{1}{2}\left[ (\Delta u_1)^2 \frac{\partial^2 f}{\partial u_1{}^2} + \cdots + (\Delta u_n)^2 \frac{\partial^2 f}{\partial u_n{}^2} \right.$$

$$\left. + 2\Delta u_1 \Delta u_2 \frac{\partial^2 f}{\partial u_1 \partial u_2} + \cdots \right] + \cdots .$$

Now since the errors $\Delta u_1, \Delta u_2, \cdots \Delta u_n$ are always relatively small,* we may neglect their squares, products, and higher powers and write

(5: 3)  $N + \Delta N = f(u_1, u_2, u_3, \cdots u_n)$

$$+ \Delta u_1 \frac{\partial f}{\partial u_1} + \Delta u_2 \frac{\partial f}{\partial u_2} + \cdots + \Delta u_n \frac{\partial f}{\partial u_n}$$

Subtracting (5: 1) from (5: 3), we get

$$\Delta N = \frac{\partial f}{\partial u_1}\Delta u_1 + \frac{\partial f}{\partial u_2}\Delta u_2 + \cdots + \frac{\partial f}{\partial u_n}\Delta u_n,$$

or

(5:4)  $$\Delta N = \frac{\partial N}{\partial u_1}\Delta u_1 + \frac{\partial N}{\partial u_2}\Delta u_2 + \frac{\partial N}{\partial u_3}\Delta u_3 + \cdots + \frac{\partial N}{\partial u_n}\Delta u_n.$$

This is the general formula for computing the error of a function, and it includes all possible cases. It will be observed that the right-hand member of (5: 4) is merely the total differential of the function $N$.

For the relative error of the function $N$ we have

(5: 5)  $$E_r = \frac{\Delta N}{N} = \frac{\partial N}{\partial u_1}\frac{\Delta u_1}{N} + \frac{\partial N}{\partial u_2}\frac{\Delta u_2}{N} + \cdots + \frac{\partial N}{\partial u_n}\frac{\Delta u_n}{N}.$$

When $N$ is a function of the form

(5: 6)  $$N = \frac{K a^m b^n c^p}{d^q e^r},$$

then by (5: 5) the relative error is

* A quantity $P$ is said to be relatively small in comparison with a second quantity $Q$ when the ratio $P/Q$ is small in comparison with unity. The squares and products of such small ratios are negligible in most calculations.

$$E_r = \frac{\Delta N}{N} = m\frac{\Delta a}{a} + n\frac{\Delta b}{b} + p\frac{\Delta c}{c} - q\frac{\Delta d}{d} - r\frac{\Delta e}{e} .$$

But since the errors $\Delta a, \cdots \Delta e$, etc. are just as likely to be negative as positive, we must take all the terms with the positive sign in order to be sure of the maximum error in the function $N$. Hence we write

$$(5:7) \qquad E_r \leqq m\left|\frac{\Delta a}{a}\right| + n\left|\frac{\Delta b}{b}\right| + p\left|\frac{\Delta c}{c}\right| + q\left|\frac{\Delta d}{d}\right| + r\left|\frac{\Delta e}{e}\right| .$$

**6. Application of the Error Formulas to the Fundamental Operations of Arithmetic and to Logarithms.** We shall now apply the preceding results to the fundamental operations of arithmetic.

*6a). Addition.* Let

$$N = u_1 + u_2 + \cdots + u_n.$$

Then

$$\Delta N = E_a = \Delta u_1 + \Delta u_2 + \cdots + \Delta u_n.$$

The absolute error of a sum of approximate numbers may therefore equal the sum of their absolute errors.

The proper way to add approximate numbers of different accuracies is shown in the two examples below.

*Example 1.* Find the sum of the approximate numbers 561.32, 491.6, 86.954, and 3.9462, each being correct to its last figure but no farther.

*Solution.* Since the second number is known only to the first decimal place, it would be useless and absurd to retain more than two decimals in any of the other numbers. Hence we round them off to two decimals, add the four numbers, and give the result to one decimal place, as shown below:

$$
\begin{array}{r}
491.6 \\
561.32 \\
86.95 \\
3.97 \\
\hline
1143.8
\end{array}
$$

By retaining two decimals in the more accurate numbers we eliminate the errors inherent in these numbers and thus reduce the error of the sum to that of the least accurate number. The final result, however, is uncertain by one unit in its last figure.

*Example 2.* Find the sum of 36490, 994, 557.32, 29500, and 86939, assuming that the number 29500 is known to only three significant figures.

*Solution.* Since óne of the numbers is known only to the nearest hundred, we round off the others to the nearest ten, add, and give the sum to hundreds, as shown below:

$$29500$$
$$86940$$
$$36490$$
$$990$$
$$560$$

$$154500 \text{ or } 1.545 \times 10^5.$$

The result is uncertain by one unit in the last significant figure.

In general, if we find the sum of $m$ numbers each of which has been rounded off correctly to the same place, the error in the sum may be as great as $m/2$ units in the last significant figure.

*6b). Averages.* An important case in the addition of numbers must here be considered. Suppose we are to find the mean of several approximate numbers. Is this mean reliable to any more figures than are the numbers from which it was obtained? The answer is yes, but in order to see why let us consider the following concrete case.

The first column below contains the mantissas of ten consecutive logarithms taken from a six-place table. The second column contains these same mantissas rounded off to five decimals. The third column gives the errors due to rounding, expressed in units of the sixth decimal place.

| $N$ | $N'$ | $E$ |
|---|---|---|
| 0.961421 | 0.96142 | 1 |
| 0.961469 | 0.96147 | −1 |
| 0.961516 | 0.96152 | −4 |
| 0.961563 | 0.96156 | 3 |
| 0.961611 | 0.96161 | 1 |
| 0.961658 | 0.96166 | −2 |
| 0.961706 | 0.96171 | −4 |
| 0.961753 | 0.96175 | 3 |
| 0.961801 | 0.96180 | 1 |
| 0.961848 | 0.96185 | −2 |

Average, 0.9616346        Av., 0.961635        Sum, −4
  = 0.961635                                    Av.,  −0.4

Here we have the relation

$$N = N' + E$$

for each of the numbers and therefore the further relations

$$\Sigma N = \Sigma N' + \Sigma E$$

and

$$\frac{\Sigma N}{n} = \frac{\Sigma N'}{n} + \frac{\Sigma E}{n}.$$

It will be noticed that the average of the rounded numbers is in error by only 0.4 of a unit in the sixth decimal place. We may therefore call it correct to six decimals, or to one more place than the rounded numbers.

The entries in all numerical tables and the results of all measurements are rounded numbers in which the error is not greater than half a unit in the last significant figure. These errors (due to rounding) are in general as likely to be positive as negative and hence their algebraic sum is never large. Usually it is less than half a unit in the last figure. We may therefore write

$$\Sigma E < |E|$$

and

$$\frac{\Sigma E}{n} < \left|\frac{E}{n}\right|,$$

where $\Sigma E/n$ denotes the error of the average.

When $n \geq 10$, it is therefore evident that the average of ten or more numbers which are given to $n$ significant figures is usually true to $(n+1)$ significant figures.

The foregoing considerations justify the computer in retaining one more figure in the mean of a set of numbers than are given in the numbers themselves. But rarely should he retain the mean to more than one additional figure.

*6c). Subtraction.* Here

$$N = u_1 - u_2$$

and

$$\Delta N = E_a = \Delta u_1 - \Delta u_2.$$

Since the errors $\Delta u_1$ and $\Delta u_2$ may be either positive or negative, however, we must take the sum of the absolute values of the errors. We then have the result that the absolute error of the difference of two approximate numbers may equal the *sum* of their absolute errors.

When one approximate number is to be subtracted from another, they must both be rounded off to the same place before subtracting. Thus, to subtract 46.365 from 779.8, assuming that each number is approximate and correct only to its last figure, we have

$$779.8 - 46.4 = 733.4.$$

It would be absurd to write $779.800 - 46.365 = 733.435$, because the last two figures in the larger number as here written are not zeros.

The most serious error connected with the subtraction of approximate numbers arises from the subtraction of numbers which are nearly equal. Suppose, for example, that the numbers 64.395 and 63.994 are each correct to five figures, but no more. Their difference, $64.395 - 63.994 = 0.401$, is correct to only *three* figures. Again, if the numbers 16950 and 16870 are each correct to only four significant figures, their difference $16950 - 16870 = 80$ is correct to only *one* significant figure, and even this figure may be in error by one unit.

Errors arising from the disappearance of the most important figures on the left, as in the two examples of the preceding paragraph, are of frequent occurrence and sometimes render the result of a computation worthless. They must be carefully guarded against and eliminated wherever possible. They can be avoided in cases where the two nearly equal numbers can be approximated to any desired number of figures. Thus, if we desire the difference $\sqrt{2.03} - \sqrt{2}$ to five significant figures, we can obtain it by taking $\sqrt{2.03} = 1.424781$ and $\sqrt{2} = 1.414214$; for then $1.424781 - 1.414214 = 0.010567$.

In general, if we desire the difference of two approximate numbers to $n$ significant figures, and if it is known beforehand that the first $m$ figures at the left will disappear by subtraction, we must start with $m + n$ significant figures in *each* of the given numbers.

*6d). Multiplication.* In this case

$$N = u_1 u_2 u_3 \cdots u_n.$$

Since this is of the form (5:6), in which $m = n = \cdots = r = 1$, we have by (5:7)

$$E_r = \frac{\Delta N}{N} = \frac{\Delta u_1}{u_1} + \frac{\Delta u_2}{u_2} + \cdots + \frac{\Delta u_n}{u_n}.$$

The relative error of a product of $n$ approximate numbers may therefore possibly equal the arithmetic sum of the relative errors of the separate numbers if all the errors happen to be of the same sign.

The accuracy of a product should always be investigated by means of the relative error. The absolute error, if desired, can be found from the relation $E_a = E_r N$.

When it is desired to find the product of two or more approximate numbers of different accuracies, the more accurate numbers should be rounded off so as to contain one more significant figure than the least accurate factor, for by so doing we eliminate the error due to the more accurate factors and thus make the error of the product due solely to the errors of the less accurate numbers. The final result should be given to as many significant figures as are contained in the least accurate factor, and no more. The proper method of procedure in such cases will be illustrated by examples later on.

*6e). Division.* Here we have

$$N = \frac{u_1}{u_2}.$$

This is also of the form (5: 6), where the exponents are all unity. Hence by (5: 7)

$$E_r = \frac{\Delta u_1}{u_1} + \frac{\Delta u_2}{u_2}.$$

The relative error of a quotient may therefore equal the sum of the relative errors of divisor and dividend.

As in the case of products, the accuracy of a quotient should always be investigated by means of the relative error, and all the statements made above in regard to products hold for quotients. In particular, if one of the numbers (divisor or dividend) is more accurate than the other, the more accurate number should be rounded off so as to contain one more significant figure than the less accurate one. The result should be given to as many significant figures as the less accurate number, and no more. The following examples will illustrate the proper methods of investigating the accuracy of products and quotients.

*Example 1.* Find the product of 349.1×863.4 and state how many figures of the result are trustworthy.

*Solution.* Assuming that each number is correct to four figures but no more, we have $\Delta u_1 \leqq 0.05$, $\Delta u_2 \leqq 0.05$. Hence

$$E_r \leqq \frac{0.05}{349.1} + \frac{0.05}{863.4} = 0.000143 + 0.000057 = 0.00020.$$

The product of the given numbers is 301413 to six figures. The absolute error of this product is

$$E_a = 301413 \times 0.00020 = 60, \text{ possibly}.$$

The true result therefore lies between 301473 and 301353, and the best we can do is to take the mean of these numbers to four significant figures, or

$$349.1 \times 863.4 = 301400 = 3.014 \times 10^5.$$

Even then there is some uncertainty about the last figure.

Theorem II of Art. 4 also tells us that the above result is uncertain in the fourth figure, but that the error in that figure is less than a unit.

*Example 2.* Find the number of correct figures in the quotient $56.3/\sqrt{5}$, assuming that the numerator is correct to its last figure but no farther.

*Solution.* Here we take $\sqrt{5} = 2.236$ so as to make the divisor free from error in comparison with the dividend. Then

$$E_r \leqq \frac{0.05}{56.3} < 0.0009;$$

and since $56.3/2.236 = 25.2$ we have

$$E_a < 25.2 \times 0.0009 < 0.023.$$

Since this error does not affect the third figure of the quotient, we take 25.2 as the correct result.

We could have seen at a glance, without any investigation, that the error of the quotient in this example would be less than 0.025; for the denominator is free from error and the possible error of 0.05 in the numerator is to be divided by 2.236, thereby making the error of the quotient less than half that amount.

*Example 3.* Find how many figures of the quotient $4.89\pi/6.7$ are trustworthy, assuming that the denominator is true to only two figures.

*Solution.* The only appreciable error to be considered here is the possible 0.05 in the denominator. The corresponding relative error is

$$E_r \leqq \frac{0.05}{6.7} < 0.0075.$$

The quotient to three figures is

$$\frac{4.89 \times 3.14}{6.7} = 2.29.$$

Hence the possible absolute error is $E_a \leqq 2.29 \times 0.0075 < 0.02$. Since the third figure of the quotient may be in error by nearly two units, we are not justified in calling the result anything but 2.3, or

$$\frac{4.89\pi}{6.7} = 2.3.$$

*6f). Powers and Roots.* Here $N$ has the form

$$N = u^m.$$

Hence by (5: 7)

$$E_r \leqq m\frac{\Delta u}{u}.$$

For the $p$th power of a number we put $m = p$ and have

$$E_r \leqq p\frac{\Delta u}{u}.$$

The relative error of the $p$th power of a number is thus $p$ times the relative error of the given number.

For the $r$th root of a number we put $m = 1/r$ and get

$$E_r \leqq \frac{1}{r}\frac{\Delta u}{u}.$$

Hence the relative error of the $r$th root of an approximate number is only $1/r$th of the relative error of the given number.

*Example.* Find the number of trustworthy figures in $(0.3862)^4$, assuming that the number in parentheses is correct to its last figure but no farther.

*Solution.* Here the relative error of the given number is

$$E_r = \frac{0.00005}{0.3862} < 0.00013.$$

The relative error of the result is therefore less than $4 \times 0.00013$, or 0.00052.

The required number to five figures is $(0.3862)^4 = 0.022246$. Hence the absolute error of the result is $0.022246 \times 0.00052 = 0.000012$. Since this error affects the fourth significant figure of the result, the best we can do is to write

$$(0.3862)^4 = 0.02225$$

and say that the last figure is uncertain by one unit.

The relative error of the fourth root of 0.3862 is less than $\frac{1}{4}(0.00013)$ = 0.000032, and since this fourth root is 0.78832 the absolute error of the result is about $0.78832 \times 0.000032 = 0.000026$. Hence the fourth root is 0.7883 correct to four figures.

*6g). Logarithms.* Here we have

$$N = \log_{10} u = 0.43429 \log_e u.$$

Hence

$$\Delta N = 0.43429\frac{\Delta u}{u},$$

or

$$\Delta N < \frac{1}{2} \frac{\Delta u}{u}.$$

The absolute error in the common logarithm of a number is thus less than half the relative error of the given number.

An error in a logarithm may cause a disastrous error in the anti-logarithm or corresponding number, for from the first formula for $\Delta N$ above we have

$$\Delta u = \frac{u \Delta N}{0.43429} = 2.3026 u \Delta N.$$

The error in the antilog may thus be many times the error in the logarithm. For this reason it is of the utmost importance that the logarithm of a result be as free from error as possible.

*Example 1.*    Suppose $N = \log_{10} u = 3.49853$ and $\Delta N < 0.000005$, so that the given logarithm is correct to its last figure.    Then $u = 3151.6$ and therefore

$$\Delta u = 2.3 \times 3151.6 \times 0.000005 = 0.036.$$

Since this error does not affect the fifth figure in $u$, the antilog is correct to five figures.

*Example 2.*    Suppose $N = \log_{10} u = 2.96384$ and $\Delta N = 0.00001$.    Then $u = 920.11$ and

$$\Delta u = 2.3 \times 920.11 \times 0.00001 = 0.021.$$

This error affects the fifth figure in $u$ and makes it uncertain by two units.

Inasmuch as the logarithm of most results is obtained by the addition of other logarithms, it is evident that such a logarithm is likely to be in error by a unit in the last figure, due to the addition of rounded numbers. Hence the corresponding number may frequently be in error by one or two units in its last significant figure when the number of significant figures in the antilog is the same as the number of decimals in the logarithm.

*Remarks.*    The reader should bear in mind the fact that the number of correct figures in the antilog corresponds to the number of correct *decimals* in the logarithm. The integral part, or characteristic, of the logarithm plays no part in determining the accuracy of the antilog. This fact is at once evident from a consideration of the equation

$$\frac{\Delta u}{u} = 2.3 \Delta N.$$

For inasmuch as the number of correct figures in the antilog $u$ is measured by its relative error, and since this latter quantity depends only on the absolute error $\Delta N$ and not at all on the characteristic, it is plain that the accuracy of the antilog depends only on the number of correct decimals in the mantissa.

It is an easy matter to determine the number of correct figures in any antilog when the number of correct decimals in the mantissa is given. Suppose, for example, that we are using $m$-place log tables and that the possible error in the logarithm of a result is one unit in the last decimal place, as is usually the case. Then $\Delta N = 1/10^m$ and we have

$$\frac{\Delta u}{u} = \frac{2.3}{10^m} = \frac{2.3}{10 \times 10^{m-1}} = \frac{1}{4.34 \times 10^{m-1}} < \frac{1}{2 \times 10^{m-1}}.$$

Hence by Corollary 4, Art. 4, the antilog $u$ is certainly correct to $m-1$ significant figures.

The equation $\Delta u/u = 1/(4.34 \times 10^{m-1})$ shows that if the mantissa is in error by two units in its last figure the antilog is still correct to $m-1$ significant figures, for in this case the relative error of the antilog is

$$\frac{\Delta u}{u} = \frac{1}{2.17 \times 10^{m-1}},$$

which is less than $1/(2 \times 10^{m-1})$. We are therefore justified in asserting that if the mantissa of a logarithm is not in error by more than two units in the last decimal place the antilog is certainly correct to $m-1$ significant figures.

7. **The Impossibility, in General, of Obtaining a Result More Accurate than the Data Used.** The reader will have observed that in all the examples worked in the preceding pages no result has been more accurate than the numbers used in obtaining it. This, of course, is what we should have expected, but sometimes computers seem to try to get more figures in the result than are used in the data. When we apply corollaries 1 and 4 of Art. 4 to the errors of products, quotients, powers, roots, logarithms, and antilogarithms, we find that in no case is the result true to more figures than are the numbers used in computing it. The results for these operations are as follows:

(a) *Products and Quotients.* If $k_1$ and $k_2$ are the first significant figures of two numbers which are each correct to $n$ significant figures, and if neither number is of the form $k(1.000 \cdots) \times 10^p$, then their product or quotient is correct to

$n - 1$ significant figures if $k_1 \geq 2$ and $k_2 \geq 2$,

$n - 2$ significant figures if either $k_1 = 1$ or $k_2 = 1$.

(b) *Powers and Roots.* If $k$ is the first significant figure of a number which is correct to $n$ significant figures, and if this number contains more than one digit different from zero, then its $p$th power is correct to

$n-1$ significant figures if $p \leq k$,
$n-2$ significant figures if $p \leq 10k$;

and its $r$th root is correct to

$n$ significant figures if $rk \geq 10$,
$n-1$ significant figures if $rk < 10$.

(c) *Logs and Antilogs.* If $k$ is the first significant figure of a number which is correct to $n$ significant figures, and if this number contains more than one digit different from zero, then for the absolute error in its common logarithm we have

$$E_a < \frac{1}{4k \times 10^{n-1}}.$$

If a logarithm (to the base 10) is not in error by more than two units in the $m$th decimal place, the antilog is certainly correct to $m-1$ significant figures.

To prove the foregoing results for the accuracy of products and quotients let $k_1$ and $k_2$ represent the first significant figures of the given numbers. Then by corollary 1 of Art. 4 the relative errors of the numbers are less than $1/(2k_1 \times 10^{n-1})$ and $1/(2k_2 \times 10^{n-1})$, respectively; and since the relative error of the product or quotient of two numbers may equal the sum of their relative errors, we have

Relative error of result

$$< \frac{1}{2k_1 \times 10^{n-1}} + \frac{1}{2k_2 \times 10^{n-1}} = \left(\frac{1}{k_1} + \frac{1}{k_2}\right)\frac{1}{2 \times 10^{n-1}}.$$

Now if $(1/k_1 + 1/k_2) \leq 1$ we have $E_r < 1/(2 \times 10^{n-1})$, and the product or quotient is certainly correct to $n-1$ significant figures. But this quantity is not greater than 1 if $k_1 \geq 2$ and $k_2 \geq 2$. Hence in this case the result is correct to $n-1$ significant figures. If, however, either $k_1 = 1$ or $k_2 = 1$, the quantity $(1/k_1 + 1/k_2) > 1$ and therefore the relative error of the result may be greater than $1/(2 \times 10^{n-1})$. Hence the result may not be correct to $n-1$ significant figures, but it is certainly correct to $n-2$ figures.

To prove the above results for the accuracy of powers and roots let $k$ represent the first significant figure of the given number. Then the relative error of this number is less than $1/(2k \times 10^{n-1})$. Hence the relative error of its $p$th power is less than

$$\frac{p}{2k \times 10^{n-1}} = \frac{p}{k}\frac{1}{2 \times 10^{n-1}}.$$

The result will therefore be correct to $n-1$ significant figures if $(p/k) \leq 1$, or $p \leq k$, and to $n-2$ significant figures if $p \leq 10k$.

The error of the $r$th root is less than

$$\frac{1}{r}\frac{1}{2k\times10^{n-1}} = \frac{1}{rk}\frac{1}{2\times10^{n-1}} = \frac{10}{rk}\frac{1}{2\times10^{n}}.$$

Hence the result will be correct to $n$ significant figures if $rk \geqq 10$ and to $n-1$ significant figures if $rk < 10$.

To prove the result for the error of the common logarithm we recall that $\Delta N < \frac{1}{2}\Delta u/u$, and since $\Delta u/u < 1/(2k\times10^{n-1})$ we have

$$\Delta N < \frac{1}{4k\times10^{n-1}}.$$

The proof for the accuracy of the antilog has already been given at the end of Art. 6.

Since the separate processes of multiplication, division, raising to powers, and extraction of roots can not give a result more accurate than the data used in obtaining it, no combination of these processes could be expected to give a more accurate result except by accident. Hence when only these processes are involved in a computation, the result should never be given to more significant figures than are contained in the least accurate of the factors used. Even then the last significant figure will usually be uncertain. In a computation involving several distinct steps, retain at the end of each step one more significant figure than is required in the final result.

While it is true in general that a computed result cannot be more accurate than the numbers used in obtaining it, an exception must be made in the cases of addition and subtraction. When only these processes are involved, the result may be much more accurate than one of the quantities added or subtracted. For example, the sum $3463+\sqrt{3}$ $= 3463+1.7 = 3464.7$ is correct to five significant figures (assuming 3463 to be an exact number) even though one of the numbers used in obtaining it is correct to only two figures. A similar result would evidently follow in the case of subtraction.

## 8. Accuracy in the Evaluation of a Formula or Complex Expression.

The two fundamental problems under this head are the following:

(a) Given the errors of several independent quantities or approximate numbers, to find the error of any function of these quantities.

(b) To find the allowable errors in several independent quantities in order to obtain a prescribed degree of accuracy in any function of these quantities.

*8a). The Direct Problem.* The first of these problems is solved by replacing the given *approximate* numbers by the letters $a, b, c, \cdots$ or $u_1, u_2, u_3$, taking the partial derivatives of the function with respect to each of these letters, and then substituting in formula $(5:4)$ or $(5:5)$.

An *exact* number, such as 2, 3, 10, etc., is *not* replaced by a letter before taking the derivatives.* We shall now work some examples to show the method of procedure.

*Example 1.*    Find the error in the evaluation of the fraction $\cos 7°10'/\log_{10} 242.7$, assuming that the angle may be in error by $1'$ and that the number 242.7 may be in error by a unit in its last figure.

*Solution.* Since this is a quotient of two functions, it is better to compute the relative error from the formula $E_r \leqq \Delta u_1/u_1 + \Delta u_2/u_2$ and then find the absolute error from the relation $E_a = NE_r$. Hence if we write

$$N = \frac{\cos 7° 10'}{\log_{10} 242.7} = \frac{\cos x}{\log_{10} y} = \frac{u_1}{u_2},$$

we have

$$\Delta u_1 = \Delta \cos x = - \sin x \Delta x,$$

$$\Delta u_2 = \Delta \log_{10} y = 0.43429 \frac{\Delta y}{y}.$$

$$\therefore E_r \leqq \frac{\sin x}{\cos x} \Delta x + \frac{0.43429}{y \log y} \Delta y,$$

or

$$E_r \leqq \tan x \Delta x + \frac{0.435}{y \log y} \Delta y.$$

Now taking $x = 7°10'$, $\Delta x = 1' = 0.000291$ radian, $y = 242$, $\Delta y = 0.1$, and using a slide rule for the computation, we have

$$E_r < 0.126 \times 0.000291 + \frac{0.435 \times 0.1}{242 \times 2.38} = 0.00011.$$

Since $N = \cos 7°10'/\log 242.7 = 0.41599$, we have

$$E_a = 0.00011 \times 0.416 = 0.000046,$$

or $E_a < 0.00005$.

The value of the fraction is therefore between 0.41604 and 0.41594, and we take the mean of these numbers to four figures as the best value of the fraction, or

$$\underline{N = 0.4160.}$$

---

* Adopted or accepted values of physical, chemical, and astronomical constants are to be treated as exact numbers, but results obtained by using these numbers as multipliers or divisors are not to be relied upon to more significant figures than are used in the constants themselves.

*Example 2.* The hypotenuse and a side of a right triangle are found by measurement to be 75 and 32, respectively. If the possible error in the hypotenuse is 0.2 and that in the side is 0.1, find the possible error in the computed angle $A$.

*Solution.* Lettering the triangle in the usual manner, we have

$$\sin A = \frac{32}{75} = \frac{a}{c}.$$

$$\therefore A = \sin^{-1}\left(\frac{a}{c}\right),$$

and

$$\Delta A = \frac{\partial A}{\partial a}\Delta a + \frac{\partial A}{\partial c}\Delta c.$$

Now

$$\frac{\partial A}{\partial a} = \frac{1}{\sqrt{c^2 - a^2}},$$

$$\frac{\partial A}{\partial c} = \frac{-a}{c\sqrt{c^2 - a^2}}.$$

Taking the numerical values of $c$ and $a$ in such a manner as to give the upper limits for $\partial A/\partial a$ and $\partial A/\partial c$, and remembering that $\Delta a = 0.1$, $\Delta c = 0.2$, we have

$$\Delta A < \frac{1}{\sqrt{(74.8)^2 - (32.1)^2}} \times 0.1 + \frac{32.1}{74.8\sqrt{(74.8)^2 - (32.1)^2}} \times 0.2 = 0.00275,$$

or

$$\Delta A < 0.0028 \text{ radian} = \underline{9' \ 38''}.$$

The possible error in $A$ is therefore 9'38''.

*8b). The Inverse Problem.* We now turn our attention to the second fundamental problem mentioned at the beginning of this article: that of finding the allowable errors in $u_1, u_2, \cdots u_n$ when the function $N$ is desired to a given degree of accuracy. This problem is mathematically indeterminate, since it would be possible to choose the errors $\Delta u_1$, $\Delta u_2$, etc. in a variety of ways so as to make $\Delta N$ less than any prescribed quantity. The problem is solved with the least labor by using what is known as the *principle of equal effects.** This principle assumes that all the partial differentials $(\partial N/\partial u_1)\Delta u_1$, $(\partial N/\partial u_2)\Delta u_2$, etc., contribute an equal amount in making up the total error $\Delta N$. Under these conditions

* See Palmer's *Theory of Measurements*, pp. 147–148.

all the terms in the right-hand member·of equation (5: 4) are equal to one another, so that

$$\Delta N = n\frac{\partial N}{\partial u}\Delta u_1 = n\frac{\partial N}{\partial u_2}\Delta u_2 = \cdots = n\frac{\partial N}{\partial u_n}\Delta u_n.$$

Hence

$$\Delta u_1 = \frac{\Delta N}{n\dfrac{\partial N}{\partial u_1}}, \quad \Delta u_2 = \frac{\Delta N}{n\dfrac{\partial N}{\partial u_2}}, \quad \cdots \quad \Delta u_n = \frac{\Delta N}{n\dfrac{\partial N}{\partial u_n}}.$$

*Example 3.* Two sides and the included angle of a triangular city lot are approximately 96 ft., 87 ft., and 36°, respectively. Find the allowable errors in these quantities in order that the area of the lot may be determined to the nearest square foot.

*Solution.* Writing $b = 96$, $c = 87$, $A = 36°$, and denoting the area by $u$, we have

$$u = \tfrac{1}{2}bc \sin A = \tfrac{1}{2}(96 \times 87 \sin 36°) = 2455 \text{ sq.ft.}$$

Hence

$$\frac{\partial u}{\partial b} = \frac{1}{2}c \sin A, \quad \frac{\partial u}{\partial c} = \frac{1}{2}b \sin A, \quad \frac{\partial u}{\partial A} = \frac{1}{2}bc \cos A.$$

Substituting these quantities in (5: 5), we find

$$\frac{\Delta u}{u} = \frac{\Delta b}{b} + \frac{\Delta c}{c} + \frac{\Delta A}{\tan A}.$$

Now since the area is to be determined to the nearest square foot we must have $\Delta u < 0.5$; and by the principle of equal effects we must have

$$\frac{\Delta b}{b} = \frac{1}{3}\frac{\Delta u}{u} < \frac{0.5}{3 \times 2455} = \frac{1}{14730} < 0.000068.$$

Hence $\Delta b < 96 \times 0.000068 = 0.0065$ ft.

In like manner

$$\frac{\Delta c}{c} = \frac{1}{3}\frac{\Delta u}{u}, \text{ or } \Delta c < 87 \times 0.000068 = 0.0059 \text{ ft.};$$

and

$$\frac{\Delta A}{\tan A} = \frac{1}{3}\frac{\Delta u}{u}, \text{ or } \Delta A < \tan 36° \times 0.000068 = 0.000049 \text{ radian.}$$

Hence from a table for converting radians to degrees we find $\Delta A = 10''$.

It thus appears that in order to attain the desired accuracy in the area the sides must be measured to the nearest hundredth of a foot and the included angle to the nearest $20''$ of arc.

This problem could also be solved by assuming that the possible errors in the measured sides might be 0.005 ft. and then computing the permissible error in the measured angle.

*Example 4.* The value of the function $6x^2(\log_{10} x - \sin 2y)$ is required correct to two decimal places. If the approximate values of $x$ and $y$ are 15.2 and 57°, respectively, find the permissible errors in these quantities.

*Solution.* Putting

$$u = 6x^2(\log_{10} x - \sin 2y) = 6(15.2)^2(\log_{10} 15.2 - \sin 114°)$$
$$= 371.9,$$

we have

$$\frac{\partial u}{\partial x} = 12x(\log_{10} x - \sin 2y) + 6x \times 0.43429 = 88.54,$$

$$\frac{\partial u}{\partial y} = -12x^2 \cos 2y = 1127.7.$$

Hence

$$\Delta u = \frac{\partial u}{\partial x}\Delta x + \frac{\partial u}{\partial y}\Delta y = 88.54\Delta x + 1127.7\Delta y.$$

In order that the required result be correct to two decimal places we must have $\Delta u < 0.005$. Then by the principle of equal effects we have

$$\Delta x = \frac{\Delta u}{2\dfrac{\partial u}{\partial x}} < \frac{0.005}{2 \times 88.54} = 0.000028,$$

$$\Delta y = \frac{\Delta u}{2\dfrac{\partial u}{\partial y}} < \frac{0.005}{2 \times 1127.7} = 0.0000022 \text{ rad.}$$

$$= 0''.45.$$

Since the permissible error in $x$ is only 0.00003, it will be necessary to take $x$ to seven significant figures in order to attain the required degree of accuracy in the result. The value of $y$ can then be taken to the nearest second.

*Remark.* It is neither necessary nor desirable to investigate the accuracy of all proposed computations. But when we are in doubt about the possibility of attaining a certain degree of accuracy in the final result, we should make the necessary investigation. It usually suffices to carry all computations to one more figure than is desired in the final result and then round off the result to the desired number of figures, if the accuracy of the given independent quantities is such as to permit this.

**9. Accuracy in the Determination of Arguments from a Tabulated Function.** In many problems it is necessary to compute some function of an unknown quantity and then determine the quantity from tabulated values of the function. Examples of this kind are the determination of numbers from a table of logarithms, and angles from trigonometric tables. If the computed function happens to be affected with an error, the argument determined from this function is necessarily incorrect in some degree. The purpose of this article is to investigate the accuracy of the argument whose value is required.

In tables of single entry are tabulated functions of a single argument. Calling $x$ the argument and $y$ the tabulated function, we have

(9: 1) $$y = f(x).$$

From this we get the relation

(9: 2) $$\Delta y = f'(x)\Delta x, \quad \text{approximately,}$$

from which we have

**(9: 3)** $$\Delta x = \frac{\Delta y}{f'(x)}.$$

This is the *fundamental equation* for computing the error in arguments taken from a table. Here $\Delta y$ represents the error in the computed function whose values are tabulated, and $\Delta x$ is the corresponding error in the argument. It will be noted that the magnitude of $\Delta x$ depends upon three things: the error in the function, the nature of the function, and the magnitude of the argument itself. We shall now apply (9: 3) to several functions whose values are tabulated.

*1. Logarithms.*

(a) $$f(x) = \log_e x.$$

$$f'(x) = \frac{1}{x}.$$

(9: 4) $$\therefore \Delta x = x\Delta y, \quad \text{from (9: 3).}$$

(b)                    $f(x) = \log_{10} x.$

$f'(x) = \dfrac{M}{x},$ where $M = 0.43429.$

$\therefore \Delta x = \dfrac{x\Delta y}{M} = 2.3026 x\Delta y.$

Hence

(9:5)                    $\Delta x < 2.31 x\Delta y.$

2. *Trigonometric Functions.*

(a)                    $f(x) = \sin x.$

$f'(x) = \cos x.$

(9:6)        $\therefore \Delta x = \dfrac{\Delta y}{\cos x} = \sec x\Delta y$ radians,

or

(9:7)          $(\Delta x)'' = 206264.8 \sec x\Delta y$ seconds.

(b)                    $f(x) = \tan x.$

$f'(x) = \sec^2 x.$

(9:8)        $\therefore \Delta x = \cos^2 x\Delta y$ radians,

or

(9:9)          $(\Delta x)'' = 206264.8 \cos^2 x\Delta y$ seconds.

(c)                    $f(x) = \log_{10} \sin x.$

$f'(x) = M\dfrac{\cos x}{\sin x} = M \cot x.$

(9:10)      $\therefore \Delta x = \dfrac{\Delta y}{M \cot x} = 2.3026 \tan x\Delta y$ radians,

or

(9:11)          $(\Delta x)'' < 475000 \tan x\Delta y$ seconds.

$$(d) \qquad f(x) = \log_{10} \tan x.$$

$$f'(x) = M \frac{\sec^2 x}{\tan x} = \frac{M}{\sin x \cos x} = \frac{2M}{\sin 2x}.$$

$$\therefore \Delta x = \frac{\sin 2x \Delta y}{2M} = 1.1513 \sin 2x \Delta y,$$

or

$$(9:12) \qquad \Delta x < 1.16 \sin 2x \Delta y \text{ radians;}$$

and

$$(9:13) \qquad (\Delta x)'' < 238000 \sin 2x \Delta y \text{ seconds.}$$

### 3. Exponential Functions.

$$f(x) = e^x.$$
$$f'(x) = e^x.$$

$$(9:14) \qquad \therefore \Delta x = \frac{\Delta y}{e^x}.$$

4. *Other Tabulated Functions.* By means of the fundamental equation (9:3) we can compute the error in any argument when the derivative of the given function is given or can be easily found. In Jahnke and Emde's *Funktionentafeln*, for instance, are tabulated the derivatives of $\log \Gamma(x+1)$, the error function $\int_0^x e^{-x^2} dx$, the Weierstrass $p$-function, $p(u)$, and Legendre's polynomials $P_n(x)$. Hence by means of these tables we can determine the argument and also its error.

Elliptic integrals are functions of two arguments. The error in each of these arguments can not be determined uniquely, but by using formula (5:4) and assuming the principle of equal effects we can find definite formulas for the errors in the arguments. Thus, denoting an elliptic integral by $I$ and the function of the arguments by $F(\theta, \phi)$, we have

$$I = F(\theta, \phi).$$

Hence

$$\Delta I = \frac{\partial F}{\partial \theta} \Delta \theta + \frac{\partial F}{\partial \phi} \Delta \phi.$$

By assuming that the two terms on the right-hand side are equal, we get

$$\Delta \theta = \frac{\Delta I}{2 \dfrac{\partial F}{\partial \theta}}, \qquad \Delta \phi = \frac{\Delta I}{2 \dfrac{\partial F}{\partial \phi}}.$$

Knowing the error $\Delta I$ of the integral, we can find from these formulas the corresponding errors in $\theta$ and $\phi$.

*Remarks.* Comparison of formulas (9: 6) and (9: 8) shows that the error made in finding an angle from its tangent is always less than when finding it from its sine, because $\cos^2 x$ is less than $\sec x$. The latter may have any value from 1 to $\infty$, whereas the value of the former never exceeds 1.

Formulas (9: 10) and (9: 12) show still more clearly the advantage of determining an angle from its tangent. It is evident from (9: 12) that the error in $x$ can rarely exceed the error in $y$, since $\sin 2x$ can not exceed 1, but (9: 10) shows that when the angle is determined from its log sine the error in $x$ may be many times that in $y$.

Let us consider a numerical case. Suppose we are to find $x$ from a 5-place table of log sines. Since all the tabular values are rounded numbers, the value of $\Delta y$ may be as large as 0.000005, due to the inherent errors of the table itself. Taking $x = 60°$ and substituting in (9: 10), we get

$$\Delta x = 2.3026\sqrt{3} \times 0.000005$$

$$= 0.00002 \text{ radian, about,}$$

$$= 4''.1.$$

The unavoidable error may therefore be as great as 4 seconds if we find $x$ from its log sine.

If, on the other hand, we find $x$ from a table of log tangents we have from (9: 12)

$$\Delta x < 1.16 \times \tfrac{1}{2}\sqrt{3} \times 0.000005 = 0.000005 \text{ rad.}$$

$$= 1''.$$

The error is thus only one-fourth as great as in the preceding case.

The foregoing formulas simply substantiate what has long been known by computers: that an angle can be determined more accurately from its tangent or cotangent than from its sine or cosine.

**10. The Accuracy of Series Approximations.** It is frequently easier to find the numerical value of a function by expanding it into a power series and evaluating the first few terms than by any other method. In fact, this is sometimes the only possible method of computing it. The general method for expanding functions into power series is by means of Taylor's formula. The two standard forms of this formula are the following:

$$(10{:}1) \quad f(x) = f(a) + (x-a)f'(a) + \frac{(x-a)^2}{2!}f''(a) + \cdots + \frac{(x-a)^{n-1}}{(n-1)!}f^{(n-1)}(a)$$

$$+ \frac{(x-a)^n}{n!}f^{(n)}[a+\theta(x-a)], \quad 0 < \theta < 1.$$

$$(10{:}2) \quad f(x+h) = f(x) + hf'(x) + \frac{h^2}{2!}f''(x) + \cdots + \frac{h^{n-1}}{(n-1)!}f^{(n-1)}(x)$$

$$+ \frac{h^n}{n!}f^{(n)}(x+\theta h), \quad 0 < \theta < 1.$$

On putting $a = 0$ in $(10{:}1)$ we get Maclaurin's formula:

$$(10{:}3) \quad f(x) = f(0) + xf'(0) + \frac{x^2}{2!}f''(0) + \cdots + \frac{x^{n-1}}{(n-1)!}f^{(n-1)}(0)$$

$$+ \frac{x^n}{n!}f^{(n)}(\theta x), \quad 0 < \theta < 1.$$

The last term in each of these three formulas is the *remainder after n terms*. This remainder term is the quantity in which we shall be interested in this article. The forms of the remainder given above are not the only ones, however. Another useful form will be given below.

*10a). The Remainder Terms in Taylor's and Maclaurin's Series.* Denoting by $R_n(x)$ the remainder after $n$ terms in the Taylor and Maclaurin expansions, we have the following useful forms:

1. For Taylor's formula $(10{:}1)$:

(a) $\qquad R_n(x) = \dfrac{(x-a)^n}{n!}f^{(n)}[a + \theta(x - a)], \quad 0 < \theta < 1.$

(b) $\qquad R_n(x) = \dfrac{1}{(n-1)!}\displaystyle\int_0^{x-a} f^{(n)}(x - t)t^{n-1}dt.$

2. For Taylor's formula $(10{:}2)$:

(a) $\qquad R_n(x) = \dfrac{h^n}{n!}f^{(n)}(x + \theta h), \quad 0 < \theta < 1.$

(b) $\qquad R_n(x) = \dfrac{1}{(n-1)!}\displaystyle\int_0^h f^{(n)}(x + h - t)t^{n-1}dt.$

3. For Maclaurin's formula:

(a) $\qquad R_n(x) = \dfrac{x^n}{n!}f^{(n)}(\theta x), \quad 0 < \theta < 1.$

(b) $\qquad R_n(x) = \dfrac{1}{(n-1)!}\displaystyle\int_0^x f^{(n)}(x - t)t^{n-1}dt.$

It will be observed that the second form (the integral form) is perfectly definite and contains no uncertain factor $\theta$. In using either form, however, it is necessary first to find the $n$th derivative of $f(x)$.

Since the integral form of $R_n(x)$ is not usually given in the text books on calculus, we shall show how to apply it to an example.

*Example.* Find the remainder after $n$ terms in the expansion of $\log_e (x+h)$.

*Solution.* Here

$$f(x) = \log_e x,$$

$$\therefore f'(x) = \frac{1}{x},$$

$$f''(x) = -\frac{1}{x^2},$$

$$f'''(x) = \frac{2}{x^3},$$

$$f^{iv}(x) = -\frac{6}{x^4},$$

$$\cdots \cdots \cdots \cdots$$

$$f^{(n)}(x) = \frac{(-1)^{n-1}(n-1)!}{x^n}.$$

$$\therefore R_n(x) = (-1)^{n-1} \frac{(n-1)!}{(n-1)!} \int_0^h \frac{1}{(x+h-t)^n} t^{n-1} dt.$$

Now since $t$ varies from 0 to $h$, the greatest value of $R_n(x)$ is obtained by putting $t=h$ in the integrand. We then have, omitting the factor $(-1)^{n-1}$, which is never greater than 1,

$$R_n(x) < \int_0^h \frac{t^{n-1} dt}{x^n} = \frac{1}{x^n} \int_0^h t^{n-1} dt = \frac{1}{x^n} \frac{h^n}{n}$$

$$= \frac{1}{n} \left(\frac{h}{x}\right)^n.$$

Suppose $x=1$, $h=0.01$. Then $h/x=0.01$. If, therefore, we wish to know how many terms in the expansion of $\log_e 1.01$ are necessary in order to get a result correct to seven decimal places we take $R_n \leqq 0.00000005$.

$$\therefore \frac{1}{n}(0.01)^n = 0.00000005.$$

It is evident by inspection that $n=4$ will give a remainder much smaller than the allowable error. Hence we take four terms of the expansion of log $(x+h)$.

The reader can easily verify that the first form of remainder gives the same result as that just found.

10b). *Alternating Series.* An alternating series is an infinite series in which the terms are alternately positive and negative. Such a series is convergent if (a) each term is numerically less than the preceding and (b) the limit of the $n$th term is zero when $n$ becomes infinite.

Alternating series are of frequent occurrence in applied mathematics and are the most satisfactory for purposes of computation, because it is always an easy matter to determine the error of a computed result. The rule for determining the error is simply this:

*In a convergent alternating series the error committed in stopping with any term is always less than the first term neglected.*

Thus, since

$$\log_e (1 + x) = x - \frac{x^2}{2} + \frac{x^3}{3} - \frac{x^4}{4} + \frac{x^5}{5} - \cdots,$$

we have

$$\log_e (1.01) = 0.01 - \frac{(0.01)^2}{2} + \frac{(0.01)^3}{3} + R,$$

where $R < |(0.01)^4/4| = 0.0000000025$.

We therefore get a result true to eight decimal places by taking only three terms of the expansion.

10c). *Some Important Series and Their Remainder Terms.* Below are given some of the most useful series and their remainder terms, alternating series not being included because their remainder terms can be computed by the rule given above.

1. *The Binomial Series.*

$$(1 + x)^m = 1 + mx + \frac{m(m - 1)}{2!}x^2 + \frac{m(m - 1)(m - 2)}{3!}x^3 + \cdots$$

$$+ \frac{m(m - 1)(m - 2) \cdots (m - n + 2)}{(n - 1)!}x^{n-1} + R_n,$$

where

(a)    $R_n = \dfrac{m(m - 1)(m - 2) \cdots (m - n + 1)}{n!}x^n(1 + \theta x)^{m-n}, 0 < \theta < 1,$

in all cases.

(b) $\qquad R_n < \left| \dfrac{m(m-1)(m-2)\cdots(m-n+1)}{n!} x^n \right|$ if $x > 0$.

(c) $\qquad R_n < \left| \dfrac{m(m-1)(m-2)\cdots(m-n+1)}{n!} \dfrac{x^n}{(1+x)^{n-m}} \right|$

if $x < 0$ and $n > m$.

(d) $\qquad\qquad R_n < |x^n| (1+x)^m$ if $-1 < m < 0$.

If $m$ is a fraction, positive or negative, or a negative integer, the binomial expansion is valid only when $|x| < 1$. Also, except when $m$ is a *positive integer*, a binomial such as $(a+b)^m$ must be written in the form

$$a^m \left(1 + \frac{b}{a}\right)^m \text{ if } a > b, \text{ or } b^m \left(1 + \frac{a}{b}\right)^m \text{ if } b > a,$$

before expanding it.

2. *Exponential Series.*

(a) $e^x = 1 + x + \dfrac{x^2}{2!} + \dfrac{x^3}{3!} + \cdots + \dfrac{x^{n-1}}{(n-1)!} + \dfrac{x^n}{n!} e^{\theta x}.$

(b) $a^x = 1 + x \log a + \dfrac{(x \log a)^2}{2!} + \cdots + \dfrac{(x \log a)^{n-1}}{(n-1)!} + \dfrac{(x \log a)^n}{n!} a^{\theta x}.$

If in (a) we put $x = 1$ we get the following series for computing $e$:

(c) $\qquad e = 1 + 1 + \dfrac{1}{2} + \dfrac{1}{3!} + \dfrac{1}{4!} + \cdots + \dfrac{1}{(n-1)!} + \dfrac{e^\theta}{n!}.$

Here

$$R_n = \frac{e^\theta}{n!}.$$

But since $e < 3$ and $\theta \leqq 1$, it is plain that

(d) $\qquad\qquad\qquad R_n < \dfrac{3}{n!}.$

A more definite formula for $R_n$ can be found as follows:

Writing more than $n$ terms of the series (c), we have

$$e = \left[ 1 + 1 + \frac{1}{2!} + \frac{1}{3!} + \cdots + \frac{1}{(n-1)!} \right]$$
$$+ \frac{1}{n!} + \frac{1}{(n+1)!} + \frac{1}{(n+2)!} + \cdots,$$

where the remainder after $n$ terms is

$$R_n = \frac{1}{n!} + \frac{1}{(n+1)!} + \frac{1}{(n+2)!} + \cdots$$

$$= \frac{1}{n!}\left(1 + \frac{1}{n+1} + \frac{1}{(n+1)(n+2)} + \cdots\right).$$

The quantity in parenthesis on the right is clearly less than the sum of the geometric series

$$1 + \frac{1}{n} + \frac{1}{n^2} + \frac{1}{n^3} + \cdots,$$

the sum of which is

$$\frac{1}{1 - \dfrac{1}{n}} = \frac{n}{n-1}.$$

Hence

(e)    $$R_n < \frac{1}{n!}\,\frac{n}{n-1}, \text{ or } R_n < \frac{1}{(n-1)(n-1)!}.$$

By means of this formula (e) we can find the requisite number of terms in the expansion (c) to give the value of $e$ correct to any desired number of decimal places. Thus, if we wished to find $e$ correct to ten decimal places by means of the series (c) we would find $n$ from the equation $1/(n-1)(n-1)! = 0.00000000005$. With the aid of a table of the reciprocals of the factorials we find that $n-1 = 13$, or $n = 14$. We should therefore take 14 terms of the series (c). We find in like manner that in order to compute $e$ correct to 100 decimal places we should take 71 terms of the series (c).

3. *Logarithmic Series.*

$$\log(m+1) = \log m + 2\left[\frac{1}{2m+1} + \frac{1}{3(2m+1)^3} + \frac{1}{5(2m+1)^5} + \cdots \right.$$

$$\left. + \frac{1}{(2n-1)(2m+1)^{2n-1}}\right] + R_n,$$

where

$$R_n < \frac{4}{(2n+1)(2m+1)^{2n+1}}.$$

Thus, to find $\log_e 5$ correct to ten decimal places we have $m+1 = 5$, or $m = 4$. Then

$$\frac{4}{(2n + 1)(5)^{2n+1}} = \frac{1}{10^{10}} \times \frac{1}{2}.$$

We find by trial that $n = 7$ is more than sufficient to insure the desired accuracy. We should therefore take seven terms of the series within the brackets.

10d). *Some nth Derivatives.* In computing the remainder term in a series it is necessary to have the $n$th derivative of the given function. To facilitate the calculation of $R_n$ we therefore give below a list of $n$th derivatives of some simple functions. The symbol $D$ denotes differentiation with respect to $x$, or $D = d/dx$.

(a) $$D^n a^x = a^x (\log_e a)^n.$$

(b) $$D^n \sin x = \sin \left( x + n\frac{\pi}{2} \right).$$

(c) $$D^n \cos x = \cos \left( x + n\frac{\pi}{2} \right).$$

(d) $$D^n \left( \frac{1}{a + bx} \right) = \frac{(-1)^n n! b^n}{(a + bx)^{n+1}}.$$

(e) $$D^n \left( \frac{1}{\sqrt{a + bx}} \right) = \frac{(-1)^n 1 \cdot 3 \cdot 5 \cdots (2n - 1)}{2^n (a + bx)^{(2n+1)/2}} b^n.$$

(f) $$D^n \log_e (a + bx) = \frac{(-1)^n (n - 1)! b^n}{(a + bx)^n}.$$

(g) $$D^n \left( \frac{\log_e x}{x} \right) = \frac{(-1)^n n!}{x^{n+1}} \left[ \log_e x - \left( 1 + \frac{1}{2} + \frac{1}{3} + \cdots + \frac{1}{n} \right) \right].$$

(h) $$D^n \log_e (1 + x^2) = \frac{(-1)^{n-1} 2(n - 1)! \cos \left[ n \sin^{-1} \left( \frac{1}{\sqrt{1 + x^2}} \right) \right]}{(1 + x^2)^{n/2}}.$$

(i) $$D^n \tan^{-1} x = \frac{(-1)^n (n - 1)!}{(1 + x^2)^{n/2}} \sin \left[ n \sin^{-1} \left( \frac{1}{\sqrt{1 + x^2}} \right) \right].$$

(j) $$D^n \left( \frac{1}{1 + x^2} \right) = \frac{(-1)^n n!}{(1 + x^2)^{(n+1)/2}} \sin \left[ (n + 1) \sin^{-1} \left( \frac{1}{\sqrt{1 + x^2}} \right) \right].$$

(k) $$D^n \log_e \Gamma(x) = \frac{(-1)^n (n - 2)!}{x^n} [x + \theta(n - 1)], \quad 0 < \theta < 1,$$

$$x > 0, \quad n > 1.$$

For an extensive investigation of $n$th derivatives the reader is referred to Steffensen's *Interpolation*, pp. 231–241.

## EXAMPLES ON CHAPTER I

1. Round off the following numbers correctly to four significant figures:

63.8543, 93487, 0.0063945, 83615, 363042, 0.090038, 53908.

2. A carpenter measures a 10-foot beam to the nearest eighth of and inch, and a machinist measures a $\frac{1}{2}$-inch bolt to the nearest thousandth of an inch. Which measurement is the more accurate?

3. The following numbers are all approximate and are correct as far as their last digits only. Find their sum.

136.421, 28.3, 321, 68.243, 17.482.

4. Find the sum of the following approximate numbers, each being correct only to the number of significant figures given:

0.15625, 86.43, 191.6, 432.0×10, 930.42.

5. The numbers 48.392 and 6852.4 are both approximate and true only to their last digits. Find their difference and state how many figures in the result are trustworthy.

6. Find the value of $\sqrt{10} - \pi$ correct to five significant figures.

7. The theoretical horsepower available in a stream is given by the formula

$$H.P. = \frac{whQ}{550},$$

where $h$ = head in feet, $Q$ = discharge in cubic feet per second, and $w$ = weight of a cubic foot of water. The weight of fresh water varies from 62.3 to 62.5 lbs. per cubic foot, depending upon its temperature and purity.

If the measured values of $Q$ and $h$ are $Q$ = 463 cu. ft./sec. and $h$ = 16.42 ft., find the H.P. of the stream and state how many figures of the result are reliable.

8. The velocity of water flowing in long pipes is given by the formula

$$v = \sqrt{\frac{2ghd}{fl}} \text{ ft./sec.,}$$

where     $g$ = acceleration of gravity = 32.2 ft./sec.$^2$,
$h$ = head in feet,
$d$ = diameter of pipe in feet,
$l$ = length of pipe in feet,
$f$ = coefficient of pipe friction.

In this problem the factor $f$ is the most uncertain. It varies from 0.01 to 0.05 and is usually somewhere between 0.02 and 0.03. Assuming that $f$ is within the limits 0.02 and 0.03 and taking

$$g = 32.2,$$
$$h = 112 \text{ feet},$$
$$d = \tfrac{1}{2} \text{ foot},$$
$$l = 1865 \text{ feet},$$

find $v$ and state how many figures of the result are reliable.

9. The velocity of water in a short pipe is given by the formula

$$v = \sqrt{\frac{2gh}{1.5 + fl/d}},$$

where $g$, $h$, $f$, $l$, and $d$ have the same meanings as in the preceding example. Taking $l = 75$ feet and the other data the same as in Ex. 8, find $v$ and state how many figures of the result are trustworthy.

10. The acceleration of gravity at any point on the earth's surface is given by the formula

$$g = 32.1721 - 0.08211 \cos 2L - 0.000003H,$$

where $H =$ altitude in feet above sea level, and $L =$ latitude of the place. It thus appears that the value of $g$ is not 32, nor 32.2, nor even 32.17.

Compute the kinetic energy of a 100-pound projectile moving with a velocity of 2000 feet per second by taking $g$ equal to 32, 32.2, and 32.17 in succession and note the extent to which the results disagree after the first two or three figures.

11. The approximate latitude of a place can be easily found by measuring the altitude $h$ of Polaris at a known time $t$ and using the formula

$$L = h - p \cos t,$$

where $p =$ polar distance $= 90° -$ declination.

Treating $p$ as a constant and equal to $1°07'30''$, and taking $h = 41°25'$, $t = 0°38'42''$, find the error in $L$ due to errors of $1'$ in $h$ and $5^s$ in $t$.

12. In the preceding example find the allowable errors in $h$ and $t$ in order that the error in $L$ shall not exceed $1'$, using the same values of $p$, $t$, and $h$ as before.

13. The distance between any two points $P_1$ and $P_2$ on the earth's surface is given by the formula

$$\cos D = \sin L_1 \sin L_2 + \cos L_1 \cos L_2 \cos (\lambda_1 - \lambda_2),$$

where $L_1$, $L_2$ and $\lambda_1$, $\lambda_2$ denote the respective latitudes and longitudes of the two places. Find the allowable errors in $L_1$, $L_2$, $\lambda_1$, $\lambda_2$ in order that the error in $D$ shall not exceed $1'$ (a geographical mile), taking

$$L_1 = 36°10'N, \quad L_2 = 58°43'N, \quad \lambda_1 = 82°15'W, \quad \lambda_2 = 125°42'W.$$

14. The fundamental equations of practical astronomy are:

(1) $$\sin h = \sin \delta \sin L + \cos \delta \cos L \cos t,$$

(2) $$\cos h \cos A = - \sin \delta \cos L + \cos \delta \sin L \cos t,$$

(3) $$\cos h \sin A = \cos \delta \sin t,$$

where $\delta$ denotes declination, $t$ hour angle, $h$ altitude, and $A$ azimuth of a celestial body and $L$ denotes the latitude of a place on the earth. The declination $\delta$ is always accurately known and may therefore be considered free from error.

Differentiating (1) by considering $\delta$ constant and $h$, $L$, $t$ as variables, we have

$$\cos h \, dh = \sin \delta \cos L \, dL - \cos \delta \sin L \cos t \, dL - \cos \delta \cos L \sin t \, dt.$$

Replacing $\cos \delta \sin L \cos t$ and $\cos \delta \sin t$ on the right by their values from (2) and (3), respectively, we get

$$dh = - (\cos A \, dL + \sin A \cos L \, dt).$$

Solving for $dL$,

(4) $$dL = - (\sec A \, dh + \tan A \cos L \, dt).$$

This equation shows that the numerical value of $dL$ is least when $A$ is near $0°$ or $180°$, that is, when the body is near the *meridian*. If $A$ should be near $90°$, that is, if the body should be near the prime vertical, the error in $L$ might be enormous. Hence when determining latitude the observed body should be as near the meridian as possible.

Using equation (4), compute $dL$ when $dh = 1'$, $dt = 10^s$, $L = 40°$, $A = 10°$, and $A = 80°$.

15. Using the formula $dL = - (\sec A \, dh + \tan A \cos L \, dt)$, find the allowable errors in $t$ and $h$ in order that the error in $L$ may not exceed $1'$ when $L = 40°$ and (a) $A = 10°$ and (b) $A = 75°$.

16. From the relation

$$\cos h \, dh = (\sin \delta \cos L - \cos \delta \sin L \cos t) dL - \cos \delta \cos L \sin t \, dt$$

we find by means of (2) and (3) of Ex. 14

$$dt = - \left( \frac{dh + \cos A \, dL}{\sin A \cos L} \right).$$

This equation shows that $dt$ is least numerically when $A$ is near $90°$, that is, when the observed body is near the prime vertical; it also shows that when the body is on or near the prime vertical an error in the assumed latitude has practically no effect on the error in $t$.

Compute $dt$ when $dh=1'$, $dL=5'$, $L=40°$, $A=10°$, and $A=80°$.

17. Using the formula for $dt$ in the preceding example, find the allowable errors in $L$ and $h$ in order that $dt$ may not exceed $3^s$, taking $L=40°$, $A=10°$, and $A=80°$.

18. Using the formula of Ex. 16, take $dt=3^s$, $dh=1'$, and find $dL$ for $A=10°$ and $A=80°$.

19. In the equation

$$x = a \sin (kt + \alpha)$$

suppose $a$, $k$, and $\alpha$ are subject to the errors $\Delta a$, $\Delta k$, $\Delta \alpha$, respectively. Compute $\Delta x$ and see which of the errors $\Delta a$, $\Delta k$, $\Delta \alpha$ is the most potent in causing an error in $x$.

20. Find the value of

$$I = \int_0^{0.8} \frac{\sin x}{x} dx$$

to five decimal places and estimate the accuracy of your result.

21. Compute the value of the integral

$$I = \int_0^{\pi/2} \sqrt{1 - 0.162 \sin^2 \phi} \, d\phi$$

by first expanding the integrand by the binomial theorem and then integrating the result term by term. Estimate the accuracy of your result.

# CHAPTER II

## INTERPOLATION

### DIFFERENCES.  NEWTON'S FORMULAS OF INTERPOLATION

**11. Introduction.** Interpolation has been defined as the art of reading between the lines of a table, and in elementary mathematics the term usually denotes the process of computing intermediate values of a function from a set of given or tabular values of that function. The general problem of interpolation, however, is much larger than this. In higher mathematics we frequently have to deal with functions whose analytical form is either totally unknown or else is of such a nature (complicated or otherwise) that the function can not easily be subjected to such operations as may be required.  In either case it is desirable to replace the given function by another which can be more readily handled.  This operation of replacing or representing a given function by a simpler one constitutes interpolation in the broad sense of the term.

The general problem of interpolation consists, then, in representing a function, known or unknown, in a form chosen in advance, with the aid of given values which this function takes for definite values of the independent variable.

Thus, let $y = f(x)$ be a function given by the values $y_0, y_1, y_2, \cdots y_n$ which it takes for the values $x_0, x_1, x_2, \cdots x_n$ of the independent variable $x$, and let $\phi(x)$ denote an arbitrary simpler function so constructed that it takes the same values as $f(x)$ for the values $x_0, x_1, x_2, \cdots x_n$. Then if $f(x)$ is replaced by $\phi(x)$ over a given interval, the process constitutes interpolation, and the function $\phi(x)$ is a formula of interpolation.

The function $\phi(x)$ can take a variety of forms.  When $\phi(x)$ is a polynomial, the process of representing $f(x)$ by $\phi(x)$ is called *parabolic* or *polynomial* interpolation; and when $\phi(x)$ is a finite trigonometric series, the process is trigonometric interpolation.  In like manner, $\phi(x)$ may be a series of exponential functions, Legendre polynomials, Bessel functions, etc.  In practical problems we always choose for $\phi(x)$ the simplest function which will represent the given function over the interval in question.  Since polynomials are the simplest functions, we usually take a polynomial for $\phi(x)$, and nearly all the standard formulas

38

of interpolation are polynomial formulas.  In case the given function is
known to be periodic, however, it is better to represent it by a trigonometric series.

The justification for replacing a given function by a polynomial or
by a trigonometric series rests on two remarkable theorems proved by
Weierstrass* in 1885.  These theorems may be stated as follows:

I.  Every function which is continuous in an interval $(a, b)$ can be
represented in that interval, to any desired degree of accuracy, by a
polynomial; that is, it is possible to find a polynomial $P(x)$ such that
$\left|f(x) - P(x)\right| < \epsilon$ for every value of $x$ in the interval $(a, b)$, where $\epsilon$ is
any preassigned positive quantity.

II.  Every continuous function of period $2\pi$ can be represented by a
finite trigonometric series of the form

$$g(x) = a_0 + a_1 \sin x + a_2 \sin 2x + \cdots + a_n \sin nx$$

$$+ b_1 \cos x + b_2 \cos 2x + \cdots + b_n \cos nx;$$

or $\left|f(x) - g(x)\right| < \delta$ for all values of $x$ in the interval considered, where
$\delta$ represents any preassigned positive quantity.

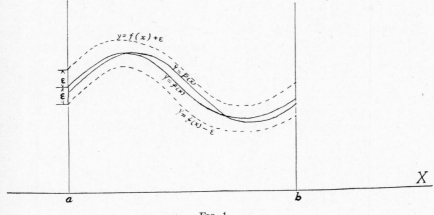

FIG. 1

Geometrically these theorems mean that, having drawn the graphs
of $y = f(x)$, $y = f(x) + \epsilon$, and $y = f(x) - \epsilon$, it is possible to find a polynomial
or a finite trigonometric series whose graph remains within the region
bounded by $y = f(x) + \epsilon$ and $y = f(x) - \epsilon$ for all values of $x$ between $a$ and
$b$, however small $\epsilon$ may be.  (See Fig. 1.)  These theorems mean, therefore,

* *Über die analytische Darstellbarkeit sogenannter willkürlicher Funktionen einer
reelen Veränderlichen* (Sitzungsberichte der Kgl. Ak. der Wiss., 1885).

that the given function may be replaced by a polynomial or by a finite trigonometric series to any desired degree of accuracy.

**12. Differences.** If $y_0$, $y_1$, $y_2$, $\cdots y_n$ denote a set of values of any function $y = f(x)$, then $y_1 - y_0$, $y_2 - y_1$, $y_3 - y_2$, $\cdots y_n - y_{n-1}$ are called the *first differences* of the function $y$. Denoting these differences by $\Delta y_0$, $\Delta y_1$, $\Delta y_2$, etc., we have $\Delta y_0 = y_1 - y_0$, $\Delta y_1 = y_2 - y_1$, $\cdots \Delta y_{n-1} = y_n - y_{n-1}$, $\Delta y_n = y_{n+1} - y_n$.

The differences of these first differences are called *second differences*. Denoting them by $\Delta^2 y_0$, $\Delta^2 y_1$, etc., we have

$$\Delta^2 y_0 = \Delta y_1 - \Delta y_0 = y_2 - 2y_1 + y_0,$$

$$\Delta^2 y_1 = \Delta y_2 - \Delta y_1 = y_3 - 2y_2 + y_1,$$

etc.

In like manner, the *third differences* are

$$\Delta^3 y_0 = \Delta^2 y_1 - \Delta^2 y_0 = y_3 - 3y_2 + 3y_1 - y_0,$$

$$\Delta^3 y_1 = \Delta^2 y_2 - \Delta^2 y_1 = y_4 - 3y_3 + 3y_2 - y_1,$$

etc.

The following *difference table* shows how the differences of all orders are formed:

| $x$ | $y$ | $\Delta y$ | $\Delta^2 y$ | $\Delta^3 y$ | $\Delta^4 y$ | $\Delta^5 y$ | $\Delta^6 y$ | $\Delta^7 y$ | $\Delta^8 y$ |
|---|---|---|---|---|---|---|---|---|---|
| $x_0$ | $y_0$ | | | | | | | | |
| | | $\Delta y_0$ | | | | | | | |
| $x_1$ | $y_1$ | | $\Delta^2 y_0$ | | | | | | |
| | | $\Delta y_1$ | | $\Delta^3 y_0$ | | | | | |
| $x_2$ | $y_2$ | | $\Delta^2 y_1$ | | $\Delta^4 y_0$ | | | | |
| | | $\Delta y_2$ | | $\Delta^3 y_1$ | | $\Delta^5 y_0$ | | | |
| $x_3$ | $y_3$ | | $\Delta^2 y_2$ | | $\Delta^4 y_1$ | | $\Delta^6 y_0$ | | |
| | | $\Delta y_3$ | | $\Delta^3 y_2$ | | $\Delta^5 y_1$ | | $\Delta^7 y_0$ | |
| $x_4$ | $y_4$ | | $\Delta^2 y_3$ | | $\Delta^4 y_2$ | | $\Delta^6 y_1$ | | $\Delta^8 y_0$ |
| | | $\Delta y_4$ | | $\Delta^3 y_3$ | | $\Delta^5 y_2$ | | $\Delta^7 y_1$ | |
| $x_5$ | $y_5$ | | $\Delta^2 y_4$ | | $\Delta^4 y_3$ | | $\Delta^6 y_2$ | | |
| | | $\Delta y_5$ | | $\Delta^3 y_4$ | | $\Delta^5 y_3$ | | | |
| $x_6$ | $y_6$ | | $\Delta^2 y_5$ | | $\Delta^4 y_4$ | | | | |
| | | $\Delta y_6$ | | $\Delta^3 y_5$ | | | | | |
| $x_7$ | $y_7$ | | $\Delta^2 y_6$ | | | | | | |
| | | $\Delta y_7$ | | | | | | | |
| $x_8$ | $y_8$ | | | | | | | | |

TABLE 1.  Diagonal Difference Table.

This table is called a *diagonal* difference table.  The majority of difference tables are of this kind, but for many purposes a more compact table, called a *horizontal* difference table, is preferable.  In the horizontal difference tables the differences of different order are denoted by subscripts instead of exponents.  Using the notation for horizontal differences, we can rewrite the preceding difference table in the horizontal form as follows:

| $x$ | $y$ | $\Delta_1 y$ | $\Delta_2 y$ | $\Delta_3 y$ | $\Delta_4 y$ | $\Delta_5 y$ | $\Delta_6 y$ | $\Delta_7 y$ | $\Delta_8 y$ |
|---|---|---|---|---|---|---|---|---|---|
| $x_0$ | $y_0$ | | | | | | | | |
| $x_1$ | $y_1$ | $\Delta_1 y_1$ | | | | | | | |
| $x_2$ | $y_2$ | $\Delta_1 y_2$ | $\Delta_2 y_2$ | | | | | | |
| $x_3$ | $y_3$ | $\Delta_1 y_3$ | $\Delta_2 y_3$ | $\Delta_3 y_3$ | | | | | |
| $x_4$ | $y_4$ | $\Delta_1 y_4$ | $\Delta_2 y_4$ | $\Delta_3 y_4$ | $\Delta_4 y_4$ | | | | |
| $x_5$ | $y_5$ | $\Delta_1 y_5$ | $\Delta_2 y_5$ | $\Delta_3 y_5$ | $\Delta_4 y_5$ | $\Delta_5 y_5$ | | | |
| $x_6$ | $y_6$ | $\Delta_1 y_6$ | $\Delta_2 y_6$ | $\Delta_3 y_6$ | $\Delta_4 y_6$ | $\Delta_5 y_6$ | $\Delta_6 y_6$ | | |
| $x_7$ | $y_7$ | $\Delta_1 y_7$ | $\Delta_2 y_7$ | $\Delta_3 y_7$ | $\Delta_4 y_7$ | $\Delta_5 y_7$ | $\Delta_6 y_7$ | $\Delta_7 y_7$ | |
| $x_8$ | $y_8$ | $\Delta_1 y_8$ | $\Delta_2 y_8$ | $\Delta_3 y_8$ | $\Delta_4 y_8$ | $\Delta_5 y_8$ | $\Delta_6 y_8$ | $\Delta_7 y_8$ | $\Delta_8 y_8$ |

TABLE 2.  Horizontal Difference Table.

In order to see the relation between horizontal and diagonal differences of the same order, we give in Tables 3 and 4 the differences of both kinds in terms of the $y$'s.

Inspection of these tables shows that the top diagonal line is the same in both, but that the bottom upwardly inclined diagonal in Table 3 is the same as the bottom horizontal line in Table 4.  Also, from Table 3 we have, for example,

$$\Delta^3 y_1 = y_4 - 3y_3 + 3y_2 - y_1.$$

Likewise, from Table 4 we have

$$\Delta_3 y_4 = y_4 - 3y_3 + 3y_2 - y_1.$$

Hence

$$\Delta^3 y_1 = \Delta_3 y_4.$$

A glance at Tables 3 and 4 will show that the general relation between the $\Delta$'s affected with exponents and those affected with subscripts is

$$\Delta^m y_k = \Delta_m y_{k+m} \qquad \text{(going forward from } y_k),$$

or

$$\Delta_m y_n = \Delta^m y_{n-m} \qquad \text{(going backward from } y_n),$$

where $m$ denotes the order of differences and $k$ and $n$ the number of the tabulated value.

| $y$ | $\Delta y$ | $\Delta^2 y$ | $\Delta^3 y$ | $\Delta^4 y$ | $\Delta^5 y$ |
|---|---|---|---|---|---|
| $y_0$ | | | | | |
| | $y_1 - y_0$ | | | | |
| $y_1$ | | $y_2 - 2y_1 + y_0$ | | | |
| | $y_2 - y_1$ | | $y_3 - 3y_2 + 3y_1 - y_0$ | | |
| $y_2$ | | $y_3 - 2y_2 + y_1$ | | $y_4 - 4y_3 + 6y_2 - 4y_1 + y_0$ | |
| | $y_3 - y_2$ | | $y_4 - 3y_3 + 3y_2 - y_1$ | | $y_5 - 5y_4 + 10y_3 - 10y_2 + 5y_1 - y_0$ |
| $y_3$ | | $y_4 - 2y_3 + y_2$ | | $y_5 - 4y_4 + 6y_3 - 4y_2 + y_1$ | |
| | $y_4 - y_3$ | | $y_5 - 3y_4 + 3y_3 - y_2$ | | $y_6 - 5y_5 + 10y_4 - 10y_3 + 5y_2 - y_1$ |
| $y_4$ | | $y_5 - 2y_4 + y_3$ | | $y_6 - 4y_5 + 6y_4 - 4y_3 + y_2$ | |
| | $y_5 - y_4$ | | $y_6 - 3y_5 + 3y_4 - y_3$ | | $y_7 - 5y_6 + 10y_5 - 10y_4 + 5y_3 - y_2$ |
| $y_5$ | | $y_6 - 2y_5 + y_4$ | | $y_7 - 4y_6 + 6y_5 - 4y_4 + y_3$ | |
| | $y_6 - y_5$ | | $y_7 - 3y_6 + 3y_5 - y_4$ | | $y_8 - 5y_7 + 10y_6 - 10y_5 + 5y_4 - y_3$ |
| $y_6$ | | $y_7 - 2y_6 + y_5$ | | $y_8 - 4y_7 + 6y_6 - 4y_5 + y_4$ | |
| | $y_7 - y_6$ | | $y_8 - 3y_7 + 3y_6 - y_5$ | | |
| $y_7$ | | $y_8 - 2y_7 + y_6$ | | | |
| | $y_8 - y_7$ | | | | |
| $y_8$ | | | | | |

TABLE 3. Diagonal Differences.

| $y$ | $\Delta_1 y$ | $\Delta_2 y$ | $\Delta_3 y$ | $\Delta_4 y$ | $\Delta_5 y$ |
|---|---|---|---|---|---|
| $y_0$ | $y_1 - y_0$ | $y_2 - 2y_1 + y_0$ | $y_3 - 3y_2 + 3y_1 - y_0$ | $y_4 - 4y_3 + 6y_2 - 4y_1 + y_0$ | $y_5 - 5y_4 + 10y_3 - 10y_2 + 5y_1 - y_0$ |
| $y_1$ | $y_2 - y_1$ | $y_3 - 2y_2 + y_1$ | $y_4 - 3y_3 + 3y_2 - y_1$ | $y_5 - 4y_4 + 6y_3 - 4y_2 + y_1$ | $y_6 - 5y_5 + 10y_4 - 10y_3 + 5y_2 - y_1$ |
| $y_2$ | $y_3 - y_2$ | $y_4 - 2y_3 + y_2$ | $y_5 - 3y_4 + 3y_3 - y_2$ | $y_6 - 4y_5 + 6y_4 - 4y_3 + y_2$ | $y_7 - 5y_6 + 10y_5 - 10y_4 + 5y_3 - y_2$ |
| $y_3$ | $y_4 - y_3$ | $y_5 - 2y_4 + y_3$ | $y_6 - 3y_5 + 3y_4 - y_3$ | $y_7 - 4y_6 + 6y_5 - 4y_4 + y_3$ | $y_8 - 5y_7 + 10y_6 - 10y_5 + 5y_4 - y_3$ |
| $y_4$ | $y_5 - y_4$ | $y_6 - 2y_5 + y_4$ | $y_7 - 3y_6 + 3y_5 - y_4$ | $y_8 - 4y_7 + 6y_6 - 4y_5 + y_4$ | |
| $y_5$ | $y_6 - y_5$ | $y_7 - 2y_6 + y_5$ | $y_8 - 3y_7 + 3y_6 - y_5$ | | |
| $y_6$ | $y_7 - y_6$ | $y_8 - 2y_7 + y_6$ | | | |
| $y_7$ | $y_8 - y_7$ | | | | |
| $y_8$ | | | | | |

TABLE 4. Horizontal Differences.

**13. Effect of an Error in a Tabular Value.** Let $y_0$, $y_1$, $y_2$, $\cdots$ $y_n$ be the true values of a function, and suppose the value $y_5$ to be affected with an error $\epsilon$, so that its erroneous value is $y_5 + \epsilon$. Then the successive differences of the $y$'s are as shown below:

| $y$ | $\Delta y$ | $\Delta^2 y$ | $\Delta^3 y$ | $\Delta^4 y$ |
|---|---|---|---|---|
| $y_0$ | | | | |
| | $\Delta y_0$ | | | |
| $y_1$ | | $\Delta^2 y_0$ | | |
| | $\Delta y_1$ | | $\Delta^3 y_0$ | |
| $y_2$ | | $\Delta^2 y_1$ | | $\Delta^4 y_0$ |
| | $\Delta y_2$ | | $\Delta^3 y_1$ | |
| $y_3$ | | $\Delta^2 y_2$ | | $\Delta^4 y_1 + \epsilon$ |
| | $\Delta y_3$ | | $\Delta^3 y_2 + \epsilon$ | |
| $y_4$ | | $\Delta^2 y_3 + \epsilon$ | | $\Delta^4 y_2 - 4\epsilon$ |
| | $\Delta y_4 + \epsilon$ | | $\Delta^3 y_3 - 3\epsilon$ | |
| $y_5 + \epsilon$ | | $\Delta^2 y_4 - 2\epsilon$ | | $\Delta^4 y_3 + 6\epsilon$ |
| | $\Delta y_5 - \epsilon$ | | $\Delta^3 y_4 + 3\epsilon$ | |
| $y_6$ | | $\Delta^2 y_5 + \epsilon$ | | $\Delta^4 y_4 - 4\epsilon$ |
| | $\Delta y_6$ | | $\Delta^3 y_5 - \epsilon$ | |
| $y_7$ | | $\Delta^2 y_6$ | | $\Delta^4 y_5 + \epsilon$ |
| | $\Delta y_7$ | | $\Delta^3 y_6$ | |
| $y_8$ | | $\Delta^2 y_7$ | | $\Delta^4 y_6$ |
| | $\Delta y_8$ | | $\Delta^3 y_7$ | |
| $y_9$ | | $\Delta^2 y_8$ | | |
| | $\Delta y_9$ | | | |
| $y_{10}$ | | | | |

TABLE 5. Showing the effect of an error.

This table shows that the effect of an error increases with the successive differences, that the coefficients of the $\epsilon$'s are the binomial coefficients with alternating signs, and that *the algebraic sum of the errors in any difference column is zero.* It shows also that *the maximum error in the differences is in the same horizontal line as the erroneous tabular value.*

The following table shows the effect of an error in a horizontal difference table:

| $y$ | $\Delta_1 y$ | $\Delta_2 y$ | $\Delta_3 y$ | $\Delta_4 y$ |
|---|---|---|---|---|
| $y_0$ | | | | |
| $y_1$ | $\Delta_1 y_1$ | | | |
| $y_2$ | $\Delta_1 y_2$ | $\Delta_2 y_2$ | | |
| $y_3$ | $\Delta_1 y_3$ | $\Delta_2 y_3$ | $\Delta_3 y_3$ | |
| $y_4$ | $\Delta_1 y_4$ | $\Delta_2 y_4$ | $\Delta_3 y_4$ | $\Delta_4 y_4$ |
| $y_5 + \epsilon$ | $\Delta_1 y_5 + \epsilon$ | $\Delta_2 y_5 + \epsilon$ | $\Delta_3 y_5 + \epsilon$ | $\Delta_4 y_5 + \epsilon$ |
| $y_6$ | $\Delta_1 y_6 - \epsilon$ | $\Delta_2 y_6 - 2\epsilon$ | $\Delta_3 y_6 - 3\epsilon$ | $\Delta_4 y_6 - 4\epsilon$ |
| $y_7$ | $\Delta_1 y_7$ | $\Delta_2 y_7 + \epsilon$ | $\Delta_3 y_7 + 3\epsilon$ | $\Delta_4 y_7 + 6\epsilon$ |
| $y_8$ | $\Delta_1 y_8$ | $\Delta_2 y_8$ | $\Delta_3 y_8 - \epsilon$ | $\Delta_4 y_8 - 4\epsilon$ |
| $y_9$ | $\Delta_1 y_9$ | $\Delta_2 y_9$ | $\Delta_3 y_9$ | $\Delta_4 y_9 + \epsilon$ |
| $y_{10}$ | $\Delta_1 y_{10}$ | $\Delta_2 y_{10}$ | $\Delta_3 y_{10}$ | $\Delta_4 y_{10}$ |

TABLE 6.

Here, again, the effect of the error is the same as in the preceding table, but in this table *the first erroneous difference of any order is in the same horizontal line as the erroneous tabular value.*

The law according to which an error is propagated in a difference table enables us to trace such an error to its source and correct it. As an illustration of the process of detecting and correcting an error in a tabulated function, let us consider the following table:*

| $x$ | $y$ | $\Delta_1 y$ | $\Delta_2 y$ | $\Delta_3 y$ | $\Delta_4 y$ | $\epsilon$ |
|------|---------|------|-------|------|------|-------|
| 0.10 | 0.09983 |      |       |      |      |       |
| 0.15 | 0.14944 | 4961 |       |      |      |       |
| 0.20 | 0.19867 | 4923 | − 38  |      |      |       |
| 0.25 | 0.24740 | 4873 | − 50  | −12  |      |       |
| 0.30 | 0.29552 | 4812 | − 61  | −11  | 1    |       |
| 0.35 | 0.34290 | 4738 | − 74  | −13  | − 1  |       |
| 0.40 | 0.38945 | 4655 | − 83  | − 9  | 4    | $\epsilon$ |
| 0.45 | 0.43497 | 4552 | −103  | −20  | −11  | $-4\epsilon$ |
| 0.50 | 0.47943 | 4446 | −106  | − 3  | 17   | $6\epsilon$ |
| 0.55 | 0.52269 | 4326 | −120  | −14  | −11  | $-4\epsilon$ |
| 0.60 | 0.56464 | 4195 | −131  | −11  | 3    | $\epsilon$ |
| 0.65 | 0.60519 | 4055 | −140  | − 9  | 2    |       |
| 0.70 | 0.64422 | 3903 | −152  | −12  | − 3  |       |

Here the third differences are quite irregular near the middle of the column, and the fourth differences are still more irregular. The irregularity begins in each column on the horizontal line corresponding to $x = 0.40$.

Since the algebraic sum of the fourth differences is 1, the average value of the fourth differences is only about 0.1 of a unit in the fifth decimal place. Hence the fourth differences found in this example are mostly accumulated errors. Referring now to Table 6, we have

$$- 4\epsilon = - 11, \quad 6\epsilon = 17, \text{ etc.}$$

Hence, $\epsilon = 3$ to the nearest unit. The true value of $y$ corresponding to $x = 0.40$ is therefore $0.38945 - 0.00003 = 0.38942$, since $(y_k + \epsilon) - \epsilon = y_k$. The columns of differences can now be corrected, and it will be found that the third differences are practically constant.

If several tabular values of the function are affected with errors the

---

* *Note.* When writing numerical difference tables, or when substituting numerical differences in formulas, it is customary to omit the zeros between the decimal point and the first significant figure to the right of it; in other words, the differences are expressed in units of the last figure retained. Thus, instead of writing −0.00038 as the first number in the column $\Delta_2 y$ we write simply −38. This practice will be followed throughout this book, except in a few instances where the zeros are written for the sake of clearness.

successve differences of the function will become irregular, but it is not an easy matter to determine the sources and magnitudes of the separate errors.

In the case where *each* of the tabulated $y$'s is affected with an error of magnitude $\epsilon$, each of the third differences is affected with an error $\epsilon_k - 3\epsilon_{k-1} + 3\epsilon_{k-2} - \epsilon_{k-3}$, each of the fourth differences with an error $\epsilon_k - 4\epsilon_{k-1} + 6\epsilon_{k-2} - 4\epsilon_{k-3} + \epsilon_{k-4}$, etc., as is evident from Tables 3 and 4. In practical problems the tabulated values of the function $y$ are obtained by measurement or by computation. They are thus liable to be affected with errors of measurement or with errors due to rounding off the computed results to the given number of figures. In either case these errors would be magnified in the process of taking differences and they alone would be sufficient to cause the higher differences to become irregular.*

**14. Differences of a Polynomial.** Let us now compute the successive differences of a polynomial of the $n$th degree. We have

$$(14:1) \qquad y = f(x) = ax^n + bx^{n-1} + cx^{n-2} + \cdots + kx + l.$$

$$(14:2) \quad \therefore \; y + \Delta y = a(x+h)^n + b(x+h)^{n-1} + c(x+h)^{n-2} + \cdots$$
$$+ k(x+h) + l,$$

where $h = \Delta x$.

Subtracting (14:1) from (14:2), we get

$$\Delta y = a[(x+h)^n - x^n] + b[(x+h)^{n-1} - x^{n-1}]$$
$$+ c[(x+h)^{n-2} - x^{n-2}] + \cdots + kh.$$

Expanding the quantities $(x+h)^n$, $(x+h)^{n-1}$, etc. by the binomial theorem, we have

$$\Delta y = a\left[ x^n + nhx^{n-1} + \frac{n(n-1)}{2}h^2x^{n-2} + \frac{n(n-1)(n-2)}{3!}h^3x^{n-3} \right.$$
$$\left. + \cdots - x^n \right] + b\left[ x^{n-1} + (n-1)hx^{n-2} + \frac{(n-1)(n-2)}{2}h^2x^{n-3} \right.$$
$$\left. + \cdots - x^{n-1} \right] + c\left[ x^{n-2} + (n-2)hx^{n-3} + \frac{(n-2)(n-3)}{2}h^2x^{n-4} \right.$$
$$\left. + \cdots - x^{n-2} \right] + \cdots + kh,$$

or

* For an exhaustive discussion of errors in the tabular values of a function, see Rice's *Theory and Practice of Interpolation*, pages 7–15 and 46–62. Also O. Biermann's *Vorlesungen über Mathematische Näherungsmethoden*, p. 136.

$$\Delta y = anhx^{n-1} + \left[ ah^2 \frac{n(n-1)}{2} + b(n-1)h \right] x^{n-2}$$

$$+ \left[ ah^3 \frac{n(n-1)(n-2)}{3!} + bh^2 \frac{(n-1)(n-2)}{2} + ch(n-2) \right] x^{n-3} + \cdots$$

Now if $\Delta x(=h)$ is constant, the bracketed coefficients of $x^{n-2}$, $x^{n-3}$, etc. are constants, so that we may replace them by the single constant coefficients $b'$, $c'$, etc. Hence we have

(14: 3)      $\Delta y = anhx^{n-1} + b'x^{n-2} + c'x^{n-3} + \cdots + k'x + l'.$

The first difference of a polynomial of the $n$th degree is thus another polynomial of degree $n-1$.

To find the second difference we give $x$ an increment $\Delta x = h$ in (14:3) and therefore have

(14: 4) $\Delta y + \Delta(\Delta y) = anh(x + h)^{n-1} + b'(x + h)^{n-2}$
$$+ c'(x + h)^{n-3} + \cdots + k'(x + h) + l'.$$

Subtracting (14:3) from (14:4), we get

$\Delta(\Delta y) = \Delta^2 y = anh[(x + h)^{n-1} - x^{n-1}]$
$$+ b'[(x + h)^{n-2} - x^{n-2}] + c'[(x + h)^{n-3} - x^{n-3}] + \cdots + k'h.$$

Expanding $(x+h)^{n-1}$, $(x+h)^{n-2}$, etc. by the binomial theorem and replacing the constant coefficients of $x^{n-3}$, $x^{n-4}$, etc. by a single letter as before, we have

$$\Delta^2 y = an(n - 1)h^2 x^{n-2} + b''x^{n-3} + c''x^{n-4} \cdots + k''x + l''.$$

The second difference is thus a polynomial of degree $n-2$.

By continuing the calculation in this manner we arrive at a polynomial of zero degree for the $n$th difference; that is,

$$\Delta^n y = a[n(n - 1)(n - 2) \cdots 1]h^n x^{n-n} = an!h^n x^0 = ah^n n!.$$

The $n$th difference is therefore constant, and all higher differences are zero.

The reader should bear in mind that this result is true only when $h$ is a constant, that is, when the values of $x$ are in arithmetic progression.

The proposition which we have just proved may be stated as follows:

*The nth differences of a polynomial of the nth degree are constant when the values of the independent variable are taken in arithmetic progression, that is, at equal intervals apart.*

The converse of this proposition is also true, namely:

*If the nth differences of a tabulated function are constant when the values of the independent variable are taken in arithmetic progression, the function is a polynomial of degree n.*

This second proposition enables us to replace any function by a polynomial if its differences of some order become constant or nearly so. Thus, the function tabulated in Art. 13 can be represented by a polynomial of the third degree, since the corrected third differences are approximately constant.

### 15. Newton's Formula for Forward Interpolation.

Our next problem is to find suitable polynomials for replacing any given function over a given interval. Let $y = f(x)$ denote a function which takes the values $y_0, y_1, y_2, \cdots y_n$ for the equidistant values $x_0, x_1, x_2, \cdots x_n$ of the independent variable $x$, and let $\phi(x)$ denote a polynomial of the $n$th degree. This polynomial may be written in the form

$$(15:1) \quad \phi(x) = a_0 + a_1(x - x_0) + a_2(x - x_0)(x - x_1)$$
$$+ a_3(x - x_0)(x - x_1)(x - x_2)$$
$$+ a_4(x - x_0)(x - x_1)(x - x_2)(x - x_3)$$
$$+ \cdots + a_n(x - x_0)(x - x_1)(x - x_2) \cdots (x - x_{n-1}).$$

We shall now determine the coefficients $a_0, a_1, a_2, \cdots a_n$ so as to make $\phi(x_0) = y_0$, $\phi(x_1) = y_1$, $\phi(x_2) = y_2$, $\cdots \phi(x_n) = y_n$.

Substituting in (15:1) the successive values $x_0, x_1, x_2, \cdots x_n$ for $x$, at the same time putting $\phi(x_0) = y_0$, $\phi(x_1) = y_1$, etc., and remembering that $x_1 - x_0 = h$, $x_2 - x_0 = 2h$, etc., we have

$$y_0 = a_0, \quad \text{or} \quad a_0 = y_0.$$

$$y_1 = a_0 + a_1(x_1 - x_0) = y_0 + a_1 h.$$

$$\therefore \quad a_1 = \frac{y_1 - y_0}{h} = \frac{\Delta y_0}{h}.$$

$$y_2 = a_0 + a_1(x_2 - x_0) + a_2(x_2 - x_0)(x_2 - x_1) = y_0 + \frac{y_1 - y_0}{h}(2h)$$
$$+ a_2(2h)(h).$$

$$\therefore \quad a_2 = \frac{y_2 - 2y_1 + y_0}{2h^2} = \frac{\Delta^2 y_0}{2h^2}.$$

$$y_3 = a_0 + a_1(x_3 - x_0) + a_2(x_3 - x_0)(x_3 - x_1)$$
$$+ a_3(x_3 - x_0)(x_3 - x_1)(x_3 - x_2)$$

$$= y_0 + \frac{y_1 - y_0}{h}(3h) + \frac{y_2 - 2y_1 + y_0}{2h^2}(3h)(2h) + a_3(3h)(2h)(h).$$

* For the proof of this proposition see Rice's *Theory and Practice of Interpolation*, p. 24.

$$\therefore \; a_3 = \frac{y_3 - 3y_2 + 3y_1 - y_0}{6h^3} = \frac{\Delta^3 y_0}{3!h^3}.$$

$$y_4 = a_0 + a_1(x_4 - x_0) + a_2(x_4 - x_0)(x_4 - x_1) + a_3(x_4 - x_0)(x_4 - x_1)(x_4 - x_2)$$
$$+ a_4(x_4 - x_0)(x_4 - x_1)(x_4 - x_2)(x_4 - x_3)$$

$$= y_0 + \frac{y_1 - y_0}{h}(4h) + \frac{y_2 - 2y_1 + y_0}{2h^2}(4h)(3h)$$

$$+ \frac{y_3 - 3y_2 + 3y_1 - y_0}{6h^3}(4h)(3h)(2h) + a_4(4h)(3h)(2h)(h).$$

$$\therefore \; a_4 = \frac{y_4 - 4y_3 + 6y_2 - 4y_1 + y_0}{4!h^4} = \frac{\Delta^4 y_0}{4!h^4}.$$

By continuing this method of calculating the coefficients we shall find that

$$a_5 = \frac{\Delta^5 y_0}{5!h^5}, \quad a_6 = \frac{\Delta^6 y_0}{6!h^6}, \; \cdots \; a_n = \frac{\Delta^n y_0}{n!h^n}.$$

Substituting these values of $a_0, a_1, \cdots a_n$ in (15:1), we get

$$(15:2) \quad \phi(x) = y_0 + \frac{\Delta y_0}{h}(x - x_0) + \frac{\Delta^2 y_0}{2h^2}(x - x_0)(x - x_1)$$

$$+ \frac{\Delta^3 y_0}{3!h^3}(x - x_0)(x - x_1)(x - x_2)$$

$$+ \frac{\Delta^4 y_0}{4!h^4}(x - x_0)(x - x_1)(x - x_2)(x - x_3) + \cdots$$

$$+ \frac{\Delta^n y_0}{n!h^n}(x - x_0)(x - x_1)(x - x_2) \cdots (x - x_{n-1}).$$

This is Newton's formula for *forward* interpolation, written in terms of $x$.

The formula can be simplified by a change of variable. Let us first write (15:2) in the following equivalent form:

$$(15:2a) \quad \phi(x) = y_0 + \Delta y_0\left(\frac{x - x_0}{h}\right) + \frac{\Delta^2 y_0}{2}\left(\frac{x - x_0}{h}\right)\left(\frac{x - x_1}{h}\right)$$

$$+ \frac{\Delta^3 y_0}{3!}\left(\frac{x - x_0}{h}\right)\left(\frac{x - x_1}{h}\right)\left(\frac{x - x_2}{h}\right)$$

$$+ \frac{\Delta^4 y_0}{4!}\left(\frac{x - x_0}{h}\right)\left(\frac{x - x_1}{h}\right)\left(\frac{x - x_2}{h}\right)\left(\frac{x - x_3}{h}\right) + \cdots.$$

Now put

$$\frac{x - x_0}{h} = u, \quad \text{or} \quad x = x_0 + hu.$$

Then since $x_1 = x_0 + h$, $x_2 = x_0 + 2h$, etc., we have

$$\frac{x - x_1}{h} = \frac{x - (x_0 + h)}{h} = \frac{x - x_0 - h}{h} = \frac{x - x_0}{h} - \frac{h}{h} = u - 1,$$

$$\frac{x - x_2}{h} = \frac{x - (x_0 + 2h)}{h} = \frac{x - x_0}{h} - \frac{2h}{h} = u - 2,$$

$$\cdot \quad \cdot \quad \cdot \quad \cdot \quad \cdot \quad \cdot \quad \cdot \quad \cdot \quad \cdot \quad \cdot \quad \cdot \quad \cdot \quad \cdot \quad \cdot \quad \cdot$$

$$\frac{x - x_{n-1}}{h} = \frac{x - [x_0 + (n-1)h]}{h} = \frac{x - x_0}{h} - \frac{(n-1)h}{h}$$

$$= u - (n-1) = u - n + 1.$$

Substituting in (15:2a) these values of $(x - x_0)/h$, $(x - x_1)/h$, etc., we get

$$\textbf{(I)} \quad \phi(x) = \phi(x_0 + hu) = g(u) = y_0 + u\Delta y_0 + \frac{u(u-1)}{2!}\Delta^2 y_0$$

$$+ \frac{u(u-1)(u-2)}{3!}\Delta^3 y_0 + \frac{u(u-1)(u-2)(u-3)}{4!}\Delta^4 y_0$$

$$+ \cdots + \frac{u(u-1)(u-2) \cdots (u-n+1)}{n!}\Delta^n y_0.$$

This is the form in which Newton's formula for forward interpolation is usually written. We shall refer to it hereafter as Newton's formula (I). It will be observed that the coefficients of the $\Delta$'s are the binomial coefficients.

The reason for the name "forward" interpolation formula lies in the fact that the formula contains values of the tabulated function from $y_0$ onward to the right (forward from $y_0$) and none to the left of this value. Because of this fact this formula is used mainly for interpolating the values of $y$ near the *beginning* of a set of tabular values and for extrapolating values of $y$ a short distance backward (to the left) from $y_0$.

The starting point $y_0$ may be any tabular value, but then the formula will contain only those values of $y$ which come *after* the value chosen as starting point.

**16. Newton's Formula for Backward Interpolation.** The formulas of the preceding section can not be used for interpolating a value of $y$ near the end of the tabular values. To derive a formula for this case we write the polynomial $\phi(x)$ in the following form:

$$(16:1) \quad \phi(x) = a_0 + a_1(x - x_n) + a_2(x - x_n)(x - x_{n-1})$$

$$+ a_3(x - x_n)(x - x_{n-1})(x - x_{n-2})$$

$$+ a_4(x - x_n)(x - x_{n-1})(x - x_{n-2})(x - x_{n-3}) + \cdots$$

$$+ a_n(x - x_n)(x - x_{n-1}) \cdots (x - x_1).$$

Then we determine the coefficients $a_1$, $a_1$, $a_2$, $\cdots a_n$ so as to make $\phi(x_n) = y_n$, $\phi(x_{n-1}) = y_{n-1}$, etc. Substituting in (16:1) the values $x_n$, $x_{n-1}$, etc. for $x$ and at the same time putting $\phi(x_n) = y_n$, $\phi(x_{n-1}) = y_{n-1}$, etc., we have

$$y_n = a_0, \quad \text{or} \quad a_0 = y_n.$$

$$y_{n-1} = a_0 + a_1(x_{n-1} - x_n) = y_n + a_1(-h).$$

$$\therefore a_1 = \frac{y_n - y_{n-1}}{h} = \frac{\Delta_1 y_n}{h}.$$

$$y_{n-2} = a_0 + a_1(x_{n-2} - x_n) + a_2(x_{n-2} - x_n)(x_{n-2} - x_{n-1})$$

$$= y_n + \frac{y_n - y_{n-1}}{h}(-2h) + a_2(-2h)(-h).$$

$$\therefore a_2 = \frac{y_n - 2y_{n-1} + y_{n-2}}{2h^2} = \frac{\Delta_2 y_n}{2h^2}.$$

By continuing the calculation of the coefficients in this manner we shall find

$$a_3 = \frac{\Delta_3 y_n}{3!h^3}, \quad a_4 = \frac{\Delta_4 y_n}{4!h^4}, \quad \cdots \quad a_n = \frac{\Delta_n y_n}{n!h^n}.$$

Substituting these values of $a_0$, $a_1$, $a_2$, etc. in (16:1), we have

$$(16:2) \quad \phi(x) = y_n + \frac{\Delta_1 y_n}{h}(x - x_n) + \frac{\Delta_2 y_n}{2h^2}(x - x_n)(x - x_{n-1})$$

$$+ \frac{\Delta_3 y_n}{3!h^3}(x - x_n)(x - x_{n-1})(x - x_{n-2})$$

$$+ \frac{\Delta_4 y_n}{4!h^4}(x - x_n)(x - x_{n-1})(x - x_{n-2})(x - x_{n-3}) + \cdots$$

$$\cdots \cdots \cdots$$

$$+ \frac{\Delta_n y_n}{n!h^n}(x - x_n)(x - x_{n-1}) \cdots (x - x_1).$$

This is Newton's formula for *backward* interpolation, written in terms of $x$. It can be simplified by making a change of variable, as was done in Art. 15.

Let us first write (16:2) in the equivalent form

$$(16:2a) \quad \phi(x) = y_n + \Delta_1 y_n \left(\frac{x - x_n}{h}\right) + \frac{\Delta_2 y_n}{2}\left(\frac{x - x_n}{h}\right)\left(\frac{x - x_{n-1}}{h}\right)$$

$$+ \frac{\Delta_3 y_n}{3!}\left(\frac{x - x_n}{h}\right)\left(\frac{x - x_{n-1}}{h}\right)\left(\frac{x - x_{n-2}}{h}\right)$$

$$+ \frac{\Delta_4 y_n}{4!}\left(\frac{x - x_n}{h}\right)\left(\frac{x - x_{n-1}}{h}\right)\left(\frac{x - x_{n-2}}{h}\right)\left(\frac{x - x_{n-3}}{h}\right) + \cdots$$

$$+ \frac{\Delta_n y_n}{n!}\left(\frac{x - x_n}{h}\right)\left(\frac{x - x_{n-1}}{h}\right) \cdots \left(\frac{x - x_1}{h}\right).$$

Now put

$$u = \frac{x - x_n}{h}, \quad \text{or} \quad x = x_n + hu.$$

Then since $x_{n-1} = x_n - h$, $x_{n-2} = x_n - 2h$, etc., we have

$$\frac{x - x_{n-1}}{h} = \frac{x - (x_n - h)}{h} = \frac{x - x_n + h}{h} = \frac{x - x_n}{h} + \frac{h}{h} = u + 1,$$

$$\frac{x - x_{n-2}}{h} = \frac{x - (x_n - 2h)}{h} = \frac{x - x_n}{h} + \frac{2h}{h} = u + 2,$$

. . . . . . . . . . . . . . . . . . . . . .

$$\frac{x - x_1}{h} = \frac{x - [x_n - (n-1)h]}{h} = \frac{x - x_n}{h} + \frac{(n-1)h}{h} = u + n - 1.$$

Substituting in (16:2a) these values of $(x - x_n)/h$, $(x - x_{n-1})/h$, etc., we get

$$\textbf{(II)} \quad \phi(x) = \phi(x_n + hu) = \psi(u) = y_n + u\Delta_1 y_n + \frac{u(u+1)}{2}\Delta_2 y_n$$

$$+ \frac{u(u+1)(u+2)}{3!}\Delta_3 y_n + \frac{u(u+1)(u+2)(u+3)}{4!}\Delta_4 y_n + \cdots$$

$$+ \frac{u(u+1)(u+2) \cdots (u+n-1)}{n!}\Delta_n y_n.$$

This is the form in which Newton's formula for backward interpolation is usually written. We shall refer to this formula hereafter as Newton's formula (II). It is to be observed that this formula employs *horizontal* differences, whereas the formula for forward interpolation employs diagonal differences.

(II) is called the formula for "backward" interpolation because it contains values of the tabulated function for $y_n$ *backward* to the left and none to the right of $y_n$. This formula is used mainly for interpolating values of $y$ near the *end* of a set of tabular values, and also for extrapolating values of $y$ a short distance ahead (to the right) of $y_n$.

We shall now illustrate the use of Newton's formulas by working some examples.

*Example 1.* Find $\log_{10}\pi$, having given
$$\log 3.141 = 0.4970679364,$$
$$\log 3.142 = 0.4972061807,$$
$$\log 3.143 = 0.4973443810,$$
$$\log 3.144 = 0.4974825374,$$
$$\log 3.145 = 0.4976206498.$$

*Solution.* We first form the table of differences, as shown below:

| $x$ | $y = \log x$ | $\Delta y$ | $\Delta^2 y$ | $\Delta^3 y$ |
|---|---|---|---|---|
| 3.141 | 0.4970679364 | | | |
| | | 1382443 | | |
| 3.142 | 0.4972061807 | | −440 | |
| | | 1382003 | | 1 |
| 3.143 | 0.4973443810 | | −439 | |
| | | 1381564 | | −1 |
| 3.144 | 0.4974825374 | | −440 | |
| | | 1381124 | | |
| 3.145 | 0.4976206498 | | | |

Here $x = \pi = 3.1415926536$, $x_0 = 3.141$, $h = 0.001$. Hence

$$u = \frac{x - x_0}{h} = \frac{3.1415926536 - 3.141}{0.001} = 0.5926536,$$

$$u - 1 = -0.4073464, \text{ etc.}$$

Substituting these values in (I), Art. 15, we get

$$\log_{10}\pi = 0.4970679364 + 0.5926536(1382443)$$

$$+ \frac{0.5926536(-0.4073464)(-440)}{2}$$

$$= 0.4970679364 + 0.0000819310 + 0.0000000053$$

$$= \underline{0.4971498727}.$$

This result is correct to its last figure.

*Example 2.* Using the tabular values of the preceding example, find $\log_{10} 3.140$.

*Solution.* Here $x = x_{-1} = 3.140$, $x_0 = 3.141$, $h = 0.001$. Hence

$$u = \frac{x - x_0}{h} = \frac{x_{-1} - x_0}{h} = \frac{-h}{h} = -1,$$

$$u - 1 = -2, \text{ etc.}$$

$$\therefore \log_{10} 3.140 = 0.4970679364 + (-1)(1382443) + \frac{(-1)(-2)}{2}(-440)$$

$$= 0.4970679364 - 0.0001382443 - 0.0000000440$$

$$= 0.4969296481.$$

This result is also correct to its last figure.

*Note.* The process of computing the value of a function outside the range of given values, as in the example above, is called *extrapolation.* It should be used with caution; but if the function is known to run smoothly near the ends of the range of given values, and if $h$ is taken as small as it should be, we are usually safe in extrapolating for a distance $h$ outside the range of given values.

*Example 3.* The hourly declination of the moon for January 1, 1918, is given in the following table. Find the declination at $3^h$ $35^m$ $15^s$.

| Hour | Declination | $\Delta_1$ | $\Delta_2$ | $\Delta_3$ |
|------|-------------|------------|------------|------------|
| 0 | $8°$ $29'$ $53''.7$ | | | |
| 1 | $8$ $18$ $19$ $.4$ | $-11'$ $34''.3$ | | |
| 2 | $8$ $6$ $43$ $.5$ | $-11$ $35$ $.9$ | $-1''.6$ | |
| 3 | $7$ $55$ $6$ $.1$ | $-11$ $37$ $.4$ | $-1$ $.5$ | $0''.1$ |
| 4 | $7$ $43$ $27$ $.2$ | $-11$ $38$ $.9$ | $-1$ $.5$ | $0$ $.0$ |

*Solution.* Since the desired declination is near the *end* of the values given we use Newton's formula (II), and we therefore form a horizontal difference table, as shown above. Denoting the time in hours by $t$, we have $t_n = 4$, $t = 3^h$ $35^m$ $15^s$, $h = 1$. Hence

$$u = \frac{t - t_n}{h} = \frac{-0^h 24^m 45^s}{1^h} = \frac{-1485^s}{3600^s} = -0.3569.$$

$$\therefore u + 1 = 0.6431.$$

Substituting these values in (II) and denoting the required declination by $\delta$, we get

$$\delta = 7°43'\,27''.2 + (-0.3569)(-11'\,38''.9) + \frac{(0.\,6431)(-0.\,3569)}{2}(-1''.5)$$

$$= 7°\,43'\,27''.2 + 4'\,9''.4 + 0''.2$$

$$= \underline{7°\,47'\,36''.8}.$$

*Example 4.* Using the data of the preceding problem, find the declination of the moon at $t = 5^{\mathrm{h}}$.

*Solution.* Here $t = t_{n+1} = 5$, $t_n = 4$.

$$\therefore u = \frac{t_{n+1} - t_n}{h} = \frac{h}{h} = 1, \; u + 1 = 2.$$

Substituting in (II), we have

$$\delta_{n+1} = 7°\,43'\,27''.2 + (1)(-11'\,38''.9) + \frac{(1)(2)}{2}(-1''.5)$$

$$= \underline{7°\,31'\,46''.8}.$$

The true value, as given in the *American Ephemeris and Nautical Almanac*, is 7° 31′ 46″.9, the error in the extrapolated value thus being only 0″.1.

## EXAMPLES ON CHAPTER II

1. Find and correct by means of differences the error in the following table:

48440
50898
53355
55800
58268
60724
63179
65634
68089.

2. Correct the error in this table:

| | | | |
|---|---|---|---|
| 19° | 12′ | 22″ | .4 |
| 19 | 25 | 54 | .7 |
| 19 | 39 | 7 | .3 |
| 19 | 51 | 53 | .8 |
| 20 | 4 | 31 | .9 |
| 20 | 16 | 43 | .5 |
| 20 | 28 | 34 | .3. |

3. Find $\log_{10} \sin 37' \, 23''$, given

$$\log \sin 37' = 8.0319195 - 10$$
$$\text{``} \quad \text{``} \quad 38' = 8.0435009 - 10$$
$$\text{``} \quad \text{``} \quad 39' = 8.0547814 - 10$$
$$\text{``} \quad \text{``} \quad 40' = 8.0657763 - 10$$
$$\text{``} \quad \text{``} \quad 41' = 8.0764997 - 10$$
$$\text{``} \quad \text{``} \quad 42' = 8.0869646 - 10$$
$$\text{``} \quad \text{``} \quad 43' = 8.0971832 - 10.$$

4. The following table gives the longitude of the moon at twelve-hour intervals for the first four days of April, 1918. Find the moon's longitude at 8:50 P.M. on April 2, the day beginning at noon.

| Apr. | 1 | 0 | 244° | 44′ | 20″.5 |
|------|---|----|------|-----|-------|
| "    | 1 | 12 | 250  | 57  | 35 .7 |
| "    | 2 | 0  | 257  | 14  | 22 .1 |
| "    | 2 | 12 | 263  | 35  | 8 .6  |
| "    | 3 | 0  | 270  | 0   | 24 .6 |
| "    | 3 | 12 | 276  | 30  | 39 .6 |
| "    | 4 | 0  | 283  | 6   | 22 .1 |

5. Using the data of Example 3, find $\log \sin 42' \, 13''$.

6. Using the data of Example 4, find the moon's longitude at 8:43 P.M., Apr. 3.

# CHAPTER III

## INTERPOLATION

### CENTRAL-DIFFERENCE FORMULAS

**17. Introduction.** Newton's formulas (I) and (II) are fundamental and are applicable to nearly all cases of interpolation, but in general they do not converge as rapidly as another class of formulas called *central-difference* formulas. These latter formulas employ differences taken as nearly as possible from a horizontal line through a diagonal difference table, and a glance at Table 3 shows that these differences contain values of the function both preceding and following the value through which the horizontal line is drawn. The central-difference formulas are therefore particularly suited for interpolating values of the function near the *middle* of a tabulated set.

The most important central-difference formulas are the two known as Stirling's formula and Bessel's formula, respectively. They can be derived in several ways, but are most simply derived by an algebraic transformation of Newton's formula (I).

**18. Stirling's Interpolation Formula.** To derive Stirling's formula we first write a diagonal difference table and mark for special consideration the tabular value $y_0$ and the differences lying as near as possible to the horizontal line through $y_0$. These quantities are printed in heavy type in the table given below.

| $y$ | $\Delta y$ | $\Delta^2 y$ | $\Delta^3 y$ | $\Delta^4 y$ | $\Delta^5 y$ | $\Delta^6 y$ | $\Delta^7 y$ | $\Delta^8 y$ |
|---|---|---|---|---|---|---|---|---|
| $y_{-4}$ | | | | | | | | |
| | $\Delta y_{-4}$ | | | | | | | |
| $y_{-3}$ | | $\Delta^2 y_{-4}$ | | | | | | |
| | $\Delta y_{-3}$ | | $\Delta^3 y_{-4}$ | | | | | |
| $y_{-2}$ | | $\Delta^2 y_{-3}$ | | $\Delta^4 y_{-4}$ | | | | |
| | $\Delta y_{-2}$ | | $\Delta^3 y_{-3}$ | | $\Delta^5 y_{-4}$ | | | |
| $y_{-1}$ | | $\Delta^2 y_{-2}$ | | $\Delta^4 y_{-3}$ | | $\Delta^6 y_{-4}$ | | |
| | $\boldsymbol{\Delta y_{-1}}$ | | $\Delta^3 y_{-2}$ | | $\boldsymbol{\Delta^5 y_{-3}}$ | | $\boldsymbol{\Delta^7 y_{-4}}$ | |
| $\boldsymbol{y_0}$ | | $\boldsymbol{\Delta^2 y_{-1}}$ | | $\boldsymbol{\Delta^4 y_{-2}}$ | | $\boldsymbol{\Delta^6 y_{-3}}$ | | $\boldsymbol{\Delta^8 y_{-4}}$ |
| | $\boldsymbol{\Delta y_0}$ | | $\boldsymbol{\Delta^3 y_{-1}}$ | | $\boldsymbol{\Delta^5 y_{-2}}$ | | $\boldsymbol{\Delta^7 y_{-3}}$ | |
| $y_1$ | | $\Delta^2 y_0$ | | $\Delta^4 y_{-1}$ | | $\Delta^6 y_{-2}$ | | $\Delta^8 y_{-3}$ |
| | $\Delta y_1$ | | $\Delta^3 y_0$ | | $\Delta^5 y_{-1}$ | | $\Delta^7 y_{-2}$ | |
| $y_2$ | | $\Delta^2 y_1$ | | $\Delta^4 y_0$ | | $\Delta^6 y_{-1}$ | | |
| | $\Delta y_2$ | | $\Delta^3 y_1$ | | $\Delta^5 y_0$ | | | |
| $y_3$ | | $\Delta^2 y_2$ | | $\Delta^4 y_1$ | | | | |
| | $\Delta y_3$ | | $\Delta^3 y_2$ | | | | | |
| $y_4$ | | $\Delta^2 y_3$ | | | | | | |
| | $\Delta y_4$ | | | | | | | |
| $y_5$ | | | | | | | | |

TABLE 7.

Newton's formula (I), when setting out from $y_0$, is

$$(A) \qquad y = y_0 + u\Delta y_0 + \frac{u(u-1)}{2}\Delta^2 y_0 + \frac{u(u-1)(u-2)}{3!}\Delta^3 y_0$$

$$+ \frac{u(u-1)(u-2)(u-3)}{4!}\Delta^4 y_0$$

$$+ \frac{u(u-1)(u-2)(u-3)(u-4)}{5!}\Delta^5 y_0 + \cdots,$$

which may be written in the form

$$(B) \qquad y = y_0 + C_1\Delta y_0 + C_2\Delta^2 y_0 + C_3\Delta^3 y_0 + C_4\Delta^4 y_0 + C_5\Delta^5 y_0 + \cdots,$$

where the $C$'s denote the binomial coefficients.

Let us now put

$$(a) \qquad m_1 = \frac{\Delta y_{-1} + \Delta y_0}{2}, \qquad\qquad (b) \qquad m_3 = \frac{\Delta^3 y_{-2} + \Delta^3 y_{-1}}{2},$$

$$(c) \qquad m_5 = \frac{\Delta^5 y_{-3} + \Delta^5 y_{-2}}{2}, \qquad\qquad (d) \qquad m_7 = \frac{\Delta^7 y_{-4} + \Delta^7 y_{-3}}{2},$$

etc.

These $m$'s are thus the arithmetic means of the *odd* differences immediately above and below the horizontal line through $y_0$.

Our immediate object now is to express $\Delta y_0$, $\Delta^2 y_0$, $\Delta^3 y_0$, etc. in terms of the $m$'s and the *even* differences lying on the horizontal line through $y_0$. This will be done by a process of elimination by working from $\Delta y_0$, $\Delta^2 y_0$, etc. diagonally upward to the right until the quantities in the horizontal line are reached. As an aid to this we shall underline the even differences $\Delta^2 y_{-1}$, $\Delta^4 y_{-2}$, $\Delta^6 y_{-3}$, $\Delta^8 y_{-4}$ wherever they occur in the algebraic work which follows, the purpose of the underlining being to call attention to the fact that the underlined quantities are *not* to be eliminated.

From the definition of differences we have

$$\underline{\Delta^2 y_{-1}} = \Delta y_0 - \Delta y_{-1}.$$

$$\therefore \Delta y_0 = \underline{\Delta^2 y_{-1}} + \Delta y_{-1}.$$

But

$$\Delta y_{-1} = 2m_1 - \Delta y_0, \text{ from (a)}.$$

$$\therefore \Delta y_0 = \underline{\Delta^2 y_{-1}} + 2m_1 - \Delta y_0.$$

$$(18:1) \qquad \therefore \Delta y_0 = m_1 + \tfrac{1}{2}\underline{\Delta^2 y_{-1}}.$$

To find the value of $\Delta^2 y_0$ in terms of the desired quantities we have

$$\Delta^3 y_{-1} = \Delta^2 y_0 - \underline{\Delta^2 y_{-1}},$$

(e)  or    $\Delta^2 y_0 = \underline{\Delta^2 y_{-1}} + \Delta^3 y_{-1}.$

But

(f)        $\underline{\Delta^4 y_{-2}} = \Delta^3 y_{-1} - \Delta^3 y_{-2},$ by definition,

(g)  and    $\Delta^3 y_{-1} = 2m_3 - \Delta^3 y_{-2},$ from (b).

Subtracting (f) from (g) and solving for $\Delta^3 y_{-1}$,

(h)        $\Delta^3 y_{-1} = m_3 + \frac{1}{2}\Delta^4 y_{-2}.$

Substituting (h) in (e),

(18: 2)        $\Delta^2 y_0 = \underline{\Delta^2 y_{-1}} + m_3 + \frac{1}{2}\underline{\Delta^4 y_{-2}}.$

To find $\Delta^3 y_0$ we start with

$$\Delta^4 y_{-1} = \Delta^3 y_0 - \Delta^3 y_{-1},$$

(i)  or    $\Delta^3 y_0 = \Delta^3 y_{-1} + \Delta^4 y_{-1}$

$$= m_3 + \frac{1}{2}\Delta^4 y_{-2} + \Delta^4 y_{-1}, \text{ from (h).}$$

But

$$\Delta^5 y_{-2} = \Delta^4 y_{-1} - \underline{\Delta^4 y_{-2}},$$

(j)  or    $\Delta^4 y_{-1} = \underline{\Delta^4 y_{-2}} + \Delta^5 y_{-2}.$

(k) Also,    $\underline{\Delta^6 y_{-3}} = \Delta^5 y_{-2} - \Delta^5 y_{-3}$

(l)  and    $\Delta^5 y_{-2} = 2m_5 - \Delta^5 y_{-3},$ from (c).

Subtracting (k) from (l) and solving for $\Delta^5 y_{-2}$,

(m)        $\Delta^5 y_{-2} = m_5 + \frac{1}{2}\Delta^6 y_{-3}.$

Substituting (m) in (j),

(n)        $\Delta^4 y_{-1} = \underline{\Delta^4 y_{-2}} + m_5 + \frac{1}{2}\underline{\Delta^6 y_{-3}}.$

Substituting (n) in (i),

(18: 3)        $\Delta^3 y_0 = m_3 + \frac{3}{2}\underline{\Delta^4 y_{-2}} + m_5 + \frac{1}{2}\underline{\Delta^6 y_{-3}}.$

For $\Delta^4 y_0$ we start with

$$\Delta^5 y_{-1} = \Delta^4 y_0 - \Delta^4 y_{-1},$$

(o)  or    $\Delta^4 y_0 = \Delta^4 y_{-1} + \Delta^5 y_{-1}$

$$= \underline{\Delta^4 y_{-2}} + m_5 + \frac{1}{2}\underline{\Delta^6 y_{-3}} + \Delta^5 y_{-1}, \text{ from (n).}$$

But

(p) $$\Delta^6 y_{-2} = \Delta^5 y_{-1} - \Delta^5 y_{-2}$$
$$= \Delta^5 y_{-1} - m_5 - \tfrac{1}{2}\Delta^6 y_{-3}, \text{ from (m)};$$

(q) and   $\Delta^7 y_{-3} = \Delta^6 y_{-2} - \underline{\Delta^6 y_{-3}}.$

(r) Also,   $\underline{\Delta^8 y_{-4}} = \Delta^7 y_{-3} - \Delta^7 y_{-4}$

(s) and   $\Delta^7 y_{-3} = 2m_7 - \Delta^7 y_{-4}, \text{ from (d)}.$

Subtracting (r) from (s) and solving for $\Delta^7 y_{-3}$,

(t) $$\Delta^7 y_{-3} = m_7 + \tfrac{1}{2}\Delta^8 y_{-4}.$$

Substituting (t) in (q) and solving for $\Delta^6 y_{-2}$,

(u) $$\Delta^6 y_{-2} = \underline{\Delta^6 y_{-3}} + m_7 + \tfrac{1}{2}\Delta^8 y_{-4}.$$

Substituting (u) in (p) and solving for $\Delta^5 y_{-1}$,

(v) $$\Delta^5 y_{-1} = m_5 + \tfrac{3}{2}\underline{\Delta^6 y_{-3}} + m_7 + \tfrac{1}{2}\Delta^8 y_{-4}.$$

Substituting (v) in (o),

(18:4) $$\Delta^4 y_0 = \underline{\Delta^4 y_{-2}} + 2m_5 + 2\underline{\Delta^6 y_{-3}} + m_7 + \tfrac{1}{2}\Delta^8 y_{-4}.$$

Now substituting (18:1), (18:2), (18:3), (18:4) in (B), we get

$$y = y_0 + C_1(m_1 + \tfrac{1}{2}\Delta^2 y_{-1}) + C_2(m_3 + \Delta^2 y_{-1} + \tfrac{1}{2}\Delta^4 y_{-2})$$
$$+ C_3(m_3 + m_5 + \tfrac{3}{2}\Delta^4 y_{-2} + \tfrac{1}{2}\Delta^6 y_{-3})$$
$$+ C_4(2m_5 + m_7 + \Delta^4 y_{-2} + 2\Delta^6 y_{-3} + \tfrac{1}{2}\Delta^8 y_{-4}),$$

or

$$y = y_0 + C_1 m_1 + \left(\frac{C_1}{2} + C_2\right)\Delta^2 y_{-1} + (C_2 + C_3)m_3$$

$$+ \left(\frac{C_2}{2} + \frac{3C_3}{2} + C_4\right)\Delta^4 y_{-2} + \text{ terms in } m_5, \Delta^6 y_{-3}, \text{ etc.}$$

Replacing the $C$'s and $m$'s by their values, we get

$$y = y_0 + u \frac{\Delta y_{-1} + \Delta y_0}{2} + \left(\frac{u}{2} + \frac{u(u-1)}{2}\right)\Delta^2 y_{-1}$$

$$+ \left(\frac{u(u-1)}{2} + \frac{u(u-1)(u-2)}{6}\right)\frac{\Delta^3 y_{-2} + \Delta^3 y_{-1}}{2}$$

$$+ \left(\frac{u(u-1)}{4} + \frac{3u(u-1)(u-2)}{12} + \frac{u(u-1)(u-2)(u-3)}{24}\right)\Delta^4 y_{-2} + \cdots,$$

or

$$y = y_0 + u\frac{\Delta y_{-1} + \Delta y_0}{2} + \frac{u^2}{2}\Delta^2 y_{-1} + \frac{u(u^2 - 1)}{3!}\frac{\Delta^3 y_{-2} + \Delta^3 y_{-1}}{2}$$

$$+ \frac{u^2(u^2 - 1)}{4!}\Delta^4 y_{-2} + \cdots.$$

By continuing the calculation as above outlined we arrive at *Stirling's* formula, namely:

$$(\text{III}) \quad y = y_0 + u\frac{\Delta y_{-1} + \Delta y_0}{2} + \frac{u^2}{2}\Delta^2 y_{-1} + \frac{u(u^2 - 1^2)}{3!}\frac{\Delta^3 y_{-2} + \Delta^3 y_{-1}}{2}$$

$$+ \frac{u^2(u^2 - 1^2)}{4!}\Delta^4 y_{-2} + \frac{u(u^2 - 1^2)(u^2 - 2^2)}{5!}\frac{\Delta^5 y_{-3} + \Delta^5 y_{-2}}{2}$$

$$+ \frac{u^2(u^2 - 1^2)(u^2 - 2^2)}{6!}\Delta^6 y_{-3} + \cdots\cdots$$

$$+ \frac{u(u^2 - 1^2)(u^2 - 2^2)(u^2 - 3^2)\cdots[u^2 - (n - 1)^2]}{(2n - 1)!}$$

$$\times \frac{\Delta^{2n-1} y_{-n} + \Delta^{2n-1} y_{-(n-1)}}{2}$$

$$+ \frac{u^2(u^2 - 1^2)(u^2 - 2^2)(u^2 - 3^2)\cdots[u^2 - (n - 1)^2]}{(2n)!}\Delta^{2n} y_{-n},$$

where $u = (x - x_0)/h$.

In this formula there are $2n+1$ terms, and the polynomial coincides with the given function at the $2n+1$ points

$$u = -n, -(n - 1), -(n - 2), \cdots -2, -1, 0, 1, 2, \cdots n - 2, n - 1, n;$$

or

$$x = x_0 - nh, x_0 - (n - 1)h, \cdots x_0 - h, x_0, x_0 + h, \cdots x_0 + (n - 1)h, x_0 + nh.$$

**19. Bessel's Interpolation Formulas.** The derivation of Bessel's formula of interpolation is similar to that of Stirling's. We first write down a diagonal difference table as before, and mark for special consideration the quantities lying as near as possible to the horizontal line drawn half-way between $y_0$ and $y_1$. These quantities are printed in heavy type in the table below.

| $y$ | $\Delta y$ | $\Delta^2 y$ | $\Delta^3 y$ | $\Delta^4 y$ | $\Delta^5 y$ | $\Delta^6 y$ | $\Delta^7 y$ | $\Delta^8 y$ |
|---|---|---|---|---|---|---|---|---|
| $y_{-4}$ | | | | | | | | |
| | $\Delta y_{-4}$ | | | | | | | |
| $y_{-3}$ | | $\Delta^2 y_{-4}$ | | | | | | |
| | $\Delta y_{-3}$ | | $\Delta^3 y_{-4}$ | | | | | |
| $y_{-2}$ | | $\Delta^2 y_{-3}$ | | $\Delta^4 y_{-4}$ | | | | |
| | $\Delta y_{-2}$ | | $\Delta^3 y_{-3}$ | | $\Delta^5 y_{-4}$ | | | |
| $y_{-1}$ | | $\Delta^2 y_{-2}$ | | $\Delta^4 y_{-3}$ | | $\Delta^6 y_{-4}$ | | |
| | $\Delta y_{-1}$ | | $\Delta^3 y_{-2}$ | | $\Delta^5 y_{-3}$ | | $\Delta^7 y_{-4}$ | |
| $\mathbf{y_0}$ | | $\mathbf{\Delta^2 y_{-1}}$ | | $\mathbf{\Delta^4 y_{-2}}$ | | $\mathbf{\Delta^6 y_{-3}}$ | | $\mathbf{\Delta^8 y_{-4}}$ |
| | $\mathbf{\Delta y_0}$ | | $\mathbf{\Delta^3 y_{-1}}$ | | $\mathbf{\Delta^5 y_{-2}}$ | | $\mathbf{\Delta^7 y_{-3}}$ | |
| $\mathbf{y_1}$ | | $\mathbf{\Delta^2 y_0}$ | | $\mathbf{\Delta^4 y_{-1}}$ | | $\mathbf{\Delta^6 y_{-2}}$ | | $\mathbf{\Delta^8 y_{-3}}$ |
| | $\Delta y_1$ | | $\Delta^3 y_0$ | | $\Delta^5 y_{-1}$ | | $\Delta^7 y_{-2}$ | |
| $y_2$ | | $\Delta^2 y_1$ | | $\Delta^4 y_0$ | | $\Delta^6 y_{-1}$ | | |
| | $\Delta y_2$ | | $\Delta^3 y_1$ | | $\Delta^5 y_0$ | | | |
| $y_3$ | | $\Delta^2 y_2$ | | $\Delta^4 y_1$ | | | | |
| | $\Delta y_3$ | | $\Delta^3 y_2$ | | | | | |
| $y_4$ | | $\Delta^2 y_3$ | | | | | | |
| | $\Delta y_4$ | | | | | | | |
| $y_5$ | | | | | | | | |

TABLE 8.

Let us now put

$$(a) \quad m_0 = \frac{y_0 + y_1}{2}, \qquad\qquad (b) \quad m_2 = \frac{\Delta^2 y_{-1} + \Delta^2 y_0}{2},$$

$$(c) \quad m_4 = \frac{\Delta^4 y_{-2} + \Delta^4 y_{-1}}{2}, \qquad\qquad (d) \quad m_6 = \frac{\Delta^6 y_{-3} + \Delta^6 y_{-2}}{2},$$

$$(e) \quad m_8 = \frac{\Delta^8 y_{-4} + \Delta^8 y_{-3}}{2}, \qquad \text{etc.}$$

The $m$'s in this case are thus the arithmetic means of the ordinates $y_0$ and $y_1$, and of the *even* differences just above and below the horizontal line through $y_{1/2}$.

We next write down Newton's formula (I), starting from the entry $y_0$, as was done in Art. 18. Our problem is to express $y_0$, $\Delta y_0$, $\Delta^2 y_0$, $\cdots \Delta^n y_0$ in terms of the $m$'s and the *odd* differences lying on the horizontal line through $y_{1/2}$. This will be done by an elimination process, by working from $\Delta^2 y_0$, $\Delta^3 y_0$, etc. diagonally upward to the right until we reach the quantities in the horizontal line. The odd differences in the horizontal line will be underlined in the work which follows, to indicate that they are *not* to be eliminated.

By definition we have

$$\underline{\Delta y_0} = y_1 - y_0.$$

$$\therefore y_0 = y_1 - \underline{\Delta y_0}.$$

But $\qquad\qquad y_1 = 2m_0 - y_0$, from (a).

$$\therefore y_0 = 2m_0 - y_0 - \underline{\Delta y_0}.$$

(19:1) $\qquad\qquad\qquad \therefore y_0 = m_0 - \frac{1}{2}\Delta y_0.$

To find $\Delta^2 y_0$ we start with

$$\underline{\Delta^3 y_{-1}} = \Delta^2 y_0 - \Delta^2 y_{-1}, \text{ by definition.}$$

$$\therefore \Delta^2 y_0 = \underline{\Delta^3 y_{-1}} + \Delta^2 y_{-1}.$$

But $\qquad\quad \Delta^2 y_{-1} = 2m_2 - \Delta^2 y_0$, from (b).

$$\therefore \Delta^2 y_0 = \underline{\Delta^3 y_{-1}} + 2m_2 - \Delta^2 y_0,$$

or

(19:2) $\qquad\qquad\qquad \Delta^2 y_0 = m_2 + \frac{1}{2}\underline{\Delta^3 y_{-1}}.$

For $\Delta^3 y_0$ we have

$$\Delta^4 y_{-1} = \Delta^3 y_0 - \underline{\Delta^3 y_{-1}}, \text{ by definition.}$$

(f) $\qquad\qquad \therefore \Delta^3 y_0 = \underline{\Delta^3 y_{-1}} + \Delta^4 y_{-1}.$

(g) But $\qquad \Delta^4 y_{-1} = 2m_4 - \Delta^4 y_{-2}$, from (c),

(h) and $\qquad \underline{\Delta^5 y_{-2}} = \Delta^4 y_{-1} - \Delta^4 y_{-2}$, by definition.

Subtracting (h) from (g) and solving for $\Delta^4 y_{-1}$,

(i) $\qquad\qquad \Delta^4 y_{-1} = m_4 + \frac{1}{2}\underline{\Delta^5 y_{-2}}.$

Substituting (i) in (f),

(19:3) $\qquad\qquad \Delta^3 y_0 = \underline{\Delta^3 y_{-1}} + m_4 + \frac{1}{2}\underline{\Delta^5 y_{-2}}.$

To find $\Delta^4 y_0$ we start with

$$\Delta^5 y_{-1} = \Delta^4 y_0 - \Delta^4 y_{-1}, \text{ by definition.}$$

(j) $\qquad\qquad \therefore \Delta^4 y_0 = \Delta^4 y_{-1} + \Delta^5 y_{-1}$

$$= m_4 + \frac{1}{2}\underline{\Delta^5 y_{-2}} + \Delta^5 y_{-1}, \text{ from (i).}$$

(k) Now $\qquad \Delta^6 y_{-2} = \Delta^5 y_{-1} - \underline{\Delta^5 y_{-2}}$, by definition.

(l)  Also  $\Delta^7 y_{-3} = \Delta^6 y_{-2} - \Delta^6 y_{-3}$, by definition,

(m) and  $\Delta^6 y_{-2} = 2m_6 - \Delta^6 y_{-3}$, from (d).

Subtracting (l) from (m) and solving for $\Delta^6 y_{-2}$,

(n)  $\Delta^6 y_{-2} = m_6 + \tfrac{1}{2}\Delta^7 y_{-3}$.

Equating (k) and (n) and solving for $\Delta^5 y_{-1}$,

(o)  $\underline{\Delta^5 y_{-1} = \Delta^5 y_{-2} + m_6 + \tfrac{1}{2}\Delta^7 y_{-3}}$.

Substituting (o) in (j), we get

(19:4)  $\Delta^4 y_0 = m_4 + \tfrac{3}{2}\Delta^5 y_{-2} + m_6 + \tfrac{1}{2}\Delta^7 y_{-3}$.

Now substituting these values of $y_0$, $\Delta^2 y_0$, $\Delta^3 y_0$, etc. in (A) of Art. 18, we have

$$y = m_0 - \frac{1}{2}\Delta y_0 + u\Delta y_0 + \frac{u(u-1)}{2}\left(m_2 + \frac{1}{2}\Delta^3 y_{-1}\right)$$
$$+ \frac{u(u-1)(u-2)}{6}\left(m_4 + \Delta^3 y_{-1} + \frac{1}{2}\Delta^5 y_{-2}\right)$$
$$+ \frac{u(u-1)(u-2)(u-3)}{24}\left(m_4 + \frac{3}{2}\Delta^5 y_{-2} + m_6 + \frac{1}{2}\Delta^7 y_{-3}\right),$$

or, rearranging,

$$y = m_0 + \left(u - \frac{1}{2}\right)\Delta y_0 + \frac{u(u-1)}{2}m_2 + \left[\frac{u(u-1)}{4} + \frac{u(u-1)(u-2)}{6}\right]\Delta^3 y_{-1}$$
$$+ \left[\frac{u(u-1)(u-2)}{6} + \frac{u(u-1)(u-2)(u-3)}{24}\right]m_4$$
$$\left[\frac{u(u-1)(u-2)}{12} + \frac{u(u-1)(u-2)(u-3)}{16}\right]\Delta^5 y_{-2}$$

+ terms in $\Delta^5 y$, $m_6$, and $\Delta^7 y_{-3}$.

Simplifying and replacing the $m$'s by their values, we get

$$y = \frac{y_0 + y_1}{2} + \left(u - \frac{1}{2}\right)\Delta y_0 + \frac{u(u-1)}{2}\frac{\Delta^2 y_{-1} + \Delta^2 y_0}{2}$$
$$+ \frac{u(u-1)(u-\frac{1}{2})}{3!}\Delta^3 y_{-1} + \frac{u(u-1)(u+1)(u-2)}{4!}\frac{\Delta^4 y_{-2} + \Delta^4 y_{-1}}{2}$$
$$+ \cdots.$$

By continuing the calculation as carried out above we arrive at *Bessel's* formula of interpolation:

$$\text{(IV)} \quad y = \frac{y_0 + y_1}{2} + \left(u - \frac{1}{2}\right)\Delta y_0 + \frac{u(u-1)}{2}\frac{\Delta^2 y_{-1} + \Delta^2 y_0}{2}$$

$$+ \frac{(u-\frac{1}{2})u(u-1)}{3!}\Delta^3 y_{-1} + \frac{u(u-1)(u+1)(u-2)}{4!}\frac{\Delta^4 y_{-2} + \Delta^4 y_{-1}}{2}$$

$$+ \frac{(u-\frac{1}{2})u(u-1)(u+1)(u-2)}{5!}\Delta^5 y_{-2}$$

$$+ \frac{u(u-1)(u+1)(u-2)(u+2)(u-3)}{6!}\frac{\Delta^6 y_{-3} + \Delta^6 y_{-2}}{2} + \cdots$$

$$+ \frac{u(u-1)(u+1)(u-2)(u+2)\cdots(u-n)(u+n-1)}{(2n)!}$$

$$\times \frac{\Delta^{2n}y_{-n} + \Delta^{2n}y_{-n+1}}{2}$$

$$+ \frac{(u-\frac{1}{2})u(u-1)(u+1)(u-2)(u+2)\cdots(u-n)(u+n-1)}{(2n+1)!}\Delta^{2n+1}y_{-n}.$$

In this formula it will be noticed that all terms involving differences of odd order contain the factor $u - \frac{1}{2}$. Hence if $u = \frac{1}{2}$, these terms all drop out and we get the simple formula

$$\textbf{(V)} \quad y = \frac{y_0 + y_1}{2} - \frac{1}{8}\frac{\Delta^2 y_{-1} + \Delta^2 y_0}{2} + \frac{3}{128}\frac{\Delta^4 y_{-2} + \Delta^4 y_{-1}}{2}$$

$$- \frac{5}{1024}\frac{\Delta^6 y_{-3} + \Delta^6 y_{-2}}{2} + \cdots$$

$$+ (-1)^n\frac{[1\cdot 3\cdot 5\cdots(2n-1)]^2}{2^{2n}(2n)!}\frac{\Delta^{2n}y_{-n} + \Delta^{2n}y_{-n+1}}{2}.$$

This important special case of Bessel's formula is called the *formula for interpolating to halves*. It is used for computing values of the function midway between any two given values.

A more symmetrical form of Bessel's formula is obtained by putting $u - \frac{1}{2} = v$, or $u = v + \frac{1}{2}$. Making this substitution in (IV), we get

**(VI)** $y = \dfrac{y_0 + y_1}{2} + v\Delta y_0 + \dfrac{(v^2 - \frac{1}{4})}{2}\dfrac{\Delta^2 y_{-1} + \Delta^2 y_0}{2} + \dfrac{v(v^2 - \frac{1}{4})}{3!}\Delta^3 y_{-1}$

$+ \dfrac{(v^2 - \frac{1}{4})(v^2 - \frac{9}{4})}{4!}\dfrac{\Delta^4 y_{-2} + \Delta^4 y_{-1}}{2} + \dfrac{v(v^2 - \frac{1}{4})(v^2 - \frac{9}{4})}{5!}\Delta^5 y_{-2}$

$+ \dfrac{(v^2 - \frac{1}{4})(v^2 - \frac{9}{4})(v^2 - \frac{25}{4})}{6!}\dfrac{\Delta^6 y_{-3} + \Delta^6 y_{-2}}{2} + \cdots$

$+ \dfrac{(v^2 - \frac{1}{4})(v^2 - \frac{9}{4}) \cdots [v^2 - (2n-1)^2/4]}{(2n)!}\dfrac{\Delta^{2n} y_{-n} + \Delta^{2n} y_{-n+1}}{2}$

$+ \dfrac{v(v^2 - \frac{1}{4})(v^2 - \frac{9}{4}) \cdots [v^2 - (2n-1)^2/4]}{(2n+1)!}\Delta^{2n+1} y_{-n}.$

This is the most convenient form of Bessel's formula.

In formulas (IV) and (VI) there are $2n+2$ terms, and the polynomials represented by them coincide with the given function at the $2n+2$ points

$u = -n, \; -n+1, \; -n+2, \cdots -1, 0, 1, 2, \cdots n, n+1;$

$v = -\dfrac{2n+1}{2}, \; -\dfrac{2n-1}{2}, \cdots -\dfrac{3}{2}, \; -\dfrac{1}{2}, \; \dfrac{1}{2}, \; \dfrac{3}{2}, \cdots \dfrac{2n-1}{2}, \dfrac{2n+1}{2};$

$x = x_0 - nh, x_0 - (n-1)h, \cdots x_0 - h, x_0, x_0 + h, \cdots x_0 + nh, x_0 + (n+1)h.$

The zero point for the $v$'s is $x_0 + h/2$, whereas for the $u$'s it is $x_0$.

We shall now apply Stirling's and Bessel's formulas to some numerical examples.

*Example 1.* The following table gives the values of the probability integral

$$f(x) = \frac{2}{\sqrt{\pi}} \int_0^x e^{-x^2} dx$$

for certain equidistant values of $x$. Find the value of this integral when $x = 0.5437$.

| $x$ | $f(x)$ | $\Delta f(x)$ | $\Delta^2 f(x)$ | $\Delta^3 f(x)$ | $\Delta^4 f(x)$ |
|------|-----------|--------|--------|------|------|
| 0.51 | 0.5292437 | | | | |
| | | 86550 | | | |
| 0.52 | 0.5378987 | | −896 | | |
| | | 85654 | | −7 | |
| 0.53 | 0.5464641 | | −903 | | 0 |
| | | 84751 | | −7 | |
| 0.54 | 0.5549392 | | −910 | | 0 |
| | | 83841 | | −7 | |
| 0.55 | 0.5633233 | | −917 | | 1 |
| | | 82924 | | −6 | |
| 0.56 | 0.5716157 | | −923 | | |
| | | 82001 | | | |
| 0.57 | 0.5798158 | | | | |

*Solution.* Here we take $x_0 = 0.54$ and $x = 0.5437$. Since $h = 0.01$, we have

$$u = \frac{x - x_0}{h} = \frac{0.5437 - 0.54}{0.01} = \frac{0.0037}{0.01} = 0.37.$$

(a) Using Stirling's formula, (III), we have

$$f(0.5437) = 0.5549392 + 0.37 \frac{(84751 + 83841)}{2}$$

$$+ \frac{(0.37)^2}{2}(-910) + \frac{0.37(0.37^2 - 1)}{2} \frac{(-7-7)}{6}$$

$$= 0.5549392 + 0.00311895 - 0.00000623 + 0.00000004.$$

$$= \underline{0.5580520.}$$

(b) To find $f(0.5437)$ by Bessel's formula it is more convenient to use (VI). Here

$$v = u - \tfrac{1}{2} = 0.37 - 0.50 = -0.13.$$

Substituting in (VI), we have

$$f(0.5437) = \frac{0.5549392 + 0.5633233}{2} + (-0.13)(83841)$$

$$+ \frac{0.0169 - 0.25}{2}\left(\frac{-910 - 917}{2}\right) + \frac{-0.13(0.0169 - 0.25)(-7)}{6}$$

$$= 0.55913125 - 0.00108993 + 0.00001065$$

$$= \underline{0.5580520.}$$

*Example 2.* The values of $e^{-x}$ for certain equidistant values of $x$ are given in the following table. Find the value of $e^{-x}$ when $x = 1.7489$.

| $x$ | $e^{-x}$ | $\Delta$ | $\Delta^2$ | $\Delta^3$ | $\Delta^4$ |
|------|-----------|-----------|-------------|-------------|-------------|
| 1.72 | 0.1790661479 | | | | |
| | | −17817379 | | | |
| 1.73 | 0.1772844100 | | 177285 | | |
| | | −17640094 | | −1762 | |
| 1.74 | 0.1755204006 | | 175523 | | +13 |
| | | −17464571 | | −1749 | |
| 1.75 | 0.1737739435 | | 173774 | | +22 |
| | | −17290797 | | −1727 | |
| 1.76 | 0.1720448638 | | 172047 | | +15 |
| | | −17118750 | | −1712 | |
| 1.77 | 0.1703329888 | | 170335 | | |
| | | −16948415 | | | |
| 1.78 | 0.1686381473 | | | | |

*Solution.*

(a)  By Stirling's formula.

Here we take $x = 1.7489$, $x_0 = 1.75$, $h = 0.01$.

Hence

$$u = \frac{1.7489 - 1.75}{0.01} = -\frac{0.0011}{0.01} = -0.11.$$

Substituting in (III), we have

$$f(1.7489) = 0.1737739435 - 0.11\frac{(-17464571 - 17290797)}{2}$$

$$+ \frac{0.0121}{2}(173774) - 0.11\left(\frac{0.0121 - 1}{6}\right)\left(\frac{-1749 - 1727}{2}\right)$$

$$+ 0.0121\left(\frac{0.0121 - 1}{24}\right)(22)$$

$$= 0.1737739435 + 0.00019115452$$

$$+ 0.00000010513 - 0.00000000315;$$

or $f(1.7489) = e^{-1.7489} = \underline{0.1739652000}.$

This value is correct to ten decimal places.

(b)  By Bessel's formula.

Since the value 1.7489 is nearer to the middle of the interval 1.74 − 1.75 than it is to the middle of the interval 1.75 − 1.76, we take $x_0 = 1.74$ so as to make $v$ as small as possible.  Hence we have

$$u = \frac{1.7489 - 1.74}{0.01} = 0.89,$$

$$v = u - \tfrac{1}{2} = 0.89 - 0.50 = 0.39.$$

$$\therefore f(1.7489) = \frac{0.1755204006 + 0.1737739435}{2} + 0.39(-17464571)$$

$$+ \left(\frac{0.39^2 - 0.25}{2}\right)\left(\frac{175523 + 173774}{2}\right)$$

$$+ 0.39\left(\frac{0.39^2 - 0.25}{6}\right)(-1749)$$

$$+ \frac{(0.39^2 - 0.25)(0.39^2 - 2.25)}{24}\left(\frac{13 + 22}{2}\right)$$

$$= 0.17464717205 - 0.00068111827$$

$$- 0.00000085490 + 0.00000000111$$

$$+ 0.00000000001;$$

or $f(1.7489) = 0.1739652000$, as before.

We could also take $x_0 = 1.75$, in which case we should have $v = -0.61$. This would give

$$f(1.7489) = 0.17290940365 + 0.00105473862$$

$$+ 0.000\ 0105562 + 0.00000000214$$

$$- 0.00000000002 \doteq 0.1739652000.$$

This value is also correct to ten decimal places, but the series converges slightly less rapidly than in the preceding case; and both of these series given by Bessel's formula converge a little less rapidly than the one given by Stirling's formula.

*Remark.* The question naturally arises at this point as to which is the more accurate, Stirling's formula or Bessel's. The answer is that one is about as accurate as the other. For a given table of differences the rapidity of convergence depends upon the magnitude of $u$ in the case of formula (III) and upon the magnitude of $v$ in the case of formula (VI). The smaller the values of $u$ and $v$ the more rapidly the series converge. We should therefore always choose the starting point $x_0$ so as to make $u$ and $v$ as small as possible. In most cases it is possible to choose the starting point so as to make $-0.5 \leq u \leq 0.5$ and $-0.5 \leq v \leq 0.5$. Thus, in Example 1 the starting point was so chosen that $u = 0.37$,

$v = -0.13$; and in Example 2 we had $u = -0.11$, $v = 0.39$. It is to be noted that Bessel's formula converged the more rapidly in the first example and Stirling's the more rapidly in the second, the reason being that $v$ was smaller than $u$ in the first case and $u$ smaller than $v$ in the second.

As a general rule it may be stated that Bessel's formula will give a more accurate result when interpolating near the middle of an interval, say from $u = 0.25$ to $0.75$ ($v = -0.25$ to $0.25$); whereas Stirling's formula will give the better result when interpolating near the beginning or end of an interval—from $u = -0.25$ to $0.25$, say.

For another phase of this question see Chapter V.

*Example 3.* The following table gives the values of the elliptic integral

$$F(\phi) = \int_0^\phi \frac{d\phi}{\sqrt{1 - \tfrac{1}{2} \sin^2 \phi}}$$

for certain equidistant values of $\phi$.   Find the value of $F(23°.5)$.

| $\phi$ | $F(\phi)$ | $\Delta F$ | $\Delta^2 F$ | $\Delta^3 F$ | $\Delta^4 F$ |
|--------|-----------|------------|--------------|--------------|--------------|
| 21° | 0.370634373 | | | | |
| | | 18070778 | | | |
| 22 | 0.388705151 | | 59002 | | |
| | | 18129780 | | 2707 | |
| 23 | 0.406834931 | | 61709 | | 4 |
| | | 18191489 | | 2711 | |
| 24 | 0.425026420 | | 64420 | | −7 |
| | | 18255909 | | 2704 | |
| 25 | 0.443282329 | | 67124 | | |
| | | 18323033 | | | |
| 26 | 0.461605362 | | | | |

*Solution.* Since we are to find the value of the function half-way between two given tabular values, we use formula (V) for interpolating to halves.  Hence we have

$$F(23°.5) = \frac{0.406834931 + 0.425026420}{2} - \frac{1}{8} \cdot \frac{61709 + 64420}{2}$$

$$+ \frac{3}{128} \cdot \frac{4 - 7}{2}$$

$$= 0.4159306755 - 0.0000078831 = \underline{0.415922792}.$$

This result is probably correct to its last figure, since the differences in the table are perfectly regular and decrease rapidly.

### EXAMPLES ON CHAPTER III

1. Find $\log_{10} \tan 56' \, 43''.5$ by Bessel's formula (VI), given

$$\log \tan 52' = 8.1797626 - 10$$
$$\text{``    ``    } 53 = 8.1880364 - 10$$
$$\text{``    ``    } 54 = 8.1961556 - 10$$
$$\text{``    ``    } 55 = 8.2041259 - 10$$
$$\text{``    ``    } 56 = 8.2119526 - 10$$
$$\text{``    ``    } 57 = 8.2196408 - 10$$
$$\text{``    ``    } 58 = 8.2271953 - 10$$
$$\text{``    ``    } 59 = 8.2346208 - 10.$$

2. Find $\sin 56° \, 50' \, 31''.58$ by Stirling's formula, given

$$\sin 56° \, 50' \, 00'' = 0.8370827$$
$$\text{``    ``    ``    } 10'' = 0.8371093$$
$$\text{``    ``    ``    } 20'' = 0.8371358$$
$$\text{``    ``    ``    } 30'' = 0.8371623$$
$$\text{``    ``    ``    } 40'' = 0.8371888$$
$$\text{``    ``    ``    } 50'' = 0.8372153$$
$$\text{``    } 57° \, 51' \, 00'' = 0.8372418.$$

3. Compute the value of $(2/\sqrt{\pi})\int_0^x e^{-x^2}dx$ when $x = 0.6538$, given the following table:

| $x$ | $(2/\sqrt{\pi})\int_0^x e^{-x^2}dx$ |
| --- | --- |
| 0.62 | 0.6194114 |
| 0.63 | 0.6270463 |
| 0.64 | 0.6345857 |
| 0.65 | 0.6420292 |
| 0.66 | 0.6493765 |
| 0.67 | 0.6566275 |
| 0.68 | 0.6637820. |

4. The mean atmospheric refraction, $R$, for a star at various altitudes $h°$ above the horizon is given in the table below. Using Bessel's formula for interpolating to halves, find the refraction for a star at an altitude of 27° above the horizon.

| $h$ | $R$ |
|---|---|
| 22° | 2′ 23″.3 |
| 24 | 2 10 .2 |
| 26 | 1 58 .9 |
| 28 | 1 49 .2 |
| 30 | 1 40 .6 |
| 32 | 1 33 .0 |

5. The declination of the moon at the beginning (noon) of certain · days in August, 1918, was as given below. Compute the declination for 9:35 P.M., August 25.

| Aug. 20, | $-16°$ | 0′ | 51″ | .0 |
|---|---|---|---|---|
| " 21 | 11 | 24 | 51 | .8 |
| " 22 | 6 | 3 | 29 | .4 |
| " 23 | $-0$ | 17 | 25 | .8 |
| " 24 | $+5$ | 30 | 21 | .5 |
| " 25 | 10 | 56 | 40 | .3 |
| " 26 | 15 | 39 | 57 | .8 |
| " 27 | 19 | 22 | 3 | .7 |
| " 28 | 21 | 49 | 48 | .3 |
| " 29 | 22 | 56 | 22 | .8 |
| " 30 | 22 | 41 | 54 | .1 |

6. The values of an elliptic integral for certain values of the amplitude $\phi$ are given in the table below. Compute the value of the integral when $\phi = 24° 36′ 42″$.

| $\phi$ | $F(\phi)$ |
|---|---|
| 21° | 0.370634373 |
| 22 | 0.388705151 |
| 23 | 0.406834931 |
| 24 | 0.425026420 |
| 25 | 0.443282329 |
| 26 | 0.461605362 |
| 27 | 0.479998225 |

# CHAPTER IV

## LAGRANGE'S FORMULA. INVERSE INTERPOLATION

### I. LAGRANGE'S FORMULA OF INTERPOLATION

**20. Introduction.** The interpolation formulas derived in the preceding sections are applicable only when the values of the independent variable are given at equidistant intervals. It is sometimes inconvenient or even impossible to obtain values of a function for equidistant values of the independent variable, and in such cases it is desirable to have an interpolation formula which involves only such data as may be at hand. We shall now derive such a formula.

**21. Lagrange's Formula.** Let $(x_0, y_0)$, $(x_1, y_1)$, $(x_2, y_2)$, $\cdots (x_n, y_n)$ denote $n+1$ corresponding pairs of values of any two variables $x$ and $y$, where $y = f(x)$. We replace the given function by a polynomial of the $n$th degree, which may be written in the following form:

$$(21\colon 1) \quad \phi(x) = A_0(x - x_1)(x - x_2)(x - x_3) \cdots (x - x_n)$$

$$+ A_1(x - x_0)(x - x_2)(x - x_3) \cdots (x - x_n)$$

$$+ A_2(x - x_0)(x - x_1)(x - x_3) \cdots (x - x_n)$$

$$+ \cdots$$

$$+ A_n(x - x_0)(x - x_1)(x - x_2) \cdots (x - x_{n-1}).$$

Here there are $n+1$ terms and $n$ factors in each term.

We next determine the $n+1$ constants $A_0, A_1, A_2, \cdots A_n$ so as to make $\phi(x_0) = y_0$, $\phi(x_1) = y_1$, $\cdots \phi(x_n) = y_n$. Putting $x = x_0$ and $\phi(x_0) = y_0$ in (21: 1), we get

$$y_0 = A_0(x_0 - x_1)(x_0 - x_2) \cdots (x_0 - x_n).$$

$$\therefore A_0 = \frac{y_0}{(x_0 - x_1)(x_0 - x_2) \cdots (x_0 - x_n)}.$$

Again, putting $x = x_1$, $\phi(x_1) = y_1$ in (21:1), we have

$$v_1 = A_1(x_1 - x_0)(x_1 - x_2) \cdots (x_1 - x_n).$$

$$\therefore A_1 = \frac{y_1}{(x_1 - x_0)(x_1 - x_2) \cdots (x_1 - x_n)}.$$

72

In a similar manner we find

$$A_2 = \frac{y_2}{(x_2 - x_0)(x_2 - x_1)(x_2 - x_3) \cdots (x_2 - x_n)},$$

$$\cdots \cdots \cdots \cdots \cdots \cdots \cdots$$

$$A_n = \frac{y_n}{(x_n - x_0)(x_n - x_1) \cdots (x_n - x_{n-1})}.$$

Substituting in $(21:1)$ these values of the $A$'s, we get

$$\textbf{(VII)} \qquad \phi(x) = \frac{(x - x_1)(x - x_2) \cdots (x - x_n)}{(x_0 - x_1)(x_0 - x_2) \cdots (x_0 - x_n)} y_0$$

$$+ \frac{(x - x_0)(x - x_2) \cdots (x - x_n)}{(x_1 - x_0)(x_1 - x_2) \cdots (x_1 - x_n)} y_1$$

$$+ \frac{(x - x_0)(x - x_1)(x - x_3) \cdots (x - x_n)}{(x_2 - x_0)(x_2 - x_1)(x_2 - x_3) \cdots (x_2 - x_n)} y_2 + \cdots$$

$$+ \frac{(x - x_0)(x - x_1) \cdots (x - x_{n-1})}{(x_n - x_0)(x_n - x_1) \cdots (x_n - x_{n-1})} y_n.$$

This formula (VII) is known as *Lagrange's formula of interpolation.* The values of the independent variable may or may not be equidistant. It is to be noted that Lagrange's formula does not involve the successive differences of the function concerned, and that there is nothing in it by which we can estimate the reliability of the results obtained.

Since Lagrange's formula is merely a relation between two variables, either of which may be taken as the independent variable, it is evident that by considering $y$ as the independent variable we can write a formula giving $x$ as a function of $y$. Hence, on interchanging $x$ and $y$ in the right-hand member of (VII) we get

$$\textbf{(VIII)} \qquad \psi(y) = \frac{(y - y_1)(y - y_2) \cdots (y - y_n)}{(y_0 - y_1)(y_0 - y_2) \cdots (y_0 - y_n)} x_0$$

$$+ \frac{(y - y_0)(y - y_2) \cdots (y - y_n)}{(y_1 - y_0)(y_1 - y_2) \cdots (y_1 - y_n)} x_1$$

$$+ \frac{(y - y_0)(y - y_1) \cdots (y - y_n)}{(y_2 - y_0)(y_2 - y_1) \cdots (y_2 - y_n)} x_2 + \cdots$$

$$+ \frac{(y - y_0)(y - y_1) \cdots (y - y_{n-1})}{(y_n - y_0)(y_n - y_1) \cdots (y_n - y_{n-1})} x_n.$$

The chief uses of Lagrange's formula are two: (1) to find any value of a function when the given values of the independent variables are not equidistant, and (2) to find the value of the independent variable corresponding to a given value of the function. This second problem is solved by means of formula (VIII).

We shall now work two examples to illustrate these uses.

*Example 1.* The following table gives certain corresponding values of $x$ and $\log_{10}x$. Compute the value of log 323.5.

| $x$ | 321.0 | 322.8 | 324.2 | 325.0 |
|---|---|---|---|---|
| $\log_{10} x$ | 2.50651 | 2.50893 | 2.51081 | 2.51188 |

*Solution.* Here $x = 323.5$, $x_0 = 321.0$, $x_1 = 322.8$, $x_2 = 324.2$, $x_3 = 325.0$. Substituting these values in (VII), we get

$$
\begin{aligned}
\log_{10} 323.5 &= \frac{(323.5 - 322.8)(323.5 - 324.2)(323.5 - 325.0)}{(321 - 322.8)(321 - 324.2)(321 - 325)} \times 2.50651 \\
&+ \frac{(323.5 - 321)(323.5 - 324.2)(323.5 - 325)}{(322.8 - 321)(322.8 - 324.2)(322.8 - 325)} \times 2.50893 \\
&+ \frac{(323.5 - 321)(323.5 - 322.8)(323.5 - 325)}{(324.2 - 321)(324.2 - 322.8)(324.2 - 325)} \times 2.51081 \\
&+ \frac{(323.5 - 321)(323.5 - 322.8)(323.5 - 324.2)}{(325 - 321)(325 - 322.8)(325 - 324.2)} \times 2.51188 \\
&= -0.07996 + 1.18794 + 1.83897 - 0.43708 \\
&= \underline{2.50987}.
\end{aligned}
$$

This result is correct to the last figure.

*Example 2.* The following table gives the values of the probability integral $(2/\sqrt{\pi})\int_0^x e^{-x^2}dx$ corresponding to certain values of $x$. For what value of $x$ is this integral equal to $\frac{1}{2}$?

| $(2/\sqrt{\pi})\int_0^x e^{-x^2}dx$ | $x$ |
|---|---|
| 0.4846555 | 0.46 |
| 0.4937452 | 0.47 |
| 0.5027498 | 0.48 |
| 0.5116683 | 0.49 |

*Solution.* Calling $y$ the value of the probability integral, we have

$$y = \tfrac{1}{2} = 0.5, \quad x_0 = 0.46, \quad x_1 = 0.47, \quad x_2 = 0.48, \quad x_3 = 0.49.$$

Substituting these in (VIII), we get

$$x = \frac{(0.5 - 0.4937452)(0.5 - 0.5027498)(0.5 - 0.5116683)}{(0.4846555 - 0.4937452)(0.4846555 - 0.5027498)(0.4846555 - 0.5116683)} \times 0.46$$

$$+ \frac{(0.5 - 0.4846555)(0.5 - 0.5027498)(0.5 - 0.5116683)}{(0.4937452 - 0.4846555)(0.4937452 - 0.5027498)(0.4937452 - 0.5116683)} \times 0.47$$

$$+ \frac{(0.5 - 0.4846555)(0.5 - 0.4937452)(0.5 - 0.5116683)}{(0.5027498 - 0.4846555)(0.5027498 - 0.4937452)(0.5027498 - 0.5116683)} \times 0.48$$

$$+ \frac{(0.5 - 0.4846555)(0.5 - 0.4937452)(0.5 - 0.5027498)}{(0.5116683 - 0.4846555)(0.5116683 - 0.4937452)(0.5116683 - 0.5027498)} \times 0.49$$

$$= - \frac{62458 \times 27498 \times 116683}{90897 \times 180943 \times 270128} \times 0.46$$

$$+ \frac{153445 \times 27498 \times 116683}{90897 \times 90046 \times 179231} \times 0.47$$

$$+ \frac{153445 \times 62548 \times 116683}{180943 \times 90046 \times 89185} \times 0.48$$

$$- \frac{153445 \times 62548 \times 27498}{270128 \times 179231 \times 89185} \times 0.49$$

$$= - 0.0207787 + 0.157737 + 0.369928 - 0.0299495$$

$$= \underline{0.476937}.$$

The true value to six decimal places is 0.476936.

*Note.* The computation in this problem should be performed by logarithms unless a calculating machine is available.

*Remark.* The reader who has followed through the computation in the two preceding examples will have noticed that Lagrange's formula is tedious to apply and involves a great deal of computation. It must also be used with care and caution, for if the values of the independent variable are not taken close together the results are liable to be very inaccurate. For these reasons Lagrange's formula should not be used except in cases where Newton's, Stirling's, and Bessel's formulas are inapplicable.

## II. INVERSE INTERPOLATION

**22. Definition.** *Inverse interpolation* is the process of finding the value of the *argument* corresponding to a given value of the function when the latter is intermediate between two tabulated values. The problem of inverse interpolation can be solved by several methods, but in this book we shall explain only three.

**23. By Lagrange's Formula.** One method of dealing with the problem is to use Lagrange's interpolation formula in the form (VIII), in which $x$ is expressed as a function of $y$. Example 2 of the preceding article was really a problem in inverse interpolation. We shall therefore not explain this method further.

**24. By Successive Approximations.** A second method is that of *successive approximations* or *iteration*. To see how this method is applied let us consider Newton's formula (I), namely,

$$y = y_0 + u\Delta y_0 + \frac{u(u-1)}{2}\Delta^2 y_0 + \frac{u(u-1)(u-2)}{3!}\Delta^3 y_0$$

$$+ \frac{u(u-1)(u-2)(u-3)}{4!}\Delta^4 y_0 + \cdots .$$

Transposing and dividing through by $\Delta y_0$, we have

$$(1) \qquad u = \frac{y-y_0}{\Delta y_0} - \frac{u(u-1)\Delta^2 y_0}{2\Delta y_0} - \frac{u(u-1)(u-2)\Delta^3 y_0}{3!}\frac{}{\Delta y_0}$$

$$- \frac{u(u-1)(u-2)(u-3)}{4!}\frac{\Delta^4 y_0}{\Delta y_0} .$$

To get a first approximation for $u$, we neglect all differences higher than the first and therefore have

$$u^{(1)} = \frac{y-y_0}{\Delta y_0} .$$

The second approximation is obtained by substituting $u^{(1)}$ in the right-hand side of (1). We then have

$$(2) \quad u^{(2)} = \frac{y-y_0}{\Delta y_0} - \frac{u^{(1)}(u^{(1)}-1)}{2}\frac{\Delta^2 y_0}{\Delta y_0} - \frac{u^{(1)}(u^{(1)}-1)(u^{(1)}-2)}{3!}\frac{\Delta^3 y_0}{\Delta y_0}$$

$$- \frac{u^{(1)}(u^{(1)}-1)(u^{(1)}-2)(u^{(1)}-3)}{4!}\frac{\Delta^4 y_0}{\Delta y_0} .$$

The third approximation is

$$(3) \quad u^{(3)} = \frac{y-y_0}{\Delta y_0} - \frac{u^{(2)}(u^{(2)}-1)}{2}\frac{\Delta^2 y_0}{\Delta y_0} - \frac{u^{(2)}(u^{(2)}-1)(u^{(2)}-2)}{3!}\frac{\Delta^3 y_0}{\Delta y_0}$$

$$- \frac{u^{(2)}(u^{(2)}-1)(u^{(2)}-2)(u^{(2)}-3)}{4!}\frac{\Delta^4 y_0}{\Delta y_0} .$$

And so on for higher approximations.

We shall now illustrate the method by working an example.

*Example 1.* Given a table of values of the probability integral $(2/\sqrt{\pi})\int_0^x e^{-x^2}dx$, for what value of $x$ is this integral equal to $\frac{1}{2}$?

| $x$ | $y$ | $\Delta y$ | $\Delta^2 y$ | $\Delta^3 y$ | $\Delta^4 y$ |
|------|--------|--------|--------|--------|--------|
| 0.45 | 0.4754818 | | | | |
| | | 91737 | | | |
| 0.46 | 0.4846555 | | $-840$ | | |
| | | 90897 | | $-11$ | |
| 0.47 | 0.4937452 | | $-851$ | | 1 |
| | | 90046 | | $-10$ | |
| 0.48 | 0.5027498 | | $-861$ | | 2 |
| | | 89185 | | $-8$ | |
| 0.49 | 0.5116683 | | $-869$ | | |
| | | 88316 | | | |
| 0.50 | 0.5204999 | | | | |

*Solution.* Here it is better to use a central-difference formula. Inspection shows that the desired value of $x$ lies between 0.47 and 0.48, and a rough linear interpolation shows that it is about $0.47\frac{2}{3}$. Hence we take $x_0 = 0.47$ and use Bessel's formula. We therefore have

$$x_0 = 0.47, \quad h = 0.01, \quad y = \tfrac{1}{2} = 0.5.$$

Substituting in Bessel's formula (VI) this value of $y$ and the appropriate quantities from the table, we have

$$0.5 = 0.4982475 + 0.0090046v + \frac{(v^2 - 0.25)}{2}(-0.0000856)$$

$$+ \frac{v(v^2 - 0.25)}{6}(-0.0000010).$$

Transposing and dividing through by 0.0090046, we get

$$(4) \qquad v = 0.194623 - (v^2 - 0.25)(-0.004753) - v(v^2 - 0.25)(-0.0000185).$$

A first approximation for $v$ is obtained by neglecting all terms beyond the first in the right-hand member of (4). Hence

$$v^{(1)} = 0.194623.$$

Substituting this for $v$ in the right-hand member of (4), we find the second approximation to be

$$v^{(2)} = 0.194623 - [(0.194623)^2 - 0.25](-0.004753)$$

$$- 0.194623[(0.194623)^2 - 0.25](-0.0000185)$$

$$= 0.194623 - 0.001008 - 0.000001 = 0.193614.$$

Now substituting this value for $v$ in the right-hand member of (4), we find

$$v^{(3)} = 0.194623 - 0.0010101 - 0.000001 = 0.193612.$$

This value differs only slightly from the preceding, and we therefore make no further approximations.

Since $u = v + \frac{1}{2}$ and $x = x_0 + hu$, we have

$$u = 0.693612,$$

$$x = 0.47 + 0.01(0.693612) = \underline{0.47693612}.$$

This value is correct to six decimal places.

*Note.* In this example it is not possible to obtain more than five trustworthy figures in the value of $v$, because the right-hand member of (4) is the result of a division by the approximate number 0.0090046, the fifth significant figure of which is uncertain. As a matter of fact, only the first four figures in $v$ are correct.

If all differences higher than the second are negligible, the problem of inverse interpolation amounts only to the solution of a quadratic equation. The following example illustrates this.

*Example 2.* Given sinh $x = 62$, to find $x$.

*Solution.* Forming a difference table as shown below, we find that all differences above the second are zero. We also notice that the required value of $x$ is slightly greater than 4.82. Hence we take $x_0 = 4.82$ and use Stirling's formula.

| $x$ | $y = \sinh x$ | $\Delta y$ | $\Delta^2 y$ | $\Delta^3 y$ |
|------|------|------|------|------|
| 4.80 | 60.7511 | | | |
| | | 6106 | | |
| 4.81 | 61.3617 | | 62 | |
| | | 6168 | | 0 |
| 4.82 | 61.9785 | | 62 | |
| | | 6230 | | 0 |
| 4.83 | 62.6015 | | 62 | |
| | | 6292 | | |
| 4.84 | 63.2307 | | | |

Substituting $y = 62$ in Stirling's formula, (III), we have

$$62 = 61.9785 + 0.6199u + 0.0031u^2,$$

or

$$31u^2 + 6199u = 215.$$

$$\therefore \quad u = \frac{-6199 + \sqrt{(6199)^2 + 4 \times 31 \times 215}}{62} = \frac{-6199 \pm 6201.15}{62}$$

$$= \frac{2.15}{62} = 0.0347.$$

Since $h = 0.01$ and $x = x_0 + hu$, we get

$$x = 4.82 + 0.01(0.0347) = 4.8203.$$

**25. By Reversion of Series.** The most obvious method of solving the problem of inverse interpolation is by reversion of series; for all the interpolation formulas thus far developed are in the form of a power series, and any convergent power series can be reverted. Thus, the power series

$$(25:1) \qquad y = a_0 + a_1 x + a_2 x^2 + a_3 x^3 + \cdots a_n x^n + \cdots$$

when reverted becomes

$$(25:2) \quad x = \left(\frac{y - a_0}{a_1}\right) + c_1\left(\frac{y - a_0}{a_1}\right)^2 + c_2\left(\frac{y - a_0}{a_1}\right)^3$$

$$+ c_3\left(\frac{y - a_0}{a_1}\right)^4 + \cdots + c_{n-1}\left(\frac{y - a_0}{a_1}\right)^n + \cdots,$$

where

$$(25:3) \begin{cases} c_1 = -\dfrac{a_2}{a_1}, \\[2ex] c_2 = -\dfrac{a_3}{a_1} + 2\left(\dfrac{a_2}{a_1}\right)^2, \\[2ex] c_3 = -\dfrac{a_4}{a_1} + 5\left(\dfrac{a_2 a_3}{a_1^2}\right) - 5\left(\dfrac{a_2}{a_1}\right)^3, \\[2ex] c_4 = -\dfrac{a_5}{a_1} + 6\dfrac{a_2 a_4}{a_1^2} + 3\left(\dfrac{a_3}{a_1}\right)^2 - 21\dfrac{a_2^2 a_3}{a_1^3} + 14\left(\dfrac{a_2}{a_1}\right)^4, \\[2ex] c_5 = -\dfrac{a_6}{a_1} + 7\left(\dfrac{a_2 a_5 + a_3 a_4}{a_1^2}\right) - 28\left(\dfrac{a_2^2 a_4 + a_2 a_3^2}{a_1^3}\right) + 84\dfrac{a_2^3 a_3}{a_1^4} \\[2ex] \qquad - 42\left(\dfrac{a_2}{a_1}\right)^5, \text{ etc.} \end{cases}$$

When reverting a series with numerical coefficients, it is better to compute the $c$'s from equations (25:3) and then substitute their values in (25:2).

We shall now write Newton's, Stirling's, and Bessel's formulas in the form of power series and then write down the values of $a_0, a_1, \cdots a_4$ in each case. We stop with fourth differences, but the reader will have no difficulty in extending them to higher differences if necessary.

a) *Newton's Formula* (I).

$$y = y_0 + u\Delta y_0 + \frac{u(u-1)}{2}\Delta^2 y_0 + \frac{u(u-1)(u-2)}{3!}\Delta^3 y_0$$

$$+ \frac{u(u-1)(u-2)(u-3)}{4!}\Delta^4 y_0$$

$$= y_0 + \left(\Delta y_0 - \frac{\Delta^2 y_0}{2} + \frac{\Delta^3 y_0}{3} - \frac{\Delta^4 y_0}{4}\right)u + \left(\frac{\Delta^2 y_0}{2} - \frac{\Delta^3 y_0}{2} + \frac{11\Delta^4 y_0}{24}\right)u^2$$

$$+ \left(\frac{\Delta^3 y_0}{6} - \frac{\Delta^4 y_0}{4}\right)u^3 + \frac{\Delta^4 y_0}{24}u^4.$$

Here

$$a_0 = y_0,$$

$$a_1 = \Delta y_0 - \frac{\Delta^2 y_0}{2} + \frac{\Delta^3 y_0}{3} - \frac{\Delta^4 y_0}{4},$$

$$a_2 = \frac{\Delta^2 y_0}{2} - \frac{\Delta^3 y_0}{2} + \frac{11\Delta^4 y_0}{24},$$

$$a_3 = \frac{\Delta^3 y_0}{6} - \frac{\Delta^4 y_0}{4},$$

$$a_4 = \frac{\Delta^4 y_0}{24}.$$

b) *Stirling's Formula.*

$$y = y_0 + um_1 + \frac{u^2}{2}\Delta^2 y_{-1} + \frac{u(u^2-1)}{3!}m_3 + \frac{u^2(u^2-1)}{4!}\Delta^4 y_{-2}$$

$$= y_0 + \left(m_1 - \frac{m_3}{6}\right)u + \left(\frac{\Delta^2 y_{-1}}{2} - \frac{\Delta^4 y_{-2}}{24}\right)u^2 + \frac{m_3 u^3}{6} + \frac{\Delta^4 y_{-2}}{24}u^4,$$

where $m_1$ and $m_3$ have the values given in Art. 18. Here

$$a_0 = y_0, \quad a_1 = m_1 - \frac{m_3}{6}, \quad a_2 = \frac{\Delta^2 y_{-1}}{2} - \frac{\Delta^4 y_{-2}}{24},$$

$$a_3 = \frac{m_3}{6}, \quad a_4 = \frac{\Delta^4 y_{-2}}{24}.$$

c) *Bessel's Formula* (VI).

$$y = m_0 + v\Delta y_0 + \frac{(v^2 - \frac{1}{4})}{2} m_2 + v\frac{(v^2 - \frac{1}{4})}{3!}\Delta^3 y_{-1} + \frac{(v^2 - \frac{1}{4})(v^2 - \frac{9}{4})}{4!} m_4$$

$$= \left(m_0 - \frac{m_2}{8} + \frac{3m_4}{128}\right) + \left(\Delta y_0 - \frac{\Delta^3 y_{-1}}{24}\right)v + \left(\frac{m_2}{2} - \frac{5m_4}{48}\right)v^2$$

$$+ \frac{\Delta^3 y_{-1}}{6}v^3 + \frac{m_4}{24}v^4,$$

where $m_0$, $m_2$, $m_4$ have the values given in Art. 19. Here

$$a_0 = m_0 - \frac{m_2}{8} + \frac{3m_4}{128}, \qquad a_1 = \Delta y_0 - \frac{\Delta^3 y_{-1}}{24},$$

$$a_2 = \frac{m_2}{2} - \frac{5m_4}{48}, \qquad a_3 = \frac{\Delta^3 y_{-1}}{6}, \qquad a_4 = \frac{m_4}{24}.$$

We shall now work Examples 1 and 2 of the preceding article by reverting the series. For Example 1 we use Bessel's formula as before. From the table on page 77 we get

$$m_0 = 0.4982475, \quad m_2 = -0.0000856, \quad m_4 = 0.00000015.$$

Hence

$$a_0 = 0.4982475 + \frac{0.0000856}{8} = 0.4982582,$$

$$a_1 = 0.0090046 + \frac{0.0000010}{24} = 9.00900464,$$

$$a_2 = -\frac{0.0000856}{2} = -0.0000428,$$

$$a_3 = -\frac{0.0000010}{6} = -0.00000017,$$

$a_4 = 0$, practically.

Since $y = \frac{1}{2} = 0.5$, we have

$$\frac{y - a_0}{a_1} = \frac{0.5 - 0.4982582}{0.00900464} = 0.1934336.$$

Also

$$\frac{a_2}{a_1} = -\frac{0.0000428}{0.00900464} = -0.004753.$$

$$\therefore \quad \left(\frac{a_2}{a_1}\right)^2 = (-0.004753)^2 = 0.0000225910,$$

$$\left(\frac{a_2}{a_1}\right)^3 = -0.0000001074,$$

$$\frac{a_3}{a_1} = -\frac{0.00000017}{0.00900464} = -0.00001888.$$

Hence

$$c_1 = -\frac{a_2}{a_1} = 0.004753,$$

$$c_2 = 0.00001888 + 2(0.000022591) = 0.00006406,$$

$$c_3 = 0 + 5(-0.004753)(-0.00001888) - 5(-0.0000001074)$$

$$= 0.000000986.$$

Substituting these quantities in (25: 2), we get

$$v = 0.1934336 + 0.004753(0.1934336)^2 + 0.00006406(0.1934336)^3$$

$$= 0.1934336 + 0.0001778 + 0.00000046$$

$$= 0.193612.$$

Hence

$$u = v + \tfrac{1}{2} = 0.693612$$

and

$$x = x_0 + hu = 0.47 + 0.01(0.693612) = \underline{0.47693612,}$$

which is the same value as found by the method of successive approximations.

To solve Example 2 we use Stirling's formula, as before. Here

$$a_0 = y_0 = 61.9785,$$

$$a_1 = 0.6199,$$

$$a_2 = \frac{0.0062}{2} = 0.0031,$$

$$a_3 = a_4 = 0.$$

Since $y = 62$, we have

$$y - a_0 = 62 - 61.9785 = 0.0215.$$

$$\therefore \quad \frac{y - a_0}{a_1} = \frac{0.0215}{0.6199} = 0.034683,$$

$$\frac{a_2}{a_1} = \frac{0.0031}{0.6199} = 0.005001.$$

Hence

$$c_1 = -0.005001, \quad c_2 = 2(0.005001)^2 = 0.00005002,$$

$$c_3 = 0, \quad \text{practically.}$$

Substituting these values in (25: 2), we have

$$u = 0.034683 - 0.005001(0.034683)^2$$

$$= 0.0347.$$

$$\therefore \quad x = 4.82 + 0.01(0.0347) = \underline{4.8203},$$

as previously found by the method of iteration.

*Remark.* The problem of inverse interpolation should be dealt with in practice by the iteration process or by the reversion of series. The former will usually be the shorter.

### EXAMPLES ON CHAPTER IV

1. From the data in the following table find by Lagrange's formulas the value of $y$ when $x = 102$ and the value of $x$ when $y = 13.5$.

| $x$ | $y$ |
|---|---|
| 93.0 | 11.38 |
| 96.2 | 12.80 |
| 100.0 | 14.70 |
| 104.2 | 17.07 |
| 108.7 | 19.91 |

2. If $\cosh x = 1.285$, find $x$ by inverse interpolation, using the data in the following table:

| $x$ | $\cosh x$ |
|---|---|
| 0.735 | 1.2824937 |
| 0.736 | 1.2832974 |
| 0.737 | 1.2841023 |
| 0.738 | 1.2849085 |
| 0.739 | 1.2857159 |
| 0.740 | 1.2865247 |
| 0.741 | 1.2873348 |
| 0.742 | 1.2881461 |

# CHAPTER V

## THE ACCURACY OF INTERPOLATION FORMULAS

**26. Introduction.** In the preceding articles we have dealt with polynomial formulas for representing a given function over an interval. These polynomials coincide with the given function at the points $(x_0, y_0)$, $(x_1, y_1)$, $(x_2, y_2)$, etc. Hence it is reasonable to suppose that we can make these polynomials approximate the given function as closely as desired by merely increasing the number of coinciding points. Such indeed is the case if we don't attempt to spread over too wide an interval, but the necessity for caution in this matter will appear from the following considerations.

When the number of points $x_0, x_1, x_2, \ldots x_n$ increases indefinitely, the polynomial interpolation formulas become infinite series, called *interpolation series*; and just as a power series converges in a certain interval and diverges outside the interval, so likewise an interpolation series converges and represents the given function over a certain interval but fails to represent it outside of that interval. For example, if we should attempt to represent the function $1/(1+x^2)$ over the interval $-5 \leq x \leq 5$ by an interpolation series, we should find that the series would not represent the function at all when $x = 4$. As a matter of fact, the series would converge and represent the function to any desired degree of accuracy between $x = -3.63$ and $x = +3.63$, but would diverge and fail to represent it outside of this interval.[*] The investigation of the convergence of interpolation series is a somewhat lengthy matter and requires the use of functions of a complex variable.[†] We shall therefore not enter into it, but shall merely derive expressions for the remainder terms in the polynomial formulas previously considered.

**27. Remainder Term in Newton's Formula (I) and in Lagrange's Formula.** The derivation of the remainder term in a polynomial

---

[*] Runge, "Über empirische Funktionen und die Interpolation zwischen äquidistanten Ordinaten." *Zeitschrift fur Math. und Physik.* Vol. XLVI (1901), p. 229. See also Steffensen's *Interpolation*, pp. 35–38.

[†] The interested reader should consult the paper by Runge, cited above, and also the following Borel Monographs: Nörlund, *Lecons sur les Series d'Interpolation*, Paris, 1926. Borel, *Leçons sur les Fonctions de Variables Réelles et les Developpements en Séries de Polynomes*, Paris, 1905. Montel, *Leçons sur les Séries de Polynomes à une Variable Complexe*, Paris, 1910. Also Runge's *Theorie und Praxis der Reihe*, Leipzig, 1904.

interpolation formula is very similar to that of finding the remainder in Taylor's expansion. Thus, to find the remainder term in Newton's formula (I) and in Lagrange's formula, we write down the arbitrary function.

$$(27:1)\ F(z) = f(z) - \phi(z) - [f(x) - \phi(x)]\frac{(z - x_0)(z - x_1) \cdots (z - x_n)}{(x - x_0)(x - x_1) \cdots (x - x_n)},$$

where $f(x)$ denotes the given function, $\phi(x)$ a polynomial interpolation formula, and $z$ a real variable. We shall assume that $f(x)$ is continuous and possesses continuous derivatives of all orders within the interval from $x_0$ to $x_n$.

Now $F(z)$ vanishes for the $n+2$ values $z = x, x_0, x_1, \cdots x_n$; and since $f(x)$ is continuous and has continuous derivatives of all orders, the same is true of $f(z)$ and hence of $F(z)$. $F(z)$ therefore satisfies the conditions of Rolle's theorem. Hence the first derivative of $F(z)$ vanishes at least once between every two consecutive zero values of $F(z)$. Therefore in the interval from $x_0$ to $x_n$ $F'(z)$ must vanish $n+1$ times, $F''(z)$ $n$ times, $F'''(z)$ $n-1$ times, etc. Hence the $(n+1)$th derivative of $F(z)$ will vanish at least once at some point whose abscissa is $\xi$.

Since $\phi(z)$ is a polynomial of the $n$th degree, its $(n+1)$th derivative is zero. Furthermore, since the expression $(z-x_0)(z-x_1)(z-x_2) \cdots (z-x_n)$ is a polynomial of degree $n+1$, it follows that its $(n+1)$th derivative is the same as the $(n+1)$th derivative of $z^{n+1}$, which is $(n+1)!$ On differentiating $(27:1)$ $n+1$ times with respect to $z$ we therefore have

$$F^{(n+1)}(z) = f^{(n+1)}(z) - 0 - [f(x) - \phi(x)]\frac{(n + 1)!}{(x - x_0)(x - x_1) \cdots (x - x_n)}.$$

But since $F^{(n+1)}(z) = 0$ at some point $z = \xi$, we have

$$0 = f^{(n+1)}(\xi) - [f(x) - \phi(x)]\frac{(n + 1)!}{(x - x_0)(x - x_1) \cdots (x - x_n)}.$$

Hence

$$f(x) - \phi(x) = \frac{f^{(n+1)}(\xi)}{(n + 1)!}(x - x_0)(x - x_1) \cdots (x - x_n).$$

Now since $f(x) - \phi(x)$ is the difference between the given function and the polynomial at any point whose abscissa is $x$, it represents the *error* committed by replacing the given function by the polynomial. Hence we have

$$(27:2)\quad \text{Error} = R_n = \frac{f^{(n+1)}(\xi)}{(n + 1!)}(x - x_0)(x - x_1) \cdots (x - x_n),$$

where $\xi$ is some value of $x$ between $x_0$ and $x_n$. This is the remainder term in formula (15: 2) and in Lagrange's formula (VII).

To get the remainder term in formula (I) of Art. 15 we recall that $x - x_0 = hu$, $x - x_1 = h(u-1)$, $x - x_2 = h(u-2)$, $\cdots x - x_n = h(u-n)$. Substituting these values of $x - x_0$, $x - x_1$, etc. in (27: 2) above, we have

$$(27: 3) \qquad R_n = \frac{h^{n+1} f^{(n+1)}(\xi)}{(n + 1)!} u(u - 1)(u - 2) \cdots (u - n).$$

If the analytical form of the given function $f(x)$ is unknown, then the best we can do is to replace $f^{(n+1)}(\xi)$ by its value in terms of differences. The general relations between differences and derivatives are expressed by the following formulas:*

$(a)$ $$\Delta^n f(x) = (\Delta x)^n f^{(n)}(x + \theta n \Delta x), \ 0 < \theta < 1.$$

$(b)$ $$\lim_{\Delta x \to 0} \frac{\Delta^n f(x)}{(\Delta x)^n} = f^{(n)}(x).$$

Putting $x = x_0$ and $\Delta x = h$, we have from $(a)$

$(c)$ $$f^{(n)}(x_0 + \theta n h) = \frac{\Delta^n f(x_0)}{h^n}.$$

Now since $x_0 + nh$ and $\xi$ are values of $x$ at points within the interval of interpolation (that is, between $x_0$ and $x_n$) we may, for practical purposes, put $\xi = x_0 + \theta n h$. Making this substitution in $(c)$, we get

$(d)$ $$f^{(n)}(\xi) = \frac{\Delta^n f(x)}{h^n}.$$

Hence we have

$(e)$ $$f^{(n+1)}(\xi) = \frac{\Delta^{n+1} f(x_0)}{h^{n+1}},$$

practically. Substituting this value of $f^{(n+1)}(\xi)$ in (27: 3), we get

$$(27:4) \qquad R_n = \frac{\Delta^{n+1} y_0}{(n + 1)!} u(u - 1)(u - 2) \cdots (u - n).$$

The smaller the interval $h$ is taken the more nearly does (27: 4) give the actual error.

## 28. Remainder Term in Newton's Formula (II).

To find a formula for the remainder in Newton's formula for *backward* interpolation we write down the function

* See Vallée-Poussin's *Cours d'Analyse Infinitesimale*, I, pp. 72–73.

$$F(z) = f(z) - \phi(z) - [f(x) - \phi(x)]\frac{(z - x_n)(z - x_{n-1}) \cdots (z - x_0)}{(x - x_n)(x - x_{n-1}) \cdots (x - x_0)},$$

differentiate it $n+1$ times with respect to $z$, and put $F^{(n+1)}(z) = 0$ for $z = \xi$. We thus find

$$f(x) - \phi(x) = \frac{f^{(n+1)}(\xi)}{(n + 1)!}(x - x_n)(x - x_{n-1}) \cdots (x - x_0),$$

or

(28: 1)   Error $= R_n = \dfrac{f^{(n+1)}(\xi)}{(n + 1)!}(x - x_n)(x - x_{n-1})(x - x_{n-2}) \cdots (x - x_0).$

This is the remainder term for formula (16: 2).

To find the corresponding formula in terms of $u$ we recall that

$$\frac{x - x_n}{h} = u, \quad \frac{x - x_{n-1}}{h} = u + 1, \quad \frac{x - x_{n-2}}{h} = u + 2, \cdots \frac{x - x_0}{h} = u + n.$$

Substituting these values $x - x_n$ etc. in (28: 1) above, we get

(28: 2)   $R_n = \dfrac{h^{n+1}f^{(n+1)}(\xi)}{(n + 1)!}u(u + 1)(u + 2) \cdots (u + n).$

To find a formula for $R_n$ when the analytical form of the given function is unknown, we replace $f^{(n+1)}(\xi)$ by $\Delta_{n+1}y_n/h^{n+1}$ in (28: 2). The result is

(28: 3)   $R_n = \dfrac{\Delta_{n+1}y_n}{(n + 1)!} u(u + 1)(u + 2) \cdots (u + n).$

## 29. Remainder Term in Stirling's Formula.

We next turn our attention to the central-difference formulas of Stirling and Bessel. To find the remainder term in Stirling's formula we write down the arbitrary function

(29: 1) $F(z) = f(z) - \phi(z)$

$$- [f(x) - \phi(x)]\frac{(z - x_0)(z - x_1)(z - x_{-1}) \cdots (z - x_n)(z - x_{-n})}{(x - x_0)(x - x_1)(x - x_{-1}) \cdots (x - x_n)(x - x_{-n})}.$$

This function vanishes for the $2n+2$ values $z = x$, $x_0$, $x_1$, $\cdots x_n$, $x_{-1}$, $x_{-2}$, $\cdots x_{-n}$. We assume that $f(x)$ is continuous and has continuous derivatives of all orders up to $2n+1$. Hence $F(z)$ satisfies the conditions of Rolle's theorem. Also, since $\phi(z)$ is a polynomial of degree $2n$, its $(2n+1)$th derivative is zero. Hence on differentiating $F(z)\,2n+1$ times and putting $F^{(2n+1)}(z) = 0$ for some value $z = \xi$, we get

$$0 = f^{(2n+1)}(\xi) - 0 - [f(x) - \phi(x)] \frac{(2n+1)!}{(x-x_0)(x-x_1)(x-x_{-1}) \cdots (x-x_n)(x-x_{-n})},$$

from which

$$f(x) - \phi(x) = \frac{f^{(2n+1)}(\xi)}{(2n+1)!}(x - x_0)(x - x_1)(x - x_{-1}) \cdots x - x_n)(x - x_{-n}),$$

or

$$(29:2) \quad \text{Error} = R_n = \frac{f^{(2n+1)}(\xi)}{(2n+1)!}(x-x_0)(x-x_1)(x-x_{-1}) \cdots (x-x_n)(x-x_{-n}).$$

We write this formula in terms of $u$ as follows: Since

$$x - x_0 = hu, \ x - x_1 = h(u-1), \ \cdots x - x_n = h(u - n), \text{ and}$$

$$x - x_{-1} = x - (x_0 - h) = x - x_0 + h = hu + h = h(u + 1),$$

$$x - x_{-2} = h(u + 2), \ \cdots x - x_{-n} = h(u + n),$$

we have

$$(29:3) \quad R_n = \frac{h^{2n+1}f^{(2n+1)}(\xi)}{(2n+1)!}u(u^2 - 1)(u^2 - 2^2)(u^2 - 3^2) \cdots (u^2 - n^2),$$

where $\xi$ is some value of $x$ between $x_{-n}$ and $x_n$.

If the analytical form of $f(x)$ is unknown, we replace $f^{(2n+1)}(\xi)$ by $m_{2n+1}$, where

$$m_{2n+1} = \frac{\Delta^{2n+1}y_{-n-1} + \Delta^{2n+1}y_{-n}}{2}.$$

Hence we get from (29:3)

$$(29:4) \quad R_n = \frac{m_{2n+1}}{(2n+1)!} \ u(u^2 - 1)(u^2 - 2^2) \cdots (u^2 - n^2).$$

In formulas (29:3) and (29:4) $n$ is the number of intervals *on each side* of $x_0$.

**30. Remainder Terms in Bessel's Formulas.** The remainder term in Bessel's formulas is derived by first writing down the arbitrary function

$$(30:1) \quad F(z) = f(z) - \phi(z)$$

$$- [f(x) - \phi(x)] \frac{(z - x_0)(z - x_1)(z - x_{-1}) \cdots (z - x_n)(z - x_{-n})(z - x_{n+1})}{(x - x_0)(x - x_1)(x - x_{-1}) \cdots (x - x_n)(x - x_{-n})(x - x_{n+1})}.$$

This function vanishes at the $2n+3$ points $z = x, x_0, x_1, x_{-1}, \cdots x_n$,

$x_{-n}$, $x_{n+1}$. Since $\phi(z)$ is a polynomial of degree $2n+1$, its $(2n+2)$th derivative is zero. Hence on differentiating $(30:1)$ $2n+2$ times with respect to $z$ and putting $F^{(2n+2)}(z)=0$ for some value $z=\xi$, we get

$$0 = f^{(2n+2)}(\xi) - 0$$

$$- [f(x) - \phi(x)]\frac{(2n+2)!}{(x-x_0)(x-x_1)(x-x_{-1}) \cdots (x-x_n)(x-x_{-n})(x-x_{n+1})},$$

from which

$$f(x)-\phi(x)=\frac{f^{(2n+2)}(\xi)}{(2n+2)!}(x-x_0)(x-x_1)(x-x_{-1}) \cdots (x-x_n)(x-x_{-n})(x-x_{n+1}),$$

or

$(30:2)$   $\text{Error} = R_n$

$$=\frac{f^{(2n+2)}(\xi)}{(2n+2)!}(x-x_0)(x-x_1)(x-x_{-1}) \cdots (x-x_n)(x-x_{-n})(x-x_{n+1}).$$

Putting $x-x_0=hu$, $x-x_1=h(u-1)$, $x-x_{-1}=h(u+1)$, etc., as in the case of Stirling's formula, we get

$(30:3)$ $R_n=\dfrac{h^{2n+2}f^{(2n+2)}(\xi)}{(2n+2)!}u(u-1)(u+1)(u-2) \cdots (u-n)(u+n)(u-n-1).$

This is the remainder term in formula (IV) of Art. 19. In terms of differences it becomes

$(30:4)$ $R_n = \dfrac{m_{2n+2}}{(2n+2)!}u(u-1)(u+1)(u-2)(u+2)$

$$\cdots (u-n)(u+n)(u-n-1),$$

where

$$m_{2n+2} = \frac{\Delta^{2n+2}y_{-n-1} + \Delta^{2n+2}y_{-n}}{2}.$$

On putting $u=v+\frac{1}{2}$ in $(30:3)$ and $(30:4)$, we get

$(30:5)$   $R_n = \dfrac{h^{2n+2}f^{(2n+2)}(\xi)}{(2n+2)!}\left(v^2 - \dfrac{1}{4}\right)\left(v^2 - \dfrac{9}{4}\right) \cdots \left(v^2 - \dfrac{(2n+1)^2}{4}\right),$

$(30:6)$   $R_n = \dfrac{m_{2n+2}}{(2n+2)!}\left(v^2 - \dfrac{1}{4}\right)\left(v^2 - \dfrac{9}{4}\right) \cdots \left(v^2 - \dfrac{(2n+1)^2}{4}\right).$

These are the remainder terms in formula (VI) of Art. 19.

Putting $v=0$ in $(30:5)$ and $(30:6)$, we get the remainder terms in the formula for interpolating to halves, namely

$$(30: 7) \quad R_n = \frac{h^{2n+2}f^{(2n+2)}(\xi)}{(2n+2)!}(-1)^{n+1}\frac{[1\cdot 3\cdot 5 \cdots (2n+1)]^2}{2^{2n+2}},$$

$$(30: 8) \quad R_n = \frac{m_{2n+2}}{(2n+2)!}(-1)^{n+1}\frac{[1\cdot 3\cdot 5 \cdots (2n+1)]^2}{2^{2n+2}}.$$

**31. Recapitulation of Formulas for the Remainder.** We now collect for easy reference the most important of the formulas derived in this chapter.

*1. Newton's Formula* (I)

(a) $$R_n = \frac{h^{n+1}f^{(n+1)}(\xi)}{(n+1)!} \, u(u-1)(u-2)\cdots(u-n).$$

(b) $$R_n = \frac{\Delta^{n+1}y_0}{(n+1)!} \, u(u-1)(u-2)\cdots(u-n).$$

*2. Newton's Formula* (II)

(a) $$R_n = \frac{h^{n+1}f^{(n+1)}(\xi)}{(n+1)!}u(u+1)(u+2)\cdots(u+n).$$

(b) $$R_n = \frac{\Delta_{n+1}y_n}{n+1!}u(u+1)(u+2)\cdots(u+n).$$

*3. Stirling's Formula,* (III)

(a) $$R_n = \frac{h^{2n+1}f^{(2n+1)}(\xi)}{(2n+1)!}u(u^2-1)(u^2-2^2)(u^2-3^2)\cdots(u^2-n^2).$$

(b) $$R_n = \frac{m_{2n+1}}{(2n+1)!}u(u^2-1)(u^2-2^2)(u^2-3^2)\cdots(u^2-n^2).$$

*4. Bessel's Formula* in terms of $u$, (IV)

(a) $$R_n = \frac{h^{2n+2}f^{(2n+2)}(\xi)}{(2n+2)!}u(u-1)(u+1)(u-2)\cdots(u-n)(u+n)(u-n-1).$$

(b) $$R_n = \frac{m_{2n+2}}{(2n+2)!}u(u-1)(u+1)(u-2)\cdots(u-n)(u+n)(u-n-1).$$

*5. Bessel's Formula* in terms of $v$, (VI)

(a) $$R_n = \frac{h^{2n+2}f^{(2n+2)}(\xi)}{(2n+2)!}\left(v^2-\frac{1}{4}\right)\left(v^2-\frac{9}{4}\right)\cdots\left(v^2-\frac{(2n+1)^2}{4}\right).$$

(b) $$R_n = \frac{m_{2n+2}}{(2n+2)!}\left(v^2-\frac{1}{4}\right)\left(v^2-\frac{9}{4}\right)\cdots\left(v^2-\frac{(2n+1)^2}{4}\right).$$

6. *Formula for Interpolating to Halves*, (V)

(a) $$R_n = \frac{h^{2n+2}f^{(2n+2)}(\xi)}{(2n+2)!}(-1)^{n+1}\frac{[1\cdot 3\cdot 5\cdots(2n+1)]^2}{2^{2n+2}}.$$

(b) $$R_n = \frac{m_{2n+2}}{(2n+2)!}(-1)^{n+1}\frac{[1\cdot 3\cdot 5\cdots(2n+1)]^2}{2^{2n+2}}.$$

7. *Lagrange's Formula*, (VII)

$$R_n = \frac{f^{(n+1)}(\xi)}{(n+1)!}(x-x_0)(x-x_1)(x-x_2)\cdots(x-x_n).$$

Where the formulas are given in pairs, the second form (b) should be used when the analytic form of the function is not known.

To lessen the labor of computing $R_n$ from these formulas the student should, when possible, use the expressions for the $n$th derivatives given on page 33.

It is not worth while to compute the remainder term in many applications of Newton's, Stirling's, and Bessel's formulas, because if the starting point is so chosen that $u$ and $v$ are numerically less than 1 and if the differences of some order are practically constant, the interpolated result will usually be correct to as many figures as are given in the tabular values of the function. This statement is based on the assumption that all available differences are used in the interpolation formula, or at least all differences which will contribute anything to the last figure retained. It is in those cases where the differences do not become constant or where it is impracticable to make use of differences above a certain order that we should compute the remainder term.

When using Lagrange's formula, however, the case is very different. Here there are no differences available and there is nothing in the formula itself by which we can estimate the reliability of the results obtained. We should therefore compute the remainder term in every application of this formula.

The student should observe that the remainder term in Stirling's formula contains *odd* differences, whereas in Bessel's formula it contains *even* differences. If, therefore, when using a central difference formula we stop with *even* differences and wish to estimate the error, we should use Stirling's formula, whereas if we stop with *odd* differences we should use Bessel's formula. If this rule is followed, the remainder term will always be the next term after the one at which we stop.

There should never be any difficulty in determining the proper value of $n$ to be substituted in the remainder formulas. Thus, if we are using Bessel's formula and stop with third differences, the remainder term will contain fourth differences. Hence we must have $2n+2=4$ or $n=1$. On the other hand, if we are using Stirling's formula and stop with fourth differences the remainder term will contain fifth differences. Hence we shall then have $2n+1=5$, from which $n=2$.

We shall now compute the remainder term in an application of Bessel's formula.

*Example.* The following table contains values of the function $y=x^4+10x^5$ for certain values of $x$. Find $y$ when $x=2.27$.

| $x$ | $y$ | $\Delta y$ | $\Delta^2 y$ | $\Delta^3 y$ | $\Delta^4 y$ |
|---|---|---|---|---|---|
| 2.0 | 336.0000 | | | | |
| | | 91.8582 | | | |
| 2.1 | 427.8582 | | 19.0724 | | |
| | | 110.9306 | | 2.8266 | |
| 2.2 | 538.7888 | | 21.8990 | | 0.2664 |
| | | 132.8296 | | 3.0930 | |
| 2.3 | 671.6184 | | 24.9920 | | 0.2784 |
| | | 157.8216 | | 3.3714 | |
| 2.4 | 829.4400 | | 28.3634 | | |
| | | 186.1850 | | | |
| 2.5 | 1015.6250 | | | | |

*Solution.* Since we wish to use Bessel's formula and compute the remainder term, we stop with third differences. Taking $x_0=2.2$, $x=2.27$, $h=0.1$, we have

$$u = \frac{2.27 - 2.20}{0.1} = \frac{0.07}{0.1} = 0.7.$$

$$\therefore \quad v = u - \tfrac{1}{2} = 0.2.$$

$$\therefore \quad y = \frac{538.7888 + 671.6184}{2} + 0.2(132.8296)$$

$$+ \left(\frac{0.04 - 0.25}{2}\right)\left(\frac{21.8990 + 24.9920}{2}\right)$$

$$+ 0.2\left(\frac{0.04 - 0.25}{6}\right)(3.0930)$$

$$= 605.2036 + 26.56592 - 2.46178 - 0.02165,$$

or

$$y = 629.28609.$$

To find $R_n$ we have $2n+2=4$ or $n=1$. Also

$$f^{\text{iv}}(x) = 24 + 1200x.$$

Hence
$$f^{iv}(\xi) = 24 + 1200\xi.$$

Now since $\xi$ lies somewhere between 2.0 and 2.5, we can express it in the form
$$\xi = 2.25 + 0.1\eta,$$

where $\eta$ lies between $-2.5$ and $+2.5$. Substituting this value of $\xi$ in $f^{iv}(\xi)$ above, we get

$$f^{iv}(\xi) = f^{iv}(2.25+0.1\eta) = 24 + 2700 + 120\eta$$
$$= 2724 + 120\eta.$$

Hence by (30:5) we have

$$R_n = \frac{h^4 f^{iv}(\xi)}{4!}\left(v^2 - \frac{1}{4}\right)\left(v^2 - \frac{9}{4}\right)$$

$$= \frac{(0.1)^4(2724 + 120\eta)}{24}(0.04 - 0.25)(0.04 - 2.25)$$

$$= 0.00527 + 0.000232\eta$$

$$= 0.00527 \pm 0.00058.$$

We therefore have

$$y = 629.28609 + 0.00527 \pm 0.00058$$
$$= \underline{629.29136 \pm 0.00058}.$$

The value of $y$ is thus between 629.2919 and 629.2908, or between 629.292 and 629.291. The correct value to four decimal places is 629.2914, and this happens to be the mean of the two limits found above.

If we substitute differences instead of the derivative in $R_n$, we have $m_{2n+2} = m_4 = (0.2664+0.2784)/2 = 0.2724$; and therefore by (30:6)

$$R_n = \frac{m_4}{4!}\left(v^2 - \frac{1}{4}\right)\left(v^2 - \frac{9}{4}\right)$$

$$= \frac{0.2784}{24}(0.04 - 0.25)(0.04 - 2.25)$$

$$= \underline{0.00527,}$$

which is the definite part of the remainder term found by using the derivative. We then have $y = 629.28609 + 0.00527 = 629.29136$, which is correct to four decimal places.

*Note.* The substitution $\xi = x_m + h\eta$, where $x_m$ denotes the mid-point of the range of given values of the function, gives the remainder as the sum of two terms, the larger of which is perfectly definite and un-affected by the uncertain factor $\eta$. It also saves the trouble of finding the greatest and least values of $f^{iv}(x)$ in order to find the limits between which the true value of the computed function lies. For Newton's formulas (I) and (II) we make the substitutions $\xi = x_0 + h\eta$ and $\xi = x_n - h\eta$, respectively, where $\eta$ is now *positive* in each case. For computing $R_n$ in Lagrange's formula we should put $\xi = x_m + h\eta$, as in the example worked above.

A final remark concerning accuracy must now be made. When the analytical form of a function is totally unknown, and the sum total of our knowledge of the function consists merely of a set of tabular values of the argument, the problem of interpolation is really indeterminate; for it is theoretically possible to construct a large number of functions which would take the values $y_0, y_1, y_2, \cdots y_n$ corresponding to the values $x_0, x_1, x_2, \cdots x_n$ of the argument. Nevertheless, if we have some knowledge of the nature of the function with which we are dealing and have no reason to believe that it behaves in an erratic manner within the range of values considered, we may fairly assume that its graph is a *smooth curve*, in which case the function can safely be replaced by a polynomial.

**32. The Accuracy of Linear Interpolation from Tables.** We shall now derive a simple formula for the maximum error inherent in linear interpolation from tables.

In the remainder after $n+1$ terms in Newton's formula (I) let us put $n = 1$. Then $R_n$ becomes

$$(32:1) \qquad R_1 = \frac{h^2 f''(\xi)}{2} u(u-1) = \frac{h^2 M}{2}(u^2 - u),$$

where $M$ denotes the maximum absolute value of $f''(x)$ in any interval of width $h$. To find the maximum numerical value of $R_1$ we differentiate it with respect to $u$, put the derivative equal to zero, solve for $u$, and then substitute this value of $u$ in (32:1). Hence we have

$$\frac{dR_1}{du} = \frac{h^2 M}{2}(2u - 1) = 0.$$

$$\therefore \quad u = \tfrac{1}{2} \quad \text{and}$$

$$|R_{max}| = \frac{h^2 M}{2}\left|\frac{1}{4} - \frac{1}{2}\right| = \frac{h^2 M}{8}.$$

The formula for the maximum error is therefore

$$(32:2) \qquad\qquad E \leqq \frac{h^2 M}{8}.$$

*Example.*  The function $1/N$ is tabulated in Barlow's Tables at unit intervals from 1 to 10000.  Find the possible error in the linear interpolation of this function when

$$N = 650.$$

*Solution.*

$$f(N) = \frac{1}{N} \cdot$$

$$\therefore \quad f''(N) = \frac{2}{N^3} \cdot$$

Taking $h = 1$, $N = 650$, and substituting in (32 : 2), we find

$$E \leqq \frac{1}{4 \times (650)^3} = \frac{1}{1,098,500,000},$$

or

$$E < 0.000000001.$$

*Note.*  The student should ever bear in mind that linear interpolation is permissible only when first differences are constant, or practically so. He should therefore always compute a few first differences and see if they are constant before using linear interpolation.

## EXAMPLES ON CHAPTER V

1.  Estimate the error in your answers to Examples 3 and 4 of Chapter II.

2.  Compute the error in your answers to Examples 2, 3, 5, and 6 of Chapter III.

3.  Compute the error in your answers to Example 1 of Chapter IV.

# CHAPTER VI

## INTERPOLATION WITH TWO INDEPENDENT VARIABLES
## TRIGONOMETRIC INTERPOLATION

**33. Introduction.** Occasionally it becomes necessary to interpolate a function of two arguments. For example, a table of elliptic integrals contains the two arguments $\theta$ and $\phi$, on both of which the value of the integral depends.

The problem of double interpolation can be solved in two ways. The simplest method in theory is to interpolate first with respect to one variable and then with respect to the other. In making these interpolations any one of the standard interpolation formulas—Newton's, Stirling's, or Bessel's—may be used for either the first interpolations or the second. We always choose the most suitable formula for the problem at hand.

**34. Double Interpolation by a Double Application of Single Interpolation.** This method can be explained best by means of examples.

*Example 1.* The following table* gives the hour angle ($t$) of the sun corresponding to certain altitudes ($a$) and declinations ($d$) at a place in a certain latitude. Find the hour angle corresponding to $d = 12°$, $a = 16°$.

|  | $a = 10°$ | $14°$ | $18°$ | $22°$ |
|---|---|---|---|---|
| $d = 20°$ | 6ʰ 11ᵐ 26ˢ | 5ʰ 50ᵐ 17ˢ | 5ʰ 29ᵐ 27ˢ | 5ʰ 8ᵐ 48ˢ |
| $15°$ | 5  55  41 | 5  35  5 | 5  14  39 | 4  54  17 |
| $10°$ | 5  40  16 | 5  19  56 | 4  59  37 | 4  39  17 |
| $5°$ | 5  24  50 | 5  4  30 | 4  44  4 | 4  23  29 |
| $0°$ | 5  9  5 | 4  48  29 | 4  27  39 | 4  6  28 |

*Solution.* Here we take the entry 5ʰ35ᵐ5ˢ as the starting point. Then the initial values of $d$ and $a$ are $d_0 = 15°$, $a_0 = 14°$.

Let $t = f(d, a)$ denote the functional relation connecting $t$, $d$, and $a$. We first find by ordinary interpolation the values of $f(12°, 14°)$, $f(12°, 18°), f(12°, 22°)$. To this end we construct the following difference tables corresponding to $a = 14°$, $a = 18°$, and $a = 22°$.

---

* A table of this kind is called the *function table*. The entries in this table are taken from Whittaker and Robinson's *Calculus of Observations*, p. 374.

$a = 14°$

| | $f(d, 14°)$ | | $\Delta f$ | $\Delta^2 f$ | $\Delta^3 f$ |
|---|---|---|---|---|---|
| | $5^h$ | $35^m$ $05^s$ | | | |
| | | | $-15^m$ $09^s$ | | |
| | 5 | 19  56 | | $-17^s$ | |
| (a) | | | $-15$  26 | | $-18^s$ |
| | 5 | 04  30 | | $-35$ | |
| | | | $-16$  01 | | |
| | 4 | 48  29 | | | |

$a = 18°$

| | $f(d, 18°)$ | | $\Delta f$ | $\Delta^2 f$ | $\Delta^3 f$ |
|---|---|---|---|---|---|
| | $5^h$ | $14^m$ $39^s$ | | | |
| | | | $-15^m$ $02^s$ | | |
| (b) | 4 | 59  37 | | $-31^s$ | |
| | | | $-15$  33 | | $-21^s$ |
| | 4 | 44  04 | | $-52$ | |
| | | | $-16$  25 | | |
| | 4 | 27  39 | | | |

$a = 22°$

| | $f(d, 22°)$ | | $\Delta f$ | $\Delta^2 f$ | $\Delta^3 f$ |
|---|---|---|---|---|---|
| | $4^h$ | $54^m$ $17^s$ | | | |
| | | | $-15^m$  $0^s$ | | |
| (c) | 4 | 39  17 | | $-48^s$ | |
| | | | $-15$  48 | | $-25^s$ |
| | 4 | 23  29 | | $-1^m$  $13^s$ | |
| | | | $-17$  01 | | |
| | 4 | 06  28 | | | |

Since the required value $f(12°, 16°)$ of the function is near the *beginning* of the assigned values of $d$, we use Newton's formula (I) to find $f(12°, a)$. Furthermore, since the given equidistant values of $d$ decrease by steps of $5°$, we have $h = -5°$ and therefore

$$u = \frac{d - d_0}{h} = \frac{12 - 15}{-5} = 0.6.$$

Now substituting in (I) of Art. 15 this value of $u$ and the other quantities from table (a) above, we have

$$f(12°\ 14°) = 5^h 35^m 5^s + 0.6(- 15^m 9^s) + \frac{0.6(- 0.4)}{2}(- 17^s)$$

$$+ \frac{0.6(- 0.4)(- 1.4)}{6}(- 18^s)$$

$$= 5^h 26^m 1^s.$$

Using the values in table (b), we get

$$f(12°\ 18°) = 5^h 14^m 39^s + 0.6(- 15^m 2^s) + \frac{0.6(- 0.4)}{2}(- 31^s$$

$$+ \frac{0.6(- 0.4)(- 1.4)}{6}(- 21^s)$$

$$= 5^h 5^m 40^s.$$

In like manner, from table (c) we get

$$f(12°, 22°) = 4^h 54^m 17^s + 0.6(- 15^m 0^s) + \frac{0.6(- 0.4)}{2}(- 48^s)$$

$$+ \frac{0.6(- 0.4)(- 1.4)}{6}(- 25^s)$$

$$= 4^h 45^m 21^s.$$

The next step in the solution is to form a difference table of these functions just computed. Hence we have

| $f(12, a)$ | $\Delta f$ | $\Delta^2 f$ |
|---|---|---|
| 5ʰ 26ᵐ 1ˢ | | |
| | −20ᵐ 21ˢ | |
| 5  5  40 | | +2ˢ |
| | −20  19 | |
| 4  45  21 | | |

Now since the required value of the function is also near the beginning of the assigned values of $a$, we again use Newton's formula (I). Also, since the equidistant values of $a$ increase by 4°, we have $h = 4°$. Hence,

$$u = \frac{a - a_0}{h} = \frac{16° - 14°}{4°} = 0.5.$$

Substituting in (I) of Art. 15 this value of $u$ and the other quantities from the tables above, we finally get

$$f(12°, 16°) = 5^h 26^m 1^s + 0.5(- 20^m 21^s) + \frac{0.5(- 0.5)}{2}(2^s)$$

$$= \underline{5^h 15^m 50^s.}$$

*Note.* If it should be required to compute $f(14°, 20°)$, for example, we would set out from the entry $5^h 55^m 41^s$ and compute $f(14°, 10°)$, $f(14°, 14°)$, $f(14°, 18°)$, and $f(14°, 22°)$ by Newton's formula (I). Then to find $f(14°, 20°)$ we would use Newton's formula (II), because the required value is near the *end* of the given values of $a$.

*Example 2.* Find from a table of elliptic integrals the value of

$$\int_0^{\sin^{-1}(12/13)} \frac{d\phi}{\sqrt{1 - 0.78 \sin^2 \phi}}.$$

*Solution.* Comparing this integral with the standard elliptic integral of the first kind, namely

$$F(\theta, \phi) = \int_0^\phi \frac{d\phi}{\sqrt{1 - \sin^2 \theta \sin^2 \phi}},$$

we have

$$\phi = \sin^{-1} \frac{12}{13} = \sin^{-1}(0.9230769) = 67°22'48''.5$$

$$= 67°.38014,$$

$$\sin^2 \theta = 0.78,$$

$$\sin \theta = 0.8831761,$$

$$\theta = 62°01'40''.4 = 62°.02789.$$

In problems of this kind, where extensive tables are at hand, it is better to use central-difference formulas. Hence we write down the appropriate portion of the given function table, compute the necessary difference tables, and from them calculate the values of $F(60°, 67°.38014)$, $F(61°, 67°.38014)$, $F(62°, 67°.38014)$, $F(63°, 67°.38014)$, and $F(64°, 67°.38014)$ by means of Bessel's formula (VI), because $67°.38014$ is near the middle of an interval. Then we form a difference table from these computed functions and find $F(62°.02789, 67°.38014)$ by means of Stirling's formula, (III), because here the value $62°.02789$ is near the beginning of an interval.

The function table is given below, and from it the difference tables following are computed.

| $\phi$ | $\theta = 60°$ | 61° | 62° | 63° | 64° |
|---|---|---|---|---|---|
| 65° | 1.3489264 | 1.3559464 | 1.3630180 | 1.3701309 | 1.3772732 |
| 66 | 1.3772777 | 1.3847727 | 1.3923331 | 1.3999481 | 1.4076057 |
| 67 | 1.4059999 | 1.4139971 | 1.4220753 | 1.4302236 | 1.4384298 |
| 68 | 1.4350955 | 1.4436231 | 1.4522494 | 1.4609635 | 1.4697532 |
| 69 | 1.4645657 | 1.4736530 | 1.4828589 | 1.4921728 | 1.5015826 |
| 70 | 1.4944109 | 1.5040879 | 1.5139061 | 1.5238552 | 1.5339233 |

$\theta = 60°$

| $\phi$ | $F(60°, \phi)$ | $\Delta F$ | $\Delta^2 F$ | $\Delta^3 F$ | $\Delta^4 F$ | $\Delta^5 F$ | |
|---|---|---|---|---|---|---|---|
| 65° | 1.3489264 | | | | | | |
| | | 283513 | | | | | |
| 66 | 1.3772777 | | 3709 | | | | |
| | | 287222 | | 25 | | | |
| 67 | 1.4059999 | | 3734 | | −11 | | (a) |
| | | 290956 | | 14 | | −5 | |
| 68 | 1.4350955 | | 3748 | | −16 | | |
| | | 294704 | | − 2 | | | |
| 69 | 1.4645659 | | 3746 | | | | |
| | | 298450 | | | | | |
| 70 | 1.4944109 | | | | | | |

$\theta = 61°$

| $\phi$ | $F(61°, \phi)$ | $\Delta F$ | $\Delta^2 F$ | $\Delta^3 F$ | $\Delta^4 F$ | $\Delta^5 F$ | |
|---|---|---|---|---|---|---|---|
| 65° | 1.3559464 | | | | | | |
| | | 288263 | | | | | |
| 66 | 1.3847727 | | 3981 | | | | |
| | | 292244 | | 35 | | | |
| 67 | 1.4139971 | | 4016 | | −12 | | |
| | | 296260 | | 23 | | +1 | |
| 68 | 1.4436231 | | 4039 | | −11 | | (b) |
| | | 300299 | | 11 | | | |
| 69 | 1.4736530 | | 4050 | | | | |
| | | 304349 | | | | | |
| 70 | 1.5040879 | | | | | | |

$\theta = 62°$

| $\phi$ | $F(62°, \phi)$ | $\Delta F$ | $\Delta^2 F$ | $\Delta^3 F$ | $\Delta^4 F$ | $\Delta^5 F$ |
|--------|----------------|------------|--------------|--------------|--------------|--------------|
| 65° | 1.3630180 | | | | | |
| | | 293151 | | | | |
| 66 | 1.3923331 | | 4271 | | | |
| | | 297422 | | 48 | | |
| 67 | 1.4220753 | | 4319 | | −13 | |
| | | 301741 | | 35 | | +1 |
| 68 | 1.4522494 | | 4354 | | −12 | |
| | | 306095 | | 23 | | |
| 69 | 1.4828589 | | 4377 | | | |
| | | 310472 | | | | |
| 70 | 1.5139061 | | | | | |

(c)

$\theta = 63°$

| $\phi$ | $F(63°, \phi)$ | $\Delta F$ | $\Delta^2 F$ | $\Delta^3 F$ | $\Delta^4 F$ | $\Delta^5 F$ |
|--------|----------------|------------|--------------|--------------|--------------|--------------|
| 65 | 1.3701309 | | | | | |
| | | 298172 | | | | |
| 66 | 1.3999481 | | 4583 | | | |
| | | 302755 | | 61 | | |
| 67 | 1.4302236 | | 4644 | | −11 | |
| | | 307399 | | 50 | | −2 |
| 68 | 1.4609635 | | 4694 | | −13 | |
| | | 312093 | | 37 | | |
| 69 | 1.4921728 | | 4731 | | | |
| | | 316824 | | | | |
| 70 | 1.5238552 | | | | | |

(d)

$\theta = 64°$

| $\phi$ | $F(64°, \phi)$ | $\Delta F$ | $\Delta^2 F$ | $\Delta^3 F$ | $\Delta^4 F$ | $\Delta^5 F$ |
|--------|----------------|------------|--------------|--------------|--------------|--------------|
| 65° | 1.3772732 | | | | | |
| | | 303325 | | | | |
| 66 | 1.4076057 | | 4916 | | | |
| | | 308241 | | 77 | | |
| 67 | 1.4384298 | | 4993 | | −10 | |
| | | 313234 | | 67 | | −4 |
| 68 | 1.4697532 | | 5060 | | −14 | |
| | | 318294 | | 53 | | |
| 69 | 1.5015826 | | 5113 | | | |
| | | 323407 | | | | |
| 70 | 1.5339233 | | | | | |

(e)

Here
$$\phi_0 = 67°, \phi = 67°.38014, h = 1°,$$
$$u = 0.38014.$$
$$\therefore \quad v = u - \tfrac{1}{2} = -0.11986.$$

Substituting in Bessel's formula (VI) the quantities given in table $(a)$, we have

$$F(60°, 67°.38014) = 1.4205477 - 0.00348740 - 0.00004408$$
$$+ 0.00000001 - 0.00000003$$
$$= 1.4170162.$$

In a similar manner we get from tables $(b)$, $(c)$, $(d)$, $(e)$,

$$F(61°, 67°.38014) = 1.4252117,$$
$$F(62°, 67°.38014) = 1.4334946,$$
$$F(63°, 67°.38014) = 1.4418540,$$
$$F(64°, 67°.38014) = 1.4502779.$$

Forming now a table of differences from these computed functions, we have

| $\theta$ | $F(\theta, 67°.38014)$ | $\Delta F$ | $\Delta^2 F$ | $\Delta^3 F$ | $\Delta^4 F$ |
|---|---|---|---|---|---|
| 60° | 1.4170162 | | | | |
| | | 81955 | | | |
| 61 | 1.4252117 | | 874 | | |
| | | 82829 | | −109 | |
| 62 | 1.4334946 | | 765 | | −11 |
| | | 83594 | | −120 | |
| 63 | 1.4418540 | | 645 | | |
| | | 84239 | | | |
| 64 | 1.4502779 | | | | |

For this interpolation we have

$$\theta_0 = 62°, \theta = 62°.02789, h = 1°.$$
$$\therefore \quad u = \frac{\theta - \theta_0}{h} = \frac{62°.02789 - 62°}{1°} = 0.02789.$$

Substituting in Stirling's formula, (III), this value of $u$ and the appropriate quantities from the table above, we get

$$F(62°.02789, 67°.38014) = 1.4334946 + 0.00023208$$
$$+ 0.00000003 + 0.00000005$$
$$= \underline{1.4337268}.$$

**35. Double or Two-Way Differences.**  Before explaining the second method of dealing with the problem of double interpolation it is necessary to define double or two-way differences, to which we now turn our attention.

Let $z = f(x, y)$ denote any function of two independent variables $x$ and $y$, and let $z_{rs} = f(x_r, y_s)$. Let us next construct the following function table:

|       | $x_0$    | $x_1$    | $x_2$    | $x_3$    | $x_4$    |     |     |     | $x_m$    |
|-------|----------|----------|----------|----------|----------|-----|-----|-----|----------|
| $y_0$ | $z_{00}$ | $z_{10}$ | $z_{20}$ | $z_{30}$ | $z_{40}$ | ... | ... | ... | $z_{m0}$ |
| $y_1$ | $z_{01}$ | $z_{11}$ | $z_{21}$ | $z_{31}$ | $z_{41}$ | ... | ... | ... | $z_{m1}$ |
| $y_2$ | $z_{02}$ | $z_{12}$ | $z_{22}$ | $z_{32}$ | $z_{42}$ | ... | ... | ... | $z_{m2}$ |
| $y_3$ | $z_{03}$ | $z_{13}$ | $z_{23}$ | $z_{33}$ | $z_{43}$ | ... | ... | ... | $z_{m3}$ |
| $y_4$ | $z_{04}$ | $z_{14}$ | $z_{24}$ | $z_{34}$ | $z_{44}$ | ... | ... | ... | ... |
| ...   | ...      | ...      | ...      | ...      | ...      | ... | ... | ... | ...      |
| ...   | ...      | ...      | ...      | ...      | ...      | ... | ... | ... | ...      |
| ...   | ...      | ...      | ...      | ...      | ...      | ... | ... | ... | ...      |
| ...   | ...      | ...      | ...      | ...      | ...      | ... | ... | ... | ...      |
| ...   | ...      | ...      | ...      | ...      | ...      | ... | ... | ... | ...      |
| $y_n$ | $z_{0n}$ | $z_{1n}$ | $z_{2n}$ | $z_{3n}$ | $z_{4n}$ | ... | ... | ... | $z_{mn}$ |

We now define double or two-way differences as follows:

$$\Delta^{1+0}z_{00} = \Delta_x z_{00} = z_{10} - z_{00},$$
$$\Delta^{1+0}z_{01} = \Delta_x z_{01} = z_{11} - z_{01},$$
$$\Delta^{1+0}z_{02} = \Delta_x z_{02} = z_{12} - z_{02},$$

$$\cdot \quad \cdot \quad \cdot \quad \cdot \quad \cdot \quad \cdot \quad \cdot \quad \cdot$$

$$\Delta^{0+1}z_{00} = \Delta_y z_{00} = z_{01} - z_{00},$$
$$\Delta^{0+1}z_{10} = \Delta_y z_{10} = z_{11} - z_{10},$$
$$\Delta^{0+1}z_{20} = \Delta_y z_{20} = z_{21} - z_{20}.$$

$$\cdot \quad \cdot \quad \cdot \quad \cdot \quad \cdot \quad \cdot \quad \cdot \quad \cdot$$

Or, more generally,

$$\Delta^{1+0}z_{rs} = \Delta_x z_{rs} = z_{r+1,s} - z_{rs},$$
$$\Delta^{0+1}z_{rs} = \Delta_y z_{rs} = z_{r,s+1} - z_{rs}.$$

Also

$$\Delta^{1+1}z_{00} = \Delta^2_{xy}z_{00} = \Delta^{1+0}z_{01} - \Delta^{1+0}z_{00}$$
$$= \Delta^{0+1}z_{10} - \Delta^{0+1}z_{00}.$$

$$\Delta^{2+0}z_{00} = \Delta_x^2 z_{00} = z_{20} - 2z_{10} + z_{00},$$

$$\Delta^{2+0}z_{01} = \Delta_x^2 z_{01} = z_{21} - 2z_{11} + z_{01},$$

$$\Delta^{2+0}z_{02} = \Delta_x^2 z_{02} = z_{22} - 2z_{12} + z_{02},$$

$$\Delta^{0+2}z_{00} = \Delta_y^2 z_{00} = z_{02} - 2z_{01} + z_{00},$$

$$\Delta^{0+2}z_{10} = \Delta_y^2 z_{10} = z_{12} - 2z_{11} + z_{10},$$

$$\Delta^{0+2}z_{20} = \Delta_y^2 z_{20} = z_{22} - 2z_{21} + z_{20},$$

$$\Delta^{2+1}z_{00} = \Delta^{2+0}z_{01} - \Delta^{2+0}z_{00},$$

$$\Delta^{1+2}z_{00} = \Delta^{0+2}z_{10} - \Delta^{0+2}z_{00},$$

$$\Delta^{3+0}z_{00} = \Delta_x^3 z_{00} = z_{30} - 3z_{20} + 3z_{10} - z_{00},$$

$$\Delta^{3+0}z_{01} = \Delta_x^3 z_{01} = z_{31} - 3z_{21} + 3z_{11} - z_{01},$$

$$\Delta^{0+3}z_{00} = \Delta_y^3 z_{00} = z_{03} - 3z_{02} + 3z_{01} - z_{00},$$

$$\Delta^{0+3}z_{10} = \Delta_y^3 z_{10} = z_{13} - 3z_{12} + 3z_{11} - z_{10},$$

$$\Delta^{3+1}z_{00} = \Delta^{3+0}z_{01} - \Delta^{3+0}z_{00},$$

$$\Delta^{1+3}z_{00} = \Delta^{0+3}z_{10} - \Delta^{0+3}z_{00},$$

$$\Delta^{4+0}z_{00} = \Delta_x^4 z_{00} = z_{40} - 4z_{30} + 6z_{20} - 4z_{10} + z_{00},$$

$$\Delta^{0+4}z_{00} = \Delta_y^4 z_{00} = z_{04} - 4z_{03} + 6z_{02} - 4z_{01} + z_{00},$$

$$\Delta^{2+2}z_{00} = \Delta^{2+0}z_{02} - 2\Delta^{2+0}z_{01} + \Delta^{2+0}z_{00},$$

$$= \Delta^{0+2}z_{20} - 2\Delta^{0+2}z_{10} + \Delta^{0+2}z_{00}.$$

The general formula for writing down these differences is easily seen to be

$$(35:1) \quad \Delta^{m+n}z_{00} = \Delta^{m+0}z_{0n} - n\Delta^{m+0}z_{0,n-1} + \frac{n(n-1)}{2}\Delta^{m+0}z_{0,n-2} + \cdots$$
$$+ \Delta^{m+0}z_{00}$$

$$= \Delta^{0+n}z_{m0} - m\Delta^{0+n}z_{m-1,0} + \frac{m(m-1)}{2}\Delta^{0+n}z_{m-2,0} + \cdots$$
$$+ \Delta^{0+n}z_{00}.$$

The symbol $\Delta_x^m z_{00}$, for example, means that we find the $m$th difference of $z_{00}$ *with respect to $x$, $y$* being held constant.

**36. A General Formula for Double Interpolation.** We are now in a position to consider a general formula for double interpolation. The following formula is derived in O. Biermann's *Mathematische Naherüngsmethoden*, pages 138–144:

$$(36:1) \quad z = f(x, y) = z_{00} + \frac{x - x_0}{h} \Delta^{1+0} z_{00} + \frac{y - y_0}{k} \Delta^{0+1} z_{00}$$

$$\frac{1}{2!} \left[ \frac{(x - x_0)(x - x_1)}{h^2} \Delta^{2+0} z_{00} + \frac{2(x - x_0)(y - y_0)}{hk} \Delta^{1+1} z_{00} \right.$$

$$\left. + \frac{(y - y_0)(y - y_1)}{k^2} \Delta^{0+2} z_{00} \right] + \cdots$$

$$+ \frac{1}{m!} \left[ \frac{(x - x_0)(x - x_1) \cdots (x - x_{m-1})}{h^m} \Delta^{m+0} z_{00} \right.$$

$$+ \frac{m(x - x_0)(x - x_1) \cdots (x - x_{m-2})(y - y_0)}{h^{m-1} k} \Delta^{(m-1)+1} z_{00}$$

$$+ \frac{m(m - 1)(x - x_0)(x - x_1) \cdots (x - x_{m-3})(y - y_0)(y - y_1)}{2 \qquad h^{m-2} k^2}$$

$$\times \Delta^{(m-2)+2} z_{00} + \cdots$$

$$\left. + \frac{(y - y_0)(y - y_1) \cdots (y - y_{m-1})}{k^m} \Delta^{0+m} z_{00} \right] + R(x_0, y_0).$$

Here $h$ and $k$ are the intervals between the equidistant values of $x$ and $y$, respectively, and $R(x_0, y_0)$ is the remainder term.

This formula can be simplified by changing the variables from $x$ and $y$ to $u$ and $v$, as follows:
Put

$$u = \frac{x - x_0}{h}, \text{ or } x = x_0 + hu.$$

Then

$$\frac{x - x_1}{h} = \frac{x - (x_0 + h)}{h} = \frac{x - x_0}{h} - \frac{h}{h} = u - 1,$$

and

$$\frac{x - x_2}{h} = \frac{x - (x_0 + 2h)}{h} = \frac{x - x_0}{h} - \frac{2h}{h} = u - 2,$$

$$\cdots \cdots \cdots \cdots \cdots \cdots \cdots$$

$$\frac{x - x_{m-1}}{h} = u - (m - 1).$$

Also, put

$$v = \frac{y - y_0}{k}, \text{ or } y = y_0 + kv.$$

Then

$$\frac{y - y_1}{k} = \frac{y - (y_0 + k)}{k} = \frac{y - y_0}{k} - \frac{k}{k} = v - 1,$$

$$\frac{y - y_2}{k} = v - 2, \text{ etc.}$$

Substituting these values of $(x-x_0)/h$, $(y-y_0)/k$, etc. in (36:1), we get

**(IX)** $z = f(x, y) = f(x_0 + hu, y_0 + kv) = z_{00} + u\Delta^{1+0}z_{00} + v\Delta^{0+1}z_{00}$

$$+ \frac{1}{2!}[u(u-1)\Delta^{2+0}z_{00} + 2uv\Delta^{1+1}z_{00} + v(v-1)\Delta^{0+2}z_{00}]$$

$$+ \frac{1}{3!}[u(u-1)(u-2)\Delta^{3+0}z_{00} + 3u(u-1)v\Delta^{2+1}z_{00}$$

$$+ 3uv(v-1)\Delta^{1+2}z_{00} + v(v-1)(v-2)\Delta^{0+3}z_{00}]$$

$$+ \frac{1}{4!}[u(u-1)(u-2)(u-3)\Delta^{4+0}z_{00} + 4u(u-1)(u-2)v\Delta^{3+1}z_{00}$$

$$+ 6u(u-1)v(v-1)\Delta^{2+2}z_{00} + 4uv(v-1)(v-2)\Delta^{1+3}z_{00}$$

$$+ v(v-1)(v-2)(v-3)\Delta^{0+4}z_{00}] + \cdots .$$

This formula (IX) corresponds to Newton's formula (I) and reduces to that formula if we put either $u = 0$ or $v = 0$.

We shall now apply this formula to the two examples which have already been worked by the first method.

*Example 3.* Solve Example 1 of Art. 34 by means of formula (IX).

*Solution.* For the sake of clearness we repeat the function table given in Example 1, and work the problem anew from the start.

| $d$ | $a = 14°$ | $18°$ | $22°$ |
|-----|-----------|-------|-------|
| 15° | 5ʰ 35ᵐ  5ˢ | 5ʰ 14ᵐ 39ˢ | 4ʰ 54ᵐ 17ˢ |
| 10° | 5  19  56 | 4  59  37 | 4  39  17 |
| 5°  | 5   4  30 | 4  44   4 | 4  23  29 |
| 0°  | 4  48  29 | 4  27  39 | 4   6  28 |

Forming next the necessary difference tables, we have

$$a_0 = 14°$$

| | $f_{d0}$ | $\Delta^{1+0}f_{d0}$ | $\Delta^{2+0}f_{d0}$ | $\Delta^{3+0}f_{d0}$ |
|---|---------|---------|---------|---------|
| $d_0$ | 5ʰ 35ᵐ  5ˢ | | | |
| | | $-15ᵐ$  9ˢ | | |
| $d_1$ | 5  19  56 | | $-17ˢ$ | |
| | | $-15$  26 | | $-18ˢ$ |
| $d_2$ | 5   4  30 | | $-35$ | |
| | | $-16$   1 | | |
| $d_3$ | 4  48  29 | | | |

$$a_1 = 18°$$

|  | $f_{d1}$ | $\Delta^{1+0}f_{d1}$ | $\Delta^{2+0}f_{d1}$ | $\Delta^{3+0}f_{d1}$ |
|---|---|---|---|---|
| $d_0$ | $5^h\ 14^m\ 39^s$ |  |  |  |
|  |  | $-15^m\ \ 2^s$ |  |  |
| $d_1$ | 4　59　37 |  | $-31^s$ |  |
|  |  | $-15\ \ 33$ |  | $-21^s$ |
| $d_2$ | 4　44　4 |  | $-52$ |  |
|  |  | $-16\ \ 25$ |  |  |
| $d_3$ | 4　27　39 |  |  |  |

$$a_2 = 22°$$

|  | $f_{d2}$ | $\Delta^{1+0}f_{d2}$ | $\Delta^{2+0}f_{d2}$ | $\Delta^{3+0}f_{d2}$ |
|---|---|---|---|---|
| $d_0$ | $4^h\ 54^m\ 17^s$ |  |  |  |
|  |  | $-15^m\ \ 0^s$ |  |  |
| $d_1$ | 4　39　17 |  | $-48^s$ |  |
|  |  | $-15\ \ 48$ |  | $-25^s$ |
| $d_2$ | 4　23　29 |  | $-\ 1^m\ 13^s$ |  |
|  |  | $-17\ \ 1$ |  |  |
| $d_3$ | 4　6　28 |  |  |  |

These three tables, it will be observed, are the same as tables $(a)$, $(b)$, $(c)$ in Example 1.

We next form difference tables by taking constant values of $d$.

$$d_0 = 15°$$

|  | $f_{0a}$ | $\Delta^{0+1}f_{0a}$ | $\Delta^{0+2}f_{0a}$ |
|---|---|---|---|
| $a_0$ | $5^h\ 35^m\ 5^s$ |  |  |
|  |  | $-20^m\ 26^s$ |  |
| $a_1$ | 5　14　39 |  | $+4^s$ |
|  |  | $-20\ \ 22$ |  |
| $a_2$ | 4　54　17 |  |  |

$$d_1 = 10°$$

|  | $f_{1a}$ | $\Delta^{0+1}f_{1a}$ | $\Delta^{0+2}f_{1a}$ |
|---|---|---|---|
| $a_0$ | $5^h\ 19^m\ 56^s$ |  |  |
|  |  | $-20^m\ 19^s$ |  |
| $a_1$ | 4　59　37 |  | $-1^s$ |
|  |  | $-20\ \ 20$ |  |
| $a_2$ | 4　39　17 |  |  |

$$d_2 = 5°$$

|  | $f_{2a}$ | $\Delta^{0+1}f_{2a}$ | $\Delta^{0+2}f_{2a}$ |
|---|---|---|---|
| $a_0$ | $5^h \quad 4^m \; 30^s$ | | |
| | | $-20^m \; 26^s$ | |
| $a_1$ | $4 \quad 44 \quad 4$ | | $-9^s$ |
| | | $-20 \quad 35$ | |
| $a_2$ | $4 \quad 23 \quad 29$ | | |

Hence

$$\Delta^{1+1}f_{00} = \Delta^{1+0}f_{01} - \Delta^{1+0}f_{00} = -15^m2^s - (-15^m9^s) = 7^s,$$

$$\Delta^{1+2}f_{00} = \Delta^{0+2}f_{10} - \Delta^{0+2}f_{00} = -1^s - (4^s) = -5^s,$$

$$\Delta^{2+1}f_{00} = \Delta^{2+0}f_{01} - \Delta^{2+0}f_{00} = -31^s - (-17^s) = -14^s,$$

$$\Delta^{1+3}f_{00} = \Delta^{0+3}f_{10} - \Delta^{0+3}f_{00} = 0 - 0 = 0,$$

$$\Delta^{3+1}f_{00} = \Delta^{3+0}f_{01} - \Delta^{3+0}f_{00} = -21^s - (-18^s) = -3^s,$$

$$\Delta^{2+2}f_{00} = \Delta^{2+0}f_{02} - 2\Delta^{2+0}f_{01} + \Delta^{2+0}f_{00}$$
$$= -48^s - 2(-31^s) + (-17^s) = -3^s,$$

$$\Delta^{4+0}f_{00} = 0,$$

$$\Delta^{0+4}f_{00} = 0.$$

We have already found in Example 1 that

$$u = 0.6, \quad v = 0.5.$$

Substituting in (IX) these values of $u$, $v$, and the computed differences, we get

$$f(12° \; 16°) = 5^h35^m5^s + 0.6(-15^m9^s) + 0.5(-20^m26^s)$$
$$+ \tfrac{1}{2}[0.6(-0.4)(-17^s) + 0.6(7^s) + 0.5(-0.5)(4^s)]$$
$$+ \tfrac{1}{6}[0.6(-0.4)(-1.4)(-18^s) + 0.9(-0.4)(-14^s)$$
$$+ 0.9(-0.5)(-5^s) + 0]$$
$$+ \tfrac{1}{24}[0 + 1.2(-0.4)(-1.4)(-3^s) + 1.8(-0.4)(-0.5)(-3^s)$$
$$+ 0 + 0],$$

or $f(12°, 16°) = 5^h15^m50^s$, as previously found.

*Example 4.* Solve Example 2 by means of formula (IX).

*Solution.* Since (IX) is not a central-difference formula, we do not use the same function table as in Example 2. From the definition of the two-way differences $\Delta^{m+n}z_{00}$ it will be seen that the following triangular function table, starting from $F(62°, 67°)$, is all that is required for finding all differences up to the fourth order inclusive.

| $\phi$ | $\theta = 62°$ | $63°$ | $64°$ | $65°$ | $66°$ |
|--------|---------------|-----------|-----------|-----------|-----------|
| $67°$ | 1.4220753 | 1.4302236 | 1.4384298 | 1.4466803 | 1.4549598 |
| 68 | 1.4522494 | 1.4609635 | 1.4697532 | 1.4786046 | |
| 69 | 1.4828589 | 1.4921728 | 1.5015826 | | |
| 70 | 1.5139061 | 1.5238552 | | | |
| 71 | 1.5453920 | | | | |

The following difference tables are next computed:

$$\theta_0 = 62°$$

| | $F_{0\phi}$ | $\Delta^{0+1}F_{0\phi}$ | $\Delta^{0+2}F_{0\phi}$ | $\Delta^{0+3}F_{0\phi}$ | $\Delta^{0+4}F_{0\phi}$ |
|--------|-------------|------------------------|------------------------|------------------------|------------------------|
| $\phi_0$ | 1.4220753 | | | | |
| | | 301741 | | | |
| $\phi_1$ | 1.4522494 | | 4354 | | |
| | | 306095 | | 23 | |
| $\phi_2$ | 1.4828589 | | 4377 | | $-13$ |
| | | 310472 | | 10 | |
| $\phi_3$ | 1.5139061 | | 4387 | | |
| | | 314859 | | | |
| $\phi_4$ | 1.5453920 | | | | |

$$\theta_1 = 63°$$

| | $F_{1\phi}$ | $\Delta^{0+1}F_{1\phi}$ | $\Delta^{0+2}F_{1\phi}$ | $\Delta^{0+3}F_{1\phi}$ |
|--------|-------------|------------------------|------------------------|------------------------|
| $\phi_0$ | 1.4302236 | | | |
| | | 307399 | | |
| $\phi_1$ | 1.4609635 | | 4694 | |
| | | 312093 | | 37 |
| $\phi_2$ | 1.4921728 | | 4731 | |
| | | 316824 | | |
| $\phi_3$ | 1.5238552 | | | |

$$\theta_2 = 64°$$

| | $F_{2\phi}$ | $\Delta^{0+1}F_{2\phi}$ | $\Delta^{0+2}F_{2\phi}$ |
|--------|-------------|------------------------|------------------------|
| $\phi_0$ | 1.4384298 | | |
| | | 313234 | |
| $\phi_1$ | 1.4697532 | | 5060 |
| | | 318294 | |
| $\phi_2$ | 1.5015826 | | |

$$\phi_0 = 67°$$

| | $F_{\theta 0}$ | $\Delta^{1+0} F_{\theta 0}$ | $\Delta^{2+0} F_{\theta 0}$ | $\Delta^{3+0} F_{\theta 0}$ | $\Delta^{4+0} F_{\theta 0}$ |
|---|---|---|---|---|---|
| $\theta_0$ | 1.4220753 | | | | |
| | | 81483 | | | |
| $\theta_1$ | 1.4302236 | | 579 | | |
| | | 82062 | | −146 | |
| $\theta_2$ | 1.4384298 | | 433 | | 3 |
| | | 82505 | | −143 | |
| $\theta_3$ | 1.4466803 | | 290 | | |
| | | 82795 | | | |
| $\theta_4$ | 1.4549598 | | | | |

$$\phi_1 = 68°$$

| | $F_{\theta 1}$ | $\Delta^{1+0} F_{\theta 1}$ | $\Delta^{2+0} F_{\theta 1}$ | $\Delta^{3+0} F_{\theta 1}$ |
|---|---|---|---|---|
| $\theta_0$ | 1.4522494 | | | |
| | | 87141 | | |
| $\theta_1$ | 1.4609635 | | 756 | |
| | | 87897 | | −139 |
| $\theta_2$ | 1.4697532 | | 617 | |
| | | 88514 | | |
| $\theta_3$ | 1.4786046 | | | |

$$\phi_2 = 69°$$

| | $F_{\theta 2}$ | $\Delta^{1+0} F_{\theta 2}$ | $\Delta^{2+0} F_{\theta 2}$ |
|---|---|---|---|
| $\theta_0$ | 1.4828589 | | |
| | | 93139 | |
| $\theta_1$ | 1.4921728 | | 959 |
| | | 94098 | |
| $\theta_2$ | 1.5015826 | | |

Hence

$$\Delta^{1+1} F_{00} = \Delta^{1+0} F_{01} - \Delta^{1+0} F_{00} = 87141 - 81483 = 5658,$$

$$\Delta^{1+2} F_{00} = \Delta^{0+2} F_{10} - \Delta^{0+2} F_{00} = 4694 - 4354 = 340,$$

$$\Delta^{2+1} F_{00} = \Delta^{2+0} F_{01} - \Delta^{2+0} F_{00} = 756 - 579 = 177,$$

$$\Delta^{1+3} F_{00} = \Delta^{0+3} F_{10} - \Delta^{0+3} F_{00} = 37 - 23 = 14,$$

$$\Delta^{3+1} F_{00} = \Delta^{3+0} F_{01} - \Delta^{3+0} F_{00} = -\,139 - (-\,146) = 7,$$

$$\Delta^{2+2} F_{00} = \Delta^{2+0} F_{02} - 2\Delta^{2+0} F_{01} + \Delta^{2+0} F_{00} = 959 - 1512 + 579$$

$$= 26.$$

In Example 2 we found $u = 0.02789$, $v = 0.38014$. Substituting in (IX) these values of $u$, $v$, and the computed differences, we get

$F(62.^{\circ}02789, 67.^{\circ}38014) = 1.4220753 + 0.02789(81483) + 0.38014(301741)$

$\quad + \frac{1}{2}[0.02789(-0.97211)(579) + 2(0.02789)(0.38014)(5658)$

$\quad + 0.38014(-0.61986)(4354)]$

$\quad + \frac{1}{6}[0.02789)(-0.97211)(-1.97211)(-146)$

$\quad + 3(0.02789)(-0.97211)(0.38014)(177)$

$\quad + 3(0.02789)(0.38014)(-0.61986)(340)$

$\quad + 0.38014(-0.61986)(-1.61986)(23)]$

$\quad + \frac{1}{24}[0.02789(-0.97211)(-1.97211)(-2.97211)(3)$

$\quad + 4(0.02789)(-0.97211)(-1.97211)(0.38014)(7)$

$\quad + 6(0.02789)(-0.97211)(0.38014)(-0.61986)(26)$

$\quad + 4(0.02789)(0.38014)(-0.61986)(-1.61986)(14)$

$\quad + 0.38014(-0.61986)(-1.61986)(-2.61986)(-13)]$

$\quad = 1.4337264.$

This value differs from that found in Example 2 by four units in the last decimal place; but in view of the fact that different parts of the function table, different formulas, and different methods were used in the two computations the agreement is as close as could be expected.

The remainder term in formula (IX) is

$$(36{:}3)\ R_n(x_0, y_0) = \frac{1}{(n+1)!}\left[\frac{\partial^{n+1}f(\xi, \eta)}{\partial x^{n+1}}h^{n+1}u(u-1)(u-2)\cdots(u-n)\right.$$

$$+ (n+1)\frac{\partial^{n+1}f(\xi, \eta)}{\partial x^n \partial y}h^n k u(u-1)\cdots[u-(n-1)]v$$

$$+ \frac{(n+1)n}{2!}\frac{\partial^{n+1}f(\xi, \eta)}{\partial x^{n-1}\partial y^2}h^{n-1}k^2(u)(u-1) - [u-(n-2)]v(v-1)$$

$$\left.+ \cdots + \frac{\partial^{n+1}f(\xi, \eta)}{\partial y^{n+1}}k^{n+1}v(v-1)(v-2)\cdots(v-n)\right],$$

where $\xi$ and $\eta$ are mean values of $x$ and $y$ in the region considered.

The formula for $R_n$ in terms of differences is

$$(36:4) \quad R_n(x_0, y_0) = \frac{1}{(n+1)!}[u(u-1)(u-2)\cdots(u-n)\Delta^{(n+1)+0}z_{00}$$

$$+ (n+1)u(u-1)(u-2)\cdots[u-(n-1)]v\Delta^{n+1}z_{00}$$

$$+ \frac{(n+1)n}{2!}u(u-1)\cdots[u-(n-2)]v(v-1)\Delta^{(n-1)+2}z_{00}$$

$$+ \cdots + v(v-1)(v-2)\cdots(v-n)\Delta^{0+(n+1)}z_{00}].$$

*Note.* The two methods explained in this chapter are sufficient for the solution of all ordinary problems of double interpolation. As to which of these methods is preferable, it may be said that the use of formula (IX) is probably shorter if all differences above the second are negligible.

For a more extensive treatment of double interpolation the reader should consult Steffensen's *Interpolation*, pp. 203–223, and *Tracts for Computers* No. III, Part II, by Karl Pearson.

**37. Trigonometric Interpolation.** When the function we desire to represent by an interpolation formula is known to be periodic, it is better to use trigonometric interpolation. Hermite's formula for interpolating periodic functions is

$$(X) \quad y = \frac{\sin(x-x_1)\sin(x-x_2)\cdots\sin(x-x_n)}{\sin(x_0-x_1)\sin(x_0-x_2)\cdots\sin(x_0-x_n)}y_0$$

$$+ \frac{\sin(x-x_0)\sin(x-x_2)\cdots\sin(x-x_n)}{\sin(x_1-x_0)\sin(x_1-x_2)\cdots\sin(x_1-x_n)}y_1$$

$$+ \cdots$$

$$+ \frac{\sin(x-x_0)\sin(x-x_1)\cdots\sin(x-x_{n-1})}{\sin(x_n-x_0)\sin(x_n-x_1)\cdots\sin(x_n-x_{n-1})}y_n.$$

This function has the period $2\pi$, as may be seen by replacing $x$ by $x+2\pi$. It is evident also that $y=y_0$ when $x=x_0$, $y=y_1$ when $x=x_1$, etc.

This formula of Hermite's for periodic functions corresponds to Lagrange's formula for non-periodic functions (Art. 21), and applies whether the given values of $x$ are equidistant or not. By interchanging $x$ and $y$ in Hermite's formula we get a formula for the inverse interpolation of periodic functions, corresponding to (VIII) of Art. 21.

*Example.* Given the following corresponding values of $x$ and $y$, find the value of $y$ corresponding to $x=0.6$, the values of $x$ being in radians:

| $x$ | 0.4 | 0.5 | 0.7 | 0.8 |
|---|---|---|---|---|
| $y$ | 0.0977 | 0.0088 | $-0.1577$ | $-0.2192$ |

*Solution.*   Here $x_0 = 0.4$, $x_1 = 0.5$, $x_2 = 0.7$, $x_3 = 0.8$, $x = 0.6$.   Substituting these values in the formula

$$y = \frac{\sin (x - x_1) \sin (x - x_2) \sin (x - x_3)}{\sin (x_0 - x_1) \sin (x_0 - x_2) \sin (x_0 - x_3)} y_0$$

$$+ \frac{\sin (x - x_0) \sin (x - x_2) \sin (x - x_3)}{\sin (x_1 - x_0) \sin (x_1 - x_2) \sin (x_1 - x_3)} y_1$$

$$+ \frac{\sin (x - x_0) \sin (x - x_1) \sin (x - x_3)}{\sin (x_2 - x_0) \sin (x_2 - x_1) \sin (x_2 - x_3)} y_2$$

$$+ \frac{\sin (x - x_0) \sin (x - x_1) \sin (x - x_2)}{\sin (x_3 - x_0) \sin (x_3 - x_1) \sin (x_3 - x_2)} y_3,$$

we get

$$y = \frac{\sin (0.1) \sin (- 0.1) \sin (- 0.2)}{\sin (- 0.1) \sin (- 0.3) \sin (- 0.4)} (0.0977)$$

$$+ \frac{\sin (0.2) \sin (- 0.1) \sin (- 0.2)}{\sin (0.1) \sin (- 0.2) \sin (- 0.3)} (0.0088)$$

$$+ \frac{\sin (0.2) \sin (0.1) \sin (- 0.2)}{\sin (0.3) \sin (0.2) \sin (- 0.1)} (- 0.1577)$$

$$+ \frac{\sin (0.2) \sin (0.1) \sin (- 0.1)}{\sin (0.4) \sin (0.3) \sin (0.1)} (- 0.2192),$$

or

$$y = - 0.01684 + 0.00592 - 0.10601 + 0.03778$$

$$= - \underline{0.07915.}$$

This value agrees with that found by numerical integration on page 242.

The computation in this problem is conveniently performed by logarithms, the log sines being given directly in the *Smithsonian Mathematical Tables, Hyperbolic Functions*, Table III.

*Note.* The problem of trigonometric interpolation was first solved by Gauss,[*] who derived several formulas similar to Hermite's. The formula usually called Gauss's formula differs from Hermite's only in having the factor $\frac{1}{2}$ written in front of all the angles; thus, $\sin \frac{1}{2}(x - x_0)$ etc. It is believed, however, that Hermite's formula is simpler than any of the Gauss formulas.

### EXAMPLES ON CHAPTER VI

1. Using the data of Example 1, Art. 34, find by two methods the hour angle of the sun when $a = 12°$ and $d = 16°$.

2. Using the short table of elliptic functions given in Example 2, Art. 34, find $F(\theta, \phi)$ by two methods when $\theta = 60°37'40''$, $\phi = 66°17'52''$.

[*] *Werke*, Band III, pp. 265–327.

# CHAPTER VII

## NUMERICAL DIFFERENTIATION AND INTEGRATION

### I. NUMERICAL DIFFERENTIATION

**38. Numerical Differentiation** is the process of calculating the derivatives of a function by means of a set of given values of that function. The problem is solved by representing the function by an interpolation formula and then differentiating this formula as many times as desired.

If the function is given by a table of values for equidistant values of the independent variable, it should be represented by an interpolation formula employing differences, such as Newton's, Stirling's, or Bessel's. But if the given values of the function are not for equidistant values of the independent variable, we must represent the function by Lagrange's or Hermite's formulas.

The considerations governing the choice of a formula employing differences are the same as in the case of interpolation. That is, if we desire the derivative at a point near the *beginning* of a set of tabular values, we use Newton's formula (I). Whereas, if we desire the derivative at a point near the *end* of the table, we use Newton's formula (II). For points near the middle of the table we should use a central-difference formula—Stirling's or Bessel's.

The values of derivatives in terms of differences may also be found by means of those interpolation formulas which employ differences. Thus, from Stirling's formula we have, since

$$u = \frac{x - x_0}{h} \text{ and } \frac{dy}{dx} = \frac{dy}{du} \cdot \frac{du}{dx} = \frac{1}{h} \frac{dy}{du},$$

$$v = y_0 + u\frac{\Delta y_{-1} + \Delta y_0}{2} + \frac{u^2}{2}\Delta^2 y_{-1} + \frac{u(u^2 - 1)}{3!} \frac{\Delta^3 y_{-2} + \Delta^3 y_{-1}}{2}$$

$$+ \frac{u^2(u^2 - 1)}{4!}\Delta^4 y_{-2} + \frac{u(u^2 - 1)(u^2 - 2^2)}{5!} \frac{\Delta^5 y_{-3} + \Delta^5 y_{-2}}{2}$$

$$+ \frac{u^2(u^2 - 1)(u^2 - 2^2)}{6!}\Delta^6 y_{-3} + \cdots,$$

114

$$\frac{dy}{dx} = \frac{1}{h}\left[\frac{\Delta y_{-1} + \Delta y_0}{2} + u\Delta^2 y_{-1} + \frac{3u^2 - 1}{3!}\frac{\Delta^3 y_{-2} + \Delta^3 y_{-1}}{2}\right.$$

$$+ \frac{4u^3 - 2u}{4!}\Delta^4 y_{-2} + \frac{5u^4 - 15u^2 + 4}{5!}\frac{\Delta^5 y_{-3} + \Delta^5 y_{-2}}{2}$$

$$\left.+ \frac{6u^5 - 20u^3 + 8u}{6!}\Delta^6 y_{-3} + \cdots \right],$$

$$\frac{d^2 y}{dx^2} = \frac{1}{h^2}\left[\Delta^2 y_{-1} + u\frac{\Delta^3 y_{-2} + \Delta^3 y_{-1}}{2}\frac{12u^2 - 2}{4!}\Delta^4 y_{-2}\right.$$

$$\left.+ \frac{20u^3 - 30u}{5!}\frac{\Delta^5 y_{-3} + \Delta^5 y_{-2}}{2} + \frac{30u^4 - 60u^2 + 8}{6!}\Delta^6 y_{-3} + \cdots \right],$$

$$\frac{d^3 y}{dx^3} = \frac{1}{h^3}\left[\frac{\Delta^3 y_{-2} + \Delta^3 y_{-1}}{2} + u\Delta^4 y_{-2} + \frac{60u^2 - 30}{5!}\frac{\Delta^5 y_{-3} + \Delta^5 y_{-2}}{2}\right.$$

$$\left.+ \frac{120u^3 - 120u}{6!}\Delta^6 y_{-3} + \cdots \right],$$

$$\frac{d^4 y}{dx^4} = \frac{1}{h^4}\left[\Delta^4 y_{-2} + u\frac{\Delta^5 y_{-3} + \Delta^5 y_{-2}}{2} + \frac{360u^2 - 120}{6!}\Delta^6 y_{-3} + \cdots \right],$$

$$\frac{d^5 y}{dx^5} = \frac{1}{h^5}\left[\frac{\Delta^5 y_{-3} + \Delta^5 y_{-2}}{2} + u\Delta^6 y_{-3} + \cdots \right],$$

$$\frac{d^6 y}{dx^6} = \frac{1}{h^6}[\Delta^6 y_{-3} + \cdots ].$$

For the point $x = x_0$ we have $u = 0$. Hence on substituting this value of $u$ in the formulas above, we get

$$\left(\frac{dy}{dx}\right)_{x_0} = \frac{1}{h}\left[\frac{\Delta y_{-1} + \Delta y_0}{2} - \frac{1}{3!}\frac{\Delta^3 y_{-2} + \Delta^3 y_{-1}}{2} + \frac{4}{5!}\frac{\Delta^5 y_{-3} + \Delta^5 y_{-2}}{2} + \cdots \right],$$

$$\left(\frac{d^2 y}{dx^2}\right)_{x_0} = \frac{1}{h^2}\left[\Delta^2 y_{-1} - \frac{1}{12}\Delta^4 y_{-2} + \frac{8}{6!}\Delta^6 y_{-3} + \cdots \right],$$

$$\left(\frac{d^3 y}{dx^3}\right)_{x_0} = \frac{1}{h^3}\left[\frac{\Delta^3 y_{-2} + \Delta^3 y_{-1}}{2} - \frac{30}{5!}\frac{\Delta^5 y_{-3} + \Delta^5 y_{-2}}{2}\right],$$

$$\left(\frac{d^4 y}{dx^4}\right)_{x_0} = \frac{1}{h^4}\left[\Delta^4 y_{-2} - \frac{120}{6!}\Delta^6 y_{-3} + \cdots \right],$$

$$\left(\frac{d^5 y}{dx^5}\right)_{x_0} = \frac{1}{h^5}\left[\frac{\Delta^5 y_{-3} + \Delta^5 y_{-2}}{2} + \cdots \right],$$

$$\left(\frac{d^6 y}{dx^6}\right)_{x_0} = \frac{1}{h^6}[\Delta^6 y_{-3} + \cdots ].$$

Evidently we can find the derivatives in exactly the same way by differentiating Newton's, Bessel's, and Lagrange's formulas.

To find the maximum or minimum value of a tabulated function we compute the necessary differences from the given table, substitute them in the appropriate interpolation formula, put the first derivative of this formula equal to zero, and solve for $u$. Then $x$ is found from the relation $x = x_0 + hu$.

We can also find the maximum or minimum value of a function by equating to zero the first derivative of Lagrange's formula.

*Example.* Find the first and second derivatives of the function tabulated below, at the point $x = 0.6$.

| $x$ | $y$ | $\Delta y$ | $\Delta^2 y$ | $\Delta^3 y$ | $\Delta^4 y$ |
|------|-----------|---------|--------|-------|------|
| 0.4 | 1.5836494 | | | | |
| | | 2137932 | | | |
| 0.5 | 1.7974426 | | 330018 | | |
| | | 2467950 | | 34710 | |
| 0.6 | 2.0442376 | | 364728 | | 3548 |
| | | 2832678 | | 38258 | |
| 0.7 | 2.3275054 | | 403086 | | |
| | | 3235764 | | | |
| 0.8 | 2.6510818 | | | | |

*Solution.* Here $x_0 = 0.6$, $u = 0$, $h = 0.1$. Substituting in the formulas for the first and second derivatives at $x = x_0$ the appropriate differences from the table above, we get

$$\frac{dy}{dx} = 10[0.2650314 - 0.0006081] = \underline{2.644233,}$$

$$\frac{d^2y}{dx^2} = 100[0.0364728 - 0.0000296] = \underline{3.64432.}$$

The function tabulated above is

$$y = 2e^x - x - 1.$$

Hence

$$\frac{dy}{dx} = 2e^x - 1, \qquad \frac{d^2y}{dx^2} = 2e^x.$$

Putting $x = 0.6$ in these, we get

$$\frac{dy}{dx} = 2.644238, \qquad \frac{d^2y}{dx^2} = 3.644238$$

as the correct values for the first and second derivatives. The values found by numerical differentiation are therefore correct to five significant figures in the case of the first derivative and to four significant figures in the case of the second derivative.

It is to be observed that differentiation makes an interpolation formula converge more slowly, just as in the case of a power series. This is why the second derivative in the example above was correct to one less figure than the first derivative.

The student should bear in mind that approximate differentiation, whether numerical or graphical, is at best only approximate and that a high degree of accuracy is rarely attainable.

*Partial derivatives* of a tabulated function of two independent variables can be found by differentiating partially formula (IX) of Art. 36.

## II. NUMERICAL INTEGRATION

**39. Introduction.** Numerical integration is the process of computing the value of a definite integral from a set of numerical values of the integrand. When applied to the integration of a function of a single variable, the process is sometimes called *mechanical quadrature*; when applied to the computation of a double integral of a function of two independent variables it is called *mechanical cubature*.

The problem of numerical integration, like that of numerical differentiation, is solved by representing the integrand by an interpolation formula and then integrating this formula between the desired limits. Thus, to find the value of the definite integral $\int_a^b y\,dx$, we replace the function $y$ by an interpolation formula, usually one involving differences, and then integrate this formula between the limits $a$ and $b$. In this way we can derive *quadrature formulas* for the approximate integration of any function for which numerical values are known. We shall now derive some of the simplest and most useful of the quadrature formulas.

**40. Quadrature Formulas in Terms of Equidistant Ordinates.** In Newton's, Stirling's, and Bessel's interpolation formulas the relation connecting $x$ and $u$ is

(40: 1) $$x = x_0 + hu,$$

from which we get

(40: 2) $$dx = hdu.$$

Let us now integrate Newton's formula (I) over $n$ equidistant intervals of width $h(=\Delta x)$. The limits of integration for $x$ are $x_0$ and $x_0 + nh$. Hence from (40: 1) the corresponding limits for $u$ are 0 and $n$. We therefore have

$$\int_{x_0}^{x_0+nh} y\,dx = h\int_0^n \left(y_0 + u\Delta y_0 + \frac{u(u-1)}{2!}\Delta^2 y_0 + \frac{u(u-1)(u-2)}{3!}\Delta^3 y_0\right.$$

$$+ \frac{u(u-1)(u-2)(u-3)}{4!}\Delta^4 y_0 + \frac{u(u-1)(u-2)(u-3)(u-4)}{5!}\Delta^5 y_0$$

$$\left.+ \frac{u(u-1)(u-2)(u-3)(u-4)(u-5)}{6!}\Delta^6 y_0 + \cdots\right)du,$$

or

$$(40:3)\qquad \int_{x_0}^{x_0+nh} y\,dx = h\left[ny_0 + \frac{n^2}{2}\Delta y_0 + \left(\frac{n^3}{3} - \frac{n^2}{2}\right)\frac{\Delta^2 y_0}{2}\right.$$

$$+ \left(\frac{n^4}{4} - n^3 + n^2\right)\frac{\Delta^3 y_0}{3!} + \left(\frac{n^5}{5} - \frac{3n^4}{2} + \frac{11n^3}{3} - 3n^2\right)\frac{\Delta^4 y_0}{4!}$$

$$+ \left(\frac{n^6}{6} - 2n^5 + \frac{35n^4}{4} - \frac{50n^3}{3} + 12n^2\right)\frac{\Delta^5 y_0}{5!}$$

$$\left.+ \left(\frac{n^7}{7} - \frac{15n^6}{6} + 17n^5 - \frac{225n^4}{4} + \frac{274n^3}{3} - 60n^2\right)\frac{\Delta^6 y_0}{6!}\right].$$

From this general formula (40:3) we can obtain several well-known special formulas, as follows:

*40a). The Trapezoidal Rule.* Putting $n=1$ and neglecting all differences above the first,[*] we have

$$\int_{x_0}^{x_0+h} y\,dx = h\left[y_0 + \frac{\Delta y_0}{2}\right] = \frac{h}{2}[2y_0 + y_1 - y_0] = \frac{h}{2}(y_0 + y_1).$$

For the next interval from $x_1$ to $x_2$ we have in like manner

$$\int_{x_1}^{x_1+h} y\,dx = \frac{h}{2}(y_1 + y_2);$$

and so on for any number of intervals. For the $n$th interval we have

$$\int_{x_{n-1}}^{x_{n-1}+h} y\,dx = \frac{h}{2}(y_{n-1} + y_n).$$

Adding all such expressions as these from $x_0$ to $x_n$, we get

$$(40:4)\qquad \int_{x_0}^{x_0+nh} y\,dx = \frac{h}{2}(y_0 + 2y_1 + 2y_2 + \cdots + 2y_{n-1} + y_n)$$

$$= h\left(\frac{y_0}{2} + y_1 + y_2 + \cdots + y_{n-1} + \frac{y_n}{2}\right).$$

---

[*] Since we are integrating over the single interval bounded by the two ordinates $y_0$ and $y_1$, it is not possible to obtain differences higher than the first.

This formula is known as the *Trapezoidal Rule*. It is very useful for computing a definite integral when the given values $y_0$, $y_1$, etc. of the function are taken close together (that is, if the interval of width $h$ is small), and it is sufficiently accurate when the values of the function are given to only two or three significant figures.

Geometrically the trapezoidal rule means that we replace the graph of the given function by $n$ segments of straight lines and that we replace the area under the graph by that of a polygon, inscribed where the graph is concave downward and circumscribed where the graph is concave upward.

*40b). Simpson's One-Third Rule.* Putting $n = 2$ and neglecting all differences above the second, we get

$$\int_{x}^{x_0+2h} y\,dx = h\left[2y_0 + 2\Delta y_0 + \left(\frac{8}{3} - 2\right)\frac{\Delta^2 y_0}{2}\right]$$

$$= h[2y_0 + 2y_1 - 2y_0 + \tfrac{1}{3}(y_2 - 2y_1 + y_0)]$$

$$= \frac{h}{3}(y_0 + 4y_1 + y_2).$$

For the next two intervals from $x_2$ to $x_2+2h$ we get in like manner

$$\int_{x_2}^{x_2+2h} y\,dx = \frac{h}{3}(y_2 + 4y_3 + y_4).$$

Similarly for the third pair of intervals we have

$$\int_{x_4}^{x_4+2h} y\,dx = \frac{h}{3}(y_4 + 4y_5 + y_6);$$

and so on. Adding all such expressions as these from $x_0$ to $x_n$, where $n$ is *even*, we get

$$\int_{x_0}^{x_0+nh} y\,dx = \frac{h}{3}(y_0 + 4y_1 + y_2 + y_2 + 4y_3 + y_4 + y_4 + 4y_5 + y_6 + \cdots),$$

or

$$(40:5)\quad \int_{x_0}^{x_0+nh} y\,dx = \frac{h}{3}(y_0+4y_1+2y_2+4y_3+2y_4+\cdots+2y_{n-2}+4y_{n-1}+y_n)$$

$$= \frac{h}{3}[y_0 + 4(y_1 + y_3 + \cdots + y_{n-1}) + 2(y_2 + y_4 + \cdots$$

$$\cdots + y_{n-2}) + y_n].$$

This important formula is known as *Simpson's One-Third Rule*. It is probably the most useful of all the formulas for mechanical quadrature.

When using this formula the student must bear in mind that the interval of integration must be divided into an *even* number of subintervals of width $h$.

The geometric significance of Simpson's one-third rule is that we replace the graph of the given function by $n/2$ arcs of second-degree parabolas.

*40c). Simpson's Three-Eighths Rule.* Putting $n = 3$ and neglecting all differences above the third, we get

$$\int_{x_0}^{x_0+3h} y\,dx = h\left[3y_0 + \frac{9}{2}\Delta y_0 + \left(9 - \frac{9}{2}\right)\frac{\Delta^2 y_0}{2} + \left(\frac{81}{4} - 27 + 9\right)\frac{\Delta^3 y_0}{6}\right]$$

$$= h\left[3y_0 + \frac{9y_1 - 9y_0}{2} + \frac{9}{4}(y_2 - 2y_1 + y_0)\right.$$

$$\left. + \frac{3}{8}(y_3 - 3y_2 + 3y_1 - y_0) = \frac{3h}{8}(y_0 + 3y_1 + 3y_2 + y_3)\right).$$

For the next set of intervals from $x = x_3$ to $x = x_6$ we have in the same way

$$\int_{x_3}^{x_6} y\,dx = \frac{3h}{8}(y_3 + 3y_4 + 3y_5 + y_6).$$

Adding all such expressions as these from $x_0$ to $x_n$, where $n$ is now a *multiple of three*, we get

$$(40: 6) \quad \int_{x_0}^{x_0+nh} y\,dx = \frac{3h}{8}[y_0 + 3y_1 + 3y_2 + 2y_3 + 3y_4 + 3y_5 + 2y_6 + \cdots$$

$$\cdots + 3y_{n-1} + y_n]$$

$$= \frac{3h}{8}[y_0 + 3(y_1 + y_2 + y_4 + y_5 + \cdots + y_{n-1})$$

$$+ 2(y_3 + y_6 + \cdots + y_{n-3}) + y_n].$$

This formula is known as *Simpson's Three-Eighths Rule*. It is inferior to the one-third rule and is given here merely for the purpose of comparing it later with the one-third rule. (Art. 47).

This formula replaces the graph of the given function by $n/3$ arcs of third-degree parabolas.

*40d). Weddle's Rule.* Putting $n = 6$ and neglecting all differences above the sixth, we have

$$\int_{x_0}^{x_0+6h} y\,dx = h\left[6y_0 + 18\Delta y_0 + 27\Delta^2 y_0 + 24\Delta^3 y_0 + \frac{123}{10}\Delta^4 y_0\right.$$

$$\left. + \frac{33}{10}\Delta^5 y_0 + \frac{411}{140}\Delta^6 y_0\right].$$

Here the coefficient of $\Delta^6 y_0$ differs from $3/10$ by the small fraction $1/140$. Hence if we replace this coefficient by $3/10$, we commit an error of only $\Delta^6 y_0/140$. If the value of $h$ is such that the sixth differences are small, the error committed will be negligible. We therefore change the last term to $(3/10)\Delta^6 y_0$ and replace all differences by their values in terms of the given $y$'s. The result reduces down to

$$\int_{x_0}^{x_0+6h} y\,dx = \frac{3h}{10}[y_0 + 5y_1 + y_2 + 6y_3 + y_4 + 5y_5 + y_6].$$

For the next set of six intervals from $x_6$ to $x_{12}$ we get in the same way

$$\int_{x_6}^{x_{12}} y\,dx = \frac{3h}{10}[y_6 + 5y_7 + y_8 + 6y_9 + y_{10} + 5y_{11} + y_{12}].$$

Adding all such expressions as these from $x_0$ to $x_n$, where $n$ is now a *multiple of six*, we get

$$(40:7) \quad \int_{x_0}^{x_0+nh} y\,dx = \frac{3h}{10}[y_0 + 5y_1 + y_2 + 6y_3 + y_4 + 5y_5 + 2y_6 + 5y_7 + y_8$$
$$+ 6y_9 + y_{10} + 5y_{11} + 2y_{12} + \cdots$$
$$+ 2y_{n-6} + 5y_{n-5} + y_{n-4} + 6y_{n-3} + y_{n-2} + 5y_{n-1} + y_n].$$

This formula is known as *Weddle's Rule*. It is the most accurate of the four formulas thus far developed. In usefulness it is second only to Simpson's one-third rule.

The geometric meaning of Weddle's rule is that we replace the graph of the given function by $n/6$ arcs of fifth-degree parabolas.

We shall now apply these four formulas to two examples, chosen at random.

*Example 1.* Compute the value of the definite integral

$$\int_4^{5.2} \log_e x\,dx.$$

*Solution.* We divide the interval of integration into six equal parts each of width $0.2$. Hence $h=0.2$. The values of the function $y=\log_e x$ are next computed for each point of subdivision. These values are given in the table below.

| $x$ | $\log_e x$ | $x$ | $\log_e x$ |
|-----|-----------|-----|-----------|
| 4.0 | 1.38629436 | 4.8 | 1.56861592 |
| 4.2 | 1.43508453 | 5.0 | 1.60943791 |
| 4.4 | 1.48160454 | 5.2 | 1.64865863 |
| 4.6 | 1.52605630 | | |

(a) By the trapezoidal rule we have

$$I_T = 0.2[9.13827570] = \underline{1.82765514}.$$

(b) By Simpson's one-third rule we have

$$I_{1/3} = \frac{0.2}{3}[3.03495299 + 4(4.57057874) + 2(3.05022046)] = \underline{1.82784726}.$$

(c) Using Simpson's three-eighths rule, we get

$$I_{3/8} = 3/8(0.2)[3.03495299 + 3(6.09474290 + 2(1.52605630)] = \underline{1.82784707}.$$

(d) By Weddle's rule we get

$$I_W = (0.3)(0.2)[3.03495299 + 5(3.04452244)$$
$$+ 3.05022046 + 6(1.52605630)] = \underline{1.82784741}.$$

The true value of the integral is

$$I = \int_4^{5.2} \log_e x \, dx = x \, (\log_e x - 1) \Big]_{4.0}^{5.2} = 1.82784744.$$

Hence the errors are

$$E_T = 1.82784744 - 1.82765514 = 0.00019230 = 19230 \times 10^{-8},$$
$$E_{1/3} = 0.00000018 = 18 \times 10^{-8},$$
$$E_{3/8} = 37 \times 10^{-8},$$
$$E_W = 3 \times 10^{-8}.$$

*Example 2.* Compute the value of the definite integral

$$\int_{0.2}^{1.4} (\sin x - \log_e x + e^x) dx.$$

*Solution.* We shall divide the interval of integration into twelve equal parts by taking $h = 0.1$. The values of the function $y = \sin x - \log_e x + e^x$ are then computed for each point of subdivision. These values are given in the table below.

| $x$ | $y$ | $x$ | $y$ |
|---|---|---|---|
| 0.2 | 3.02951 | 0.9 | 3.34830 |
| 0.3 | 2.84936 | 1.0 | 3.55975 |
| 0.4 | 2.79754 | 1.1 | 3.80007 |
| 0.5 | 2.82130 | 1.2 | 4.06984 |
| 0.6 | 2.89759 | 1.3 | 4.37050 |
| 0.7 | 3.01465 | 1.4 | 4.70418 |
| 0.8 | 3.16605 | | |

(a) By the trapezoidal rule:

$$I_T = 0.1[40.56179] = \underline{4.056\ 8.}$$

(b) By Simpson's one-third rule:

$$I_{1/3} = \frac{0.1}{3}[3.02951 + 4.70418 + 4(20.20418) + 2(16.49077)] = \underline{4.05106.}$$

(c) By Simpson's three-eighths rule:

$$I_{3/8} = \frac{0.3}{8}[3.02951 + 4.70418 + 3(26.90753) + 2(9.78742)] = \underline{4.05117.}$$

(d) By Weddle's rule:

$$I_W = 0.03[21.05841 + 5(13.58281) + 6(6.62137) + 2(3.16605)] = \underline{4.05098.}$$

The true value of the integral is

$$I = \int_{0.2}^{1.4} (\sin x - \log_e x + e^x)dx = -\cos x - x(\log_e x - 1) + e^x \Big]_{0.2}^{1.4}$$
$$= 4.05095.$$

Hence the errors are:

$$E_T = 4.05095 - 4.05618 = -0.00523,$$
$$E_{1/3} = -0.00011,$$
$$E_{3/8} = -0.00022,$$
$$E_W = -0.00003.$$

*Remarks.* The results of these two examples show that

1. The trapezoidal rule is much less accurate than any of the others.

2. Simpson's one-third rule is more accurate than the three-eighths rule, the error of the former being only half that of the latter.

3. Weddle's rule is more accurate than any of the others.

The trapezoidal rule has the advantage of great simplicity and is sufficiently accurate in problems where the data are given to only two or three significant figures.

Simpson's one-third rule is almost as simple as the trapezoidal, and is far more accurate.

The three-eighths rule is less simple and less accurate than the one-third rule and hence has no *raison d'être.* It will be shown later (Art. 47) that the error inherent in the three-eighths rule is generally $2\frac{1}{4}$ times that of the one-third rule.

Weddle's rule is simple in form and very accurate, but has the disadvantage of requiring that the number of subdivisions be a multiple of six.  This means that when computing the values of $y$ in many problems the assigned values of $x$ can not be taken as simple tenths, as was done in the two examples worked above.  The subdivision by tenths is nearly always possible when using Simpson's one-third rule.  However, when Simpson's rule can not give the desired degree of accuracy, Weddle's rule should be used.

Simpson's three-eighths rule should *never* be used.*

**41. Central-Difference Quadrature Formulas.**  By integrating Stirling's and Bessel's interpolation formulas we can derive rapidly converging quadrature formulas in terms of differences.  Thus, integrating Stirling's formula from $x = x_0 - h$ to $x = x_0 + h$, or $u = -1$ to $u = 1$, we have

$$I = \int_{-h}^{h} \phi(x)dx = h \int_{-1}^{1} \left( y_0 + u\frac{\Delta y_{-1} + \Delta y_0}{2} + \frac{u^2}{2}\Delta^2 y_{-1} \right.$$

$$+ \frac{u(u^2 - 1)}{3!} \frac{\Delta^3 y_{-2} + \Delta^3 y_{-1}}{2} + \frac{u^2(u^2 - 1)}{4!} \Delta^4 y_{-2}$$

$$+ \frac{u(u^2 - 1)(u^2 - 4)}{5!} \frac{\Delta^5 y_{-3} + \Delta^5 y_{-2}}{2}$$

$$\left. + \frac{u^2(u^2 - 1)(u^2 - 4)}{6!}\Delta^6 y_{-3} + \cdots \right) du$$

$$= h \left[ 2y_0 + \frac{1}{3}\Delta^2 y_{-1} + \frac{2}{24}\left(\frac{1}{5} - \frac{1}{3}\right)\Delta^4 y_{-2} + \frac{2}{720}\left(\frac{1}{7} - 1 + \frac{4}{3}\right)\Delta^6 y_{-3} \right]$$

$$= 2h \left[ y_0 + \frac{1}{6}\Delta^2 y_{-1} - \frac{1}{180}\Delta^4 y_{-2} + \frac{1}{1512}\Delta^6 y_{-3} + \cdots \right].$$

This formula gives the approximate value of the integral from $x = x_0 - h$ to $x = x_0 + h$.  By advancing the subscripts of the $y$'s by one unit we get the value of the integral from $x = x_0$ to $x = x_0 + 2h$.  Denoting this integral by $I_0^2$, we have

$$I_0^2 = 2h \left[ y_1 + \frac{1}{6}\Delta^2 y_0 - \frac{1}{180}\Delta^4 y_{-1} + \frac{1}{1512}\Delta^6 y_{-2} \right].$$

* Henceforth in this book the term "Simpson's rule" will mean Simpson's one-third rule.

The integrals $I_2{}^4$, $I_4{}^6$, $\cdots I_{n-2}^n$ are likewise seen to be

$$I_2{}^4 = 2h\left[y_3 + \frac{1}{6}\Delta^2 y_2 - \frac{1}{180}\Delta^4 y_1 + \frac{1}{1512}\Delta^6 y_0\right],$$

$$I_4{}^6 = 2h\left[y_5 + \frac{1}{6}\Delta^2 y_4 - \frac{1}{180}\Delta^4 y_3 + \frac{1}{1512}\Delta^6 y_2\right],$$

$$\cdot\ \cdot\ \cdot\ \cdot\ \cdot\ \cdot\ \cdot\ \cdot\ \cdot\ \cdot\ \cdot\ \cdot\ \cdot\ \cdot\ \cdot\ \cdot\ \cdot\ \cdot$$

$$I_{n-2}^n = 2h\left[y_{n-1} + \frac{1}{6}\Delta^2 y_{n-2} - \frac{1}{180}\Delta^4 y_{n-3} + \frac{1}{1512}\Delta^6 y_{n-4}\right].$$

Adding all these separate integrals, we get

$$(41:1)\quad I_0{}^n = 2h\left[y_1 + y_3 + y_5 + \cdots + y_{n-1}\right.$$

$$+ \frac{1}{6}(\Delta^2 y_0 + \Delta^2 y_2 + \cdots + \Delta^2 y_{n-2})$$

$$- \frac{1}{180}(\Delta^4 y_{-1} + \Delta^4 y_1 + \Delta^4 y_3 + \cdots + \Delta^4 y_{n-3})$$

$$\left.+ \frac{1}{1512}(\Delta^6 y_{-2} + \Delta^6 y_0 + \Delta^6 y_2 + \cdots + \Delta^6 y_{n-4})\right],$$

where

$$I_0{}^n = \int_{x_0}^{x_0+nh} y\,dx$$

and $n$ is *even*.

Integrating Bessel's formula (VI) over the interval $x = x_0$ to $x = x_0 + h$, or $v = -\frac{1}{2}$ to $v = \frac{1}{2}$, we have

$$I_0{}^1 = \int_{x_0}^{x_0+h} \phi(x)dx = h\int_{-1/2}^{1/2}\left(\frac{y_0 + y_1}{2} + v\Delta y_0 + \frac{(v^2 - \frac{1}{4})}{2}\frac{\Delta^2 y_{-1} + \Delta^2 y_0}{2}\right.$$

$$+ \frac{v(v^2 - \frac{1}{4})}{3!}\Delta^3 y_{-1} + \frac{(v^2 - \frac{1}{4})(v^2 - \frac{9}{4})}{4!}\frac{\Delta^4 y_{-2} + \Delta^4 y_{-1}}{2}$$

$$+ \frac{v(v^2 - \frac{1}{4})(v^2 - \frac{9}{4})}{5!}\Delta^5 y_{-2}$$

$$\left.+ \frac{(v^2 - \frac{1}{4})(v^2 - \frac{9}{4})(v^2 - \frac{25}{4})}{6!}\frac{\Delta^6 y_{-3} + \Delta^6 y_{-2}}{2} + \cdots\right)dv$$

$$= h\left[\frac{y_0 + y_1}{2} - \frac{1}{12}\frac{\Delta^2 y_{-1} + \Delta^2 y_0}{2} + \frac{11}{720}\frac{\Delta^4 y_{-2} + \Delta^4 y_{-1}}{2}\right.$$

$$\left.- \frac{191}{60480}\frac{\Delta^6 y_{-3} + \Delta^6 y_{-2}}{2}\right].$$

By advancing the subscripts a unit at a time we find the integrals over the succeeding intervals to be

$$I_1{}^2 = h\left[\frac{y_1 + y_2}{2} - \frac{1}{12}\frac{\Delta^2 y_0 + \Delta^2 y_1}{2} + \frac{11}{720}\frac{\Delta^4 y_{-1} + \Delta^4 y_0}{2}\right.$$
$$\left. - \frac{191}{60480}\frac{\Delta^6 y_{-2} + \Delta^6 y_{-1}}{2}\right],$$

$$I_2{}^3 = h\left[\frac{y_2 + y_3}{2} - \frac{1}{12}\frac{\Delta^2 y_1 + \Delta^2 y_2}{2} + \frac{11}{720}\frac{\Delta^4 y_0 + \Delta^4 y_1}{2}\right.$$
$$\left. - \frac{191}{60480}\frac{\Delta^6 y_{-1} + \Delta^6 y_0}{2}\right],$$

. . . . . . . . . . .

$$I_{n-1}{}^n = h\left[\frac{y_{n-1} + y_n}{2} - \frac{1}{12}\frac{\Delta^2 y_{n-2} + \Delta^2 y_{n-1}}{2} + \frac{11}{720}\frac{\Delta^4 y_{n-3} + \Delta^4 y_{n-2}}{2}\right.$$
$$\left. - \frac{191}{60480}\frac{\Delta^6 y_{n-4} + \Delta^6 y_{n-3}}{2}\right].$$

Adding all these separate integrals, we get

$$(41:2) \qquad I_0{}^n = h\left[\left(\frac{y_0}{2} + y_1 + y_2 + \cdots + y_{n-1} + \frac{y_n}{2}\right)\right.$$
$$- \frac{1}{12}\left(\frac{\Delta^2 y_{-1}}{2} + \Delta^2 y_0 + \Delta^2 y_1 + \cdots\right.$$
$$\left. + \Delta^2 y_{n-2} + \frac{\Delta^2 y_{n-1}}{2}\right)$$
$$+ \frac{11}{720}\left(\frac{\Delta^4 y_{-2}}{2} + \Delta^4 y_{-1} + \Delta^4 y_0 + \cdots\right.$$
$$\left. + \Delta^4 y_{n-3} + \frac{\Delta^4 y_{n-2}}{2}\right)$$
$$- \frac{191}{60480}\left(\frac{\Delta^6 y_{-3}}{2} + \Delta^6 y_{-2} + \Delta^6 y_{-1} + \cdots\right.$$
$$\left.\left. + \Delta^6 y_{n-4} + \frac{\Delta^6 y_{n-3}}{2}\right)\right],$$

where $n$ is now either even or odd.

It will be observed that formulas (41: 1) and (41: 2) involve only differences of *even* orders, that (41: 2) involves *all* the even differences, whereas (41: 1) involves only half of them. Formula (41: 2) is too cumbersome for practical use as it stands, but it can be transformed into a much simpler and more useful form, as we shall now show.

From the definition of differences we have

$$\Delta^2 y_{-1} = \Delta y_0 - \Delta y_{-1},$$

$$\Delta^2 y_0 = \Delta y_1 - \Delta y_0,$$

$$\cdot \quad \cdot \quad \cdot \quad \cdot \quad \cdot \quad \cdot \quad \cdot$$

$$\Delta^2 y_{n-1} = \Delta y_n - \Delta y_{n-1},$$

$$\Delta^4 y_{-2} = \Delta^3 y_{-1} - \Delta^3 y_{-2},$$

$$\Delta^4 y_{-1} = \Delta^3 y_0 - \Delta^3 y_{-1},$$

$$\cdot \quad \cdot \quad \cdot \quad \cdot \quad \cdot \quad \cdot \quad \cdot$$

$$\Delta^4 y_{n-2} = \Delta^3 y_{n-1} - \Delta^3 y_{n-2},$$

$$\Delta^6 y_{-3} = \Delta^5 y_{-2} - \Delta^5 y_{-3},$$

$$\Delta^6 y_{-2} = \Delta^5 y_{-1} - \Delta^5 y_{-2},$$

$$\cdot \quad \cdot \quad \cdot \quad \cdot \quad \cdot \quad \cdot \quad \cdot$$

$$\Delta^6 y_{n-3} = \Delta^5 y_{n-2} - \Delta^5 y_{n-3}, \quad \text{etc.}$$

Substituting in (41: 2) these values of the even differences, we find that all differences except those at the beginning and end of the table cancel one another and that formula (41: 2) reduces down to

$$I_0{}^n = h\left[\left(\frac{y_0}{2} + y_1 + y_2 + \cdots + y_{n-1} + \frac{v_n}{2}\right) + \frac{1}{12}\left(\frac{\Delta y_{-1} + \Delta y_0}{2}\right)\right.$$

$$- \frac{11}{720}\left(\frac{\Delta^3 y_{-2} + \Delta^3 y_{-1}}{2}\right) + \frac{191}{60480}\left(\frac{\Delta^5 y_{-3} + \Delta^5 y_{-2}}{2}\right)$$

$$- \frac{1}{12}\left(\frac{\Delta y_{n-1} + \Delta v_n}{2}\right) + \frac{11}{720}\left(\frac{\Delta^3 y_{n-2} + \Delta^3 y_{n-1}}{2}\right)$$

$$\left. - \frac{191}{60480}\left(\frac{\Delta^5 y_{n-3} + \Delta^5 y_{n-2}}{2}\right)\right],$$

which can be written in the simpler form

**(41:3)** $\quad I_0{}^n = h\left[\left(\dfrac{y_0}{2} + y_1 + y_2 + \cdots + y_{n-1} + \dfrac{y_n}{2}\right)\right.$

$\qquad\qquad - \dfrac{1}{12}\left(\dfrac{\Delta y_{n-1} + \Delta y_n}{2} - \dfrac{\Delta y_{-1} + \Delta y_0}{2}\right)$

$\qquad\qquad + \dfrac{11}{720}\left(\dfrac{\Delta^3 y_{n-2} + \Delta^3 y_{n-1}}{2} - \dfrac{\Delta^3 y_{-2} + \Delta^3 y_{-1}}{2}\right)$

$\qquad\qquad \left. - \dfrac{191}{60480}\left(\dfrac{\Delta^5 y_{n-3} + \Delta^5 y_{n-2}}{2} - \dfrac{\Delta^5 y_{-3} + \Delta^5 y_{-2}}{2}\right)\right).$

The results given by this formula are identical with those given by (41: 2), but the labor involved in obtaining them is only a small fraction of that required when using (41: 2).

The geometric significance of formulas (41: 1), (41: 2), and (41: 3) should be noted. Formula (41: 1) replaces the graph of the given function by $n/2$ arcs of parabolas of the sixth degree, whereas (41: 2) and (41: 3) replace the graph by $n$ arcs of sixth-degree parabolas.

By neglecting fourth and sixth differences in (41: 1) and replacing the second differences by their values in terms of the $y$'s, we shall find that (41: 1) then reduces to Simpson's one-third rule. This formula therefore represents Simpson's rule with correction terms.

Formulas (41: 2) and (41: 3) likewise represent the Trapezoidal rule with correction terms.

We shall now apply (41: 1) and (41: 3) to two examples.

*Example 1.* Compute the value of $\pi$ from the formula

$$\frac{\pi}{4} = \int_0^1 \frac{dx}{1 + x^2}.$$

*Solution.* We first compute the values of the function $y = 1/(1+x^2)$ from $x = -0.3$ to $x = 1.3$, taking $h = 0.1$, and then form a table of differences as shown on the following page.

Substituting in (41: 1) the appropriate differences, we have

$$\frac{\pi}{4} = 0.2\left[3.9311573 + \frac{1}{6}(-249992) - \frac{1}{180}(-7) + \frac{1}{1512}(778)\right]$$

$$= 0.78539816.$$

$$\therefore \quad \pi = 4 \times 0.78539816 = \underline{3.14159264}.$$

The true value of $\pi$ to nine figures is

$$\pi = 3.14159265.$$

Difference Table for $y = 1/(1+x^2)$.

| $x$ | $y$ | $\Delta y$ | $\Delta^2 y$ | $\Delta^3 y$ | $\Delta^4 y$ | $\Delta^5 y$ | $\Delta^6 y$ |
|---|---|---|---|---|---|---|---|
| −0.3 | 0.9174312 | | | | | | |
| | | 441073 | | | | | |
| −0.2 | 0.9615385 | | −155468 | | | | |
| | | 285605 | | −31127 | | | |
| −0.1 | 0.9900990 | | −186595 | | +19702 | | |
| | | 99010 | | −11425 | | +3148 | |
| 0 | 1.0000000 | | −198020 | | +22850 | | −6296 |
| | | − 99010 | | +11425 | | −3148 | |
| 0.1 | 0.9900990 | | −186595 | | 19702 | | −4762 |
| | | −285605 | | +31127 | | −7910 | |
| 0.2 | 0.9615385 | | −155468 | | 11792 | | −1320 |
| | | −441073 | | 42919 | | −9230 | |
| 0.3 | 0.9174312 | | −112549 | | 2562 | | +1886 |
| | | −553622 | | 45481 | | −7344 | |
| 0.4 | 0.8620690 | | − 67068 | | − 4782 | | +3323 |
| | | −620690 | | 40699 | | −4021 | |
| 0.5 | 0.8000000 | | − 26369 | | − 8803 | | 3085 |
| | | −647059 | | 31896 | | − 936 | |
| 0.6 | 0.7352941 | | + 5527 | | − 9739 | | 1983 |
| | | −641532 | | 22157 | | +1047 | |
| 0.7 | 0.6711409 | | + 27684 | | − 8692 | | 868 |
| | | −613848 | | 13465 | | +1915 | |
| 0.8 | 0.6097561 | | 41149 | | − 6777 | | 86 |
| | | −572699 | | 6688 | | 2001 | |
| 0.9 | 0.5524862 | | 47837 | | − 4776 | | − 299 |
| | | −524862 | | 1912 | | 1702 | |
| 1.0 | 0.5000000 | | 49749 | | − 3074 | | − 416 |
| | | −475113 | | − 1162 | | 1286 | |
| 1.1 | 0.4524887 | | 48587 | | − 1788 | | |
| | | −426526 | | − 2950 | | | |
| 1.2 | 0.4098361 | | 45637 | | | | |
| | | −380889 | | | | | |
| 1.3 | 0.3717472 | | | | | | |

Substituting in (41: 3) the appropriate differences from the table, we get

$$\frac{\pi}{4} = 0.1\left[7.8498150 - \frac{1}{12}(-499988) + \frac{11}{720}(375)\right.$$

$$\left. - \frac{191}{60480}(1494)\right] = 0.78539817.$$

$$\therefore \ \pi = 4 \times 0.78539817 = \underline{3.14159268}.$$

This value is slightly less accurate than that obtained by (41: 1), but either result is correct to as many figures as were used in the computed ordinates.

Simpson's rule gives for this problem the value

$$\pi = 3.14159260,$$

which is likewise correct to as many figures as are given in the computed ordinates.

*Example 2.* Compute the approximate value of the integral

$$I = \int_1^2 \frac{dx}{x}.$$

*Solution.* Taking $h = 0.1$, we compute the values of $y = 1/x$ at one-tenth unit intervals from $x = 0.7$ to $x = 2.3$ and form a table of differences.

Difference Table for $y = 1/x$.

| $x$ | $y$ | $\Delta y$ | $\Delta^2 y$ | $\Delta^3 y$ | $\Delta^4 y$ | $\Delta^5 y$ | $\Delta^6 y$ |
|---|---|---|---|---|---|---|---|
| 0.7 | 1.42857143 | | | | | | |
| | | −17857143 | | | | | |
| 0.8 | 1.25000000 | | 3968254 | | | | |
| | | −13888889 | | −1190476 | | | |
| 0.9 | 1.11111111 | | 2777778 | | 432900 | | |
| | | −11111111 | | − 757576 | | −180375 | |
| 1.0 | 1.00000000 | | 2020202 | | 252525 | | 83252 |
| | | − 9090909 | | − 505051 | | − 97123 | |
| 1.1 | 0.90909091 | | 1515151 | | 155402 | | 41618 |
| | | − 7575758 | | − 349649 | | − 55505 | |
| 1.2 | 0.83333333 | | 1165502 | | 99897 | | 22212 |
| | | − 6410256 | | − 249752 | | − 33293 | |
| 1.3 | 0.76923077 | | 915750 | | 66604 | | 12472 |
| | | − 5494506 | | − 183148 | | − 20821 | |
| 1.4 | 0.71428571 | | 732602 | | 45783 | | 7362 |
| | | − 4761904 | | − 137365 | | − 13459 | |
| 1.5 | 0.66666667 | | 595237 | | 32324 | | 4478 |
| | | − 4166667 | | − 105041 | | − 8981 | |
| 1.6 | 0.62500000 | | 490196 | | 23343 | | 2834 |
| | | − 3676471 | | − 81698 | | − 6147 | |
| 1.7 | 0.58823529 | | 408498 | | 17196 | | 1855 |
| | | − 3267973 | | − 64502 | | − 4292 | |
| 1.8 | 0.55555556 | | 343996 | | 12904 | | 1215 |
| | | − 2923977 | | − 51598 | | − 3077 | |
| 1.9 | 0.52631579 | | 292398 | | 9827 | | 843 |
| | | − 2631579 | | − 41771 | | − 2234 | |
| 2.0 | 0.50000000 | | 250627 | | 7593 | | 589 |
| | | − 2380952 | | − 34178 | | − 1645 | |
| 2.1 | 0.47619048 | | 216449 | | 5948 | | |
| | | − 2164503 | | − 28230 | | | |
| 2.2 | 0.45454545 | | 188219 | | | | |
| | | − 1976284 | | | | | |
| 2.3 | 0.43478261 | | | | | | |

Substituting in (41: 1) the appropriate differences, we get

$$I = 0.2\left[3.45953943 + \frac{1}{6}(3727034) - \frac{1}{180}(281353)\right.$$

$$\left. + \frac{1}{1512}(61266)\right] = \underline{0.693147185}.$$

The correct value is $\log_e 2 = 0.693147181$.

Substituting in (41: 3) the appropriate differences from the table, we get

$$I = 0.1\left[6.93771403 - \frac{1}{12}(7594744) + \frac{11}{720}(593339)\right.$$

$$\left. - \frac{191}{60480}(136810)\right] = \underline{0.69314714}.$$

It will be seen that formula (41: 1) gave the more accurate value in this example as was the case in the preceding.

Concerning the relative merits of formulas (41: 1) and (41: 3), it may be said that (41: 1) converges more rapidly and is therefore slightly more accurate. It utilizes fewer ordinates outside the range of integration than does (41: 3). Formula (41: 1) requires that the number of subintervals be *even*, and also requires a little more labor in its application than does (41: 3).

Formula (41: 3) has the advantage of being applicable to any number of sub-intervals and of requiring very little labor in its application. It also gives the same degree of accuracy with third or fifth differences as (41: 1) gives with fourth or sixth differences. Its chief disadvantage is that it utilizes several ordinates outside the range of integration.

The extra-interval ordinates required in formulas (41: 1) and (41: 3) can usually be found by computation, as in the examples worked above, or by extrapolation by means of Newton's formulas (I) and (II). Usually, however, it is not safe to use extrapolation for finding more than one ordinate at each end of the range.

**42. Gauss's Quadrature Formula.** The most accurate of the quadrature formulas in ordinary use is known as Gauss's formula. In Simpson's and Weddle's formulas the ordinates are equally spaced, but it occurred to Gauss that some other spacing might give a better result. Hence he set for himself this problem:

If the definite integral $\int_a^b f(x)dx$ is to be computed from a given number of values of $f(x)$, just where should these values be taken in order to get a result of the greatest possible accuracy? In other words, how shall the interval $(a, b)$ be subdivided so as to give the best possible result?

It turns out that the points of subdivision should not be equidistant, but they are symmetrically placed with respect to the mid-point of the interval of integration.

Let $I = \int_a^b y\,dx$ denote the integral to be computed, where $y = f(x)$. On changing the variable by the substitution

$$(42:1) \qquad\qquad x = a + (b - a)u$$

the limits of integration become 0 and 1. The new value of $y$ is

$$y = f(x) = f[a + (b - a)u] = \phi(u),$$

say. Then since $dx = (b-a)du$, the integral becomes

$$(42:2) \qquad\qquad I = (b - a) \int_0^1 \phi(u)du.$$

Gauss's formula is

$$(42:3) \quad \int_0^1 \phi(u)du = R_1\phi(u_1) + R_2\phi(u_2) + R_3\phi(u_3) + \cdots + R_n\phi(u_n),$$

where $u_1, u_2, \cdots u_n$ are the points of subdivision of the interval $u = 0$ to $u = 1$. The corresponding values of $x$ are therefore

$$x_1 = a + (b - a)u_1, \quad x_2 = a + (b - a)u_2, \quad \text{etc.}$$

The value of the integral $\int_a^b f(x)$ is therefore

$$(42:4) \quad I = \int_a^b f(x)dx = (b - a)[R_1\phi(u_1) + R_2\phi(u_2) + \cdots + R_n\phi(u_n)].$$

We shall not give a detailed derivation of Gauss's formula $(42:3)$, but merely show how the values of $u_1, u_2, \cdots u_n$ and $R_1, R_2, \cdots R_n$ are found and then show how to apply it to an example.

We assume that $\phi(u)$ can be expanded in a convergent power series in the interval $u = 0$ to $u = 1$. Hence we write

$$(42:5) \quad \phi(u) = a_0 + a_1u + a_2u^2 + a_3u^3 + \cdots + a_mu^m + \cdots.$$

We also assume that the integral can be expressed as a linear function of the ordinates of the form $(42:3)$. Integrating $(42:5)$ between the limits 0 and 1, we have

$$(42:6) \quad I = \int_0^1 \phi(u)du = \int_0^1 (a_0 + a_1u + a_2u^2 + \cdots + a_mu^m + \cdots)du$$

$$= a_0 + \frac{a_1}{2} + \frac{a_2}{3} + \frac{a_3}{4} + \frac{a_4}{5} + \frac{a_5}{6} + \cdots + \frac{a_m}{m + 1}.$$

From (42:5) we also have

$$\phi(u_1) = a_0 + a_1u_1 + a_2u_1{}^2 + a_3u_1{}^3 + a_4u_1{}^4 + \cdots + a_mu_1{}^m + \cdots,$$
$$\phi(u_2) = a_0 + a_1u_2 + a_2u_2{}^2 + a_3u_2{}^3 + a_4u_2{}^4 + \cdots + a_mu_2{}^m + \cdots,$$

$$\phi(u_n) = a_0 + a_1u_n + a_2u_n{}^2 + a_3u_n{}^3 + \cdots + a_mu_n{}^m + \cdots.$$

Substituting in (42:3) these values of $\phi(u_1)$, $\phi(u_2)$, $\cdots$ $\phi(u_n)$, we get

$$I = R_1(a_0 + a_1u_1 + a_2u_1{}^2 + \cdots + a_mu_1{}^m + \cdots)$$
$$+ R_2(a_0 + a_1u_2 + a_2u_2{}^2 + \cdots + a_mu_2{}^m + \cdots)$$

$$+ R_n(a_0 + a_1u_n + a_2u_n{}^2 + \cdots + a_mu_n{}^m + \cdots),$$

or, rearranging,

(42: 7)
$$I = a_0(R_1 + R_2 + R_3 + \cdots + R_n)$$
$$+ a_1(R_1u_1 + R_2 u_2 + \cdots + R_nu_n)$$
$$+ a_2(R_1u_1{}^2 + R_2u_2{}^2 + \cdots + R_nu_n{}^2)$$

$$+ a_m(R_1u_1{}^m + R_2u_2{}^m + \cdots + R_nu_n{}^m).$$

Now if the integral $I$ in (42:7) is to be identically the same as the $I$ in (42:6) for *all* values of $a_0$, $a_1$, etc.; that is, if (42:7) is to be identical with (42:6) regardless of the *form* of the function $\phi(u)$—, then corresponding coefficients of $a_0$, $a_1$, $a_2$, etc. in (42:7) and (42:6) must be equal. Hence we must have

(42: 8)
$$\begin{cases} R_1 + R_2 + R_3 + \cdots + R_n = 1, \\ R_1u_1 + R_2u_2 + R_3u_3 + \cdots + R_nu_n = \tfrac{1}{2}, \\ R_1u_1{}^2 + R_2u_2{}^2 + R_3u_3{}^2 + \cdots + R_nu_n{}^2 = \tfrac{1}{3}, \\ \quad \cdots \\ R_1u_1{}^m + R_2u_2{}^m + R_3u_3{}^m + \cdots + R_nu_n{}^m = \dfrac{1}{m+1}. \end{cases}$$

By taking $2n$ of these equations and solving them simultaneously, it would be theoretically possible to find the $2n$ quantities $u_1$, $u_2$, $\cdots u_n$ and $R_1$, $R_2$, $\cdots R_n$. However, the labor of solving these equations by the ordinary methods of algebra would be quite prohibitive even for small values of $n$. The difficulty is obviated by utilizing a result from higher mathematics.

It can be shown* quite easily that if $\phi(u)$ is a polynomial of degree not higher than $2n-1$, then $u_1, u_2, \cdots u_n$ can be found as follows: Solve the equation†

$$\frac{d^n(t^2-1)^n}{dt^n} = 0.$$

The $n$ roots of this $n$th degree equation are all real, and we may call them $t_1, t_2, \cdots t_n$. Then the $u$'s are given by the relations

$$u_1 = \frac{1+t_1}{2}, \qquad u_2 = \frac{1+t_2}{2}, \cdots u_n = \frac{1+t_n}{2}.$$

On substituting these values of the $u$'s in (42:8), we can solve the first $n$ of these equations for the $n$ $R$'s. We shall do this for the case $n=3$. The equation to be solved is

$$\frac{d^3(t^2-1)^3}{dt^3} = 0, \quad \text{or} \quad \frac{d^3}{dt^3}(t^6 - 3t^4 + 3t^2 - 1) = 0.$$

Performing the differentiations, we get

$$24t(5t^2 - 3) = 0.$$

Hence $t=0, \pm\sqrt{3/5}$, and therefore

$$t_1 = -\sqrt{3/5}, \quad t_2 = 0, \quad t_3 = \sqrt{3/5}.$$

Then

$$u_1 = \frac{1-\sqrt{3/5}}{2}, \quad u_2 = \frac{1}{2}, \quad u_3 = \frac{1+\sqrt{3/5}}{2}.$$

Substituting these values of $u_1, u_2, u_3$ in the second and third of equations (42:8), we have the following three equations for determining $R_1, R_2, R_3$:

$$R_1 + R_2 + R_3 = 1,$$

$$R_1\left(\frac{1-\sqrt{3/5}}{2}\right) + \frac{R_2}{2} + R_3\left(\frac{1+\sqrt{3/5}}{2}\right) = \frac{1}{2},$$

$$R_1\left(\frac{1-\sqrt{3/5}}{2}\right)^2 + \frac{R_2}{4} + R_3\left(\frac{1+\sqrt{3/5}}{2}\right)^2 = \frac{1}{3}.$$

* See, for example, Todhunter's *Functions of Laplace, Lamé, and Bessel*, p. 99.

† The roots of this equation are given to sixteen decimal places for $n=1$ to $n=7$ in Heine's *Handbuch der Kugelfunctionen*, Vol. II, pp. 15–16. They are also given indirectly for $n=1$ to $n=10$ in B. P. Moors's *Valeur Approximative d'une Intégrale Definie*. The $r$'s given by Moors are the half roots, that is, $r = \pm t/2$.

Solving these equations by determinants, we find

$$R_1 = \frac{5}{18}, \; R_2 = \frac{4}{9}, \; R_3 = \frac{5}{18}.$$

The numerical values of the $u$'s and $R$'s for $n = 3, 4, 5, 6, 7$ are given below.*

$n = 3$.

$u_1 = 0.1127016654,$ $\qquad R_1 = R_3 = \dfrac{5}{18},$

$u_2 = 0.5,$

$u_3 = 0.8872983346.$ $\qquad R_2 = \dfrac{4}{9}.$

$n = 4$.

$u_1 = 0.0694318442,$ $\qquad R_1 = R_4 = 0.1739274226,$

$u_2 = 0.3300094782,$ $\qquad R_2 = R_3 = 0.3260725774.$

$u_3 = 0.6699905218,$

$u_4 = 0.9305681558.$

$n = 5$.

$u_1 = 0.04691007703,$ $\qquad R_1 = R_5 = 0.1184634425,$

$u_2 = 0.2307653449,$ $\qquad R_2 = R_4 = 0.2393143352,$

$u_3 = 0.5,$

$u_4 = 0.7692346551,$ $\qquad R_3 = \dfrac{64}{225} = 0.2844444444.$

$u_5 = 0.9530899230.$

$n = 6$.

$u_1 = 0.03376524290,$ $\qquad R_1 = R_6 = 0.0856622462,$

$u_2 = 0.1693953068,$

$u_3 = 0.3806904070,$ $\qquad R_2 = R_5 = 0.1803807865,$

$u_4 = 0.6193095930,$

$u_5 = 0.8306046932,$ $\qquad R_3 = R_4 = 0.2339569673.$

$u_6 = 0.9662347571.$

* For additional values of $n$ the reader should consult B. P. Moors, *Valeur Approximative d'une Intégrale Definie*, where (Table C) the values of the $u$'s and $R$'s are given to sixteen decimals for $n = 1$ to $n = 10$. Our $u$'s and the $r$'s in Moors are connected by the relation $u = \frac{1}{2} \pm r$.

$n = 7.$

$u_1 = 0.02544604383,$        $R_1 = R_7 = 0.06474248308,$

$u_2 = 0.1292344072,$

$u_3 = 0.2970774243,$        $R_2 = R_6 = 0.1398526957,$

$u_4 = 0.5,$            $R_3 = R_5 = 0.1909150253,$

$u_5 = 0.7029225757,$

$u_6 = 0.8707655928,$        $R_4 = \dfrac{256}{1225} = 0.2089795918.$

$u_7 = 0.9745539562.$

*Note.* Some authors make the substitution

$$x = \frac{a+b}{2} + \frac{b-a}{2} t,$$

which changes the limits of integration to $-1$ and $1$. Then $y$ becomes

$$y = f(x) = f\left[\frac{a+b}{2} + \frac{b-a}{2} t\right] = \psi(t),$$

say, and the integral becomes

$$I = \frac{b-a}{2} \int_{-1}^{1} \psi(t)dt.$$

Gauss's formula in this case is

$$\int_{-1}^{1} \psi(t)dt = A_1\psi(t_1) + A_2\psi(t_2) + \cdots + A_n\psi(t_n),$$

where $A_1 = 2R_1$, $A_2 = 2R_2$, $\cdots A_n = 2R_n$, and $t_1$, $t_2$, $\cdots t_n$ are the roots of the equation $d^n(t^2-1)^n/dt^n = 0$. The formula for $I$ is then

$$I = \frac{b-a}{2}[A_1\psi(t_1) + A_2\psi(t_2) + \cdots + A_n\psi(t_n)].$$

The relation between these $t$'s and our $u$'s is

$$u = \frac{1+t}{2}.$$

We shall now apply Gauss's formula to a simple example.
*Example.* Compute the integral

$$I = \int_{5}^{12} \frac{dx}{x}.$$

*Solution.* Here we put $x = a + (b-a)u = 5 + 7u$. Hence

$$\phi(u) = \frac{1}{5 + 7u}.$$

Taking $n = 5$, we have

$$\phi(u_1) = \frac{1}{5.32837054} = 0.187674636,$$

$$\phi(u_2) = \frac{1}{6.61535741} = 0.151163412,$$

$$\phi(u_3) = \frac{1}{8.5} = 0.117647059,$$

$$\phi(u_4) = \frac{1}{10.3846426} = 0.0962960439,$$

$$\phi(u_5) = \frac{1}{11.67162946} = 0.0856778399.$$

Substituting these values in (42: 4), together with the corresponding $R$'s for $n = 5$, we get

$$I = 7 \, [0.1184634425 \times 0.187674636$$

$$+ \; 0.2393143352 \times 0.151163412$$

$$+ \; \frac{64}{225} \times 0.117647059 + 0.2393143352 \times 0.0962960439$$

$$+ \; 0.1184634425 \times 0.0856778399 \, ],$$

or

$$I_G = \underline{0.875468458}.$$

The true value of the integral is

$$I = \int_5^{12} \frac{dx}{x} = \log_e \frac{12}{5} = \log_e 2.4 = 0.875468737.$$

The error is therefore

$$E_G = 0.00000028.$$

The value of this integral by Simpson's rule, using fifteen ordinates, was found to be

$$I_{1/3} = 0.87547189.$$

The error in this case is therefore

$$E_{1/3} = 0.0000034,$$

or more than ten times as great as with Gauss's formula. The labor required to find the integral by Gauss's formula is, however, about ten times as great as with Simpson's unless a computing machine is used.

Gauss's formula is useful for another purpose besides computing definite integrals. Recalling that the mean value of a function is given by the formula

$$y_m = \frac{\displaystyle\int_a^b y\,dx}{b - a},$$

we see that the accuracy of the mean depends upon the accuracy with which the integral $\int_a^b y\,dx$ can be computed. The most accurate value of this is obtained by measuring ordinates at the points given by Gauss's formula.

Thus, if we wished to find the best value for the mean daily temperature from only four measurements, we would proceed as follows:

Denoting temperature by $T$, the hour of the day by $t$, and starting from midnight as the beginning of the day, we have

$$T = f(t), \quad T_m = \frac{\displaystyle\int_0^{24} f(t)\,dt}{24}.$$

Put $t = a + (b-a)u = 24u$. Hence

$$t_1 = 24u_1 = 24 \times 0.0694 = 1.^h67,$$

$$t_2 = 24u_2 = 24 \times 0.330 = 7.^h92,$$

$$t_3 = 24u_3 = 24 \times 0.670 = 16.^h08,$$

$$t_4 = 24u_4 = 24 \times 0.9306 = 22.^h33.$$

The best times during the day to take measurements are therefore

1:40 A.M., 7:55 A.M., 4:05 P.M., and 10:20 P.M.

In a similar manner we could find the best times of the day for making five, six, or any other number of measurements by taking the proper $u$'s for $n = 5$, 6, etc.

The same method can be applied for finding the best positions or times for taking measurements on any other physical quantity.

*Remarks.* 1. The reader should bear in mind that Gauss's formula gives an *exact* result when $f(x)$ is a polynomial of the $(2n-1)$th degree or lower.

2. Although Gauss's method is theoretically beautiful and of great accuracy, it has the disadvantage of being laborious in its application, for two reasons:

(a) If the values of $y$ are to be computed from a formula, the numerical values of $u$ to be substituted in the formula must be given to at least as many significant figures as we wish to obtain in the $y$'s.

(b) After we have found the $y$'s to the desired number of significant figures we must multiply them by $R$'s having at least as many figures.

Gauss's formula thus compels us to deal with large numbers in every step if we desire the accuracy it is capable of giving. In applying this formula it is therefore almost imperative that we use a calculating machine. Whoever doubts this statement has only to work out a simple example to be convinced.

3. Gauss's formula should be used for computing definite integrals only when few ordinates are obtainable or when the importance of the result is such as to justify a great expenditure of labor.

**43. Euler's Formula of Summation and Quadrature.** The approximate relation between integrals and sums is expressed by Euler's summation formula. Written as a quadrature formula it is*

$$\int_a^b f(x)dx = h\left[\left(\frac{f(x_0)}{2} + f(x_1) + f(x_2) + \cdots + f(x_{n-1}) + \frac{f(x_n)}{2}\right)\right.$$

$$\textbf{(43:1)} \qquad - \frac{h}{12}[f'(b) - f'(a)] + \frac{h^3}{720}[f'''(b) - f'''(a)]$$

$$\left. - \frac{h^5}{30240}[f^v(b) - f^v(a)] + \frac{h^7}{1209600}[f^{vii}(b) - f^{vii}(a)] - \cdots\right]$$

$$\cdots + R.$$

It will be observed that the first group of terms in parentheses on the right-hand side is simply the trapezoidal formula. The others may be looked upon as correction terms. By adding and subtracting $h[f(x_0)/2 + f(x_n)/2]$ on the right-hand side of (43:1) we have

$$\int_a^b f(x)dx = h[f(x_0) + f(x_1) + \cdots + f(x_n)] - \frac{h}{2_|}[f(x_0) + f(x_n)]$$

$$- \frac{h^2}{12}[f'(b) - f'(a)] + \cdots.$$

---

* For the derivation of Euler's formula see Vallée-Poussin's *Cours d'Analyse Infinitesimale*, II, p. 341; Whittaker and Robinson's *Calculus of Observations*, p. 134; or Charlier's *Mechanik des Himmels*, II, §1.

Transposing and dividing through by $h$, we get

$$f(x_0) + f(x_1) + \cdots + f(x_n) = \frac{1}{h} \int_a^b f(x)dx + \frac{1}{2}[f(x_0) + f(x_n)]$$

$$+ \frac{h}{12}[f'(b) - f'(a)] - \frac{h^3}{720}[f'''(b) - f'''(a)] + \cdots,$$

or, since $x_0 = a$, $x_n = b$,

$$\sum_{i=0}^{i=n} f(x_i) = \frac{1}{h} \int_a^b f(x)dx + \frac{1}{2}[f(a) + f(b)] + \frac{h}{12}[f'(b) - f'(a)]$$

**(43 : 2)** $\qquad - \frac{h^3}{720}[f'''(b) - f'''(a)] + \frac{h^5}{30240}[f^v(b) - f^v(a)]$

$$- \frac{h^7}{1209600}[f^{vii}(b) - f^{vii}(a)] - R.$$

Formula (43 : 2) is *Euler's summation formula.* It is useful for finding the approximate sum of any number of consecutive values of a function when these values are given for equidistant values of $x$, provided the integral $\int_a^b f(x)dx$ can be easily evaluated. In these formulas $h$ is the distance between the equidistant values of $x$, so that $nh = b - a$.

*Note.* Formulas (43 : 1) and (43 : 2) differ in an important respect from the quadrature formulas previously derived. In (43 : 1) the terms on the right-hand side, beginning with $(h/12)[f'(b) - f'(a)]$, form an *asymptotic series.* The same is true of (43 : 2), beginning with the term $(1/12)[f'(b) - f'(a)]$.

An asymptotic series is an infinite series which converges for a certain number of terms and then begins to diverge. In computing with such a series it is important to know what term to stop with in order to get the most accurate result. We should stop not with the smallest term but with *the term just before the smallest*; for the error committed is usually less than twice the first neglected term* and is therefore least when the first term neglected is the smallest term in the series. For the reason just given it is important that Euler's formula be used with caution, especially when finding sums by (43 : 2). We shall now apply each of these formulas to an example.

*Example 1.* Compute the value of $\pi$ from the formula

$$\frac{\pi}{4} = \int_0^1 \frac{dx}{1 + x^2}.$$

---

* See Charlier, loc. cit., p. 14.

*Solution.* We take $h = \frac{1}{6}$ and compute the values of $y = 1/(1+x^2)$ at each point of subdivision, as shown in the table below.

| $x$ | $y$ | $x$ | $y$ |
|-----|-----|-----|-----|
| $0$ | $1$ | $\frac{2}{3}$ | $0.69230769$ |
| $\frac{1}{6}$ | $0.97297297$ | $\frac{5}{6}$ | $0.59016393$ |
| $\frac{1}{3}$ | $0.9$ | $1$ | $0.5$ |
| $\frac{1}{2}$ | $0.8$ | | |

We next compute the derivatives of $1/(1+x^2)$, as given below.

$$f(x) = \frac{1}{1+x^2},$$

$$f'(x) = -\frac{2x}{(1+x^2)^2},$$

$$f'''(x) = \frac{24x(1-x^2)}{(1+x^2)^4},$$

$$f^v(x) = \frac{240x}{(1+x^2)^6}[10x^2 - 3x^4 - 3],$$

$$f^{vii}(x) = -\frac{5760x}{(1+x^2)^8}[7x^6 - 49x^4 + 49x^2 - 7].$$

Hence

$$f'(0) = 0, \quad f'(1) = -\tfrac{1}{2},$$
$$f'''(0) = 0, \quad f'''(1) = 0,$$
$$f^v(0) = 0, \quad f^v(1) = 15,$$
$$f^{vii}(0) = 0, \quad f^{vii}(1) = 0.$$

Substituting all these values in (43:1), we get

$$\frac{\pi}{4} = \frac{1}{6}[0.75 + 0.97297297 + 0.9 + 0.8 + 0.69230769 + 0.59016393]$$

$$-\frac{1}{36 \times 12}\left(-\frac{1}{2}\right) - \frac{1}{6^6 \times 30240}(15) = \underline{0.78539816},$$

which is correct to its last figure.

*Example 2.* Find the sum of

$$\frac{1}{51^2} + \frac{1}{53^2} + \frac{1}{55^2} + \cdots + \frac{1}{99^2}.$$

*Solution.* Here $f(x) = 1/x^2$ and $h = 2$. Then

$$f'(x) = -\frac{2}{x^3}, \quad f'''(x) = -\frac{24}{x^5}, \quad f^v(x) = -\frac{72}{x^7}, \quad f^{vii}(x) = -\frac{40320}{x^9}.$$

Remembering that $a = 51$, $b = 99$, and substituting in (43: 2), we get

$$\sum_{x=51}^{x=99} \frac{1}{x^2} = \frac{1}{2} \int_{51}^{99} \frac{dx}{x^2} + \frac{1}{2}\left[\frac{1}{51^2} + \frac{1}{99^2}\right] + \frac{1}{3}\left[\frac{1}{51^3} - \frac{1}{99^3}\right]$$

$$- \frac{4}{15}\left[\frac{1}{51^5} - \frac{1}{99^5}\right] + \frac{16}{21}\left[\frac{1}{51^7} - \frac{1}{99^7}\right]$$

$$- \frac{64}{15}\left[\frac{1}{51^9} - \frac{1}{99^9}\right]$$

$$= 0.004753416 + 0.0002432490$$

$$+ 0.0000021694 - 0.0000000008$$

$$= \underline{0.004998833.}$$

If we had attempted to find the sum of the squares of the reciprocals of all the odd numbers from 1 to 99 we could not have obtained it accurately, for each bracketed quantity after the second would have been practically unity and therefore the various terms would have been the same as the coefficients 4/15, 16/21, 64/15, etc. To get the greatest accuracy in this case we should have to stop with the third term and even then the error might be nearly 8/15. Hence the necessity for caution in finding sums by means of Euler's formula.

**44. Caution in the Use of Quadrature Formulas.** The student should ever bear in mind that when computing the value of a definite integral by means of a quadrature formula he is really replacing the given integrand by a polynomial and integrating this polynomial over the given interval of integration. The accuracy of the result will depend upon how well the polynomial represents the integrand over this interval; or, geometrically, on how well the graph of the polynomial coincides with the graph of the integrand. Before beginning the computation of an integral by a quadrature formula the computer should ascertain the nature and behavior of the integrand over the interval of integration. In some instances it may be necessary to construct an accurate graph of the integrand. The computation can then be planned with reference to the nature and behavior of the function to be integrated. The following example will illustrate this point.

*Example 1.* Find by Simpson's rule the value of the integral

$$I = \int_{-1}^{1} \frac{x^7 \sqrt{1 - x^2}\ dx}{(2 - x)^{13/2}} .$$

*Solution.* The integrand is evidently negative from $x = -1$ to $x = 0$, and positive from $x = 0$ to $x = 1$. Hence we divide each of these intervals into four equal parts and compute the value of the integrand at each point of subdivision. The results are given in the table below.

| $x$ | $y$ | $x$ | $y$ |
|---|---|---|---|
| $-1$ | $-0$ | 0.25 | 0.000001555 |
| $-0.75$ | $-0.0001231$ | 0.50 | 0.000485 |
| $-0.50$ | $-0.00001753$ | 0.75 | 0.02070 |
| $-0.25$ | $-0.000000304$ | 1 | 0 |
| 0 | 0 | | |

On applying Simpson's rule to these tabular values we find

$$I_{-1}^{0} = -0.0000441,$$

$$I_0^1 = 0.006981.$$

$$\therefore \quad I = -0.0000441 + 0.006981 = 0.006937.$$

This result could be accepted with confidence if the tabular values were of the same order of magnitude, but the table shows that the integrand at $x = 0.50$ is enormously larger than it is for smaller values of $x$, and that at $x = 0.75$ it is enormously larger than at $x = 0.50$. Hence we had better examine this function more closely in the region from $x = 0.50$ to $x = 1$ and possibly make a new computation of the integral.

| $x$ | $y$ | $x$ | $y$ |
|---|---|---|---|
| 0.50 | 0.000485 | 0.80 | 0.038445 |
| 0.55 | 0.001136 | 0.82 | 0.048654 |
| 0.60 | 0.002514 | 0.84 | 0.061016 |
| 0.65 | 0.005297 | 0.86 | 0.075765 |
| 0.70 | 0.010688 | 0.88 | 0.092918 |
| 0.75 | 0.020701 | 0.90 | 0.11221 |
| 0.80 | 0.038445 | 0.92 | 0.13259 |
| | | 0.94 | 0.15149 |
| | | 0.96 | 0.16306 |
| | | 0.98 | 0.15190 |
| | | 1 | 0 |

The above table shows the variation of the integrand in the interval $0.50 \leq x \leq 1$, and Fig. 2 shows the graph for the whole interval from $x = -1$ to $x = 1$. A glance at the graph shows that in order

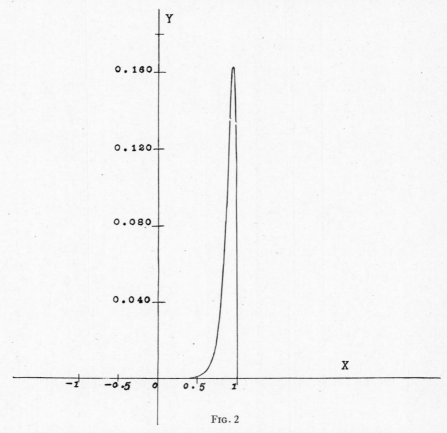

FIG. 2

to obtain a trustworthy result we should divide the computation into three distinct parts:

(1)  By taking $h = 0.25$ in the interval $-1 < x < 0.5$,
(2)  By taking $h = 0.05$ in the interval $0.5 < x < 0.8$,
(3)  By taking $h = 0.02$ in the interval $0.8 < x < 1$.

The results of these computations are

$$I_{-1}^{0.5} = -0.000035,$$

$$I_{0.5}^{0.8} = 0.002898,$$

$$I_{0.8}^{1} = 0.023548.$$

$$\therefore \quad I = -0.000035 + 0.002898 + 0.023548 = 0.0235.$$

Even when the graph of the integrand is a smooth, regular curve in the interval of integration a quadrature formula may not give a very accurate result unless the subdivisions are very small. This fact is illustrated by the following example.

*Example 2.* Find by Simpson's rule the value of

$$I = \int_{-1}^{1} \sqrt{(1 - x^2)(2 - x)} \, dx.$$

*Solution.* The values of the integrand are given in the table below.

| $x$ | $y$ | $x$ | $y$ |
|------|---------|------|----------|
| −1   | 0       | 0.1  | 1.371496 |
| −0.9 | 0.742294 | 0.2  | 1.314534 |
| −0.8 | 1.003992 | 0.3  | 1.243756 |
| −0.7 | 1.173456 | 0.4  | 1.159310 |
| −0.6 | 1.289961 | 0.5  | 1.060660 |
| −0.5 | 1.369307 | 0.6  | 0.946573 |
| −0.4 | 1.419859 | 0.7  | 0.814248 |
| −0.3 | 1.446720 | 0.8  | 0.657267 |
| −0.2 | 1.453272 | 0.9  | 0.457165 |
| −0.1 | 1.441874 | 1    | 0        |
| 0    | 1.414214 |      |          |

The correct value of the given integral to five significant figures is found from a table of elliptic integrals to be

$$I = 2.2033.$$

Simpson's rule gives the following values for different values of $h$:

(a)  $I = 2.0914$ for $h = 0.5$. Percentage error $= 5.1\%$.

(b)  $I = 2.1751$ for $h = 0.2$. Percentage error $= 1.28\%$.

(c)  $I = 2.1934$ for $h = 0.1$. Percentage error $= 0.42\%$.

It will be observed that when the interval of integration was divided into 20 subintervals the error was nearly a half of one per cent, which is less than slide-rule accuracy. Inasmuch as the tabular values are all correct to six or seven figures, the errors in the results found above are due entirely to the inherent inaccuracy of Simpson's rule. The trouble with this problem lies in the fact that the integrand cannot be approximated closely by a polynomial near the end points of the range of integration unless $h$ is taken very small in these regions. Simpson's rule would give an accurate result in this case if the computation were made in three parts, as in the previous example, and smaller values of $h$ were used for the ends of the interval of integration.

In Art. 48 several formulas will be derived for the inherent error in Simpson's rule, but occasionally a problem may arise when the exact error cannot be easily determined even with the aid of those formulas.

**45. Mechanical Cubature.** In this article we shall give two methods for finding the numerical value of a definite double integral of a function of two independent variables. The first method will be by application of a formula which may be regarded as an extension of Simpson's rule to functions of two variables. The second method is simply by repeated application of the ordinary quadrature formulas for one variable.

To derive the double quadrature formula we start with the formula for double interpolation, namely (IX) of Art. 36, and integrate this formula over two intervals in the $y$-direction and two in the $x$-direction, first omitting from the formula all terms involving the differences $\Delta^{3+0}$, $\Delta^{0+3}$, $\Delta^{4+0}$, $\Delta^{3+1}$, $\Delta^{1+3}$, $\Delta^{0+4}$, since these differences involve values of the function outside the rectangle over which we are integrating.

Since $dx = h\,du$, $dy = k\,dv$ we have, after omitting the terms just mentioned,

$$I = \int_{x_0}^{x_0+2h} \int_{y_0}^{y_0+2k} z\,dy\,dx = hk \int_0^2 \int_0^2 \left\{ z_{00} + u\Delta^{1+0}z_{00} + v\Delta^{0+1}z_{00} \right.$$

$$+ \frac{1}{2}[u(u-1)\Delta^{2+0}z_{00} + 2uv\Delta^{1+1}z_{00} + v(v-1)\Delta^{0+2}z_{00}]$$

$$+ \frac{1}{6}[3u(u-1)v\Delta^{2+1}z_{00} + 3uv(v-1)\Delta^{1+2}z_{00}]$$

$$\left. + \frac{1}{24}[6u(u-1)v(v-1)\Delta^{2+2}z_{00}] \right\} dv\,du.$$

Performing the indicated integrations and replacing the double differences by their values as given in Art. 35, we get

**(45 : 1)** $\quad I = \dfrac{hk}{9}[z_{00} + z_{02} + z_{22} + z_{20} + 4(z_{01} + z_{12} + z_{21} + z_{10}) + 16z_{11}].$

This is the formula which corresponds to Simpson's rule for a function of one variable. It can be represented diagramatically as shown in Fig. 3, the coefficients of the several $z$'s being shown on the diagram. By adding any number of unit blocks of this type we could obtain a general formula for double integration, corresponding to Simpson's rule for $n$ intervals in single integration, but it is not worth while to do this.

Formula (45: 1) can be rewritten in either of the following forms:

$$(45:2)\quad I = \frac{h}{3}\left[\frac{k}{3}(z_{00}+4z_{01}+z_{02})+4\cdot\frac{k}{3}(z_{10}+4z_{11}+z_{12})+\frac{k}{3}(z_{02}+4z_{12}+z_{22})\right],$$

$$(45:3)\quad I = \frac{h}{3}\left[\frac{k}{3}(z_{00}+4z_{10}+z_{20})+4\cdot\frac{k}{3}(z_{01}+4z_{11}+z_{21})+\frac{k}{3}(z_{02}+4z_{12}+z_{22})\right].$$

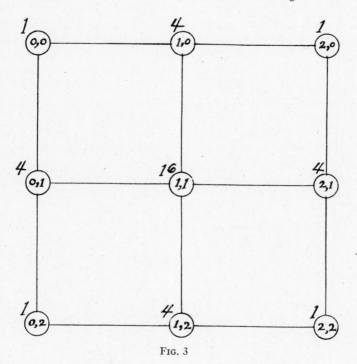

FIG. 3

Now such an expression as $(k/3)(z_{00}+4z_{10}+z_{20})$ is nothing but Simpson's rule applied to a single row in the diagram, in this case the top horizontal row. Let us put

$$A_0 = \frac{k}{3}(z_{00}+4z_{10}+z_{20}), \quad A_1 = \frac{k}{3}(z_{01}+4z_{11}+z_{21}),\ \text{etc.}$$

Then (45: 3) becomes

$$(45:4)\qquad\qquad I = \frac{h}{3}(A_0+4A_1+A_2).$$

This formula shows that formula (45: 1) is equivalent to applying Simpson's rule to each horizontal row in the diagram and then applying it again to the results thus obtained. These considerations lead to the following general statement:

*If we are given a rectangular array of values of a function of two variables, we may apply to each horizontal row or to each vertical column any quadrature formula employing equidistant ordinates, such as Simpson's and Weddle's formulas. Then to the results thus obtained for the rows (or columns) we may again apply a similar formula.*

This important result makes it unnecessary to derive general formulas for approximate double integration.

It is instructive to notice the geometric significance of this general statement. Since the double integral between constant limits of a function of two variables is represented by the volume of a solid having a rectangular base and height at any point equal to $z[=f(x, y)]$, it is evident that the integrals $A_0$, $A_1$, etc. are merely vertical cross sectional areas of this solid made by equidistant planes. Then when we apply a quadrature formula to these $A$'s, we are merely finding the volume of the solid, as if we evaluated the integral $\int_a^b A_s\, dx$.

An engineering application of mechanical cubature would be the solution of such a problem as the following:

Suppose it were necessary to determine the amount of earth to be moved in making an excavation for a large building on uneven ground, or in grading down or filling in a city block. The area to be excavated would be divided up into small rectangles by running two systems of equidistant parallel lines at right angles to each other. The distances of the corners of these rectangles above or below an assumed datum plane would be the $z$'s of this article. Knowing these $z$'s and the distances between the parallel lines (the $h$'s and $k$'s), we could find the volume of the excavation by the methods given above.

We shall now work two examples by these methods.

*Example 1.* Find by formula (45: 1) the value of the integral

$$I = \int_4^{4.4} \int_2^{2.6} \frac{dy\,dx}{xy}.$$

*Solution.* Taking $h = 0.2$ and $k = 0.3$, we compute the values of $z = 1/xy$ shown in the table below.

| $y$ \ $x$ | 4.0 | 4.2 | 4.4 |
|---|---|---|---|
| 2.0 | 0.125000 | 0.119048 | 0.113636 |
| 2.3 | 0.108696 | 0.103520 | 0.0988142 |
| 2.6 | 0.096154 | 0.0915751 | 0.0874126 |

Substituting these in (45:1), we get

$$I = \frac{0.2 \times 0.3}{9} [0.12500 + 0.096154 + 0.0874126 + 0.113636$$
$$+ 4(0.108696 + 0.0915751 + 0.0988142$$
$$+ 0.119048) + 16 \times 0.103520]$$
$$= 0.0250070.$$

The true value of the integral is

$$\int_{4}^{4.4} \int_{2}^{2.6} \frac{dy\,dy}{x\,y} = \log_e 1.1 \times \log_e 1.3$$
$$= 0.0953108 \times 0.262364$$
$$= 0.0250061.$$

The error is therefore

$$E = 0.0250061 - 0.0250070 = -0.0000009.$$

*Example 2.* Find by numerical integration the value of the integral

$$I = \int_{4}^{5.2} \int_{2}^{3.2} \frac{dy\,dx}{x\,y}.$$

*Solution.* Here we take $h = 0.2$, $k = 0.3$ as before, and compute the following table of values of $z = 1/xy$.

| y \ x | 4.0 | 4.2 | 4.4 | 4.6 | 4.8 | 5.0 | 5.2 |
|---|---|---|---|---|---|---|---|
| 2.0 | 0.125000 | 0.119048 | 0.113636 | 0.108696 | 0.104167 | 0.100000 | 0.096154 |
| 2.3 | 0.108696 | 0.103520 | 0.0988142 | 0.0945180 | 0.0905797 | 0.0869565 | 0.0836120 |
| 2.6 | 0.096154 | 0.0915751 | 0.0874126 | 0.0836120 | 0.0801282 | 0.0769231 | 0.0739645 |
| 2.9 | 0.0862069 | 0.0821018 | 0.0783699 | 0.0749625 | 0.0718391 | 0.0689655 | 0.0663130 |
| 3.2 | 0.078125 | 0.0744048 | 0.0710227 | 0.0679348 | 0.0651042 | 0.0625000 | 0.0600962 |

Applying Weddle's rule to each horizontal row, we have

$$A_0 = 0.06[0.125000 + 5(0.119048) + 0.113636 + 6(0.108696)$$
$$+ 0.104167 + 5(0.100000) + 0.096154]$$
$$= 0.131182,$$

$$A_1 = 0.114072, \quad A_2 = 0.100909, \quad A_3 = 0.090470,$$
$$A_4 = 0.081989.$$

Now applying Simpson's rule to the $A$'s, we get

$$I = 0.1[0.131182 + 4(0.114072) + 2(0.100909)$$
$$+ 4(0.090470) + 0.081989 = 0.123316.$$

The true value of this integral is

$$\int_{4}^{5.2} \int_{2}^{3.2} \frac{dy\,dx}{x\,y} = \log_e 1.3 \times \log_e 1.6 = 0.123321,$$

and the error is therefore

$$E = 0.123321 - 0.123316 = 0.000005.$$

### EXAMPLES ON CHAPTER VII

1. In the table below are given corresponding values of a variable $x$ and an unknown function $y$. For what value of $x$ is $y$ a minimum?

| $x$ | $y$ |
|-----|------|
| 3 | −205 |
| 4 | −240 |
| 5 | −259 |
| 6 | −262 |
| 7 | −250 |
| 8 | −224 |

2. For what value of $x$ is the following tabulated function a minimum?

| $x$ | $y$ |
|-----|--------|
| 0.2 | 0.9182 |
| 0.3 | 0.8975 |
| 0.4 | 0.8873 |
| 0.5 | 0.8862 |
| 0.6 | 0.8935 |
| 0.7 | 0.9086 |

3. In the year 1918 the declination of the sun at Greenwich mean noon on certain dates was as given below. Find when the declination was a maximum.

| Date | Declination |
|------|-------------|
| June 19 | 23° 25′ 23″5 |
| " 20 | " 26 19 .4 |
| " 21 | " 26 50 .5 |
| " 22 | " 26 56 .8 |
| " 23 | " 26 38 .3 |
| " 24 | " 25 55 .1 |
| " 25 | " 24 47 .1 |

4. Compute the value of

$$I = \int_0^{\pi/2} \sqrt{1 - 0.162 \sin^2 \phi}\, d\phi$$

by Simpson's one-third rule and by Weddle's rule, taking

$$\phi = 0°,\ 15°,\ 30°,\ 45°,\ 60°,\ 75°,\ 90°.$$

Compare your results with that found by the series method in Example 21, Chapter I. Also compare the amount of labor involved in each case.

5. Compute by Gauss's method the value of the integral

$$I = \int_0^{\pi/2} \frac{d\phi}{\sqrt{1 - 0.5 \sin^2 \phi}},$$

taking $n = 5$, and compare your result with the known value

$$1.8540746773.$$

6. Compute by central-difference formulas (41: 1) and (41: 3) the value of the integral

$$I = \int_{100}^{1000} \frac{dx}{\log_{10} x},$$

taking ten subintervals.

7. Find by Weddle's rule the value of the integral

$$I = \int_{0.4}^{1.6} \frac{x\,dx}{\sinh x},$$

taking twelve subintervals.

8. Find by Euler's quadrature formula the value of the integral

$$I = \int_0^{\pi/2} \cos x^2\, dx.$$

9. Find by Euler's summation formula the sum of

$$\frac{1}{400} + \frac{1}{402} + \cdots + \frac{1}{498} + \frac{1}{500}.$$

10. Find the value of the integral

$$I = \int_{30°}^{90°} \log_{10} \sin x\, dx$$

by (a) Euler's formula; (b) Gauss's formula, taking $n=5$; (c) central-difference formula (41 : 3), taking ten subintervals.

11. Compute by any method the value of the integral

$$I = \int_0^{\pi/3} \sqrt{\cos \theta} d\theta.$$

12. Compute to five decimal places the value of

$$I = \int_0^{1/2} \frac{x dx}{\cos x}.$$

# CHAPTER VIII

## THE ACCURACY OF QUADRATURE FORMULAS

**46. Introduction.** A computer should have some means of estimating the reliability of every computed result. It is not always possible to have an explicit formula giving the error committed, but usually there exists some means for ascertaining the magnitude of most unavoidable errors.

The purpose of this chapter is to determine the relative accuracy of several well-known quadrature formulas and then give explicit formulas for the error inherent in the most useful of these. We hope to show, incidentally, that Simpson's three-eighths rule is inferior to the one-third rule in every respect and is therefore not worth mentioning in any future textbooks in which approximate integration is touched upon.

**47. The Relative Accuracy of Simpson's Rules and Weddle's Rule.** In order to compare the accuracy of these three quadrature formulas we must apply each of them to the same interval and divide this interval into the same number of subintervals. The smallest number of sub-intervals to which all three formulas can be applied is six. We therefore consider an interval of width $6h$, and let $x = k$ be the mid-point of this interval. The points of subdivision, including the end points, will then be $x = k-3h,\ k-2h,\ k-h,\ k,\ k+h,\ k+2h,\ k+3h$.

Let $y = f(x)$ denote the function to be integrated. We shall assume that this function is continuous and has continuous derivatives of all orders throughout the interval $(k-3h, k+3h)$. We shall further assume that the value of $h$ is such that $f(x)$ can be represented in the given interval by a convergent power series in $h$. Such a power series is given by a Taylor expansion of the given function.

Now let $F(x)$ denote the integral of $f(x)$, so that

$$\int_k^x f(x)dx = F(x) + C.$$

Then the true value of the integral $\int_{k-3h}^{k+3h} f(x)dx$ is

$$I = \int_{k-3h}^{k+3h} f(x)dx = F(k + 3h) - F(k - 3h).$$

Expanding the functions $F(k+3h)$ and $F(k-3h)$ into a Taylor series and remembering that $F'(x) = f(x)$, $F''(x) = f'(x)$, etc., we have

$$F(k + 3h) = F(k) + 3hf(k) + \frac{9h^2}{2}f'(k) + \frac{27h^3}{6}f''(k) + \cdots$$

$$F(k - 3h) = F(k) - 3hf(k) + \frac{9h^2}{2}f'(k) - \frac{27h^3}{6}f''(k) - \cdots$$

Hence

$$(47:1) \quad I = \int_{k-3h}^{k+3h} f(x)dx = 6hf(k) + 9h^3f''(k) + \frac{81}{20}h^5f^{\mathrm{iv}}(k)$$

$$+ \frac{243}{280}h^7f^{\mathrm{vi}}(k) + \cdots .$$

The value of this integral by Simpson's one-third rule is

$$I_{1/3} = \frac{h}{3}\{f(k - 3h) + f(k + 3h) + 4[f(k - 2h) + f(k) + f(k + 2h)]$$

$$+ 2[f(k - h) + f(k + h)]\}.$$

Replacing the functions $f(k-3h)$, $f(k+3h)$, etc. by their Taylor expansions, we get

$$(47:2) \quad I_{1/3} = 6hf(k) + 9h^3f''(k) + \frac{49}{12}h^5f^{\mathrm{iv}}(k) + \frac{329}{360}h^7f^{\mathrm{vi}}(k) + \cdots .$$

Subtracting $(47:2)$ from $(47:1)$, we have

$$(47:3) \quad E_{1/3} = I - I_{1/3} = -\frac{h^5}{30}f^{\mathrm{iv}}(k) - \frac{17}{420}f^{\mathrm{vi}}(k) \cdots .$$

Simpson's three-eighths rule gives for the integral $(47:1)$

$$I_{3/8} = \frac{3h}{8}\{f(k - 3h) + f(k + 3h) + 3[f(k - 2h) + f(k + 2h)$$

$$+ f(k - h) + f(k + h)] + 2f(k)\}.$$

Replacing the several functions on the right by their Taylor expansions, we get

$$(47:4) \quad I_{3/8} = 6hf(k) + 9h^3f''(k) + \frac{33}{8}h^5f^{\mathrm{iv}}(k) + \frac{77}{80}h^7f^{\mathrm{vi}}(k) + \cdots .$$

Subtracting $(47:4)$ from $(47:1)$, we have

$$(47:5) \qquad E_{3/8} = I - I_{3/8} = -\frac{3h^5}{40}f^{iv}(k) - \frac{53}{560}h^7 f^{vi}(k) - \cdots .$$

The value of the integral $(47:1)$ by Weddle's rule is

$$I_W = \frac{3h}{10}\{f(k - 3h) + f(k + 3h) + 5[f(k - 2h) + f(k + 2h)]$$

$$+ f(k - h) + f(k + h) + 6f(k)]\} .$$

Replacing the functions on the right by their Taylor expansions as before, we get

$$(47:6) \; I_W = 6hf(k) + 9h^3 f''(k) + \frac{81}{20}h^5 f^{iv}(k) + \frac{7}{8}h^7 f^{vi}(k) + \cdots .$$

Subtracting $(47:6)$ from $(47:1)$, we find

$$(47:7) \qquad\qquad E_W = I - I_W = -\frac{h^7}{140}f^{vi}(k)$$

as the error in Weddle's rule.*

In order to compare the errors inherent in the two Simpson rules, let us write them in the forms

$$E_{1/3} = -\frac{4h^5}{120}\left[ f^{iv}(k) + \frac{51}{42}h^2 f^{vi}(k) \right],$$

$$E_{3/8} = -\frac{9h^5}{120}\left[ f^{iv}(k) + \frac{53}{42}h^2 f^{vi}(k) \right].$$

It is evident that the quantities within the brackets are nearly equal, and all the more so if $h$ is small. Hence when $h$ is sufficiently small the errors inherent in the two rules are in the ratio of the coefficients of the bracketed expressions, that is

$$\frac{E_{1/3}}{E_{3/8}} = \frac{4}{9}, \quad \text{or } E_{1/3} = \frac{4}{9}E_{3/8}.$$

The inherent error of the one-third rule is thus less than half that of the three-eighths rule.

Since the one-third rule is simpler in form, more flexible and convenient in its application, and more accurate than the three-eighths rule, there is no reason why the latter should not be relegated to the category of useless things.

* In terms of differences the error for six subintervals is
$$E_W = \frac{h}{140}\left| \Delta^6 f(x) \right| = \frac{h}{140}\left| \Delta^6 y \right| .$$

As to the inherent error in Weddle's rule, it is evident that when $h$ is such that the Taylor series converges rapidly and the principle part of the error is therefore given by the first term of the series representing the error, Weddle's rule is far more accurate than either of the Simpson rules. If, however, $h$ is so large that the error series converges very slowly or even not at all, Simpson's one-third rule may give just as accurate a result as Weddle's. In the vast majority of cases Weddle's rule is more accurate than Simpson's and should be used in problems where considerable accuracy is desired.

*Remark.* The reader should bear in mind that the comparison of the accuracy of the three quadrature formulas considered in this article is based on the assumption that the value of $h$ is such that the given function can be represented over the interval of integration by a convergent power series in $h$. If the interval $h$ is taken so large that this is not true, or if the series converges very slowly, there no longer exists any basis for an analytical comparison and there is no certainty as to what quadrature formula will give the best result.

**48. Formulas for the Error in Simpson's One-Third Rule.** The formula usually given for the error inherent in Simpson's rule is*

$$(48:1) \qquad E_{1/3} = -\frac{h^4}{180}(b-a)f^{iv}(\xi), \ a \leqq \xi \leqq b,$$

where $(a, b)$ is the interval of integration. This formula evidently applies only when the analytical form of the function $f(x)$ is known. Its usefulness is further limited by its indefinite magnitude, due to the factor $f^{iv}(\xi)$, and by the amount of labor which would sometimes be required in finding the fourth derivative of $f(x)$.

*48a). A Series Formula for the Error.* A more definite and useful formula for the error can be derived as follows:

Let $x = k$ be the mid-point of an interval of width $2h$. Then the true value of the integral $\int f(x)dx$ over this interval is

$$(48:2) \qquad I = \int_{k-h}^{k+h} f(x)dx = F(k+h) - F(k-h).$$

Expanding $F(k+h)$ and $F(k-h)$ by Taylor's theorem and remembering that $F'(x) = f(x)$, $F''(x) = f'(x)$, etc., we have

$$F(k+h) = F(k) + hf(k) + \frac{h^2}{2!}f'(k) + \frac{h^3}{3!}f''(k) + \cdots$$

$$F(h-k) = F(k) - hf(k) + \frac{h^2}{2!}f'(k) - \frac{h^3}{3!}f''(k) + \cdots .$$

---

*For an elegant derivation of this formula see Vallée-Poussin's *Cours d'Analyse Infinitesimale*, I, pp. 330–331.

Hence

$$(48\colon 3)\; I = \int_{k-h}^{k+h} f(x)dx = 2\left[ hf(k) + \frac{h^3}{3!}f''(k) + \frac{h^5}{5!}f^{iv}(k) + \cdots \right].$$

The value of this integral by Simpson's rule is

$$(48\colon 4)\qquad I_{1/3} = \frac{h}{3}[f(k-h) + 4f(k) + f(k+h)].$$

Replacing $f(k-h)$ and $f(k+h)$ by their Taylor expansions, we have

$$(48\colon 5)\qquad I_{1/3} = \frac{h}{3}\left[6f(k) + h^2 f''(k) + \frac{2h^4}{4!}f^{iv}(k) + \frac{2h^6}{6!}f^{vi}(k) + \cdots \right].$$

Subtracting (48: 5) from (48: 3), we find the error inherent in Simpson's rule to be

$$(48\colon 6)\; E = I - I_{1/3} = -\frac{h^5}{90}\left[ f^{iv}(k) + \frac{h^2}{21}f^{vi}(k) + \frac{h^4}{1008}f^{viii}(k) + \cdots \right].$$

This is the error for the two subintervals from $x = k - h$ to $x = k + h$. To get the error for the whole interval $(a, b)$, where $x_0 = a$ and $x_n = b$, we put $k = x_1, x_3, x_5, \cdots x_{n-1}$ in (48: 6) and add the results. We thus have

$$(48\colon 7)\qquad E = -\frac{h^5}{90}\Bigg\{ f^{iv}(x_1) + f^{iv}(x_3) + \cdots + f^{iv}(x_{n-1})$$

$$+ \frac{h^2}{21}[f^{vi}(x_1) + f^{vi}(x_3) + \cdots + f^{vi}(x_{n-1})]$$

$$+ \frac{h^4}{1008}[f^{viii}(x_1) + f^{viii}(x_3) + \cdots + f^{viii}(x_{n-1})] + \cdots \Bigg\}.$$

This is the fundamental formula from which more useful formulas will be derived.

*48b). A Formula in Terms of Differences.* In many applications of Simpson's rule the analytical form of the function to be integrated is either totally unknown or else is of such a nature that its fourth and higher derivatives are difficult to calculate. In either case formula (48: 7) can not be applied as it stands. We get around the difficulty by transforming it into another form.

Let us replace the derivatives $f^{iv}(x_1)$, $f^{iv}(x_3)$, $\cdots f^{viii}(x_1)$, etc. by their values in terms of differences. For this purpose we write Stirling's interpolation formula in the form

$$y = f(x) = f(k + hu) = y_k + u\frac{\Delta y_k + \Delta y_{k-h}}{2} + \frac{u^2}{2}\Delta^2 y_{k-h}$$

$$+ \frac{u(u^2 - 1^2)}{3!}\frac{\Delta^3 y_{k-h} + \Delta^3 y_{k-2h}}{2} + \cdots$$

to eighth differences.

Differentiating this formula with respect to $x$ by means of the formula $dy/dx = (dy/du)(du/dx)$ and the relation $x = k + hu$, or $u = (x - k)/h$, and then putting $u = 0$ in each derivative, we get

$$f^{iv}(k) = \frac{1}{h^4}\left(\Delta^4 y_{k-2h} - \frac{1}{6}\Delta^6 y_{k-3h} + \frac{7}{240}\Delta^8 y_{k-4h} \cdots\right),$$

$$f^{vi}(k) = \frac{1}{h^6}\left(\Delta^6 y_{k-3h} - \frac{1}{4}\Delta^8 y_{k-4h} \cdots\right),$$

$$f^{viii}(k) = \frac{1}{h^8}\left(\Delta^8 y_{k-4h} + \cdots\right).$$

Now putting $k = x_1, x_3, \cdots x_{n-1}$, writing $\Delta^4 y_{x_1-2h} = \Delta^4 y_{-1}$, etc., neglecting all eighth differences, and substituting in (48: 7) these values of the fourth and sixth derivatives, we get

$$(\textbf{48: 8}) \quad E_{1/3} = -\frac{h}{90}(\Delta^4 y_{-1} + \Delta^4 y_1 + \Delta^4 y_3 + \cdots + \Delta^4 y_{n-3})$$

$$+ \frac{h}{756}(\Delta^6 y_{-2} + \Delta^6 y_0 + \Delta^6 y_2 + \cdots + \Delta^6 y_{n-4}).$$

This expression for the error in Simpson's rule is identical with the last two terms of our central-difference quadrature formula (41: 1). That formula is therefore Simpson's rule plus its correction terms, as was stated on page 128.

*48c). A Formula in Terms of the Given Ordinates.* To get a formula for $E_{1/3}$ in terms of the given ordinates, we replace the differences in (48: 8) by their values in terms of the $y$'s as given in Art. 12, Table 3. Since in many problems the $y$'s are obtained by measurement or by computation, they are liable to be affected with small errors, and these errors are cumulative in the process of taking differences, as pointed out in Art. 13. Hence in such problems the sixth differences may consist largely of accumulated errors. For this reason we will neglect the sixth differences in formula (48: 8) and replace only the fourth differences by their values in terms of the $y$'s.

Since

$$\Delta^4 y_{-1} = y_3 - 4y_2 + 6y_1 - 4y_0 + y_{-1},$$

$$\Delta^4 y_1 = y_5 - 4y_4 + 6y_3 - 4y_2 + y_1,$$

$$\cdot \ \cdot \ \cdot \ \cdot \ \cdot \ \cdot \ \cdot \ \cdot \ \cdot \ \cdot \ \cdot \ \cdot \ \cdot \ \cdot \ \cdot \ \cdot$$

$$\Delta^4 y_{n-3} = y_{n+1} - 4y_n + 6y_{n-1} - 4y_{n-2} + y_{n-3},$$

we have, on substituting these in (48: 8),

(48: 9) $E_{1/3} = -\dfrac{h}{90}[y_{-1} + y_{n+1} - 4(y_0 + y_n) + 7(y_1 + y_{n-1})$

$$- 8(y_2 + y_4 + \cdots + y_{n-2}) + 8(y_3 + y_5 + \cdots + y_{n-3})]$$

when $n \geqq 6$.

If the number of subintervals be less than six, the formulas for $E_{1/3}$ are

(48: 10) $E_{1/3} = -\dfrac{h}{90}[y_{-1} + y_3 - 4(y_0 + y_2) + 6y_1]$, for $n = 2$.

(48: 11) $E_{1/3} = -\dfrac{h}{90}[y_{-1} + y_5 - 4(y_0 + y_4) + 7(y_1 + y_3) - 8y_2]$, for $n = 4$.

The ordinates $y_{-1}$ and $y_{n+1}$, which are outside the interval of integration, can be found in one or more ways. If the values of $y$ are computed from a formula and the formula holds outside the interval of integration, then we merely compute $y_{-1}$ and $y_{n+1}$ from this formula by substituting the proper values of $x$. But if we are given only a tabular set of $y$'s, we find $y_{-1}$ and $y_{n+1}$ by extrapolation, the former by using Newton's formula (I) and the latter by using Newton's formula (II).

*48d). Chevilliet's Formula.* The fundamental formula (48: 7) can be transformed in still another way so as to yield a very simple formula for $E_{1/3}$.

Let us go back for a moment to formula (48: 3). Putting $k = x_1$, $x_3, \cdots x_{n-1}$ in this formula, we have

$$I_1 = \int_{x_0}^{x_2} f(x)dx = 2\left[ hf(x_1) + \frac{h^3}{3!}f''(x_1) + \frac{h^5}{5!}f^{iv}(x_1) + \cdots \right],$$

$$I_2 = \int_{x_2}^{x_4} f(x)dx = 2\left[ hf(x_3) + \frac{h^3}{3!}f''(x_3) + \frac{h^5}{5!}f^{iv}(x_3) + \right],$$

$$\cdot \ \cdot \ \cdot \ \cdot \ \cdot \ \cdot \ \cdot \ \cdot \ \cdot \ \cdot \ \cdot \ \cdot \ \cdot \ \cdot \ \cdot \ \cdot \ \cdot \ \cdot$$

$$I_{n/2} = \int_{x_{n-2}}^{x_n} f(x)dx = 2\left[ hf(x_{n-1}) + \frac{h^3}{3!}f''(x_{n-1}) + \frac{h^5}{5!}f^{iv}(x_{n-1}) \right].$$

Adding these, we have

$$(48\text{:}12)\ I = \int_{x_0}^{x_n} f(x)dx = [2hf(x_1) + 2hf(x_3) + \cdots + 2hf(x_{n-1})]$$

$$+ \frac{2h^3}{3!}[f''(x_1) + f''(x_3) + \cdots + f''(x_{n-1})]$$

$$+ \frac{2h^5}{5!}[f^{iv}(x_1) + f^{iv}(x_3) + \cdots + f^{iv}(x_{n-1})] + \cdots$$

$$= R + C_1 + C_2 + \cdots,\ \text{say.}$$

The geometric interpretation of this formula is as follows: The integral $I$ represents the area under the graph of $y = f(x)$ from $x = x_0$ to $x = x_n$. The top bracketed line represents the sum of the areas of $n/2$ rectangles having altitudes $y_1, y_3, \cdots y_{n-1}$ and bases of width $2h$. The remaining terms on the right-hand side represent the error committed by replacing the area under the graph by the sum of the areas of these rectangles.

Let us now consider the geometric interpretation of our fundamental formula (48: 7), which can be written in the form

$$(48\text{:}13)\ E_{1/3} = -\frac{h^4}{180}\left\{ 2hf^{iv}(x_1) + 2hf^{iv}(x_3) + \cdots + 2hf^{iv}(x_{n-1})\right.$$

$$+ \frac{2h^3}{21}[f^{vi}(x_1) + f^{vi}(x_3) + \cdots + f^{vi}(x_{n-1})]$$

$$\left. + \frac{2h^5}{1008}[f^{viii}(x_1) + f^{viii}(x_3) + \cdots + f^{viii}(x_{n-1})] + \cdots \right\}$$

$$= -\frac{h^4}{180}\left[ R + \frac{2}{7}C_1 + \frac{5}{42}C_2 + \cdots \right].$$

This formula may be interpreted as follows: The sum $2hf^{iv}(x_1) + 2hf^{iv}(x_3) + \cdots + 2hf^{iv}(x_{n-1})$ represents the sum of the areas of $n/2$ rectangles having altitudes $y_1^{iv}, y_3^{iv}, \cdots y_{n-1}^{iv}$ and bases of width $2h$. The other terms within the braces are correction terms. The whole series within the braces therefore represents a close approximation to the area under the graph of $y = f^{iv}(x)$ from $x = x_0$ to $x = x_n$, the magnitude of the error being $(5/7)C_1 + (37/42)C_2$.

Now if $h$ is relatively small in comparison with the interval of integration $b - a$ or $x_n - x_0$, the correction terms $C_1$, $C_2$, etc. will be small. Hence in such cases the area under the graph will be closely approximated by the sum of the rectangles plus $(2/7)C_1$ etc.

The true value of the area under the graph of $y = f^{iv}(x)$ is

$$\int_a^b f^{iv}(x)dx = \left[ f'''(x) \right]_a^b = f'''(b) - f'''(a).$$

Substituting this expression for the quantity enclosed by the braces in (48:13), we get

**(48:14)**
$$E_{1/3} = -\frac{h^4}{180}[f'''(b) - f'''(a)].$$

This is Chevilliet's formula* for the error inherent in Simpson's rule. It is less accurate than any of the preceding formulas for $E_{1/3}$, but has one advantage not possessed by any of the others. That advantage will become apparent in the following paragraphs.

We notice, incidentally, that if we double the number of subintervals by decreasing $h$ to half its previous value we cut down the error to one-sixteenth of its previous value.

*48e). Formulas in Terms of Two Computed Results.* Suppose two computations of a definite integral are made by Simpson's rule, using a different value of $h$ for each computation. Let $R_1$, $h_1$, $E_1$ denote the result, the value of $h$, and the error in the first computation, and let $R_2$, $h_2$, $E_2$ denote the corresponding quantities in the second computation. Then by (48:14) we have

$$\frac{E_1}{E_2} = \frac{h_1^4}{h_2^4}, \text{ or } E_1 = \frac{h_1^4}{h_2^4}E_2.$$

Hence if $h_2 = h_1/m$, where $m$ is a positive integer, we have

$$E_1 = m^4 E_2.$$

Let $I$ denote the true value of the given integral. Then for the two computations we have

$$I = R_1 + E_1 = R_1 + m^4 E_2,$$
$$I = R_2 + E_2.$$

Subtracting the upper equation from the lower and solving for $E_2$, we get

(48:15)
$$E_2 = \frac{R_2 - R_1}{m^4 - 1}.$$

From this general formula we can get particular ones by assigning different values to $m$. Thus, for $m = 2$ we have

(48:16)
$$E_2 = \frac{R_2 - R_1}{15}.$$

This formula tells us that if we compute the value of a definite integral

* *Comptes Rendus* 78(1874), p. 1841.

by using a certain value for $h$ and then compute it again by using twice as many subdivisions, the error of the second result will be about 1/15th of the difference of the two results.

In like manner, on putting $m = 3$ we find

(48: 17)
$$E_2 = \frac{R_2 - R_1}{80}.$$

*Remarks.* The reader should bear in mind that the three formulas just derived are based on Chevilliet's formula and that they are therefore no more accurate than it is. They will give reliable results if the value of $h$ in *each* computation is small enough for Chevilliet's formula to give a reliable result for the error. Formula (48: 16), for example, fails to give the true value of the error in Example 2 of Art. 44, the reason being that the values of $h$ there used are not small enough near the ends of the interval for Chevilliet's formula to give a reliable result.

Of the several formulas derived in this article for the error in Simpson's rule the most reliable and useful is (48: 9). It gives the principal part of the error in both magnitude and sign, and it involves only the quantities used in the rule itself—with the exception of the two extreme ordinates $y_{-1}$ and $y_{n+1}$. These can usually be computed directly from the integrand when given or else by extrapolation from the tabular values.

**49. To Find the Value of $h$ for a Stipulated Degree of Accuracy in the Integral.** Suppose we should wish to know the proper value of $h$ to insure five-figure accuracy in the computed integral. Chevilliet's formula gives us a means of finding it.

If the analytic form of the function is known and the third derivative is easily calculated, substitute in (48: 14) the stipulated $E$ and the calculated values of $f'''(b)$ and $f'''(a)$; then solve for $h$.

If the form of the function is not known, or if known but the third derivative is not easily found, assume a convenient value, $h_1$, for $h$ and find the corresponding $E_1$ by means of (48: 9). Then if $E_p$ is the prescribed or stipulated error in the computed integral, we have from (48: 14)

$$\frac{E_1}{E_p} = \frac{h_1^4}{h^4},$$

from which

(49: 1)
$$h = h_1 \left(\frac{E_p}{E_1}\right)^{1/4}.$$

By means of this formula we can determine the proper value of $h$

to insure a prescribed degree of accuracy in the computed integral, provided $h_1$ and $h$ are small enough for Chevilliet's formula to give a correct result.

**50. The Error Due to Inaccurate Data.** In many problems to which Simpson's rule is applied the given values of the function are less accurate than Simpson's rule. In such cases it is useless to compute the inherent error in the rule by any of the formulas so far given in this chapter, because this would be less than the error due to the data.

To find the error due to inaccurate data we assume that each value of $y$ is affected with an error $\epsilon$. Then applying Simpson's rule to these inaccurate $y$'s, we have

$$I_{1/3} = \frac{h}{3}[\overline{y_0 + \epsilon_0} + 4(\overline{y_1 + \epsilon_1} + \overline{y_3 + \epsilon_3} + \cdots + \overline{y_{n-1} + \epsilon_{n-1}})$$

$$+ 2(\overline{y_2 + \epsilon_2} + \overline{y_4 + \epsilon_4} + \cdots + \overline{y_{n-2} + \epsilon_{n-2}}) + \overline{y_n + \epsilon_n}]$$

$$= \frac{h}{3}[y_0 + 4(y_1 + y_3 + \cdots + y_{n-1}) + 2(y_2 + y_4 + \cdots y_{n-2}) + y_n]$$

$$+ \frac{h}{3}[\epsilon_0 + 4(\epsilon_1 + \epsilon_3 + \cdots + \epsilon_{n-1}) + 2(\epsilon_2 + \epsilon_4 + \cdots + \epsilon_{n-2}) + \epsilon_n)].$$

Hence the error due to the inaccuracy of the data is

$$(50:1) \quad E_D = \frac{h}{3}[\epsilon_0 + 4(\epsilon_1 + \epsilon_3 + \cdots \epsilon_{n-1}) + 2(\epsilon_2 + \epsilon_4 + \cdots + \epsilon_{n-2}) + \epsilon_n].$$

If all these $\epsilon$'s should be of the same magnitude and sign, the maximum possible error due to the inaccurate $y$'s would be

$$(E_D)_{max} = \frac{h}{3}\left[1 + 4\left(\frac{n}{2}\right) + 2\frac{(n-2)}{2}\right]\epsilon$$

$$= \frac{h}{3}(3n\epsilon) = hn\epsilon = (b-a)\epsilon,$$

or

$$(50:2) \qquad\qquad (E_D)_{max} = (b-a)\epsilon.$$

Such a result, however, would probably never occur, since the $\epsilon$'s would not be all of the same sign, but would, on the contrary, be of different signs and largely neutralize one another.

We shall now apply formulas (48:9) and (48:14) to the first example worked in Art. 40.

*Example.* Compute by means of (48:9) and (48:14) the error in the evaluation of $\int_4^{5.2} \log_e x\, dx$ by Simpson's rule.

*Solution.* We must first compute $y_{-1}$ and $y_{n+1}$ from the given function $y = \log_e x$. For these we have

$$y_{-1} = \log_e 3.8 = 1.33500107,$$

$$y_{n+1} = \log_e 5.4 = 1.68639895.$$

The values of $y$ from $y_0$ to $y_n$ inclusive are given in the table on page 121. Substituting these $y$'s in (48: 9), we get

$$E_{1/3} = -\frac{0.2}{90}[3.02140002 - 4(3.03495299)$$

$$+ 7(3.04452244) - 8(3.05022046)$$

$$+ 8(1.52605630)]$$

$$= 0.00000015.$$

The true error was found in Art. 40 to be 0.00000018.

To compute the error by Chevilliet's formula we first find $f'''(x)$ from the equation $f(x) = \log_e x$. We thus have

$$f'''(x) = \frac{2}{x^3}.$$

Hence

$$f'''(5.2) = \frac{2}{(5.2)^3} = 0.0142239,$$

$$f'''(4.0) = \frac{1}{4^3} = \frac{1}{64} = 0.0156250,$$

and therefore

$$E_{1/3} = -\frac{(0.2)^4}{180}(0.0142239 - 0.0156250)$$

$$= 0.00000001.$$

This error is much too small, and the reason is that the value of $h$ in this problem is too large for Chevilliet's formula to give a reliable result for the error.

Suppose we wished to know the value of $h$ necessary to give the integral correct to ten decimal places. Since we have already found the error corresponding to a particular value of $h$, we can find the desired value by substituting in formula (49: 1). Here

$$h_1 = 0.2, \ E_1 = 0.00000015, \ E_p < 0.00000000005.$$

Hence we have

$$h < 0.2 \left( \frac{0.00000000005}{0.00000015} \right)^{1/4} = \underline{0.027}.$$

Since $b - a = nh$, we find that we should have to divide the interval $(4, 5.2)$ into more than 45 subintervals in order to get a result correct to ten decimal places.

**51. The Remainder Terms in Central-Difference Formulas (41:1) and (41: 3).** The remainder terms in these formulas can be found by integrating the remainder terms in Stirling's and Bessel's interpolation formulas from which (41: 1) and (41: 3) were derived. Since (41: 1) is at least as accurate as (41: 3), and since a more definite formula can be derived for the remainder term in the latter than in the former, we shall derive the remainder term for (41: 3) only and use it for computing the error in both formulas. In Art. 30 we found the remainder term in Bessel's formula (VI) to be

$$R_n = \frac{h^{2n+2} f^{(2n+2)}(\xi)}{(2n+2)!} \left( v^2 - \frac{1}{4} \right)\left( v^2 - \frac{9}{4} \right) \cdots \left( v^2 - \frac{(2n+1)^2}{4} \right).$$

Since $f(x)dx$ is the quantity that is integrated by a quadrature formula, it is plain that $R_n(x)dx$ is the quantity which must be integrated to find the inherent error in the quadrature; and since $dx = hdv$, we have for the error in a single subinterval of width $h$

$$(51:1) \quad E = \int_{x_0}^{x_0+h} R_n(x)dx = h \int_{-1/2}^{1/2} \frac{h^{2n+2} f^{(2n+2)}(\xi)}{(2n+2)!} \left( v^2 - \frac{1}{4} \right)\left( v^2 - \frac{9}{4} \right)$$

$$\cdots \left( v^2 - \frac{(2n+1)^2}{4} \right) dv = \frac{2 h^{2n+3} f^{(2n+2)}(\xi)}{(2n+2)!}$$

$$\times \int_{0}^{1/2} \left( v^2 - \frac{1}{4} \right)\left( v^2 - \frac{9}{4} \right) \cdots \left( v^2 - \frac{(2n+1)^2}{4} \right) dv.$$

Let us put

$$(51:2) \quad V_n = \int_{0}^{1/2} \left( v^2 - \frac{1}{4} \right)\left( v^2 - \frac{9}{4} \right) \cdots \left( v^2 - \frac{(2n+1)^2}{4} \right) dv.$$

Then

$$E = \frac{2 h^{2n+3} f^{(2n+2)}(\xi)}{(2n+2)!} \left| V_n \right|.$$

This is the error for a single subinterval of width $h$. Let $M_n$ denote the maximum value of $f^{(2n+2)}(x)$ in the interval $(a, b)$. Then since there are $(b-a)/h$ subintervals from $x=a$ to $x=b$, we have for the total error in the interval $(a, b)$

$$(51:3) \qquad E \leqq \frac{2h^{2n+2}M_n}{(2n+2)!}(b-a)\,|\,V_n\,| \ .$$

From this general formula we get particular ones by assigning values to $n$. Thus, if we include fourth differences in (41:2) and neglect all higher differences, we put $n=2$. Then (51:2) becomes

$$V_2 = \int_0^{1/2} \left(v^2 - \frac{1}{4}\right)\left(v^2 - \frac{9}{4}\right)\left(v^2 - \frac{25}{4}\right)dv = -\frac{191}{168},$$

and therefore (51:3) becomes

$$E \leqq \frac{191h^6M_2}{60480}(b-a);$$

or, more simply,

$$(51:4) \qquad E_a{}^b < \frac{h^6M_2}{316}(b-a).$$

In terms of differences this becomes

$$(51:5) \qquad E_a{}^b < \frac{|\,\Delta^6 y\,|}{316}(b-a),$$

where $\Delta^6 y$ is the largest of the sixth differences.

If we include sixth differences in (41:2) and neglect all higher differences, then $n=3$ and (51:2) becomes

$$V_3 = \int_0^{1/2} (v^2 - \frac{1}{4})(v^2 - \frac{9}{4})(v^2 - \frac{25}{4})(v^2 - \frac{49}{4})dv = \frac{2497}{180}.$$

On substituting these in (51:3) we find

$$E_a{}^b \leqq \frac{2497h^8M_3}{3628800}(b-c$$

or

$$(51:6) \qquad E_a{}^b < \frac{h^8M_3}{1453}(b-a).$$

In terms of differences this becomes

$$(51:7) \qquad E_a{}^b < \frac{|\,\Delta^8 y\,|}{1453}(b-a),$$

where $\Delta^8 y$ is the largest of the eighth differences in the interval $(a, b)$.

When we stop with fourth differences in formula (41: 1) or with third differences in (41: 3), the error is to be computed by (51: 5); and when we stop with sixth differences in (41: 1) or with fifth differences in (41: 3), the error is to be computed by (51 :7).

**52. Expressions for the Error in Gauss's Formula.** Gauss's quadrature formula has been studied exhaustively by several eminent mathematicians, and many expressions have been derived for the error inherent in it. The majority of these expressions, however, are of little value from a practical standpoint. The following two are the most useful:

1. If $f(x)$ does not change sign in the interval of integration $(a, b)$, the inherent error is*

$$(52:1)\quad E_G = \frac{(b-a)^{2n+1}}{2n+1}\left[\frac{n!}{(n+1)(n+2)\cdots 2n}\right]^2 \frac{f^{(2n)}(\xi)}{(2n)!},$$

where $\xi$ is some value of $x$ between $a$ and $b$.

2. If $\phi(u)$ (see Art. 42) can be expanded into a convergent power series, the principal part of the inherent error in Gauss's formula is given by the expression †

$$(52:2)\ E_G = \frac{(b-a)}{(2n+1)2^{2n}}\left\{\frac{n!}{1\cdot 3\cdot 5\cdots(2n-1)}\right\}^2$$

$$\times\left\{L_{2n} + \frac{L_{2n+2}}{8}\left(\frac{(n+1)(n+2)}{2n+3} + \frac{n(n-1)}{2n-1}\right)\right\},$$

where the $L$'s are the coefficients in the power series

$$(52:3)\quad \phi(u+\tfrac{1}{2}) = L_0 + L_1 u + L_2 u^2 + \cdots + L_{2n}u^{2n} + \cdots.$$

Even these two formulas have their drawbacks, for the first requires that we find the $(2n)$th derivative of the given function and is further impaired by the indefinite factor $f^{(2n)}(\xi)$. The second formula is definite as far as it goes, but it requires us to expand $\phi(u+\tfrac{1}{2})$ into a power series —an easy matter in some examples, but practically impossible in others. When the series converges rapidly, the term involving $L_{2n+2}$ in (52: 2) may be omitted. Neither of these formulas applies when the analytic form of the function is unknown.

* *Encyklopädie der Mathematischen Wissenschaften*, II. 3.1, p. 68.
† Derived in Todhunter's *Functions of Laplace, Lamé, and Bessel*, p. 108.

We shall illustrate the use of these formulas by applying them to the simple example worked in Art. 42.

*Example.* Taking $n = 5$, find the error in the evaluation of

$$I = \int_5^{12} \frac{dx}{x}$$

by Gauss's formula.

*Solution.* (a). The $(2n)$th derivative of $f(x) = 1/x$ is $f^{(10)}(x) = 10!/x^{11}$. Then since $b - a = 7$ and $n = 5$ we have from (52: 1)

$$E_G = \frac{7^{11}}{11} \left[ \frac{5!}{6 \cdot 7 \cdot 8 \cdot 9 \cdot 10} \right]^2 \frac{\dfrac{10!}{\xi^{11}}}{10!} = \frac{7^{11}}{11} \left[ \frac{5!}{6 \cdot 7 \cdot 8 \cdot 9 \cdot 10} \right]^2 \frac{1}{\xi^{11}} .$$

The value of $\xi$ is somewhere between 5 and 12. On substituting these extreme values of $\xi$ in this expression for $E_G$ we find that the error lies between 0.000058 and 0.0000000038. These limits are far apart and the actual error is thus very indefinite. The true error was found in Art. 42 to be 0.00000028.

(b). We shall next estimate the error by formula (52:2). In Art. 42 we found that $\phi(u) = 1/(5 + 7u)$. Hence

$$\phi\left(u + \frac{1}{2}\right) = \frac{1}{5 + 7(u + 0.5)} = \frac{1}{8.5 + 7u} = \frac{2}{17}\left(1 + \frac{14}{17}u\right)^{-1}$$

$$= \frac{2}{17}\left[1 - \frac{14}{17}u + \left(\frac{14}{17}u\right)^2 - \cdots + \left(\frac{14}{17}u\right)^{10} - \left(\frac{14}{17}u\right)^{11} \right.$$

$$\left. + \left(\frac{14}{17}u\right)^{12} - \cdots \right].$$

From this series we see that

$$L_{2n} = \frac{2}{17}\left(\frac{14}{17}\right)^{10} \text{ and } L_{2n+2} = \frac{2}{17}\left(\frac{14}{17}\right)^{12} .$$

Substituting these in (52: 2), we get

$$E_G = \frac{2}{17} \times \frac{7}{11 \times 2^{10}} \left\{ \frac{5!}{1 \cdot 3 \cdot 5 \cdot 7 \cdot 9} \right\}^2 \left\{ \left(\frac{14}{17}\right)^{10} + \frac{1}{8}\left(\frac{14}{17}\right)^{12}\left(\frac{42}{13} + \frac{20}{9}\right) \right\}$$

$$= 0.00000017 + 0.00000008 = 0.00000025.$$

This result agrees well with the actual error 0.00000028 found in Art. 42. It will be found in practice that formula (52: 2) is far superior to (52: 1).

**53. The Remainder Term in Euler's Formula.** Malmsten's expression for the remainder after $n$ terms in Euler's formula of summation and quadrature is

(53: 1)                    $R_n = A_{2n}h^{2n+1}f^{(2n)}(a + \theta h),\ 0 < \theta < 1,$

for a single subinterval of width $h$.

Let $M$ denote the numerically greatest value of $f^{(2n)}(x)$ in the whole interval $(a, b)$. Then for the $n$ subintervals we have

(53: 2)                    $R_n \leqq nA_{2n}h^{2n+1}M,$

or, since $n = (b-a)/h,$

**(53: 3)**                    $R_n \leqq A_{2n}h^{2n}M(b - a).$

Here $A_{2n}$ has the following values:

$$A_2 = -\frac{1}{12}, \quad A_4 = +\frac{1}{720}, \quad A_6 = -\frac{1}{30240}, \quad A_8 = +\frac{1}{1209600},$$

$$A_{10} = -\frac{1}{47900160}.$$

More useful, perhaps, than formula (53: 3) is the following working rule due to Charlier:*

*In stopping with any term in Euler's formula the error committed is less than twice the first neglected term.*

Hence we get the most accurate result by stopping with the term just before the smallest, so that the first neglected term is the smallest of all.

We shall now show that the first two terms of Euler's formula will give a more accurate result than Simpson's rule.

Putting $n = 2$ in formula (53: 3), we have

$$R_2 \leqq A_4 h^4 M(b - a) = \frac{h^4 M}{720}(b - a),$$

where $M$ denotes the greatest numerical value of $f^{iv}(x)$ in the interval $(a, b)$.

The remainder term in Simpson's rule is (Art. 48)

$$E_{1/3} = \frac{h^4 M}{180}(b - a).$$

Hence the inherent error in Euler's formula for only two terms is just one fourth that in Simpson's rule.

* *Mechanik des Himmels*, II, pp. 13–16.

## EXAMPLES ON CHAPTER VIII

1. Estimate the inherent errors in your answers to Example 4 of Chapter VII and compare these errors with that found in Example 21 of Chapter I.

2. Compute the inherent error in your answer to Example 6 of Chapter VII.

3. Estimate the accuracy of your answer to Example 8, Ch. VII.

# CHAPTER IX

## THE SOLUTION OF NUMERICAL ALGEBRAIC AND TRANSCENDENTAL EQUATIONS

### I. EQUATIONS IN ONE UNKNOWN

**54. Introduction.** It is shown in algebra how to solve literal equations of all degrees up to and including the fourth; and it is also shown how to compute by Horner's method the roots of numerical equations of any degree. Algebra is silent, however, on the solution of such types of equations as $ax + b \log x = c$, $ae^{-x} + b \tan x = 5$, etc. These are *transcendental equations*, and no general method exists for finding their roots in terms of their coefficients. When the coefficients of such equations are pure numbers, however, it is always possible to compute the roots to any desired degree of accuracy.

The object of the present chapter is to set forth the most useful methods for finding the roots of any equation having numerical coefficients. Since Horner's method is explained in all college algebras, and since it can not be applied to transcendental equations, we shall not consider it here.

**55. Finding Approximate Values of the Roots.** In finding the real roots of a numerical equation by any method except that of Graeffe, it is necessary first to find an approximate value of the root from a graph or otherwise. Let

$$(55:1) \qquad\qquad f(x) = 0$$

denote the equation whose roots are to be found. Then if we take a set of rectangular coordinate axes and plot the graph of

$$(55:2) \qquad\qquad y = f(x),$$

it is evident that the abscissas of the points where the graph crosses the $x$-axis are the real roots of the given equation, for at these points $y$ is zero and therefore (55:1) is satisfied. Approximate values for the real roots of any numerical equation can therefore be found from the graph of the given equation. It is not necessary, however, to draw the complete graph. Only the portions in the neighborhood of the points where it crosses the $x$-axis are needed.

Even more useful and important than a graph is the following fundamental theorem:

*If $f(x)$ is continuous from $x = a$ to $x = b$ and if $f(a)$ and $f(b)$ have opposite signs, then there is at least one real root between $a$ and $b$.*

This theorem is evident from an inspection of Fig. 4, for if $f(a)$ and $f(b)$ have opposite signs the graph must cross the $x$-axis at least once between $x = a$ and $x = b$.

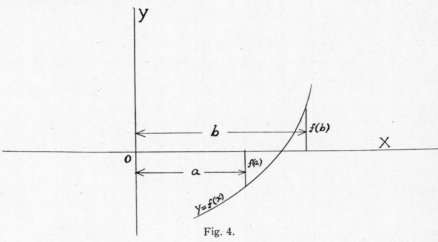

Fig. 4.

When $f(x)$ is the sum of two or more functions, it is usually better to write $f(x) = 0$ in the form

(55: 3)                      $f_1(x) = f_2(x)$

and then plot on the same axes the two equations

$$y_1 = f_1(x), \quad y_2 = f_2(x).$$

The abscissas of the points of intersection of these two curves are the real roots of the given equation, for at these points $y_1 = y_2$ and therefore $f_1(x) = f_2(x)$.   Hence (55: 3) is satisfied and consequently $f(x) = 0$ is likewise satisfied.

We shall now apply the foregoing methods to two examples.

*Example 1.*  Find approximate values for the real roots of

$$x \log_{10} x = 1.2.$$

*Solution.*  Writing the equation in the form $f(x) = x \log_{10} x - 1.2$, we first compute a set of corresponding values of $x$ and $f(x)$, as given below. Since the logarithms of negative numbers are imaginary, it is evident that only positive values of $x$ can be assigned.

| $x$ | $f(x)$ | $x$ | $f(x)$ |
|---|---|---|---|
| 0 | $-1.2$ | 1.0 | $-1.2$ |
| 0.2 | $-1.34$ | 2 | $-0.6$ |
| 0.4 | $-1.36$ | 3 | $+0.23$ |
| 0.6 | $-1.33$ | 4 | $+1.21$ |
| 0.8 | $-1.28$ | | |

Since $f(2)$ and $f(3)$ have opposite signs, a root lies between 2 and 3, and this is the only real root. There is no need of drawing the graph in this example.

*Example 2.* Find the approximate value of the root of

$$3x - \cos x - 1 = 0.$$

*Solution.* Since this equation is the difference of two functions we can write it in the form

$$3x - 1 = \cos x.$$

Then we plot separately on the same set of axes the two equations

$$y_1 = 3x - 1,$$
$$y_2 = \cos x.$$

The abscissa of the point of intersection of the graphs of these equations is seen to be about 0.61 (Fig. 5).

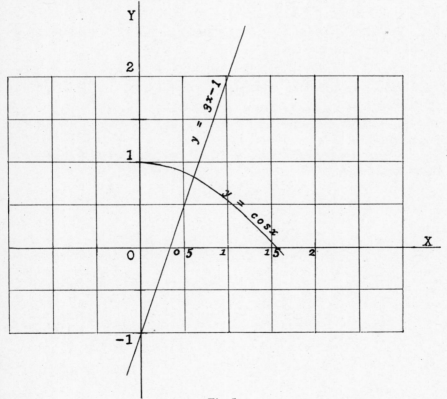

Fig. 5.

Of course we could also find this approximate value by computing a table of values of the function $f(x) = 3x - \cos x - 1$ and noting the change in sign of $f(x)$, as in Ex. 1.

**56. The Method of False Position (Regula Falsi).** The oldest method for computing the real roots of a numerical equation is the method of false position, or "regula falsi." In this method we find two numbers $x_1$ and $x_2$ between which the root lies. These numbers should be as close together as possible. Since the root lies between $x_1$ and $x_2$ the graph of $y = f(x)$ must cross the $x$-axis between $x = x_1$ and $x = x_2$, and $y_1$ and $y_2$ must have opposite signs.

Now since any portion of a smooth curve is practically straight for a short distance, it is legitimate to assume that the change in $f(x)$ is proportional to the change in $x$ over a short interval, as in the case of linear interpolation from logarithmic and trigonometric tables. The method of false position is based on this principle, for it assumes that the graph of $y = f(x)$ is a straight line between the points $(x_1, y_1)$ and $(x_2, y_2)$, these points being on opposite sides of the $x$-axis.

To derive a formula for computing the root let Fig. 6 represent a

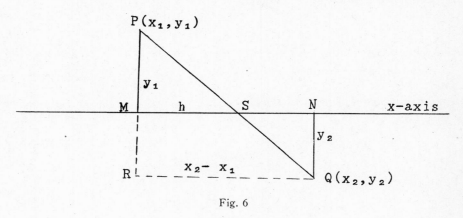

Fig. 6

magnified view of that part of the graph between $(x_1, y_1)$ and $(x_2, y_2)$. Then from the similar triangles $PMS$ and $PRQ$ we have

$$\frac{MS}{MP} = \frac{RQ}{RP}, \quad \text{or} \quad \frac{h}{|y_1|} = \frac{x_2 - x_1}{|y_1| + |y_2|}.$$

(56:1) $$\therefore \quad h = \frac{(x_2 - x_1)\,|y_1|}{|y_1| + |y_2|}.$$

The value of the desired root, under the assumptions made, is

$$x = x_1 + MS = x_1 + h.$$

Hence

(56: 2)
$$x = x_1 + \frac{(x_2 - x_1)\,|\,y_1\,|}{|\,y_1\,| + |\,y_2\,|}.$$

This value of $x$ is not, however, the true value of the root, because the graph of $y = f(x)$ is not a perfectly straight line between the points $P$ and $Q$. It is merely a closer approximation to the true root.

In the practical application of the regula falsi method we compute a short table of corresponding values of $x$ and $f(x)$ for equidistant values of $x$—units, tenths, hundredths, etc. Then by means of (56: 1) we compute corrections to be applied to the previously obtained approximate values. The following examples should make the method clear.

*Example 1.* Compute the real root of

$$x \log_{10} x - 1.2 = 0$$

correct to five decimal places.

*Solution.* The short table in Example 1 of the preceding article shows that the root lies between 2 and 3, and that it is nearer 3. Hence we make out the following table and then compute the corrections by (56: 1).

| | $x$ | $y$ | |
|---|---|---|---|
| 1st | 2 | $-0.6$ | $h_1 = \dfrac{1 \times 0.6}{0.83} = 0.72.$ |
| approx. | 3 | $+0.23$ | |
| Diff. | 1 | 0.83 | $x^{(1)} = 2 + 0.72 = 2.72.$ |

| | | | |
|---|---|---|---|
| 2nd | 2.7 | $-0.04$ | $h_2 = \dfrac{0.1 \times 0.04}{0.09} = 0.044.$ |
| approx. | 2.8 | $+0.05$ | |
| | 0.1 | 0.09 | $x^{(2)} = 2.74.$ |

| | | | |
|---|---|---|---|
| 3rd | 2.74 | $-0.0006$ | $h_3 = \dfrac{0.01 \times 0.0006}{0.0087} = 0.0007.$ |
| approx. | 2.75 | $+0.0081$ | |
| | 0.01 | 0.0087 | $x^{(3)} = 2.74 + 0.0007 = 2.7407.$ |

|          | 2.7406 | −0.000039 | $h_4 = \dfrac{0.0001 \times 0.000039}{0.000084}$ |
|----------|--------|-----------|--------------------------------------------------|

4th
approx.

2.7407   +0.000045

0.0001   0.000084

$= 0.000046.$

$x^{(4)} = 2.7406 + 0.000046$

$= 2.74065.$

*Remark.* In examples of this kind it is necessary to use logarithms to more decimal places with each succeeding approximation. In this example six-place logarithms were used in the last approximation.

*Example 2.* Find the real root of the equation

$$3x - \cos x - 1 = 0.$$

*Solution.* In Ex. 2 of the preceding article we found the approximate value of this root to be 0.61. Hence we begin by computing the following short table of corresponding values of $x$ and $f(x) = 3x - \cos x - 1 = y$.

It is evident from the table that the root lies between 0.60 and 0.61. Hence we proceed with the first approximation by the regula falsi method.

| $x$  | $f(x)$  |
|------|---------|
| 0.60 | −0.025  |
| 0.61 | +0.010  |
| 0.62 | +0.046  |

|                  | $x$   | $y$      |                                                        |
|------------------|-------|----------|--------------------------------------------------------|
|                  | 0.60  | −0.025   |                                                        |
| 1st              | 0.61  | +0.010   | $h_1 = \dfrac{0.01 \times 0.025}{0.035} = 0.0071.$     |
| approx.<br>Diff. | 0.01  | 0.035    | $x^{(1)} = 0.60 + 0.0071 = 0.607.$                     |

|                  | 0.607 | −0.00036 |                                                        |
|------------------|-------|----------|--------------------------------------------------------|
| 2nd              | 0.608 | +0.00321 | $h_2 = \dfrac{0.001 \times 0.00036}{0.00357}$          |
| approx.          | 0.001 | 0.00357  | $= 0.000101.$                                          |
|                  |       |          | $x^{(2)} = 0.6071.$                                     |

|                  | 0.6071 | 0.00000  |                            |
|------------------|--------|----------|----------------------------|
| 3rd              | 0.6072 | 0.00035  | $h_3 = 0.$                 |
| approx.          | 0.0001 | 0.00035  | $x^{(3)} = 0.60710.$       |

**57. Solution by Repeated Plotting on a Larger Scale.** The following method is the graphical equivalent of the regula falsi method and has the advantage of giving a visual representation of the approximating process.

Suppose an approximate value of the root has been found from a graph or otherwise. Plot on a large scale a small part of the graph of $y = f(x)$ for values of $x$ near the desired root, so that one can see more clearly about where the graph crosses the $x$-axis. An additional figure of the root can be read from this graph. Then plot on a still larger scale a small part of the graph for values of $x$ near the improved value of the root (the value just found), and continue the process in this manner until the root has been found to as many figures as desired. The following example should make the method clear.

*Example.* Find the positive real root of

$$x - \cos\left(\frac{0.7854 - x\sqrt{1 - x^2}}{1 - 2x^2}\right) = 0.$$

*Solution.* We first compute the value of the left member for several values of $x$, as given in table (1). This table shows that a root lies between 0.5 and 0.6. Hence we plot the graph of the given equation from $x = 0.5$ to $x = 0.6$ and assume it to be a straight line within this interval. The result is Fig. 7 (a), and it shows at a glance that the root is about 0.56 or 0.57. We therefore compute table (2) and plot the results as

|     | $x$  | $f(x)$  |     | $x$    | $f(x)$   |
|-----|------|---------|-----|--------|----------|
| (1) | 0.4  | $-0.42$ | (3) | 0.579  | $-0.001$ |
|     | 0.5  | $-0.26$ |     | 0.580  | $+0.003$ |
|     | 0.6  | $+0.14$ |     |        |          |
| (2) | 0.56 | $-0.092$| (4) | 0.5793 | $-0.0005$|
|     | 0.57 | $-0.030$|     | 0.5794 | $+0.0003$|
|     | 0.58 | $+0.003$|     |        |          |

shown in Fig. 7 (b). This graph shows that the root is about 0.579. Continuing the process in this manner by computing tables (3) and (4) and plotting the results on still larger scales as shown in Figs. 7 (c) and 7 (d), we find the desired root to be $x = 0.57936$ to five figures.

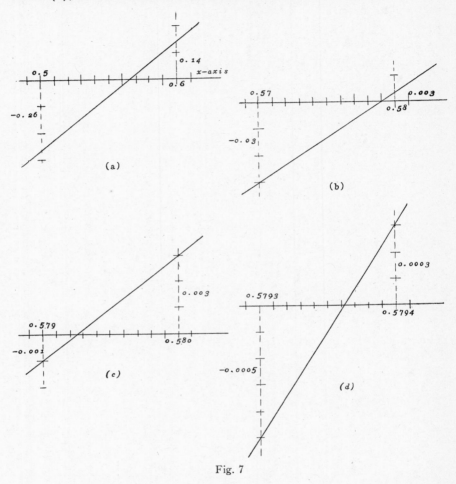

Fig. 7

This method and the regula falsi method are particularly valuable for finding the roots of complicated equations such as the one solved above.

**58. The Newton-Raphson Method.** When the derivative of $f(x)$ is a simple expression and easily found, the real roots of $f(x) = 0$ can be computed rapidly by a process called the Newton-Raphson method. The underlying idea of the method is due to Newton, but the method as now used is due to Raphson.*

* See Cajori's *History of Mathematics*, p. 203.

To derive a formula for computing real roots by this method let $a$ denote an approximate value of the desired root, and let $h$ denote the correction which must be applied to $a$ to give the exact value of the root, so that

$$x = a + h.$$

The equation $f(x) = 0$ then becomes

$$f(a + h) = 0.$$

Expanding this by Taylor's theorem, we have

$$f(a + h) = f(a) + hf'(a) + \frac{h^2}{2}f''(a + \theta h), \ 0 \leqq \theta \leqq 1.$$

Hence

$$f(a) + hf'(a) + \frac{h^2}{2}f''(a + \theta h) = 0.$$

Now if $h$ is relatively small, we may neglect the term containing $h^2$ and get the simple relation

$$f(a) + hf'(a) = 0,$$

from which

**(58: 1)**
$$h_1 = -\frac{f(a)}{f'(a)}.$$

The improved value of the root is then

**(58: 2)**
$$a_1 = a + h_1 = a - \frac{f(a)}{f'(a)}.$$

The succeeding approximations are

$$a_2 = a_1 + h_2 = a_1 - \frac{f(a_1)}{f'(a_1)}, \quad a_3 = a_2 - \frac{f(a_2)}{f'(a_2)},$$

$$\cdots a_n = a_{n-1} - \frac{f(a_{n-1})}{f'(a_{n-1})}.$$

Equation (58: 1) is the fundamental formula in the Newton-Raphson process. It is evident from this formula that the larger the derivative $f'(x)$ the smaller is the correction which must be applied to get the correct value of the root. This means that when the graph is nearly vertical where it crosses the $x$-axis the correct value of the root can be found with great rapidity and very little labor. If, on the other hand, the numerical value of the derivative $f'(x)$ should be small in the neighborhood of the root, the values of $h$ given by (58: 1) would be large and the computation of the root by this method would be a slow process or might even fail altogether. The Newton-Raphson method should never be used when the graph of $f(x)$ is nearly horizontal where it crosses the $x$-axis. The process will evidently fail if $f'(x) = 0$ in the neighborhood of the root. In such cases the regula falsi method should be used.

We shall now apply the Newton-Raphson method to two examples.

*Example 1.* Compute to four decimal places the real root of

$$x^2 + 4 \sin x = 0.$$

*Solution.* Since the term $x^2$ is positive for all real values of $x$, it is evident that the equation will be satisfied only by a negative value of $x$. We find from a graph that an approximate value of the root is $-1.9$. Since $f(x) = x^2 + 4 \sin x$ and $f'(x) = 2x + 4 \cos x$, we have from (58: 1)

$$h_1 = -\frac{(-1.9)^2 + 4 \sin(-1.9)}{2(-1.9) + 4 \cos(-1.9)} = -\frac{3.61 - 3.78}{-3.8 - 1.293}$$

$$= -0.03.$$

$$\therefore \quad a_1 = -1.9 - 0.03 = -1.93.$$

$$h_2 = -\frac{(-1.93)^2 + 4 \sin(-1.93)}{2(-1.93) + 4 \cos(-1.93)} = -\frac{-0.0198}{-5.266}$$

$$= -0.0038.$$

$$\therefore \quad a_2 = -1.9338.$$

This result is correct to its last figure, as will be shown later.

*Example 2.* Find by the Newton-Raphson method the real root of

$$3x - \cos x - 1 = 0.$$

*Solution.* Here

$$f(x) = 3x - \cos x - 1,$$

$$f'(x) = 3 + \sin x.$$

We found graphically (Fig. 5) that the approximate value of the root is 0.61. Hence

$$h_1 = -\frac{3(0.61) - \cos(0.61) - 1}{3 + \sin(0.61)} = -\frac{0.010}{3.57}$$

$$= -0.00290.$$

$$\therefore \quad a_1 = 0.61 - 0.0029 = 0.6071.$$

$$h_2 = -\frac{3(0.6071) - \cos(0.6071) - 1}{3 + \sin(0.6071)}$$

$$= 0.00000381.$$

$$\therefore \quad a_2 = 0.60710381.$$

This result also is true to its last figure.

It will be observed that the root was obtained to a higher degree of accuracy and with less labor by this method than by the regula falsi method.

**59. Geometric Significance of the Newton-Raphson Method.**  The regula falsi method assumes that the graph of the given function is replaced by the chord joining $(x_1, y_1)$ and $(x_2, y_2)$.  No such geometric assumption was made in deriving the formula for computing the roots by the Newton-Raphson method, but the formula has a simple geometric significance nevertheless.

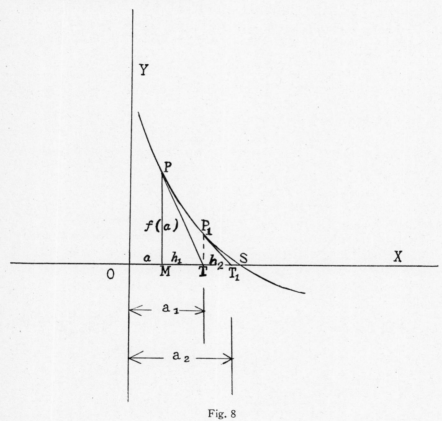

Fig. 8

Let Fig. 8 represent a magnified view of the graph of $y = f(x)$ where it crosses the $x$-axis.  Suppose we draw a tangent from the point $P$ whose abscissa is $a$.  This tangent will intersect the $x$-axis in some point $T$.  Then let us draw another tangent from $P_1$ whose abscissa is $OT$. This tangent will meet the $x$-axis in some point $T_1$ between $T$ and $S$. Then we may draw a third tangent from $P_2$ whose abscissa is $OT_1$, this tangent cutting the $x$-axis at a point $T_2$ between $T_1$ and $S$, and so on. It is evident intuitionally that if the curvature of the graph does not change sign between $P$ and $S$ the points $T$, $T_1$, $T_2$, $\cdots$ will approach the point $S$ as a limit; that is, the intercepts $OT$, $OT_1$, $OT_2$, $\cdots$ will approach the intercept $OS$ as a limit. But $OS$ represents the real root of the equation whose graph is drawn. Hence the quantities $OT$, $OT_1$, $OT_2$, $\cdots$ are successive approximations to the desired root.* This is the geometric significance of the Newton-Raphson process.

To derive the fundamental formula from this figure let $MT = h_1$, $TT_1 = h_2$, etc. The slope of the graph at $P$ is $f'(a)$. But from the figure we have

$$PM = f(a), \text{ and slope at } P = \tan \angle XTP = -\frac{f(a)}{h_1}.$$

Hence

$$f'(a) = -\frac{f(a)}{h_1}, \text{ or } h_1 = -\frac{f(a)}{f'(a)},$$

which is the fundamental formula of the Newton-Raphson method. From the triangle $P_1TT_1$ we find in exactly the same way

$$h_2 = -\frac{f(a_1)}{f'(a_1)}.$$

From the preceding discussion it is evident that in the Newton-Raphson method the graph of the given function is replaced by a tangent at each successive step in the approximation process.

**60. The Inherent Error in the Newton-Raphson Method.** If $a$ is an approximate value of a root of $f(x) = 0$ and $h$ is the necessary correction, so that $f(a+h) = 0$, then we have by Art. 58

(60: 1)        $$f(a) + hf'(a) + \frac{h^2}{2}f''(a + \theta h) = 0, 0 < \theta < 1.$$

In the Newton-Raphson method we neglected the term involving $h^2$ and got an approximate value $h_1$ from the equation

(60: 2)        $$f(a) + h_1 f'(a) = 0.$$

Subtracting (60: 2) from (60: 1), we have

---

* The assumption that the curvature does not change sign between $P$ and $S$ is not a necessary condition for convergence. The process will still converge to the true value of the root when there is a point of inflection in the arc $PS$, but the limit will be approached from both sides.

$$(h - h_1)f'(a) + \frac{h^2}{2}f''(a + \theta h) = 0.$$

(60: 3) $$\therefore \quad h - h_1 = - h^2 \frac{f''(a + \theta h)}{2f'(a)}.$$

Now since $h$ is the true value of the required correction and $h_1$ is its approximate value, it is plain that $h - h_1$ is the error in $h_1$. The error in $h_1$ is thus given by (60: 3). Let $M$ denote the maximum value of $f''(x)$ in the neighborhood of $a + h_1$. Then

(60: 4) $$h - h_1 = - \frac{h^2 M}{2f'(a)}.$$

Our next problem is to express this error in terms of the known quantity $h_1$.

Clearing (60: 4) of fractions and transposing, we have

$$Mh^2 + 2f'(a)h = 2f'(a)h_1.$$

$$\therefore \quad h = \frac{-f'(a) + \sqrt{[f'(a)]^2 + 2Mf'(a)h_1}}{M}$$

$$= \frac{1}{M}\left[-f'(a) + f'(a)\left(1 + \frac{2Mh_1}{f'(a)}\right)^{1/2}\right].$$

Now expanding the quantity $[1 + 2Mh_1/f'(a)]^{1/2}$ by the binomial theorem, we have

$$h = \frac{1}{M}\left[-f'(a) + f'(a)\left(1 + \frac{Mh_1}{f'(a)} - \frac{1}{2}\frac{M^2 h_1^2}{[f'(a)]^2} + \frac{1}{2}\frac{M^3 h_1^3}{[f'(a)]^3}\right)\right]$$

$$= \frac{1}{M}\left(-f'(a) + f'(a) + Mh_1 - \frac{1}{2}\frac{M^2 h_1^2}{f'(a)} + \frac{1}{2}\frac{M^3 h_1^3}{[f'(a)]^2}\right)$$

$$= h_1 - \frac{Mh_1^2}{2f'(a)} + \frac{M^2 h_1^3}{2[f'(a)]^2} \cdots.$$

Hence

(60: 5) $$\text{Error} = h - h_1 = -\frac{Mh_1^2}{2f'(a)} + \frac{M^2 h_1^3}{2[f'(a)]^2}.$$

Since $h_1$ is always a small decimal, it is evident that the principal part of the error is contained in the first term on the right-hand side of (60: 5), so that we may neglect the term involving $h_1^3$. The formula for the error thus reduces to

(60: 6) $$E_1 \leqq \left|\frac{Mh_1^2}{2f'(a)}\right|.$$

This is the error in $a_1$. The error in $a_n$ is therefore

**(60: 7)**
$$E_n \leqq \left| \frac{M h_n^2}{2f'(a_{n-1})} \right|.$$

Now in most equations which one would solve by the Newton-Raphson method the quantity $M/2f'(a)$ is not greater than 1. Suppose, therefore, that $\left| M/2f'(a_{n-1}) \right| \leqq 1$. Then (60: 7) reduces to

**(60: 8)**
$$\left| E_n \right| \leqq h_n^2.$$

This result is most important; for it tells us that if $h_n$ begins with $m$ zeros when expressed as a decimal fraction, then $h_n^2$ begins with $2m$ zeros. This means that when the first significant figure in $h$ is less than 7, we may safely carry the division of $f(a_{n-1})/f'(a_{n-1})$ to $2m$ decimal places; for the error in the quotient will be less than half a unit in the $2m$th decimal place. Stated otherwise, *the number of reliable significant figures in $h$ is equal to the number of zeros between the decimal point and first significant figure*, provided the number of reliable figures in both $f(a_{n-1})$ and $f'(a_{n-1})$ is as great as the number of zeros preceding the first significant figure in $h$.

We thus have a simple method for determining the accuracy of the roots found by the Newton-Raphson method, and this fact makes this method much superior to the regula falsi method when the root is desired to several decimal places.

It is now clear why we were able to say in Exs. 1 and 2 of Art. 58 that the results obtained were true to the last figure in each case.

**61. The Method of Iteration.** When a numerical equation $f(x) = 0$ can be expressed in the form

(61: 1)
$$x = \phi(x),$$

the real roots can be found by the process of *iteration*. This is the method which was used for inverse interpolation in Art. 24. The process is this: We find from a graph or otherwise an approximate value $x_0$ of the desired root. We then substitute this in the right-hand member of (61: 1) and get a better approximation $x^{(1)}$, given by the equation

$$x^{(1)} = \phi(x_0).$$

Then the succeeding approximations are

$$x^{(2)} = \phi(x^{(1)}),$$
$$x^{(3)} = \phi(x^{(2)}),$$
$$\cdot \quad \cdot \quad \cdot \quad \cdot \quad \cdot \quad \cdot \quad \cdot$$
$$x^{(n)} = \phi(x^{(n-1)}).$$

We shall apply the process to two examples.

*Example 1.* Find by the method of iteration a real root of

$$2x - \log_{10} x = 7.$$

*Solution.* The given equation can be written in the form

$$x = \tfrac{1}{2}(\log_{10} x + 7).$$

We find from the intersection of the graphs $y_1 = 2x - 7$ and $y_2 = \log_{10} x$ that an approximate value of the root is 3.8. Hence we have

$$x^{(1)} = \tfrac{1}{2}(\log 3.8 + 7) = 3.79,$$

$$x^{(2)} = \tfrac{1}{2}(\log 3.79 + 7) = 3.7893,$$

$$x^{(3)} = \tfrac{1}{2}(\log 3.7893 + 7) = \underline{3.7893}.$$

Since $x^{(3)}$ is the same as $x^{(2)}$, we do not repeat the process but take 3.7893 as the correct result to five figures. The iteration process is the shortest and easiest method for working this example.

*Example 2.* The method of iteration is especially useful for finding the real roots of an equation given in the form of an infinite series. To find an expression for the probable error (see Art. 101) of a single measurement of a set, one procedure is to find the real root of the following equation (see page 319):

$$\rho - \frac{\rho^3}{3} + \frac{\rho^5}{10} - \frac{\rho^7}{42} + \frac{\rho^9}{216} - \frac{\rho^{11}}{1320} + \cdots = 0.4431135,$$

or

(1) $$\rho = \frac{\rho^3}{3} - \frac{\rho^5}{10} + \frac{\rho^7}{42} - \frac{\rho^9}{216} + \frac{\rho^{11}}{1320} + 0.4431135.$$

We shall now find the value of $\rho$ to six decimal places.

*Solution.* Neglecting all powers of $\rho$ higher than the first, we find an approximate value of $\rho$ to be 0.44. Hence we start with this value and substitute it in the right-hand member of (1). The result is

$$\rho^{(1)} = \frac{(0.44)^3}{3} - \frac{(0.44)^5}{10} + \frac{(0.44)^7}{42} - \frac{(0.44)^9}{216} + \frac{(0.44)^{11}}{1320} + 0.4431$$

$$= 0.4699 = 0.47, \text{ say.}$$

Then the second approximation is

$$\rho^{(2)} = \frac{(0.47)^3}{3} - \frac{(0.47)^5}{10} + \frac{(0.47)^7}{42} - \frac{(0.47)^9}{216} + \frac{(0.47)^{11}}{1320} + 0.44311$$

$$= 0.47554 = 0.476, \text{ say.}$$

Writing (1) in the form

$$\rho = \phi(\rho),$$

we find the succeeding approximations to be

$$\rho^{(3)} = \phi(0.476) = 0.4767,$$

$$\rho^{(4)} = \phi(0.4767) = 0.47689,$$

$$\rho^{(5)} = \phi(0.47689) = 0.476927,$$

$$\rho^{(6)} = \phi(0.476927) = 0.476934,$$

$$\rho^{(7)} = \phi(0.476934) = \underline{0.476936}.$$

This last value is correct to its last figure.*

The reader will observe that the iteration process converges slowly in this example. This is due to nature of the given equation. In Ex. 1 the convergence was rapid.

*Note.* Usually there are two or more ways in which an equation $f(x) = 0$ can be written in the form $x = \phi(x)$. It is not a matter of indifference as to which way it is written before starting the iteration process, for in some forms the process will not converge at all. An example of this is given in Art. 64.

**62. Convergence of the Iteration Process.** We shall now determine the condition under which the iteration process converges. The true value of the root satisfies the equation

$$x = \phi(x),$$

and the first approximation satisfies

$$x^{(1)} = \phi(x_0).$$

Subtracting this equation from the preceding, we have

(62: 1)          $$x - x^{(1)} = \phi(x) - \phi(x_0).$$

By the theorem of mean value the right-hand member of (62: 1) can be written

$$\phi(x) - \phi(x_0) = (x - x_0)\phi'(\xi_0), \quad x_0 \leqq \xi_0 \leqq x.$$

Hence (62: 1) becomes

$$x - x^{(1)} = (x - x_0)\phi'(\xi_0).$$

A similar equation holds for all succeeding approximations, so that

---

* The value of $\rho$ correct to ten decimal places is 0.4769362762.

$$x - x^{(2)} = (x - x^{(1)})\phi'(\xi_1),$$

$$x - x^{(3)} = (x - x^{(2)})\phi'(\xi_2),$$

$$\cdots \cdots \cdots \cdots \cdots \cdots$$

$$x - x^{(n)} = (x - x^{(n-1)})\phi'(\xi_{n-1}).$$

Multiplying together all these equations, member for member, and dividing the result through by the common factors $x - x^{(1)}$, $x - x^{(2)}$, $\cdots x - x^{(n-1)}$, we get

$$(62:2) \qquad x - x^{(n)} = (x - x_0)\phi'(\xi_0)\phi'(\xi_1) \cdots \phi'(\xi_{n-1}).$$

Now if the maximum absolute value of $\phi'(x)$ is less than 1 throughout the interval $(x_0, x)$, so that each of the quantities $\phi'(\xi_0)$, $\phi'(\xi_1)$, etc. is not greater than a proper fraction $m$, we get from (62:2)

$$(62:3) \qquad |x - x^{(n)}| \leq |x - x_0| m^n.$$

We can therefore make the error $x - x^{(n)}$ as small as we please by repeating the iteration process a sufficient number of times.

The condition, then, for convergence is that $\phi'(x)$ be less than 1 in the neighborhood of the desired root, the smaller the value of $\phi'(x)$ the more rapid the convergence. This condition was satisfied in Examples 1 and 2 above.

## II.  SIMULTANEOUS EQUATIONS IN SEVERAL UNKNOWNS

The real roots of simultaneous algebraic and transcendental equations in several unknowns can be found either by the Newton-Raphson method or by the method of iteration. We shall give an outline of each method for the cases of two unknowns and three unknowns. The reader will have no difficulty in extending both methods to the case of any number of unknowns should the necessity arise for doing so.

## 63. The Newton-Raphson Method for Simultaneous Equations.
Let us consider first the case of two equations in two unknowns. Let the given equations be

$$(63:1) \qquad \phi(x, y) = 0,$$

$$(63:2) \qquad \psi(x, y) = 0.$$

Now if $x_0$, $y_0$ be approximate values of a pair of roots and $h$, $k$ be corrections, so that

$$x = x_0 + h,$$

$$y = y_0 + k.$$

then (63: 1) and (63: 2) become

(63: 3)                     $\phi(x_0 + h, y_0 + k) = 0,$

(63: 4)                     $\psi(x_0 + h, y_0 + k) = 0.$

Expanding (63: 3) and (63: 4) by Taylor's theorem for a function of two variables, we have

(63: 5)   $\phi(x_0 + h, y_0 + k) = \phi(x_0, y_0) + h\left(\dfrac{\partial \phi}{\partial x}\right)_0 + k\left(\dfrac{\partial \phi}{\partial y}\right)_0$

+terms in higher powers of $h$ and $k = 0.$

(63: 6)   $\psi(x_0 + h, y_0 + k) = \psi(x_0, y_0) + h\left(\dfrac{\partial \psi}{\partial x}\right)_0 + k\left(\dfrac{\partial \psi}{\partial y}\right)_0$

+terms in higher powers of $h$ and $k = 0.$

Now since $h$ and $k$ are relatively small, we neglect their squares, products, and higher powers, and then (63: 5) and (63: 6) become simply

(63: 7)            $\phi(x_0, y_0) + h\left(\dfrac{\partial \phi}{\partial x}\right)_0 + k\left(\dfrac{\partial \phi}{\partial y}\right)_0 = 0,$

(63: 8)            $\psi(x_0, y_0) + h\left(\dfrac{\partial \psi}{\partial x}\right)_0 + k\left(\dfrac{\partial \psi}{\partial y}\right)_0 = 0.$

Solving these by determinants, we find the first corrections to be

**(63: 9)**              $h_1 = \dfrac{\begin{vmatrix} -\phi(x_0, y_0) & \left(\dfrac{\partial \phi}{\partial y}\right)_0 \\ -\psi(x_0, y_0) & \left(\dfrac{\partial \psi}{\partial y}\right)_0 \end{vmatrix}}{D},$

**(63: 10)**             $k_1 = \dfrac{\begin{vmatrix} \left(\dfrac{\partial \phi}{\partial x}\right)_0 & -\phi(x_0, y_0) \\ \left(\dfrac{\partial \psi}{\partial x}\right)_0 & -\psi(x_0, y_0) \end{vmatrix}}{D},$

where

**(63: 11)**             $D = \begin{vmatrix} \left(\dfrac{\partial \phi}{\partial x}\right)_0 & \left(\dfrac{\partial \phi}{\partial y}\right)_0 \\ \left(\dfrac{\partial \psi}{\partial x}\right)_0 & \left(\dfrac{\partial \psi}{\partial y}\right)_0 \end{vmatrix}.$

Additional corrections can be found by repeated application of these formulas with the improved values of $x$ and $y$ substituted at each step.

The notation $(\partial\phi/\partial x)_0$ means the value of $\partial\phi/\partial x$ when $x_0$ and $y_0$ are substituted for $x$ and $y$. Similarly, $(\partial\phi/\partial x)_1$ means the value of $\partial\phi/\partial x$ when $x = x^{(1)}$, $y = y^{(1)}$; and so on.

In the case of three equations in three unknowns,

$$\phi(x, y, z) = 0,$$

$$\psi(x, y, z) = 0,$$

$$\chi(x, y, z) = 0,$$

let $h$, $k$, $l$, denote corrections to the approximate values $x_0$, $y_0$, $z_0$, respectively. Then proceeding exactly as in the case of two equations we get the three simple equations

$$\phi(x_0, y_0, z_0) + h\left(\frac{\partial\phi}{\partial x}\right)_0 + k\left(\frac{\partial\phi}{\partial y}\right)_0 + l\left(\frac{\partial\phi}{\partial z}\right)_0 = 0,$$

$$\psi(x_0, y_0, z_0) + h\left(\frac{\partial\psi}{\partial x}\right)_0 + k\left(\frac{\partial\psi}{\partial y}\right)_0 + l\left(\frac{\partial\psi}{\partial z}\right)_0 = 0,$$

$$\chi(x_0, y_0, z_0) + h\left(\frac{\partial\chi}{\partial x}\right)_0 + k\left(\frac{\partial\chi}{\partial y}\right)_0 + l\left(\frac{\partial\chi}{\partial z}\right)_0 = 0,$$

for determining the first corrections $h_1$, $k_1$, $l_1$. The process may be repeated as many times as desired.

We shall now apply this method to a pair of simultaneous equations, one transcendental and the other algebraic.

*Example.* Compute by the Newton-Raphson method a real solution of the equations

$$\begin{cases} x + 3\log_{10} x - y^2 = 0, \\ 2x^2 - xy - 5x + 1 = 0. \end{cases}$$

*Solution.* On plotting the graphs of these equations on the same set of axes, we find that they intersect at the points $(1.4, -1.5)$ and $(3.4, 2.2)$. We shall compute the second set of values correct to four decimal places. Let

(1) $$\phi(x, y) = x + 3\log_{10} x - y^2,$$

(2) $$\psi(x, y) = 2x^2 - xy - 5x + 1.$$

Then

$$\frac{\partial \phi}{\partial x} = 1 + \frac{3M}{x}, \quad \text{where } M = 0.43429,$$

$$\frac{\partial \phi}{\partial y} = -2y,$$

$$\frac{\partial \psi}{\partial x} = 4x - y - 5, \quad \frac{\partial \psi}{\partial y} = -x.$$

Now since $x_0 = 3.4$, $y_0 = 2.2$, we have

$$\phi(x_0, y_0) = 0.1545, \quad \psi(x_0, y_0) = -0.72,$$

$$\left(\frac{\partial \phi}{\partial x}\right)_0 = 1.383, \quad \left(\frac{\partial \phi}{\partial y}\right)_0 = -4.4, \quad \left(\frac{\partial \psi}{\partial x}\right)_0 = 6.4,$$

$$\left(\frac{\partial \psi}{\partial y}\right)_0 = -3.4.$$

Substituting these values in (63:9), (63:10), (63:11), we find

$$h_1 = 0.157, \quad k_1 = 0.085.$$

Hence

$$x^{(1)} = 3.4 + 0.157 = 3.557, \quad y^{(1)} = 2.285.$$

Now substituting $x^{(1)}$ and $y^{(1)}$ for $x$ and $y$ in $\phi(x, y)$, $\psi(x, y)$, $\partial \phi / \partial x$, etc., we get

$$\phi(x^{(1)}, y^{(1)}) = -0.011, \quad \psi(x^{(1)}, y^{(1)}) = 0.3945,$$

$$\left(\frac{\partial \phi}{\partial x}\right)_1 = 1.367, \quad \left(\frac{\partial \phi}{\partial y}\right)_1 = -4.57, \quad \left(\frac{\partial \psi}{\partial x}\right)_1 = 6.943,$$

$$\left(\frac{\partial \psi}{\partial y}\right)_1 = -3.557.$$

Substituting these in (63:11), (63:9), (63:10), we get

$$h_2 = -0.0685, \quad k_2 = -0.0229.$$

Hence

$$x^{(2)} = 3.4885, \quad y^{(2)} = 2.2621.$$

Repeating the computation with these improved values of $x$ and $y$, we find

$$h_3 = -0.0013, \quad k_3 = -0.000561.$$

Hence the third approximations are

$$x^{(3)} = \underline{3.4782}, \quad y^{(3)} = \underline{2.26154},$$

and these are correct to the last figure.

**64. The Method of Iteration for Simultaneous Equations.** In the case of two equations

$$\phi(x, y) = 0,$$
$$\psi(x, y) = 0,$$

we first write the given equations in the forms

$$x = F_1(x, y),$$
$$y = F_2(x, y).$$

Then if $x_0$, $y_0$ be the approximate values of a pair of roots, improved values are found by the steps indicated below:

1st approx.
$$\begin{cases} x^{(1)} = F_1(x_0, y_0), \\ y^{(1)} = F_2(x^{(1)}, y_0); \end{cases}$$

2nd approx.
$$\begin{cases} x^{(2)} = F_1(x^{(1)}, y^{(1)}), \\ y^{(2)} = F_2(x^{(2)}, y^{(1)}): \end{cases}$$

etc.

If we are given three equations

$$\phi(x, y, z) = 0,$$
$$\psi(x, y, z) = 0,$$
$$\chi(x, y, z) = 0,$$

we would first write them in the forms

$$x = F_1(x, y, z),$$
$$y = F_2(x, y, z),$$
$$z = F_3(x, y, z).$$

The successive steps in the computation would then be:

1st approximation
$$\begin{cases} x^{(1)} = F_1(x_0, y_0, z_0), \\ y^{(1)} = F_2(x^{(1)}, y_0, z_0), \\ z^{(1)} = F_3(x^{(1)}, y^{(1)}, z_0); \end{cases}$$

2nd approximation
$$\begin{cases} x^{(2)} = F_1(x^{(1)}, y^{(1)}, z^{(1)}) \\ y^{(2)} = F_2(x^{(2)}, y^{(1)}, z^{(1)}), \\ z^{(2)} = F_3(x^{(2)}, y^{(2)}, z^{(1)}); \end{cases}$$

etc.

We shall now apply the iteration process to the pair of equations which we have already solved (for one pair of roots) by the Newton-Raphson method:

$$\phi(x, y) = x + 3 \log_{10} x - y^2,$$

$$\psi(x, y) = 2x^2 - xy - 5x + 1.$$

*Solution.* We start with the approximate values $x_0 = 3.4$, $y_0 = 2.2$, as indicated by the intersection of the graphs. In our next step we are confronted with several possibilities, for the two equations can be written in the forms $x = F_1(x, y)$, $y = F_2(x, y)$ in several ways. In the absence of further information we start out with the simplest forms, namely

$$x = y^2 - 3 \log_{10} x,$$

$$y = \frac{1}{x} + 2x - 5.$$

Then we have

$$x^{(1)} = (2.2)^2 - 3 \log_{10} 3.4 = 3.25,$$

$$y^{(1)} = \frac{1}{3.25} + 2(3.25) - 5 = 1.81;$$

$$x^{(2)} = (1.81)^2 - 3 \log_{10} (3.25) = 1.74,$$

$$y^{(2)} = \frac{1}{1.74} + 2(1.74) - 5 = -0.95.$$

These values of $x$ and $y$ are evidently getting worse with each application of the iteration process. We must therefore write the given equations in some other form before attempting the iteration process again.

Without trying all possible forms we will make a fresh start with the only forms that will make the process converge, namely

$$x = \sqrt{\frac{x(y + 5) - 1}{2}},$$

$$y = \sqrt{x + 3 \log_{10} x}.$$

Then the successive approximations are

$$\begin{cases} x^{(1)} = \sqrt{\dfrac{3.4(2.2 + 5) - 1}{2}} = 3.426, \\[2mm] y^{(1)} = \sqrt{3.426 + 3 \log_{10} 3.426} = 2.243; \end{cases}$$

$$\begin{cases} x^{(2)} = \sqrt{\dfrac{3.426(2.243 + 5) - 1}{2}} = 3.451, \\[2mm] y^{(2)} = \sqrt{3.451 + 3 \log_{10} 3.451} = 2.2505; \end{cases}$$

$$x^{(3)} = 3.466, \quad y^{(3)} = 2.255;$$
$$x^{(4)} = 3.475, \quad y^{(4)} = 2.258;$$
$$x^{(5)} = 3.480, \quad y^{(5)} = 2.259;$$
$$x^{(6)} = 3.483, \quad y^{(6)} = 2.260.$$

Here it is evident that the iteration process converges very slowly in this example, for after having applied the process six times we have added only one reliable figure to the approximate roots we started with.

This example brings out two important facts in connection with the method of iteration. The first is that we must not start out blindly in working a problem by this method, for instead of improving the roots at each step we might make them decidedly worse. The second important fact brought out is that the iteration process should not be applied at all in some examples, for the convergence might be too slow, as was the case above. All this leads us to a consideration of the conditions under which the process converges. Having these conditions at hand, we can decide in advance as to the advisability of attempting a problem by iteration.

**65. Convergence of the Iteration Process in the Case of Several Unknowns.** To find the conditions for convergence in the case of two equations, we write them in the forms

$$x = F_1(x, y),$$
$$y = F_2(x, y).$$

These equations are satisfied by the exact values of the pair of roots $x, y$. The first approximations satisfy the equations

$$x^{(1)} = F_1(x_0, y_0),$$
$$y^{(1)} = F_2(x_0, y_0).$$

Subtracting these equations from the corresponding equations above, we have

(65: 1)          $$x - x^{(1)} = F_1(x, y) - F_1(x_0, y_0),$$
(65: 2)          $$y - y^{(1)} = F_2(x, y) - F_2(x_0, y_0).$$

Now applying to the right-hand side of the first equation the theorem of mean value for a function of two variables, we have

$$F_1(x, y) - F_1(x_0, y_0) = (x - x_0)\frac{\partial \overline{F}_1}{\partial x} + (y - y_0)\frac{\partial \overline{F}_1}{\partial y},$$

where

$$\frac{\partial \overline{F}_1}{\partial x} = \frac{\partial F_1[x_0 + \theta(x - x_0),\ y_0 + \theta(y - y_0)]}{\partial x},\ 0 \leqq \theta \leqq 1,$$

and

$$\frac{\partial \overline{F}_1}{\partial y} = \frac{\partial F_1[x_0 + \theta(x - x_0),\ y_0 + \theta(y - y_0)]}{\partial y}.$$

In a similar manner we get

$$F_2(x,\ y) - F_2(x_0,\ y_0) = (x - x_0)\frac{\partial \overline{F}_2}{\partial x} + (y - y_0)\frac{\partial \overline{F}_2}{\partial y}.$$

Substituting these expressions for the right-hand members of (65: 1) and (65: 2), we get

$$x - x^{(1)} = (x - x_0)\frac{\partial \overline{F}_1}{\partial x} + (y - y_0)\frac{\partial \overline{F}_1}{\partial y},$$

$$y - y^{(1)} = (x - x_0)\frac{\partial \overline{F}_2}{\partial x} + (y - y_0)\frac{\partial \overline{F}_2}{\partial y}.$$

Adding these two equations and considering only the absolute values of the several quantities, we have

$$(65: 3)\quad |\ x - x^{(1)}\ | + |\ y - y^{(1)}\ | \leqq |\ x - x_0\ | \left\{ \left| \frac{\partial \overline{F}_1}{\partial x} \right| + \left| \frac{\partial \overline{F}_2}{\partial x} \right| \right\}$$

$$+ |\ y - y_0\ | \left\{ \left| \frac{\partial \overline{F}_1}{\partial y} \right| + \left| \frac{\partial \overline{F}_2}{\partial y} \right| \right\}.$$

Now let the maximum value of either $|\partial F_1/\partial x| + |\partial F_2/\partial x|$ or $|\partial F_1/\partial y| + |\partial F_2/\partial y|$ be a proper fraction $m$ for all points in the region $(x_0,\ x)$ and $(y_0,\ y)$. Then (65: 3) becomes

$$|\ x - x^{(1)}\ | + |\ y - y^{(1)}\ | \leqq m \{\ |\ x - x_0\ | + |\ y - y_0\ |\ \}.$$

This relation holds for the first approximation. For the succeeding approximations we have the similar relations

$$|\ x - x^{(2)}\ | + |\ y - y^2\ | \leqq m \{\ |\ x - x^{(1)}\ | + |\ y - y^{(1)}\ |\ \},$$

$$|\ x - x^{(3)}\ | + |\ y - y^{(3)}\ | \leqq m \{\ |\ x - x^{(2)}\ | + |\ y - y^{(2)}\ |\ \},$$

$$\cdot\ \cdot\ \cdot\ \cdot\ \cdot\ \cdot\ \cdot\ \cdot\ \cdot\ \cdot\ \cdot\ \cdot\ \cdot\ \cdot\ \cdot\ \cdot\ \cdot\ \cdot\ \cdot\ \cdot\ \cdot\ \cdot$$

$$|\ x - x^{(n)}\ | + |\ y - y^{(n)}\ | \leqq m \{\ |\ x - x^{(n-1)}\ | + |\ y - y^{(n-1)}\ |\ \}.$$

Now multiplying together all these inequalities, member for member, and dividing through by the common factors $\{ |x-x^{(1)}| + |y-y^{(1)}| \}$, $\{ |x-x^{(2)}| + |y-y^{(2)}| \}$, etc., we get

$$| x - x^{(n)} | + | y - y^{(n)} | \leqq m^n \{ | x - x_0 | + | y - y_0 | \} .$$

Since $m$ is a proper fraction, it is clear that we can make the right-hand member of this inequality as small as we please by repeating the iteration process a sufficient number of times. This means that the errors $|x-x^{(n)}|$ and $|y-y^{(n)}|$ can be made as small as we like.

The iteration process for two unknowns therefore converges when, and only when, the two conditions $|\partial F_1/\partial x| + |\partial F_2/\partial x| < 1$ and $|\partial F_1/\partial y| + |\partial F_2/\partial y| < 1$ hold for all points in the neighborhood of $(x_0, y_0)$. In order for the convergence to be rapid enough to make the method advisable in any given problem it is necessary that each of the quantities $|\partial F_1/\partial x| + |\partial F_2/\partial x|$ and $|\partial F_1/\partial y| + |\partial F_2/\partial y|$ be much less than 1.

We are now able to see why the convergence was so slow in the example which we attempted to work by the iteration process in Art. 64. For that example the values of the quantities named above are

$$\left| \frac{\partial F_1}{\partial x} \right| + \left| \frac{\partial F_2}{\partial x} \right| = 0.521 + 0.304 = 0.825,$$

$$\left| \frac{\partial F_1}{\partial y} \right| + \left| \frac{\partial F_2}{\partial y} \right| = 0.162 + 0 = 0.162.$$

The first is much too large for rapid convergence.

### EXAMPLES ON CHAPTER IX

1. Find graphically or otherwise the approximate value of a real root of the equation

$$2x - \log_{10} x = 7.$$

2. Find the approximate value of a real root of

$$x \sinh \frac{10}{x} - 15 = 0.$$

3. Compute to four decimal places by the regula falsi method the root found approximately in Example 1 above.

4. Do the same for the root found approximately in Example 2.

5. Find to four decimal places by the Newton-Raphson method a real root of

$$x^2 + 4 \sin x = 0.$$

6. Solve $x = 0.21 \sin (0.5 + x)$ by the iteration process.

7. Find to three decimal places the smallest positive root of

$$x^x + 2x = 6.$$

8. Find the smallest positive root of

$$x \tan x = 1.28.$$

9. Compute a root of

$$x^{105} - 1 = 100(x - 1).$$

10. Find to five decimal places a root of

$$x \log_{10} x = -0.125.$$

11. Compute to eight decimal places a root of

$$\sin x - 0.6 x \cos x = 1.$$

12. Find a root of

$$\tan x + \tanh x = 0.$$

13. Find a real root of

$$e^x + e^{-3x} = 4.$$

14. Compute to six decimal places a root of

$$6\theta - 5 \sinh \theta = 0.$$

15. Find the smallest root of

$$1 - x + \frac{x^2}{(2!)^2} - \frac{x^3}{(3!)^2} + \frac{x^4}{(4!)^2} - \frac{x^5}{(5!)^2} + \cdots = 0.$$

16. Find a real solution of

$$4.2x^2 + 8.8y^2 = 1.42,$$
$$(x - 1.2)^2 + (y - 0.6)^2 = 1.$$

17. Find by the Newton-Raphson method a real solution of

$$x^2 y^2 - 3x^3 - 6y^3 + 8 = 0,$$
$$x^4 - 9y + 2 = 0.$$

18. Find to five decimal places a solution of

$$\sin x = y + 1.32,$$
$$\cos y = x - 0.85.$$

19. An approximate solution of the equations

$$x^7 - 5x^2y^4 + 1510 = 0,$$

$$y^5 - 3x^4y - 105 = 0,$$

is $x = 2$, $y = 3$. Find this solution to four decimal places.

20. Find by iteration a solution of

$$x = \log_{10} \frac{y}{z} + 1,$$

$$y = 0.4 + z^2 - 2x^2,$$

$$z = 2 + \frac{xy}{20},$$

approximate values being $x = 1$, $y = 2.2$, $z = 2$.

# CHAPTER X

## GRAEFFE'S ROOT-SQUARING METHOD FOR SOLVING ALGEBRAIC EQUATIONS

**66. Introduction.** The methods given in the preceding chapter are applicable only for finding the *real* roots of numerical equations. It is sometimes necessary to find also the complex roots of algebraic equations. In studying the stability of airplanes, for example, it is necessary to solve linear differential equations with constant coefficients. The solution of such a differential equation is effected, as is well known, by first solving an algebraic equation whose degree is equal to the order of the given differential equation. The algebraic equations which arise in stability theory are usually of the fourth, sixth, or eighth degree. A pair of complex roots indicates an oscillation, the real part of the root giving the damping factor and the imaginary part the period of oscillation.

No short and simple method exists for finding the complex roots of algebraic equations of high degree. Probably the root-squaring method of Graeffe* is the best to use in most cases. This method gives all the roots at once, both real and complex.

**67. Principle of the Method.** The underlying principle of Graeffe's method is this: The given equation is transformed into another whose roots are high powers of those of the original equation. The roots of the transformed equation are widely separated, and because of this fact are easily found. For example, if two of the roots of the original equation are 3 and 2, the corresponding roots of the transformed equation are $3^m$ and $2^m$, where $m$ is the power to which the roots of the given equation have been raised. Thus, if $m = 64$, we have $3^{64} = 10^{30.536}$, $2^{64} = 10^{19.266}$. The two roots of the given equation were of the same order of magnitude, but in the transformed equation the larger root is more than a hundred billion times as large as the smaller one. Stated otherwise, the ratio of the roots in the given equation is $\frac{2}{3}$, but in the transformed equation it is $10^{19.266}/10^{30.536} = 1/10^{11.27}$, or $2^{64}/3^{64} < 0.00000000001$. The smaller root in the transformed equation is therefore negligible in comparison with the larger one. The roots of the transformed equa-

---

* *Auflösung der höheren numerischen Gleichungen*, Zurich (1837).

tion are said to be separated *when the ratio of any root to the next larger is negligible in comparison with unity.*

**68. The Root-Squaring Process.** The transformed equation is obtained by repeated application of a root squaring process. The first application of this process transforms the given equation into another whose roots are the squares of those of the original equation. This second equation is then transformed into a third equation whose roots are the squares of those of the second, and therefore the fourth powers of those of the original equation. The root-squaring process is continued in this manner until the roots of the last transformed equation are completely separated.

We shall now explain the root-squaring process and show the method of applying it.

Let the given equation be

$$(68:1) \quad f(x) = a_0 x^n + a_1 x^{n-1} + a_2 x^{n-2} + \cdots + a_{n-1} x + a_n = 0.$$

Then if $x_1, x_2, \cdots x_n$ be the roots of this equation we can write it in the equivalent form

$$(68:2) \quad f(x) = a_0(x - x_1)(x - x_2)(x - x_3) \cdots (x - x_n) = 0.$$

Now let us multiply (68:2) by the function

$$(68:3) \quad (-1)^n f(-x) = (-1)^n a_0(-x - x_1)(-x - x_2) \cdots (-x - x_n)$$
$$= a_0(x + x_1)(x + x_2) \cdots (x + x_n).$$

The result is

$$(68:4) \quad (-1)^n f(-x) f(x) = a_0^2(x^2 - x_1^2)(x^2 - x_2^2) \cdots (x^2 - x_n^2).$$

Let $x^2 = y$. Then (68:4) becomes

$$(68:5) \quad \phi(y) = a_0^2(y - x_1^2)(y - x_2^2) \cdots (y - x_n^2) = 0.$$

The roots of this equation are $x_1^2, x_2^2, \cdots x_n^2$ and are thus the squares of the roots of the given equation (68:1). Hence to form an equation whose roots are the squares of those of $f(x) = 0$, we merely multiply $f(x) = 0$ by $(-1)^n f(-x)$.

This multiplication can be carried out in a simple routine manner, as we shall now show. Let us first consider the sixth degree equation

$$f(x) = a_0 x^6 + a_1 x^5 + a_2 x^4 + a_3 x^3 + a_4 x^2 + a_5 x + a_6 = 0.$$

Then

$$(-1)^6 f(-x) = a_0 x^6 - a_1 x^5 + a_2 x^4 - a_3 x^3 + a_4 x^2 - a_5 x + a_6.$$

By actual multiplication we find

$$(68\!:\!6) \quad (-1)^6 f(-x)f(x) = a_0^2\,x^{12} \;\begin{array}{l}-a_1^2\\+2a_0a_1\end{array}\Bigg|\,x^{10}\;\begin{array}{l}+a_2^2\\-2a_1a_3\\+2a_0a_4\end{array}\Bigg|\,x^8\;\begin{array}{l}-a_3^2\\2a_2a_4\\-2a_1a_5\\+2a_0a_6\end{array}\Bigg|\,x^6$$

$$\begin{array}{l}+a_4^2\\-2a_3a_5\\+2a_2a_6\end{array}\Bigg|\,x^4\;\begin{array}{l}-a_5^2\\+2a_4a_6\end{array}\Bigg|\,x^2 + a_6^2 = 0.$$

Let us consider next a seventh-degree equation,

$$f(x) = a_0x^7 + a_1x^6 + a_2x^5 + a_3x^4 + a_4x^3 + a_5x^2 + a_6x + a_7 = 0.$$

Then

$$(-1)^7 f(-x) = a_0x^7 - a_1x^6 + a_2x^5 - a_3x^4 + a_4x^3 - a_5x^2 + a_6x - a_7.$$

Multiplying these equations together in the ordinary manner, as before, we find

$$(68\!:\!7) \quad (-1)^7 f(-x)f(x) = a_0x^{14} \;\begin{array}{l}-a_1^2\\+2a_0a_2\end{array}\Bigg|\,x^{12}\;\begin{array}{l}+a_2^2\\-2a_1a_3\\+2a_0a_4\end{array}\Bigg|\,x^{10}\;\begin{array}{l}-a_3^2\\+2a_2a_4\\-2a_1a_5\\+2a_0a_6\end{array}\Bigg|\,x^8$$

$$\begin{array}{l}+a_4^2\\-2a_3a_5\\+2a_2a_6\\-2a_1a_7\end{array}\Bigg|\,x^6\;\begin{array}{l}-a_5^2\\+2a_4a_6\\-2a_3a_7\end{array}\Bigg|\,x^4\;\begin{array}{l}+a_6^2\\-2a_5a_7\end{array}\Bigg|\,x^2 - a_7^2 = 0.$$

A glance at equations (68: 6) and (68: 7) shows that the law of formation of the coefficients in the squared equation is the same whether the degree of the given equation be even or odd. In practice the multiplication is carried out with detached coefficients as indicated below:

| $a_0$ | $a_1$ | $a_2$ | $a_3$ | $a_4$ | $a_5\;\cdots$ |
|---|---|---|---|---|---|
| $a_0$ | $-a_1$ | $a_2$ | $-a_3$ | $a_4$ | $-a_5\;\cdots$ |
| $a_0^2$ | $-a_1^2$ | $a_2^2$ | $-a_3^2$ | $a_4^2$ | $-a_5^2\;\cdots$ |
| | $+2a_0a_2$ | $-2a_1a_3$ | $+2a_2a_4$ | $-2a_3a_5$ | $+2a_4a_6\;\cdots$ |
| | | $+2a_0a_4$ | $-2a_1a_5$ | $+2a_2a_6$ | $-2a_3a_7\;\cdots$ |
| | | | $+2a_0a_6$ | $-2a_1a_7$ | $+2a_2a_8\;\cdots$ |
| | | | | $+2a_0a_8$ | $-2a_1a_9\;\cdots$ |
| | | | | | $+2a_0a_{10}\;\cdots$ |
| $b_0$ | $b_1$ | $b_2$ | $b_3$ | $b_4$ | $b_5$ |

The coefficients in the new equation are the sums $b_0$, $b_1$, $b_2$, $\cdots$ $b_n$ of the several columns in the scheme above. These coefficients can evidently be written down according to the following rule:

1. *The numbers in the top row are the squares of the coefficients directly above them, with alternating signs—the second, fourth, sixth, etc. squared numbers being negative.*

2. *The quantities directly under these squared numbers are the doubled products of the coefficients equally removed from the one directly overhead, the first being twice the product of the two coefficients adjacent to the one overhead, the second the doubled product of the next two equally removed coefficients, etc.*

3. *The signs of the doubled products are changed alternately in going along the rows and also in going down the columns, the sign of the first doubled product in each row not being changed.*

We shall now apply Graeffe's method to three cases of algebraic equations.

**69. Case I. Roots all Real and Unequal.** Since the relations between the roots $x_1$, $x_2$, $\cdots$ $x_n$ and coefficients $a_0$, $a_1$, $\cdots$ $a_n$ of the general equation of the $n$th degree

$$a_0 x^n + a_1 x^{n-1} + \cdots + a_{n-1} x + a_n = 0$$

are

$$\frac{a_1}{a_0} = - (x_1 + x_2 + \cdots + x_n),$$

$$\frac{a_2}{a_0} = + (x_1 x_2 + x_1 x_3 + \cdots),$$

$$\frac{a_3}{a_0} = - (x_1 x_2 x_3 + x_1 x_2 x_4 \cdots),$$

$$\cdots \cdots \cdots \cdots \cdots \cdots$$

$$\frac{a_n}{a_0} = (-1)^n x_1 x_2 \cdots x_n,$$

it follows that the roots $x_1^m$, $x_2^m$, $\cdots$ $x_n^m$ and coefficients $b_0$, $b_1$, $\cdots$ $b_n$ of the final transformed equation

$$b_0 (x^m)^n + b_1 (x^m)^{n-1} \cdots + b_{n-1} x^m + b_n = 0$$

are connected by the corresponding relations

$$\frac{b_1}{b_0} = -\ (x_1{}^m + x_2{}^m + \cdots + x_n{}^m)$$

$$= -\ x_1{}^m\left(1 + \frac{x_2{}^m}{x_1{}^m} + \frac{x_3{}^m}{x_1{}^m} + \cdots + \frac{x_n{}^m}{x_1{}^m}\right),$$

$$\frac{b_2}{b_0} = x_1{}^m x_2{}^m + x_1{}^m x_3{}^m + \cdots = x_1{}^m x_2{}^m\left(1 + \frac{x_3{}^m}{x_1{}^m} + \frac{x_3{}^m}{x_2{}^m} + \cdots\right),$$

$$\frac{b_3}{b_0} = -\ (x_1{}^m x_2{}^m x_3{}^m + x_1{}^m x_2{}^m x_4{}^m + \cdots) = -\ x_1{}^m x_2{}^m x_3{}^m\left(1 + \frac{x_4{}^m}{x_3{}^m} + \cdots\right),$$

$$\cdots \cdots \cdots \cdots \cdots \cdots \cdots \cdots \cdots$$

$$\frac{b_n}{b_0} = (-\ 1)^n x_1{}^m x_2{}^m \cdots x_n{}^m.$$

Now if the order of magnitude of the roots is

$$|\ x_1\ | > |\ x_2\ | > |\ x_3\ | \cdots > |\ x_n\ |\ ,$$

it is evident that when the roots are sufficiently separated the ratios $x_2^m/x_1^m$, $x_3^m/x_2^m$, etc. are negligible in comparison with unity. Hence the relations between roots and coefficients in the final transformed equation are

$$\frac{b_1}{b_0} = -\ x_1{}^m, \quad \frac{b_2}{b_0} = x_1{}^m x_2{}^m, \quad \frac{b_3}{b_0} = -\ x_1{}^m x_2{}^m x_3{}^m,$$

$$\cdots \cdots \frac{b_n}{b_0} = (-\ 1)^n x_1{}^m x_2{}^m x_3{}^m \cdots x_n{}^m.$$

Dividing each of these equations after the first by the preceding equation, we obtain

$$\frac{b_2}{b_1} = -\ x_2{}^m, \quad \frac{b_3}{b_2} = -\ x_3{}^m, \quad \cdots \frac{b_n}{b_{n-1}} = -\ x_n{}^m.$$

Hence from these and the equation $b_1/b_0 = -x_1^m$, we get

(69 : 1)  $\quad b_0 x_1{}^m + b_1 = 0, \quad b_1 x_2{}^m + b_2 = 0, \quad b_2 x_3{}^m + b_3 = 0, \cdots$

$$b_{n-1} x_n{}^m + b_n = 0.$$

The root-squaring process has thus broken up the original equation into $n$ simple equations from which the desired roots can be found with ease.

The question naturally arises as to how many root-squarings are necessary to break up the original equation into linear fragments. The answer is that the required number of squarings depends upon (1) the ratios of the roots of the given equation and (2) the number of significant figures desired in the computed roots.  Since the required roots, and therefore their ratios, are not known in advance, it is not possible to determine beforehand just how many times the root-squaring process must be repeated.  This, however, is a matter of no importance, for *in practice we continue the root-squaring process until the doubled products in the second row have no effect on the coefficients of the next transformed equation.*

Since the coefficients in the given equation are not in general all positive, the signs of the doubled products will not occur in regular order as in the literal equations which we used to illustrate the root-squaring process.  The possibilities of making a mistake in the signs of these products are great, and therefore some scheme should be adopted to prevent such mistakes.  As a convenient notation for reminding us at each step as to whether or not the sign is to be changed we shall write a "*c*" after each term in which the sign is to be changed and an "*n*" (for no change) after each term where the sign is not to be changed.

Furthermore, as the root-squaring process necessarily increases the coefficients in the transformed equations until they become enormously large numbers,we shall always write these coefficients as simple numbers multiplied by powers of 10.

Finally, in the successive transformations of the equations by the root-squaring process, we shall not write down the multiplier $(-1)^n f(-x)$ as was done in the scheme on page 200, but simply apply the rule stated on page 201.  We shall now compute all the roots of an equation by Graeffe's method.

*Example* 1.  Find all the roots of the equation

$$1.23x^5 - 2.52x^4 - 16.1x^3 + 17.3x^2 + 29.4x - 1.34 = 0.$$

*Solution.*  The preliminary work of separating the roots is given on the following page and should be self-explanatory in view of what has been said above.  When doubled products are too small to be written down, a star(*) is written instead.

It is evident that further squaring will simply give the squares of the coefficients in the last line of the table, and we therefore stop with the 32d powers of the roots.  Then by (69:1) we have the following five simple equations:

$$(7.541 \times 10^2)x_1^{32} - 2.346 \times 10^{22} = 0,$$
$$(-2.346 \times 10^{22})x_2^{32} + 3.95 \times 10^{37} = 0,$$
$$(3.95 \times 10^{37})x_3^{32} - 8.744 \times 10^{46} = 0,$$
$$(-8.744 \times 10^{46})x_4^{32} + 2.148 \times 10^{47} = 0,$$
$$(2.148 \times 10^{47})x_5^{32} - 1.175 \times 10^4 = 0.$$

| | $x^5$ | $x^4$ | $x^3$ | $x^2$ | $x^1$ | $x^0$ |
|---|---|---|---|---|---|---|
| Given equa. | 1.23 | $-2.52$ | $-16.1$ | 17.3 | 29.4 | $-1.34$ |
| | 1.513 | $-0.635 \cdot 10$<br>$-3.961n$ | $+2.592 \cdot 10^2$<br>$+0.872c$<br>$+0.723n$ | $-2.993 \cdot 10^2$<br>$-9.467n$<br>$-0.068c$ | $+8.644 \cdot 10^2$<br>$+0.464c$ | $-1.796$ |
| 2nd powers | 1.513 | $-4.596 \cdot 10$ | $+4.187 \cdot 10^2$ | $-1.253 \cdot 10^3$ | $+9.108 \cdot 10^2$ | $-1.796$ |
| | 2.289 | $-2.112 \cdot 10^3$<br>$+1.267n$ | $+1.753 \cdot 10^5$<br>$-1.152c$<br>$+0.028n$ | $-1.570 \cdot 10^6$<br>$+0.763n$<br>$*$ | $+8.296 \cdot 10^5$<br>$-0.045c$ | $-3.226$ |
| 4th p. | 2.289 | $-0.845 \cdot 10^3$ | $+0.629 \cdot 10^5$ | $-0.807 \cdot 10^6$ | $+8.251 \cdot 10^5$ | $-3.226$ |
| | 5.240 | $-0.714 \cdot 10^6$<br>$+0.288n$ | $+0.396 \cdot 10^{10}$<br>$-0.136c$<br>$*$ | $-0.651 \cdot 10^{12}$<br>$+0.104n$<br>$*$ | $+6.808 \cdot 10^{11}$<br>$*$ | $-10.41$ |
| 8th p. | 5.240 | $-0.426 \cdot 10^6$ | $+0.260 \cdot 10^{10}$ | $-0.547 \cdot 10^{12}$ | $+6.808 \cdot 10^{11}$ | $-10.41$ |
| | $2.746 \cdot 10$ | $-1.815 \cdot 10^{11}$<br>$+0.272n$ | $+6.76 \cdot 10^{18}$<br>$-0.47c$ | $-2.992 \cdot 10^{23}$<br>$+0.035n$ | $+4.635 \cdot 10^{23}$ | $-1.084 \cdot 10^2$ |
| 16th p. | $2.746 \cdot 10$ | $-1.543 \cdot 10^{11}$ | $+6.29 \cdot 10^{18}$ | $-2.957 \cdot 10^{23}$ | $+4.635 \cdot 10^{23}$ | $-1.084 \cdot 10^2$ |
| | $7.541 \cdot 10^2$ | $-2.381 \cdot 10^{22}$<br>$+0.035n$ | $+3.96 \cdot 10^{37}$<br>$-0.01c$ | $-8.744 \cdot 10^{46}$<br>$*$ | $+2.148 \cdot 10^{47}$ | $-1.175 \cdot 10^4$ |
| 32nd p. | $7.541 \cdot 10^2$ | $-2.346 \cdot 10^{22}$ | $+3.95 \cdot 10^{37}$ | $-8.744 \cdot 10^{46}$ | $+2.148 \cdot 10^{47}$ | $-1.175 \cdot 10^4$ |

Solving these by logarithms, we have

$$\log x_1 = \frac{20 + \log 2.346 - \log 7.541}{32} = 0.60915.$$

$$\therefore \quad x_1 = 4.066.$$

In a similar manner we find

$$x_2 = 2.991, \quad x_3 = 1.959, \quad x_4 = 1.0285, \quad x_5 = 0.04447.$$

The signs of these roots are yet to be determined. To do this we first apply Descartes's rule of signs and find that there can not be more than three positive roots nor more than two negative roots. Then we substitute in the given equation the approximate values $\pm 4$, $\pm 3$, $\pm 2$, $\pm 1$, $\pm 0.04$ and see whether the positive or negative value comes nearer to satisfying the equation. In this manner we find that the roots are

$$x_1 = 4.066,$$

$$x_2 = -2.991,$$

$$x_3 = 1.959,$$

$$x_4 = -1.0285,$$

$$x_5 = 0.0445.$$

The sum of these roots is 2.050, whereas it should be $2.52/1.23 = 2.049$. The agreement is therefore as close as could be expected.

All roots found by Graeffe's method should be carefully checked by some means or other.

**70. Case II. Complex Roots.** When some of the roots of an algebraic equation are complex, the equation can not be expressed as a product of linear factors with real coefficients. Such an equation can, however, always be expressed as a product of real linear and real quadratic factors, each quadratic factor corresponding to a pair of complex roots. The root-squaring process can therefore never break up such an equation into linear fragments as in the case when all the roots are real and unequal.

When an equation has complex roots, the root-squaring process always breaks it up into linear and quadratic fragments. The real roots, if any, are found from the linear fragments as in Case I, while the complex roots are found from the quadratic fragments.

In transforming an equation by the root-squaring process the presence of complex roots is revealed in two ways: (1) the doubled products do not all disappear from the first row and (2) the signs of some of the coefficients fluctuate as the transformations continue. The reason for these peculiarities can be seen by considering a typical example.

*70a). Detection of Complex Roots.* Let us consider an equation having two distinct real roots and two pairs of complex roots. Let these roots be $x_1$, $r_1 e^{i\theta_1}$, $r_1 e^{-i\theta_1}$, $x_3$, $r_2 e^{i\theta_2}$, $r_2 e^{-i\theta_2}$; and let the order of their magnitude be

$$|x_1| > r_1 > |x_3| > r_2.$$

Then the equation having these roots is

$$(70\!:\!1)\quad (x - x_1)(x - r_1 e^{i\theta_1})(x - r_1 e^{-i\theta_1})(x - x_3)(x - r_2 e^{i\theta_2})(x - r_2 e^{-i\theta_2}) = 0.$$

The equation whose roots are the $m$th powers of the roots of this equation is therefore

$$(70\!:\!2)\quad (y - x_1^m)(y - r_1^m e^{im\theta_1})(y - r_1^m e^{-im\theta_1})$$
$$\times (y - x_3^m)(y - r_2^m e^{im\theta_2})(y - r_2^m e^{-im\theta_2}) = 0,$$

where $y = x^m$.

On performing the indicated multiplications in $(70\!:\!2)$, then taking out the factors $x_1^m r_1^m$, $x_1^m r_1^{2\,m}$, $x_1^m r_1^{2\,m} x_3^m$, $x_1^m r_1^{2\,m} x_3^m r_2^m$, and neglecting the ratios

$$\frac{r_1^m}{x_1^m},\ \frac{x_3^m}{x_1^m},\ \frac{r_2^m}{x_1^m},\ \frac{x_3^m}{r_1^m},\ \frac{r_2^m}{r_1^m},\ \frac{r_2^m}{x_3^m},$$

since each of these is negligible in comparison with unity, we finally get

$$(70\!:\!3)\quad y^6 - x_1^m y^5 + 2x_1^m r_1^m \cos m\theta_1 y^4 - x_1^m r_1^{2m} y^3 + x_1^m r_1^{2m} x_3^m y^2$$
$$- 2x_1^m r_1^{2m} x_3^m r_2^m \cos m\theta_2 y + x_1^m r_1^{2m} x_3^m r_2^{2m} = 0.$$

The roots of the original equation have now been separated as much as they can ever be (since in deriving $(70\!:\!3)$ we neglected such ratios as $r_1^m/x_1^m$ etc.), and the given equation has been broken up into the linear and quadratic fragments

$$(70\!:\!4)\quad \begin{cases} y^6 - x_1^m y^5 = 0,\ -x_1^m y^5 + 2x_1^m r_1^m \cos m\theta_1\, y^4 - x_1^m r_1^{2m} y^3 = 0, \\ -x_1^m r_1^{2m} y^3 + x_1^m r_1^{2m} x_3^m y^2 = 0, \\ x_3^m y^2 - 2x_1^m r_1^{2\,m} x_3^m r_2^m \cos m\theta_2 y + x_1^m r_1^{2m} x_3^m r_2^{2m} = 0, \end{cases}$$

from which we can obtain the original roots with which we started.

Suppose, now, that we apply the root-squaring process to $(70\!:\!3)$ once more, as shown below:

|  | $y^6$ | $y^5$ | $y^4$ | $y^3$ |
|---|---|---|---|---|
| $m$th p. | 1 | $-x_1{}^m$ | $2x_1{}^m r_1{}^m \cos m\theta_1$ | $-x_1{}^m r_1{}^{2m}$ |
|  | 1 | $-x_1{}^{2m}$<br>$+4x_1{}^m r_1{}^m \cos m\theta_1$ | $+4x_1{}^{2m} r_1{}^{2m} \cos^2 m\theta_1$<br>$-2x_1{}^{2m} r_1{}^{2m}$<br>$+2x_1{}^m r_1{}^{2m} x_3{}^m$ | $-x_1{}^{2m} r_1{}^{4m}$<br>$+4x_1{}^{2m} r_1{}^{3m} x_3{}^m \cos m\theta_1$<br>$-4x_1{}^{2m} r_1{}^{2m} x_3{}^m r_2{}^m \cos m\theta_2$<br>$+2x_1{}^m r_1{}^{2m} x_3{}^m r_2{}^{2m}$ |
| $2m$th p. | 1 | $-x_1{}^{2m}$ | $+4x_1{}^{2m} r_1{}^{2m} \cos^2 m\theta_1$<br>$-2x_1{}^{2m} r_1{}^{2m}$ | $-x_1{}^{2m} r_1{}^{4m}$ |

|  | $y^2$ | $y^1$ | $y^0$ |
|---|---|---|---|
| $m$th p. | $x_1{}^m r_1{}^{2m} x_3{}^m$ | $-2x_1{}^m r_1{}^{2m} x_3{}^m r_2{}^m \cos m\theta_2$ | $x_1{}^m r_1{}^{2m} x_3{}^m r_2{}^{2m}$ |
|  | $+x_1{}^{2m} r_1{}^{4m} x_3{}^{2m}$<br>$-4x_1{}^{2m} r_1{}^{4m} x_3{}^m r_2{}^m \cos m\theta_2$<br>$+4x_1{}^{2m} r_1{}^{3m} x_3{}^m r_2{}^{2m} \cos m\theta_1$ | $-4x_1{}^{2m} r_1{}^{4m} x_3{}^{2m} r_2{}^{2m} \cos^2 m\theta_2$<br>$+2x_1{}^{2m} r_1{}^{4m} x_3{}^m r_2{}^{2m}$ | $+x_1{}^{2m} r_1{}^{4m} x_3{}^{2m} r_2{}^{4m}$ |
| $2m$th p. | $+x_1{}^{2m} r_1{}^{4m} x_3{}^{2m}$ | $-4x_1{}^{2m} r_1{}^{4m} x_3{}^{2m} r_2{}^{2m} \cos^2 m\theta_2$<br>$+2x_1{}^{2m} r_1{}^{4m} x_3{}^{2m} r_2{}^{2m}$ | $+x_1{}^{2m} r_1{}^{4m} x_3{}^{2m} r_2{}^{4m}$ |

It is readily seen on dividing the doubled products in each column by the squared term at the top that all these products are negligible except two in the first row. Hence the sums of the several columns are as given above. This result shows why the doubled products in the first row do not all disappear when complex roots are present.

Furthermore, since $2\cos^2\phi - 1 = \cos 2\phi$, we can write the coefficients of $y^4$ and $y$ in the forms $2x_1{}^{2\,m} r_1{}^{2\,m} \cos 2m\theta_1$ and $-2x_1{}^{2\,m} r_1{}^{4\,m} x_3{}^{2\,m} r_2{}^{2\,m} \cos 2\theta_2$, respectively. Hence the coefficients in the last transformed equation are simply

$$(70\!:\!5) \quad 2m\text{th p. } 1 - x_1{}^{2m} + 2x_1{}^{2m} r_1{}^{2m} \cos 2m\theta_1 - x_1{}^{2m} r_1{}^{4m} + x_1{}^{2m} r_1{}^{4m} x_3{}^{2m}$$
$$- 2x_1{}^{2m} r_1{}^{4m} x_3{}^{2m} r_2{}^{2m} \cos 2m\theta_2 + x_1{}^{2m} r_1{}^{4m} x_3{}^{2m} r_2{}^{4m}.$$

On comparing this last equation with the one for the $m$th powers of the roots we see at once that each application of the root-squaring process doubles the amplitudes of the complex roots. Hence the cosines of these amplitudes must frequently change signs as the amplitudes are continually doubled. This explains the fluctuation in the signs of some of the coefficients when complex roots are present.

After the original equation has been broken up into linear and quadratic fragments by the root-squaring process, we can find the complex roots by solving the resulting quadratic equations for $x^m$ and then extracting the $m$th root of the results by means of De Moivre's theorem. But by proceeding in this manner we would have ambiguities of sign in the computed roots, and such ambiguities are not easily removed. To obtain the complex roots without ambiguity as to signs we derive some further relations between roots and coefficients.

*70b). Relations between the Coefficients of an Algebraic Equation and the Reciprocals of Its Roots.* In the general equation

$$a_0 x^n + a_1 x^{n-1} + a_2 x^{n-2} + \cdots + a_{n-1} x + a_n = 0$$

let us put $x = 1/y$. The result, after clearing of fractions, is

$$a_n y^n + a_{n-1} y^{n-1} + a_{n-2} y^{n-2} + \cdots + a_3 y^3 + a_2 y^2 + a_1 y + a_0 = 0.$$

Hence from the well-known relations between roots and coefficients (p. 201) we have

$$\frac{a_{n-1}}{a_n} = -(y_1 + y_2 + \cdots + y_n),$$

$$\frac{a_{n-2}}{a_n} = y_1 y_2 + y_1 y_3 + \cdots + y_2 y_3 + \cdots,$$

$$\cdots \cdots \cdots \cdots \cdots \cdots \cdots \cdots$$

$$\frac{a_0}{a_n} = (-1)^n y_1 y_2 \cdots y_n;$$

or, since $y = 1/x$,

$$(70:6) \quad \begin{cases} \dfrac{1}{x_1} + \dfrac{1}{x_2} + \cdots + \dfrac{1}{x_n} = -\dfrac{a_{n-1}}{a_n}, \\[2mm] \dfrac{1}{x_1 x_2} + \dfrac{1}{x_1 x_3} + \cdots + \dfrac{1}{x_2 x_3} + \cdots + \dfrac{1}{x_{n-1} x_n} = \dfrac{a_{n-2}}{a_n}, \\[2mm] \cdots \cdots \cdots \cdots \cdots \cdots \cdots \cdots \\[2mm] \dfrac{1}{x_1 x_2 x_3 \cdots x_n} = (-1)^n \dfrac{a_0}{a_n}. \end{cases}$$

These relations between the coefficients and reciprocals of the roots will help us to avoid ambiguities of sign in the computation of complex roots.

*Example 2.* Find all the roots of the equation

$$x^7 - 2x^5 - 3x^3 + 4x^2 - 5x + 6 = 0.$$

*Solution.* The preliminary work of separating the roots is shown on pages 210–211 and should be self-explanatory.

It is evident from the last application of the root-squaring process that another application would effect no further separation of the roots. Hence we stop with the 256th powers of the roots.

The given equation has now been broken up into three linear and two quadratic fragments. We first compute the real roots from the linear fragments.

For the first real root we have by (69 : 1)

$$x_1{}^{256} = 9.084 \times 10^{74},$$

from which we find by logarithms

$$x_1 = 1.9625.$$

The second real root is found from

$$(- 9.084 \cdot 10^{74}) \cdot x_2{}^{256} + 6.472 \cdot 10^{122} = 0.$$

Solving this by logarithms, we find

$$x_2 = 1.5379.$$

The next two roots are complex, but the fifth, a real root, is found from the equation

$$(3.879 \cdot 10^{179}) \cdot x_5{}^{256} - 9.852 \cdot 10^{190} = 0,$$

from which

$$x_5 = 1.1080.$$

To determine the signs of these roots we first apply Descartes's rule of signs to the original equation and find that there can not be more than one negative root. The other two real roots must therefore be positive. On substituting in the original equation the rough values $\pm 2$, we find that $-2$ nearly satisfies the equation. Hence $x_1 = -1.9625$. The three real roots are therefore

$$x_1 = -1.9625, \quad x_2 = 1.5379, \quad x_5 = 1.1080.$$

The modulus of the first pair of complex roots is found from the quadratic equation

(1) $$(6.472 \cdot 10^{122}) y^2 + (2.093 \cdot 10^{151}) y + 3.879 \cdot 10^{179} = 0,$$

where $y = x^{256}$. Let $r_1$ denote this modulus. We find $r_1$ by means of a simple theorem connecting the coefficients of a quadratic equation with the modulus of its complex roots.

Let the quadratic equation

(2) $$x^2 + bx + c = 0,$$

| | $x^7$ | $x^6$ | $x^5$ | $x^4$ | $x^3$ | $x^2$ | $x^1$ | $x^0$ |
|---|---|---|---|---|---|---|---|---|
| Given equa. | 1 | 0 | − 2 | 0 | − 3 | 4 | − 5 | 6 |
| | 1 | 0 | 4 | 0 | 9 | − 16 | 25 | − 36 |
| | | − 4n | 0c | 12n | 0c | 30n | − 48c | |
| | | | − 6n | 0c | 20n | 0c | | |
| | | | | − 10n | 0c | | | |
| 2d p. | 1 | − 4 | − 2 | 2 | 29 | 14 | − 23 | − 36 |
| | 1 | − 16 | 4 | 4 | $8.41\cdot10^2$ | $- 1.96\cdot10^2$ | $5.29\cdot10^2$ | $- 1.296\cdot10^3$ |
| | | − 4n | 16c | − 116n | − 0.56c | − 13.34n | 10.08c | |
| | | | 58n | + 112c | + 0.92n | + 1.44c | | |
| | | | | − 46n | − 2.88c | | | |
| 4th p. | 1 | − 20 | $7.8\cdot10$ | $- 5.4\cdot10$ | $+ 5.89\cdot10^2$ | $- 1.386\cdot10^3$ | $+ 1.537\cdot10^3$ | $- 1.296\cdot10^3$ |
| | 1 | $- 4.00\cdot10^2$ | $+ 6.084\cdot10^3$ | $- 0.2916\cdot10^4$ | $+ 3.4692\cdot10^5$ | $- 1.9210\cdot10^6$ | $+ 2.3624\cdot10^6$ | $- 1.680\cdot10^6$ |
| | | + 1.56n | − 2.160c | + 9.1884n | − 1.4969c | + 1.8106n | − 3.5925c | |
| | | | + 1.178n | + 5.5440c | + 2.3977n | − 0.1400c | | |
| | | | | + 0.3074n | − 0.5184c | | | |
| 8th p. | 1 | $- 2.44\cdot10^2$ | $+ 5.102\cdot10^3$ | $+ 3.660\cdot10^4$ | $+ 3.852\cdot10^5$ | $- 0.2504\cdot10^6$ | $- 1.230\cdot10^6$ | $- 1.680\cdot10^6$ |
| | 1 | $- 5.9536\cdot10^4$ | $+ 2.6030\cdot10^9$ | $- 1.3396\cdot10^9$ | $+ 1.4838\cdot10^{11}$ | $- 0.6270\cdot10^{11}$ | $+ 1.5129\cdot10^{12}$ | $- 2.8224\cdot10^{12}$ |
| | | + 1.0204n | + 1.7861c | + 3.9306n | + 0.1833c | − 9.4759n | − 0.8413c | |
| | | | + 0.0770n | − 0.1222c | − 0.1255n | + 1.2298c | | |
| | | | | − 0.0025n | − 0.0082c | | | |

| | $x^0$ | $x^1$ | $x^2$ | $x^3$ | $x^4$ | $x^5$ | $x^6$ | $x^7$ |
|---|---|---|---|---|---|---|---|---|
| 16th p. | $- 2.822 \cdot 10^{12}$ | $+ 0.6716 \cdot 10^{12}$ | $- 8.873 \cdot 10^{11}$ | $+ 1.533 \cdot 10^{11}$ | $+ 2.466 \cdot 10^{9}$ | $+ 4.466 \cdot 10^{7}$ | $- 4.933 \cdot 10^{4}$ | $1$ |
| | $- 7.964 \cdot 10^{24}$ | $+ 0.4510 \cdot 10^{24}$<br>$- 5.0079c$ | $- 7.873 \cdot 10^{23}$<br>$+ 2.059n$<br>$+ 0.139c$ | $+ 2.350 \cdot 10^{22}$<br>$+ 0.438c$<br>$+ 0.006n$<br>$*$ | $- 0.6081 \cdot 10^{19}$<br>$1.3693n$<br>$0.0088c$<br>$*$ | $+ 1.9945 \cdot 10^{15}$<br>$+ 0.2433c$<br>$+ 0.0003n$ | $- 2.433 \cdot 10^{9}$<br>$+ 0.089n$ | $1$ |
| 32d p. | $- 7.964 \cdot 10^{24}$ | $- 4.557 \cdot 10^{24}$ | $- 5.675 \cdot 10^{23}$ | $+ 2.794 \cdot 10^{22}$ | $+ 0.7524 \cdot 10^{19}$ | $+ 2.238 \cdot 10^{15}$ | $- 2.344 \cdot 10^{9}$ | $1$ |
| | $- 6.343 \cdot 10^{49}$ | $+ 2.077 \cdot 10^{49}$<br>$- 0.904c$ | $- 3.221 \cdot 10^{47}$<br>$- 2.546n$<br>$+ 0.001c$ | $+ 7.806 \cdot 10^{44}$<br>$+ 0.085c$<br>$*$ | $- 0.5661 \cdot 10^{38}$<br>$+ 1.2502n$<br>$*$ | $+ 5.009 \cdot 10^{30}$<br>$+ 0.035c$<br>$*$ | $- 5.494 \cdot 10^{18}$<br>$+ 0.004n$ | $1$ |
| 64th p. | $- 6.343 \cdot 10^{49}$ | $+ 1.173 \cdot 10^{49}$ | $- 5.766 \cdot 10^{47}$ | $+ 7.891 \cdot 10^{44}$ | $+ 6.841 \cdot 10^{37}$ | $5.044 \cdot 10^{30}$ | $- 5.490 \cdot 10^{18}$ | $1$ |
| | $- 4.023 \cdot 10^{99}$ | $+ 1.376 \cdot 10^{98}$<br>$- 0.731c$ | $- 3.325 \cdot 10^{95}$<br>$+ 0.185n$ | $+ 6.227 \cdot 10^{89}$<br>$+ 0.001c$ | $- 4.680 \cdot 10^{75}$<br>$+ 7.960n$ | $+ 2.544 \cdot 10^{61}$<br>$*c$ | $- 3.014 \cdot 10^{37}$<br>$*n$ | $1$ |
| 128th p. | $- 4.023 \cdot 10^{99}$ | $0.645 \cdot 10^{98}$ | $- 3.140 \cdot 10^{95}$ | $+ 6.228 \cdot 10^{89}$ | $+ 3.280 \cdot 10^{75}$ | $+ 2.544 \cdot 10^{61}$ | $- 3.014 \cdot 10^{37}$ | $1$ |
| | $- 1.618 \cdot 10^{199}$ | $+ 0.416 \cdot 10^{196}$<br>$- 0.253c$ | $- 9.860 \cdot 10^{190}$<br>$+ 0.008n$<br>$*$ | $+ 3.879 \cdot 10^{179}$<br>$*c$ | $- 1.076 \cdot 10^{161}$<br>$+ 3.169n$ | $+ 6.472 \cdot 10^{122}$<br>$*c$ | $- 9.084 \cdot 10^{74}$<br>$*n$ | $1$ |
| 256th p. | $- 1.618 \cdot 10^{199}$ | $+ 0.163 \cdot 10^{196}$ | $- 9.852 \cdot 10^{190}$ | $+ 3.879 \cdot 10^{179}$ | $+ 2.093 \cdot 10^{161}$ | $+ 6.472 \cdot 10^{122}$ | $- 9.084 \cdot 10^{74}$ | $1$ |

have the complex roots $re^{i\theta}$ and $re^{-i\theta}$. Then

$$x^2 + bx + c \equiv (x - re^{i\theta})(x - re^{-i\theta})$$
$$\equiv x^2 - r(e^{i\theta} + e^{-i\theta}) + r^2$$
$$\equiv x^2 - (2r\cos\theta)x + r^2.$$

Hence $c = r^2$, $-b = 2r\cos\theta$; that is, *the absolute term in the quadratic* (2) *is equal to the square of the modulus of its complex roots.*

Let $R_1$ denote the modulus of the complex roots of (1). Then on dividing the equation through by $6.472 \times 10^{122}$ and applying the theorem just stated, we get

$$R_1{}^2 = \frac{3.879 \times 10^{57}}{6.472}.$$

Since, however, $R_1 = r_1{}^{256}$, we have

$$r_1{}^{512} = \frac{3.879 \times 10^{57}}{6.472}.$$

Solving this by logarithms, we find

$$r_1 = 1.2909.$$

The modulus of the second pair of complex roots is found in like manner from the quadratic

$$(-9.852 \times 10^{190})y^2 + (0.163 \times 10^{196})y - 1.618 \times 10^{199} = 0,$$

(3)    or    $$y^2 - \frac{0.163 \times 10^6}{9.852}y + \frac{1.618 \times 10^9}{9.852} = 0.$$

Denoting this modulus by $r_2$ and that of (3) by $R_2$, we have

$$R_2{}^2 = \frac{1.618 \times 10^9}{9.852}, \quad \text{or} \quad r_2{}^{512} = \frac{1.618 \times 10^9}{9.852},$$

from which

$$r_2 = 1.0618.$$

Now let the two pairs of complex roots be denoted by

$$u_1 + iv_1, \quad u_1 - iv_1 \quad \text{and} \quad u_2 + iv_2, \quad u_2 - iv_2,$$

respectively. Then since the sum of the roots of the given equation is 0, we have

$$x_1 + x_2 + 2u_1 + x_5 + 2u_2 = 0,$$

or

(4)    $$u_1 + u_2 = -0.3417.$$

We next apply the theorem connecting the sum of the reciprocals of the roots with the coefficients of the given equation, namely

$$\frac{1}{x_1} + \frac{1}{x_2} + \frac{1}{u_1 + iv_1} + \frac{1}{u_1 - iv_1} + \frac{1}{x_5} + \frac{1}{u_2 + iv_2} + \frac{1}{u_2 - iv_2} = \frac{5}{6}.$$

Rationalizing the denominators of the complex terms and putting $u_1^2 + v_1^2 = r_1^2$, $u_2^2 + v_2^2 = r_2^2$, we get

$$\frac{1}{x_1} + \frac{1}{x_2} + \frac{2u_1}{r_1^2} + \frac{1}{x_5} + \frac{2u_2}{r_2^2} = \frac{5}{6}.$$

Now substituting in this equation the numerical values

$$\frac{1}{x_1} = -0.508386,$$

$$\frac{1}{x_2} = 0.6502374, \quad \frac{1}{x_5} = 0.902527, \quad \frac{1}{r_1^2} = 0.60010, \quad \frac{1}{r_2^2} = 0.92875$$

and dividing through by 2, we obtain

(5)        $0.6001u_1 + 0.92875u_2 = -0.10552.$

Solving (4) and (5) simultaneously, we find

$$u_1 = -0.6445, \quad u_2 = 0.3028.$$

$v_1$ and $v_2$ are found from the formulas $v_1 = \sqrt{r_1^2 - u_1^2} = \sqrt{(r_1 + u_1)(r_1 - u_1)}$ and $v_2 = \sqrt{r_2^2 - u_2^2} = \sqrt{(r_2 + u_2)(r_2 - u_2)}$ to be

$$v_1 = 1.1185, \quad v_2 = 1.018.$$

Hence the two pairs of complex roots are

$$-0.6445 \pm 1.118i \quad \text{and} \quad 0.3028 \pm 1.018i.$$

We have thus obtained the complex roots without any ambiguity of signs.

The computed roots in this example can be checked by substituting the values of the real roots and moduli in the known relation

$$x_1 x_2 r_1^2 x_5 r_2^2 = -5/6,$$

or

$$\log (x_1 x_2 r_1^2 x_5 r_2^2) = \log 5/6.$$

These logarithms are found to be

$$0.77816 = 0.77815.$$

The agreement is thus as close as could be expected.

*Remark.* If an equation contains more than two pairs of complex roots, the moduli of the roots can be found from the quadratic fragments as in the example above. Then the real parts $u_1$, $u_2$, $u_3$, $\cdots$ can be found by making further use of the relations connecting the roots and the reciprocals of the roots with the coefficients of the original equation.

In some equations of high degree it might be advantageous, after finding the real roots, to depress the original equation by taking out the real roots and leaving only the complex roots. This is conveniently done by synthetic division. The relations between the roots and coefficients of the depressed equation should then be used.

**71. Case III. Roots Real and Numerically Equal.** If two roots of an equation are numerically equal, the root-squaring process can never break up the equation into linear fragments. One of the doubled products will always remain in the first row. This product will be just half the squared term above it, as can be seen by considering an equation of the third degree.

Let the roots of

$$(71\!:1) \qquad\qquad x^3 + a_1 x^2 + a_2 x + a_3 = 0$$

be $x_1$, $x_2$, $x_3$. Then the equation whose roots are the $m$th powers of those of (71:1) is

$$(y - x_1{}^m)(y - x_2{}^m)(y - x_3{}^m) = 0, \quad \text{where } y = x^m,$$

or

$$y^3 - (x_1{}^m + x_2{}^m + x_3{}^m)y^2 + (x_1{}^m x_2{}^m + x_1{}^m x_3{}^m + x_2{}^m x_3{}^m)y - x_1{}^m x_2{}^m x_3{}^m = 0,$$

or

$$(71\!:2) \quad y^3 - x_1{}^m \left(1 + \frac{x_2{}^m}{x_1{}^m} + \frac{x_3{}^m}{x_1{}^m}\right)y^2$$

$$+ x_1{}^m x_2{}^m \left(1 + \frac{x_3{}^m}{x_2{}^m} + \frac{x_3{}^m}{x_1{}^m}\right)y - x_1{}^m x_2{}^m x_3{}^m = 0.$$

Now let $x_2 = x_3$ and let $|x_1| > |x_2|$. Then for sufficiently large values of $m$ the ratio $x_2{}^m/x_1{}^m$ is negligible in comparison with unity and (71:2) reduces to

$$(71\!:3) \qquad\qquad y^3 - x_1{}^m y^2 + 2 x_1{}^m x_2{}^m y - x_1{}^m x_2{}^{2m} = 0.$$

The roots of the given equation have now been separated as much as they can ever be, but we shall apply the root-squaring process to (71:3) to see what happens. Using only the coefficients, we have

| | | | | |
|---|---|---|---|---|
| $m$th p. | 1 | $-x_1^m$ | $2x_1^m x_2^m$ | $-x_1^m x_2^{2m}$ |
| | 1 | $-x_1^{2m}$ $+4x_1^m x_2^m$ | $+4x_1^{2m}x_2^{2m}$ $-2x_1^{2m}x_2^{2m}$ | $-x_1^{2m}x_2^{4m}$ |
| $2m$th p. | 1 | $-x_1^{2m}$ | $+2x_1^{2m}x_2^{2m}$ | $-x_1^{2m}x_2^{4m}$ |

It will be noticed that the first doubled product is negligible in comparison with the squared term above it, whereas the second is of the *same order of magnitude* as the squared term above and just *half as large*. Furthermore, in the equation for the $2m$th powers of the roots all the coefficients except one are the squares of those in the preceding equation. This remaining one is only *half* the square of the corresponding coefficient in the preceding equation. These peculiarities enable us to detect equal real roots immediately. We shall now show how to compute such roots.

*Example 3.* Solve the equation

$$5x^3 + 2x^2 - 15x - 6 = 0.$$

*Solution.*

| | | | | |
|---|---|---|---|---|
| Given equa. | 5 | 2 | $-15$ | $-6$ |
| | 25 | $-4$ $-150n$ | 225 $+24c$ | $-36$ |
| 2d p. | 25 | $-1.54\cdot10^2$ | $+2.49\cdot10^2$ | $-36$ |
| | $6.25\cdot10^2$ | $-2.3716\cdot10^4$ $+1.2450n$ | $+6.2001\cdot10^4$ $-1.1008c$ | $-1.296\cdot10^3$ |
| 4th p. | $6.25\cdot10^2$ | $-1.1266\cdot10^4$ | $+5.0993\cdot10^4$ | $-1.296\cdot10^3$ |
| | $3.9062\cdot10^5$ | $-1.269\cdot10^8$ $+0.637n$ | $+2.600\cdot10^9$ $-0.029c$ | $-1.680\cdot10^6$ |
| 8th p. | $3.906\cdot10^5$ | $-0.632\cdot10^8$ | $+2.571\cdot10^9$ | $-1.680\cdot10^6$ |
| | $1.526\cdot10^{11}$ | $-3.994\cdot10^{15}$ $+2.008$ | $+6.610\cdot10^{18}$ * | $-2.822\cdot10^{12}$ |
| 16th p. | $1.526\cdot10^{11}$ | $-1.986\cdot10^{15}$ | $6.610\cdot10^{18}$ | $-2.822\cdot10^{12}$ |

The given equation has now been broken up into the simple fragment $(6.610\cdot10^{18})x_3^{16} - 2.822\cdot10^{12} = 0$ and the quadratic fragment

$1.526 \cdot 10^{11} x_1^{32} - 1.986 \cdot 10^{15} x_1^{16} + 6.610 \cdot 10^{18} = 0$. Solving the simple fragment by logarithms, we find

$$x_3 = 0.3999.$$

To find the roots of the quadratic fragment we write the equation in the form

$$x_1^{32} - \frac{1.986 \times 10^4}{1.526} x_1^{16} + \frac{6.61 \times 10^7}{1.526} = 0.$$

Since the roots are known to be equal and since their product is equal to the absolute term of the quadratic, we have

$$x_1^{32} = \frac{6.61 \times 10^7}{1.526}.$$

Solving by logarithms, we get

$$x_1 = 1.732.$$

We check this result by putting the sum of the roots equal to the coefficient of $x_1^{16}$ with its sign changed. Since the roots are equal, we have

$$2x_1^{16} = \frac{1.986 \times 10^4}{1.526},$$

from which

$$x_1 = 1.731.$$

We shall next determine the signs of these roots. By Descartes's rule there can not be more than one positive root nor more than two negative roots. Hence we try $\pm 0.4$ and find that $-0.4$ satisfies the given equation. The other two roots are therefore $\pm 1.732$.

*Remarks.* It would be an easy matter to find the peculiarities in the transformed equation due to the presence of equal pairs of complex roots or to pairs of complex roots having equal moduli and different amplitudes, but as such roots rarely or never occur in practical problems we shall not consider them.

There are methods for improving the values of the real and imaginary parts of complex roots found by the root-squaring process, but these methods are rather long and laborious to apply. For information concerning these methods the reader is referred to Runge and König's *Numerisches Rechnen*, p. 173; Bairstow's *Applied Aerodynamics*, p. 558; and Carvallo's *Resolution Numerique des Equations*, p. 20. Sufficiently accurate values of the roots can usually be obtained by using

Barlow's Tables of squares, cubes, etc. and Crelle's Multiplication Tables, or else by means of a computing machine.

The values of the real roots can be obtained more accurately by applying the Newton-Raphson method to the values found by Graeffe's method.

Carvallo* has extended Graeffe's method to the solution of transcendental equations by expanding the equation into a Taylor series, neglecting the remainder term, and then treating the resulting polynomial as an algebraic equation.

### EXAMPLES ON CHAPTER X

Find to four significant figures all the roots of the following equations:

1. $$7.5x^5 + 5.44x^3 - 3.24x^2 - 1.85x + 0.2 = 0.$$

2. $$3.26x^6 + 4.2x^4 + 3.08x^3 - 7.16x^2 + 1.92x - 7.76 = 0.$$

3. $$x^6 - 6x^5 + 3x^4 + 5x^3 - 6x + 2 = 0.$$

* Loc. cit., p. 24.

# CHAPTER XI

## THE NUMERICAL SOLUTION OF DIFFERENTIAL EQUATIONS

### THE METHOD OF SUCCESSIVE APPROXIMATIONS

**72. Introduction.** Certain types of differential equations are dealt with in text books on calculus and differential equations, and methods are developed for solving equations of the types treated. Comparatively few differential equations, however, can be integrated in finite form. But just as there are methods for finding to any desired degree of accuracy the roots of any algebraic or transcendental equation having numerical coefficients, so likewise there are methods for finding to any desired degree of accuracy the solution of a differential equation having numerical coefficients and given initial conditions.

In the present and succeeding chapters will be set forth four general methods for solving differential equations numerically. The first method to be considered is usually called the method of successive approximations, but is also known as the method of iteration and the method of Picard.* The theoretical soundness of the method was established by Picard as an existence theorem about the year 1890, but the conditions under which the process is valid as used in this chapter were first laid down by F. R. Moulton† in 1918. The methods of applying it have been developed by many workers, beginning with Euler and extending down to the present time. This method is applicable to any ordinary differential equation or to any system of ordinary equations.

**73. Principle of the Method.** Any differential equation of the first order involving the variables $x$ and $y$ can be written in the symbolic form

$$(73:1) \qquad \frac{dy}{dx} = f(x, y).$$

Let us attempt to solve this equation for $y$ in terms of $x$, subject to the condition that $y = y_0$ when $x = x_0$.¶

From (73:1) we have

$$dy = f(x, y)dx.$$

Hence

$$y = \int f(x, y)dx + C = \int \left(\frac{dy}{dx}\right)dx + C.$$

---

* *Journal de Mathematiques*, 4th series, Vol. VI (1890) pp. 197–210.
† *New Methods in Exterior Ballistics*, Ch. V, Chicago, 1926.

Since $y$ is to have the value $y_0$ when $x = x_0$, these last equations may be written in the equivalent forms

$$(73:2) \qquad y = y_0 + \int_{x_0}^{x} f(x, y)dx = y_0 + \int_{x_0}^{x} \left(\frac{dy}{dx}\right) dx.$$

Here the integral term on the right represents the increment in $y$ which must be added to $y_0$ to get the value of $y$ corresponding to any given value of $x$.

Confining our attention for the moment to the first form in (73: 2), namely,

$$y = y_0 + \int_{x_0}^{x} f(x, y)dx ,$$

we observe that the problem is complicated by the presence of $y$ under the integration sign as well as outside. An equation of this kind is called an *integral equation* and can be solved by the method of successive approximations if certain simple conditions (see Art. 78) are satisfied and if the necessary integrations can be performed at each step.

To find a solution of (73: 2) by the method of successive approximations it is readily seen that if the function is continuous and the interval of integration $x - x_0 (= \Delta x)$ is small, the corresponding increment in $y$ is also small. Hence to get a first approximation for $y$ we put $y_0$ for $y$ in the integrand. Then

$$y^{(1)} = y_0 + \int_{x_0}^{x} f(x, y_0)dx.$$

The integrand is now a function of $x$ alone and the integral can therefore be found by a quadrature or computed by some approximation process. Here the superscript (1) denotes the first approximation to the unknown function $y$. Succeeding approximations will be denoted by $y^{(2)}, y^{(3)}, \cdots y^{(n)}$.

Having now a first approximation $y^{(1)}$ for $y$, we substitute it for $y$ in the integrand of (73: 2) and integrate again, thus obtaining a second approximation

$$y^{(2)} = y_0 + \int_{x_0}^{x} f(x, y^{(1)})dx.$$

The process is repeated in this way as many times as may be necessary or desirable, the $n$th approximation being given by the equation

$$y^{(n)} = y_0 + \int_{x_0}^{x} f(x, y^{(n-1)})dx.$$

A simple example will make the process clearer.

*Example.* Solve the differential equation

$$\frac{dy}{dx} = x + y,$$

with the initial conditions $x_0 = 0$, $y_0 = 1$.

*Solution.* To get a first approximation we substitute $y = 1$ in the right-hand member of the given equation, thus obtaining

$$y^{(1)} = 1 + \int_0^x \left(\frac{dy}{dx}\right) dx = 1 + \int_0^x (x + 1)dx = \frac{x^2}{2} + x + 1.$$

For second and third approximations we have

$$y^{(2)} = 1 + \int_0^x \left(x + \frac{x^2}{2} + x + 1\right) dx = \frac{x^3}{6} + x^2 + x + 1,$$

$$y^{(3)} = 1 + \int_0^x \left(x + \frac{x^3}{6} + x^2 + x + 1\right) dx = \frac{x^4}{24} + \frac{x^3}{3} + x^2 + x + 1.$$

We have thus found $y$ as a power series in $x$. For $x = 0.1$ we have

$$y = \frac{0.0001}{24} + \frac{0.001}{3} + 0.01 + 0.1 + 1 = 1.1103.$$

This value of $y$ is correct to four decimal places, as will be pointed out later. For $x = 0.2$ the corresponding value of $y^{(3)}$ is 1.2427, whereas the true value is known to be 1.2428. We could get a better value by continuing the approximations to $y^{(4)}$, $y^{(5)}$, etc.; but it is better to move up to the point $x = 0.1$ and start all over again.

The graphs of $y^{(1)}$, $y^{(2)}$, $y^{(3)}$, and $y = F(x)$ are shown in Fig. 9. It will be seen that the approximating curves approach the curve $y = F(x)$ more closely with each successive approximation.

Taking $x = 0.1$ and $y = 1.1103$ as initial values, we have

$$y^{(1)} = 1.1103 + \int_{0.1}^x (x + 1.1103)dx$$

$$= \frac{x^2}{2} + 1.1103x + 0.9943.$$

Then for second and third approximations we get

$$y^{(2)} = 1.1103 + \int_{0.1}^{x} \left( x + \frac{x^2}{2} + 1.1103x + 0.9943 \right) dx$$

$$= \frac{x^3}{6} + 1.0552x^2 + 0.9943x + 1.0001.$$

$$y^{(3)} = 1.1103 + \int_{0.1}^{x} \left( x + \frac{x^3}{6} + 1.0552x^2 + 0.9943x + 1.0001 \right) dx$$

$$= \frac{x^4}{24} + 0.3517x^3 + 0.9972x^2 + 1.0001x + 1.0000.$$

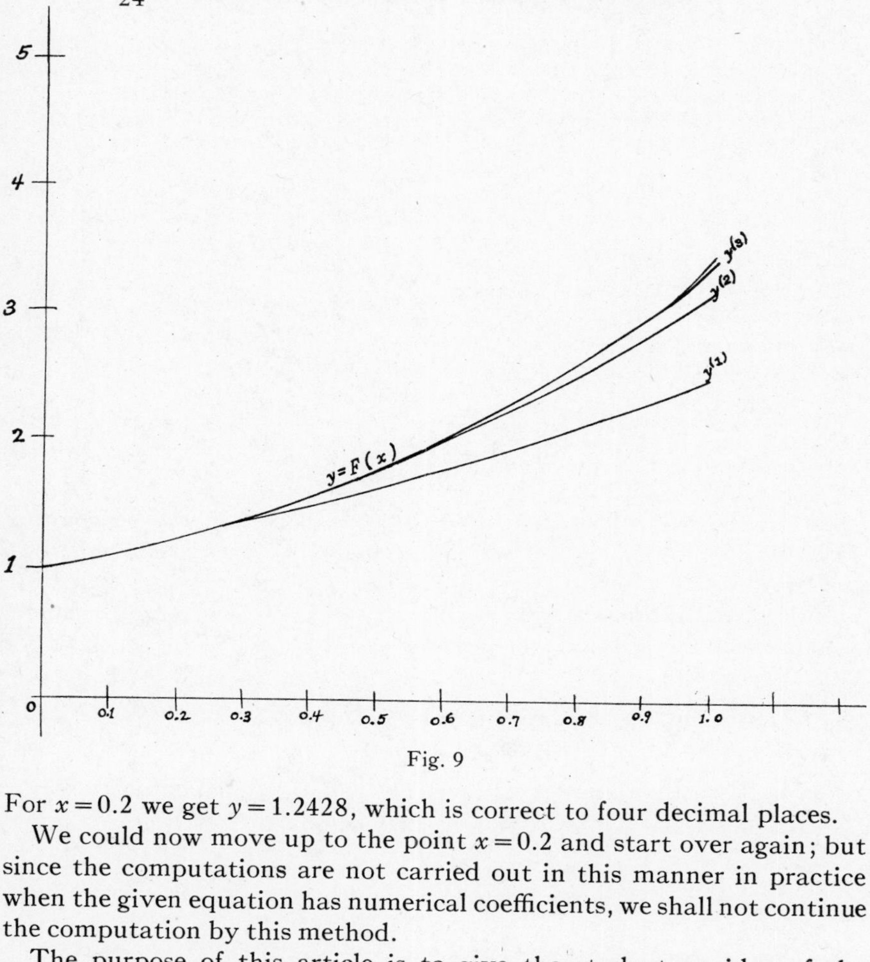

Fig. 9

For $x = 0.2$ we get $y = 1.2428$, which is correct to four decimal places.

We could now move up to the point $x = 0.2$ and start over again; but since the computations are not carried out in this manner in practice when the given equation has numerical coefficients, we shall not continue the computation by this method.

The purpose of this article is to give the student an idea of the underlying principle of the method of successive approximations and also to prepare him for a proof which is to come later. The practical difficulties associated with the method as outlined above lie mostly in the difficult and sometimes impossible integrations which would often have to be performed many times over. For example, if we wished to solve the equation $dy/dx = (y-x)/(y+x)$ with the initial conditions $x_0 = 0$, $y_0 = 1$, we should have

$$y^{(1)} = 1 + \int_0^x \frac{1-x}{1+x} dx = 1 + \int_0^x \left( \frac{2}{1+x} - 1 \right) dx$$

$$= 1 + 2 \log (1 + x) - x,$$

$$y^{(2)} = 1 + \int_0^x \frac{1 + 2 \log (1 + x) - x - x}{1 + 2 \log (1 + x) - x + x} dx$$

$$= 1 + \int_0^x \left( 1 - \frac{2x}{1 + 2 \log (1 + x)} \right) dx;$$

and our troubles would continue to pile up as we continued the approximations. The difficulties would be far greater in other examples which might come up for solution. Fortunately such difficulties and indeed all direct integrations may be avoided by the methods to be explained in the next two articles.

**74. Starting the Solution.** If we integrate the differential equation

(74: 1)
$$\frac{dy}{dx} = f(x, y),$$

we find $y$ as a function of $x$, which may be written in the symbolic form

(74: 2)
$$F(x) + C.$$

The graph of (74: 2) is a curve in the $xy$-plane; and since a smooth curve is practically straight for a short distance from any point on it, we have the approximate relation

(74: 3)
$$\Delta y = \left( \frac{dy}{dx} \right) \Delta x,$$

where the value of the derivative is to be taken at the point $(x, y)$. (If the student is in doubt about the relation (74: 3), he should draw a figure and verify it).

To find points on the graph of (74: 2) and therefore values of $x$ and $y$ satisfying the differential equation (74: 1), we start with the initial values $x = x_0$, $y = y_0$, and let $x$ change by equal increments $\Delta x = h$. Then the values of $y$ corresponding to $x_1 (= x_0 + h)$, $x_2 (= x_1 + h)$, $x_3$, etc. are approximately

$$y_1 = y_0 + \Delta y = y_0 + \left(\frac{dy}{dx}\right)_0 h, \; y_2 = y_1 + \left(\frac{dy}{dx}\right)_1 h,$$

$$y_3 = y_2 + \left(\frac{dy}{dx}\right)_2 h, \; \text{etc.}$$

By taking $h$ small enough and proceeding in this way we could tabulate the integral of (74: 1) as a set of corresponding values of $x$ and $y$. Such was the method of Euler, but it is either too slow (in case $h$ is small) or too inaccurate (in case $h$ is not small) for practical use.

The method which is actually used for starting the numerical integration of a differential equation can be explained best by means of an example. Let us return to the simple equation

$$\frac{dy}{dx} = x + y,$$

with the initial conditions $x_0 = 0$, $y_0 = 1$. The value of the derivative at the point $x_0 = 0$, $y_0 = 1$ is

$$\left(\frac{dv}{dx}\right)_0 = 0 + 1 = 1.$$

If we take $h = 0.05$, an approximate value for $y_1$ is

$$y_1^{(1)} = y_0 + \left(\frac{dy}{dx}\right)_0 h = 1 + 0.05 = 1.05.$$

An approximate value for $dy/dx$ at $(x_1, y_1)$ is therefore

$$\left(\frac{dy}{dx}\right)_1^{(1)} = 0.05 + 1.05 = 1.10.$$

A better value for the increment in $y$ is obtained by multiplying $h$ by the *average* $dy/dx$ for the ends of the interval from $x_0$ to $x_1$ (this is obvious if we think of $dy/dx$ as the rate of change of $y$ with respect to $x$). Hence for the second approximation to $y_1$ we take

$$y_1^{(2)} = y_0 + \frac{\left(\frac{dy}{dx}\right)_0 + \left(\frac{dy}{dx}\right)_1}{2} h = 1 + \frac{1 + 1.10}{2} \times 0.05 = 1.0525.$$

Then a better value for $dy/dx$ at $(x_1, y_1)$ is

$$\left(\frac{dy}{dx}\right)_1^{(2)} = 0.05 + 1.0525 = 1.1025.$$

A third approximation to $y_1$ is then

$$y_1{}^{(3)} = 1 + \frac{1 + 1.1025}{2} \times 0.05 = 1.05256.$$

Continuing the computation, we have

$$\left(\frac{dy}{dx}\right)_1^{(3)} = 0.05 + 1.05256 = 1.10256,$$

$$y_1{}^{(4)} = 1 + \frac{1 + 1.10256}{2} \times 0.05 = 1.05256.$$

Since this is the same as $y_1{}^{(3)}$, we can get no further change in $y$ by continuing the approximations. We therefore take

$$y_1 = 1.0526 \ , \ \left(\frac{dy}{dx}\right)_1 = 1.1026.$$

As a first approximation for $y_2$ we have

$$y_2{}^{(1)} = y_1 + \left(\frac{dy}{dx}\right)_1 h = 1.0526 + 1.1026 \times 0.05 = 1.1077.$$

Hence

$$\left(\frac{dy}{dx}\right)_2^{(1)} = 0.1 + 1.1077 = 1.2077.$$

Then

$$y_2{}^{(2)} = 1.0526 + \frac{1.1026 + 1.2077}{2} \times 0.05 = 1.1104,$$

and

$$\left(\frac{dy}{dx}\right)_2^{(2)} = 0.1 + 1.1104 = 1.2104.$$

Hence

$$y_2{}^{(3)} = 1.0526 + \frac{1.1026 + 1.2104}{2} \times 0.05 = 1.1104 \ ,$$

which is the same as $y_2{}^{(2)}$. We therefore take

$$y_2 = 1.1104 \ , \ \left(\frac{dy}{dx}\right)_2 = 1.2104.$$

Collecting our results in tabular form, we have the following table:

| $x$ | $y$ | $dy/dx$ |
|------|--------|--------|
| 0.00 | 1.0000 | 1.0000 |
| 0.05 | 1.0526 | 1.1026 |
| 0.10 | 1.1104 | 1.2104 |

The process by which we obtained these results in the table is an improvement over Euler's method, but it, too, is too slow for computing a large number of tabular values. It is also of limited accuracy; for the values just found are wrong by one unit in the fourth decimal place, and the inaccuracy can not be corrected by further approximations. At the beginning of the computation it is necessary to proceed as above until two or three lines in the table have been computed, but after that we use the more rapid and accurate methods developed in the next article. Incidentally those methods will enable us to correct the inaccuracies of the earlier computations.

**75. Use of Approximating Polynomials.** We found in Chapter II that any continuous function can be approximated to any desired degree of accuracy by a polynomial. The integrals of all ordinary differential equations occurring in applied mathematics are continuous functions of the argument, at least over considerable intervals, and the derivatives of these functions are also continuous except for an occasional break. The functions and their derivatives can therefore be approximated by polynomials over any intervals where there are no discontinuities in the function or in those derivatives which it is desired to approximate. We therefore assume the following polynomial for $dy/dx$:

$$(75\!:\!1) \quad \frac{dy}{dx} = y' = a_0 + a_1(x - x_n) + a_2(x - x_n)(x - x_{n-1})$$

$$+ a_3(x - x_n)(x - x_{n-1})(x - x_{n-2})$$

$$+ a_4(x - x_n)(x - x_{n-1})(x - x_{n-2})(x - x_{n-3})$$

$$+ a_5(x - x_n)(x - x_{n-1})(x - x_{n-2})(x - x_{n-3})(x - x_{n-4}).$$

This is the form of polynomial that was assumed in Art. 16 when deriving Newton's formula (II), the only difference being that we are now using $y'$ instead of $y$. This form of polynomial is assumed because in this chapter we always know the values of $y'$ behind us and are trying to find its value at the next point ahead. Newton's formula (II) for this case is therefore

$$(75.2) \quad y' = y'_n + u\Delta_1 y'_n + \frac{u(u+1)}{2}\Delta_2 y'_n + \frac{u(u+1)(u+2)}{6}\Delta_3 y'_n$$

$$+ \frac{u(u+1)(u+2)(u+3)}{24}\Delta_4 y'_n$$

$$= y'_n + \Delta_1 y'_n u + \frac{\Delta_2 y'_n}{2}(u^2 + u) + \frac{\Delta_3 y'_n}{6}(u^3 + 3u^2 + 2u)$$

$$+ \frac{\Delta_4 y'_n}{24}(u^4 + 6u^3 + 11u^2 + 6u),$$

where

$$u = \frac{x - x_n}{h} \quad \text{or} \quad x = x_n + hu.$$

Since the change in $y$ for any interval is given by the formula

$$\Delta y = \int_{x_k}^{x_{k+1}} \left(\frac{dy}{dx}\right) dx = \int_{x_k}^{x_{k+1}} y'\, dx,$$

we can find by means of (75:2) the change in $y$ over any interval where $dy/dx$ is continuous. We therefore have for any interval $x_{k+1} - x_k$

$$\Delta y = \int_{x_k}^{x_{k+1}} \left[ y'_n + \Delta_1 y'_n u + \frac{\Delta_2 y'_n}{2}(u^2 + u) \right.$$

$$\left. + \frac{\Delta_3 y'_n}{6}(u^3 + 3u^2 + 2u) + \frac{\Delta_4 y'_n}{24}(u^4 + 6u^3 + 11u^2 + 6u) \right] dx.$$

Since $x = x_n + hu$, we have $dx = h\,du$. Substituting this value for $dx$ above and changing limits, we get

$$\Delta y = h \int_{u_k}^{u_{k+1}} \left[ y'_n + \Delta_1 y'_n u + \frac{\Delta_4 y'_n}{2}(u^2 + u) + \frac{\Delta_3 y'_n}{6}(u^3 + 3u^2 + 2u) \right.$$

$$\left. + \frac{\Delta_4 y'_n}{24}(u^4 + 6u^3 + 11u^2 + 6u) \right] du,$$

or

$$(75:3) \quad \Delta y = h \left[ y'_n u + \Delta_1 y'_n \frac{u^2}{2} + \frac{\Delta_2 y'_n}{2}\left(\frac{u^3}{3} + \frac{u^2}{2}\right) + \frac{\Delta_3 y'_n}{6}\left(\frac{u^4}{4} + u^3 + u^2\right) \right.$$

$$\left. + \frac{\Delta_4 y'_n}{24}\left(\frac{u^5}{5} + \frac{3u^4}{2} + \frac{11u^3}{3} + 3u^2\right) \right]_{u_k}^{u_{k+1}}.$$

Let us now compute the value of $\Delta y$ for the intervals $x_{n+1} - x_n$,

$x_n - x_{n-1}$, $x_{n-1} - x_{n-2}$, etc. by substituting in (75: 3) the proper limits for $u$. For the interval $x_{n+1} - x_n$ the limits for $u$ are

$$u_{k+1} = (x_{n+1} - x_n)/h = h/h = 1, \quad u_k = (x_n - x_n)/h = 0.$$

On substituting these in (75: 3) and simplifying, we get

$$\Delta y = I_n^{n+1} = h\left[ y_n' + \frac{1}{2}\Delta_1 y_n' + \frac{5}{12}\Delta_2 y_n' + \frac{3}{8}\Delta_3 y_n' + \frac{251}{720}\Delta_4 y_n' \right].$$

For the interval $x_n - x_{n-1}$ the limits for $u$ are

$$u_{k+1} = \frac{x_n - x_n}{h} = 0, \quad u_k = \frac{x_{n-1} - x_n}{h} = \frac{-h}{h} = -1;$$

and therefore

$$\Delta y = I_{n-1}^{n} = h\left[ y_n' - \frac{1}{2}\Delta_1 y_n' - \frac{1}{12}\Delta_2 y_n' - \frac{1}{24}\Delta_3 y_n' - \frac{19}{720}\Delta_4 y_n' \right].$$

Proceeding in the same way for the other intervals, we get formulas for the changes in $y$ in those intervals. The results for the several intervals are:

**(75: 4)** $I_n^{n+1} = h\left[ y_n' + \frac{1}{2}\Delta_1 y_n' + \frac{5}{12}\Delta_2 y_n' + \frac{3}{8}\Delta_3 y_n' + \frac{251}{720}\Delta_4 y_n' \right]$,

**(75: 5)** $I_{n-1}^{n} = h\left[ y_n' - \frac{1}{2}\Delta_1 y_n' - \frac{1}{12}\Delta_2 y_n' - \frac{1}{24}\Delta_3 y_n' - \frac{19}{720}\Delta_4 y_n' \right]$,

(75: 6) $I_{n-2}^{n-1} = h\left[ y_n' - \frac{3}{2}\Delta_1 y_n' + \frac{5}{12}\Delta_2 y_n' + \frac{1}{24}\Delta_3 y_n' + \frac{11}{720}\Delta_4 y_n' \right]$,

(75: 7) $I_{n-3}^{n-2} = h\left[ y_n' - \frac{5}{2}\Delta_1 y_n' + \frac{23}{12}\Delta_2 y_n' - \frac{3}{8}\Delta_3 y_n' - \frac{19}{720}\Delta_4 y_n' \right]$,

(75: 8) $I_{n-4}^{n-3} = h\left[ y_n' - \frac{7}{2}\Delta_1 y_n' + \frac{53}{12}\Delta_2 y_n' - \frac{55}{24}\Delta_3 y_n' + \frac{251}{720}\Delta_4 y_u' \right]$.

By adding (75: 4) and (75: 5) and then (75: 5) and (75: 6) we get the following additional formulas:

(75: 9)    $I_{n-1}^{n+1} = h\left[ 2y_n' + \frac{1}{3}\Delta_2 y_n' + \frac{1}{3}\Delta_3 y_n' + \frac{232}{720}\Delta_4 y_n' \right]$

$$= h\left[ 2y_n' + \frac{1}{3}(\Delta_2 y_n' + \Delta_3 y_n' + \Delta_4 y_n') \right],$$

approximately.

$$(75:10) \quad I_{n-2}^{n} = 2h\left[y_n' - \Delta_1 y_n' + \frac{1}{6}\Delta_2 y_n' - \frac{1}{180}\Delta_4 y_n'\right]$$

$$= 2h\left[y_n' - \Delta_1 y_n' + \frac{1}{6}\Delta_2 y_n'\right],$$

approximately.

Now a word as to the use of these formulas. (75: 4) is the formula for *integrating ahead*; it is used for finding the approximate change in $y$ in the next interval ahead of us, thereby enabling us to find the approxmiate value of $y$ at the end of that interval. When a line in the table of corresponding values of $x$ and $y$ has been finished, the first entry in the next line is computed by (75: 4).

Formula (75: 5) is used for correcting and improving the approximate values found by (75: 4). It is not used for starting a new line in the table but for finishing the lines started by (75:4).

Formulas (75: 6), (75: 7), (75: 8) are used for checking previously computed results, such as the first two or three lines in a table when these latter were computed by the method of Art. 74.

(75: 9) is another formula for integrating ahead, by taking two intervals at a time. The increments computed from this formula are to be added not to the last values found but to those next to the last.

(75: 10) is a simple and accurate check formula for two consecutive intervals. It takes account of third and fourth differences, but only first and second differences appear in it.

Formulas (75: 4) and (75: 5) are the main tools with which we shall work from now on in this chapter. It is needless to say that all these formulas apply equally well when the variables are any quantities whatever—time and acceleration, time and velocity, etc. Their use will be illustrated by several examples.

*Example.* We return once more to the differential equation

$$\frac{dy}{dx} = x + y.$$

In Art. 74 we computed the entries in the following table, except that now we have added on the columns of differences.

| $x$ | $y$ | $y'$ | $\Delta_1 y'$ | $\Delta_2 y'$ |
|------|--------|--------|-----------|----------|
| 0.00 | 1.0000 | 1.0000 | | |
| 0.05 | 1.0526 | 1.1026 | +0.1026 | |
| 0.10 | 1.1104 | 1.2104 | +0.1078 | +52 |

Before proceeding further with the computation we had better check the values already found. If $x_n$ denotes the third value of $x$ in the table, then the second and first values will be $x_{n-1}$ and $x_{n-2}$, respectively.

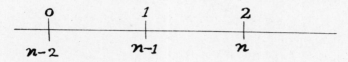

Fig. 10

(See Fig. 10.) To compute the increment in $y$ for the first interval and thereby find $y_1$ we apply formula (75: 6), since it covers the interval $x_{n-1}-x_{n-2}$. We therefore have

$$\Delta y = 0.05 \left[ 1.2104 - \frac{3}{2}(0.1078) + \frac{5}{12}(0.0052) \right] = 0.05254.$$

$$\therefore \quad y_1 = y_0 + \Delta y = 1.0525.$$

For the second interval we apply (75: 5). Then

$$\Delta y = 0.05 \left[ 1.2104 - \frac{1}{2}(0.1078) - \frac{1}{12}(0.0052) \right] = 0.05780.$$

The corrected values of $y$ are therefore $y_1 = 1.0525$,

$$y_2 = 1.0525 + 0.0578 = 1.1103.$$

We now make a new table containing the corrected values for $y$, $y'$, and the first and second differences of $y'$. We also insert in this table a column for $\Delta y$ as a matter of convenience.

| $x$ | $y$ | $\Delta y$ | $y'$ | $\Delta_1 y'$ | $\Delta_2 y'$ | $\Delta_3 y'$ |
|------|--------|---------|--------|----------|------|-----|
| 0.00 | 1.000  |         | 1.000  |          |      |     |
| 0.05 | 1.0525 | +0.0525 | 1.1025 | +0.1025  |      |     |
| 0.10 | 1.1103 | +0.0578 | 1.2103 | +0.1078  | +53  |     |
| 0.15 | 1.1736 | +0.0633 | 1.3236 | +0.1133  | +55  | +2  |
| 0.20 | 1.2427 | +0.0691 | 1.4427 | +0.1191  | +56  | +1  |

The computation is continued by adding a new line to the above table, the line for $x = 0.15$. The first step is to compute a new $\Delta y$ by means of formula (75: 4), using the data of the third line:

$$\Delta y = 0.05 \left[ 1.2103 + \frac{1}{2}(0.1078) + \frac{5}{12}(0.0053) \right] = 0.0633.$$

$$\therefore \quad y_3^{(1)} = 1.1103 + 0.0633 = 1.1736.$$

Then

$$(y')_3^{(1)} = 0.15 + 1.1736 = 1.3236.$$

The next step is to enter these values of $y$ and $y'$ in the fourth line of the table and then compute the differences of $y'$, as shown in the table. The entries in this line must now be checked and improved upon if possible by means of formula (75:5). Thus,

$$\Delta y = 0.05\left[1.3236 - \frac{1}{2}(0.1133) - \frac{1}{12}(0.0055)\right] = 0.0633.$$

Since this is the same value for $y$ as previously found, there is no possibility of improving upon the results in the fourth line and we therefore take them to be correct to four decimal places.

The fifth line in the table is computed in exactly the same way and is found to be correct at the first trial.

The fact that the correct values of $y$ were found at the first trial in lines four and five suggests that it may be expedient to double the interval of integration, in order to progress more rapidly. We therefore take $h = 0.10$ and make a new table with differences to correspond to the longer interval.

| $x$ | $y$ | $\Delta y$ | $y'$ | $\Delta_1 y'$ | $\Delta_2 y'$ | $\Delta_3 y'$ | $\Delta_4 y'$ |
|------|--------|----------|--------|----------|------|-----|----|
| 0.0 | 1.0000 |          | 1.0000 |          |      |     |    |
| 0.1 | 1.1103 | +0.1103  | 1.2103 | +0.2103  |      |     |    |
| 0.2 | 1.2427 | 0.1324   | 1.4427 | +0.2324  | +221 |     |    |
| 0.3 | 1.3995 | 0.1568   | 1.6995 | +0.2568  | +244 | +23 |    |
| 0.3 | 1.3996 | 0.1569   | 1.6996 | +0.2569  | +245 | +24 | +1 |
| 0.4 | 1.5835 | 0.1839   | 1.9835 | +0.2839  | +270 | +25 | 1  |
| 0.5 | 1.7973 | 0.2138   | 2.2973 | +0.3138  | 299  | +29 | 4  |
| 0.6 | 2.0441 | 0.2468   | 2.6441 | +0.3468  | 330  | +31 | 2  |
| 0.7 | 2.3274 | 0.2833   | 3.0274 | +0.3833  | 365  | +35 | 4  |
| 0.8 | 2.6510 | 0.3236   | 3.4510 | 0.4236   | 403  | 38  | 3  |
| 0.9 | 3.0191 | 0.3681   | 3.9191 | 0.4681   | 445  | 42  | 4  |
| 1.0 | 3.4364 | 0.4173   | 4.4364 | 0.5173   | 492  | 47  | 5  |
| 1.0 | 3.4365 | 0.4174   | 4.4365 | 0.5174   | 493  | 48  | 1  |

To start the line for $x = 0.3$, we first compute $\Delta y$ by means of (75:4), using the data in the line for $x = 0.2$. We have

$$\Delta y = 0.1[1.4427 + 0.1162 + 0.0092] = 0.1568.$$

Hence $y_{0.3}^{(1)} = 1.2427 + 0.1568 = 1.3995$, and $(y')_{0.3}^{(1)} = 1.6995$. We now enter these values in the table and compute the differences for that line.

Checking these values by means of (75: 5), we get

$$\Delta y = 0.1(1.6995 - 0.1284 - 0.0020 - 0.0001) = 0.1569.$$

Since this value of $\Delta y$ is different from that previously found, we repeat the line for $x = 0.3$ and write this value of $\Delta y$ in the new line. The second approximations for $y_{0.3}$ and $(y')_{0.3}$ are then

$$y_{0.3}^{(2)} = 1.2427 + 0.1569 = 1.3996,$$
$$(y')_{0.3}^{(2)} = 1.6996.$$

Entering these values in the new line, computing the corresponding differences, and then applying formula (75: 5) to the data of this line, we have

$$\Delta y = 0.1(1.6996 - 0.1284 - 0.0020 - 0.0002) = 0.1569.$$

Since this is the same value for $\Delta y$ as previously found, we consider the results in this second line for $x = 0.3$ to be correct.

The computations are continued up to $x = 1$, as shown in the table. It so happens that formula (75: 4) gives the correct result for every line except the last. Fourth differencies are used in formula (75: 4), but never in (75: 5). The coefficient $251/720$ in (75: 4) may be taken as $\frac{1}{3}$ to simplify the computations.

The exact solution of the differential equation $dy/dx = x+y$, with the initial conditions $x_0 = 0$, $y_0 = 1$, is

$$y = 2e^x - x - 1.$$

By means of this equation we can compute the exact value of $y$ corresponding to any value of $x$. The following table gives the correct values of $y$ for values of $x$ differing by one tenth.

| $x$ | $y$ | $x$ | $y$ |
|-----|-----|-----|-----|
| 0   | 1      | 0.6 | 2.0442 |
| 0.1 | 1.1103 | 0.7 | 2.3275 |
| 0.2 | 1.2428 | 0.8 | 2.6511 |
| 0.3 | 1.3997 | 0.9 | 3.0192 |
| 0.4 | 1.5836 | 1.0 | 3.4366 |
| 0.5 | 1.7974 |     |        |

It will be noticed that the values found by numerical integration are in error by one unit in the last decimal place, beginning with the value for $x = 0.2$. The truth is that the source of these errors is in the value 1.2427, which is in error by one unit in the last figure. This error was simply carried on by addition throughout the table. To avoid such errors it is necessary to have the first two or three lines in the table correct.

*Note.* There is another method for starting a new line in the table without the use of formula (75: 4). It consists in assuming that the third difference in the next line will be the same as in the line just finished, and then working backwards by adding the new differences to the values in the previous line. For example, suppose we take the line for $x = 0.8$ and try to find the next line. We have

| $x$ | $y$ | $\Delta y$ | $y'$ | $\Delta_1 y'$ | $\Delta_2 y'$ | $\Delta_3 y'$ |
|------|--------|--------|----------|----------|-------|------|
| 0.8 | 2.6510 | 0.3236 | 3.4510 | 0.4236 | 403 | 38 |
| 0.9 | 3.0191 | 0.3681 | (3.9187) | (0.4677) | (441) | (38) |
| 0.9 | 3.0191 | 0.3681 | 3.9191 | 0.4681 | 445 | 42 |

The first step in this procedure was to assume that the third difference in the line for $x = 0.9$ was 0.0038, the same value as given in the line above. Then we added this 0.0038 to the second difference 0.0403 in the line above. This gave us a second difference for the new line. We added this 0.0441 to the first difference in the line above and obtained a new first difference 0.4677. This was then added to the previous $y'$ to get the value 3.9187 for $y'$ in the new line.

The next step is to apply formula (75: 5) to this new line, using the quantities enclosed in parentheses (these quantities are enclosed in parentheses to indicate that they are trial or assumed values). We thus get

$$\Delta y = 0.1(3.9187 - 0.2338 - 0.0034 - 0.0002) = 0.3681.$$

This value of $\Delta y$ happens to be correct. We now add this to the previous $y$ to get the new value of $y$ and thus complete the line. But now the new $y'$ must be computed by adding the value of $x$ to this new $y$. We therefore repeat the line for $x = 0.9$ and insert the correct values of all the quantities. In some instances it would be necessary to correct this second line.

The method just outlined in this note is not as much trouble to apply as it may seem from the description above, but nevertheless it requires more labor than the method of integrating ahead by (75: 4) and will therefore not be used in this book.

**76. Equations of the Second Order and Systems of Simultaneous Equations.** Any differential equation of the second or higher order can be reduced to a system of first order equations by the introduction of auxiliary variables. Thus, the second order equation

$$(76:1) \qquad \frac{d^2y}{dx^2} + a\frac{dy}{dx} + by = 0$$

can be reduced to two first order equations by putting $y' = dy/dx$. The resulting equations are

$$(76:2) \qquad \left\{ \begin{array}{l} \dfrac{dy}{dx} = y', \\[2ex] \dfrac{dy'}{dx} = -ay' - by. \end{array} \right.$$

In like manner any equation of higher order or any system of equations of the second or higher order can be reduced to a system of equations of the first order. A few examples will serve to illustrate the method of procedure in such cases.

*Example 1.* A baseball is batted with an initial velocity of 150 feet per second at an angle of 23° with the horizon. Assuming that the air resistance is proportional to the first power of the velocity and that the resistance coefficient (proportionality factor) is 0.02, find the range of the ball and the time of flight.

*Solution.* The equations of motion under the conditions stated are

$$\left\{ \begin{array}{l} \dfrac{d^2x}{dt^2} = -0.02\dfrac{dx}{dt}, \\[2ex] \dfrac{d^2y}{dt^2} = -0.02\dfrac{dy}{dt} - g. \end{array} \right.$$

Putting

$$\dot{x} = \frac{dx}{dt}, \quad \ddot{x} = \frac{d\dot{x}}{dt} = \frac{d^2x}{dt^2},$$

$$\dot{y} = \frac{dy}{dt}, \quad \ddot{y} = \frac{d\dot{y}}{dt} = \frac{d^2y}{dt^2},$$

we have

$$\left\{ \begin{array}{l} \ddot{x} = -0.02\dot{x}, \\[1ex] \ddot{y} = -0.02\dot{y} - g. \end{array} \right.$$

Since these two equations are entirely independent of each other, the first not containing $y$ or any of its derivatives and the second not containing $x$ or any of its derivatives, we shall integrate them separately, taking the $y$-equation first. Taking $g = 32.16$ ft./sec.², the equations with which we shall work are

(1)    $\ddot{y} = -0.02\dot{y} - 32.16;$

(2)    $\Delta \dot{y} = \displaystyle\int_{t_n}^{t_{n+1}} \ddot{y}\, dt = \Delta t \left[ \ddot{y} + \frac{1}{2}\Delta_1 \ddot{y} + \frac{5}{12}\Delta_2 \ddot{y} + \frac{3}{8}\Delta_3 \ddot{y} + \frac{1}{3}\Delta_4 \ddot{y} \right],$

for starting a new line;

(3)    $\Delta \dot{y} = \displaystyle\int_{t_{n-1}}^{t_n} \ddot{y}\, dt = \Delta t \left[ \ddot{y} - \frac{1}{2}\Delta \ddot{y}_1 - \frac{1}{12}\Delta_2 \ddot{y} - \frac{1}{24}\Delta_3 \ddot{y} \right],$

for finishing the new line, except for $y$;

(4)    $\Delta y = \displaystyle\int_{t_{n-1}}^{t_n} \dot{y}\, dt = \Delta t \left[ \dot{y} - \frac{1}{2}\Delta_1 \dot{y} - \frac{1}{12}\Delta_2 \dot{y} - \frac{1}{24}\Delta_3 \dot{y} \right],$

for finding $y$ in the new line.   Here the $t_{n+1}$ in (2) represents the same instant as $t_n$ in (3) and (4).

The first step in starting the computation is to find the vertical velocity and acceleration at the instant the ball leaves the bat. For the velocity we have

$$\dot{y}_0 = 150 \sin 23° = 58.61 \text{ ft./sec.}$$

Substituting this value of $\dot{y}$ in (1), we get for the initial acceleration

$$\ddot{y}_0 = -0.02 \times 58.61 - 32.16 = -33.33 \text{ ft./sec}^2.$$

These values give the first line in the table.

To get the next line we assume that the acceleration will remain practically constant for a short time, say $\frac{1}{2}$ second. Then the decrease in velocity during the first half a second is approximately

$$\Delta \dot{y} = \tfrac{1}{2}(-33.33) = -16.66,$$

and the velocity of the ball at the *end* of this half second is therefore about

$$\overset{(1)}{\dot{y}_{1/2}} = \dot{y}_0 + \Delta \dot{y} = 58.61 - 16.66 = 41.95 \text{ ft./sec.}$$

Substituting this value of $\dot{y}$ in (1), we get a second approximation for the acceleration at the end of the first half second, namely

$$\overset{(2)}{\ddot{y}_{1/2}} = -0.02 \times 41.95 - 32.16 = -33.00 \text{ ft./sec}^2.$$

Then a better approximation for the change in velocity is obtained by multiplying the time interval by the *average* of the acceleration at the beginning and at the end of the interval. Thus,

$$\Delta \dot{y} = \frac{1}{2}\left(\frac{-33.33 - 33.00}{2}\right) = -16.58.$$

Hence $\dot{y}^{(2)}{}_{1/2} = 58.61 - 16.58 = 42.03$. Substituting this in (1), we get $\ddot{y}^{(3)}{}_{1/2} = -33.00$, which is the same as $\ddot{y}^{(2)}{}_{1/2}$.

We have therefore finished the computation for the velocity and acceleration at the end of the first half second. To find the increase in $y$ during the first interval we multiply the time by the average velocity. Hence

$$\Delta y = \frac{1}{2}\frac{(58.61 + 42.03)}{2} = 25.16 \text{ ft.}$$

The second line in the table is now complete for $y$, $\dot{y}$, $\ddot{y}$, and the first differences are entered.

To start the third line we integrate ahead by (2) to find the approximate change in velocity in the next half second. The result is

$$\Delta \dot{y} = -16.42,$$

and therefore the velocity at the end of the second interval is about

$$\dot{y}_1^{(1)} = 42.03 - 16.42 = 25.61 \text{ ft./sec.}$$

Substituting this in (1), we find the acceleration at the end of the second interval to be

$$\ddot{y} = -32.67.$$

We now enter these values in the third line, form the differences, and check the change in velocity by means of (3). The change checks up to be the same as previously found and we therefore take the values of velocity and acceleration to be correct. The corresponding increment in $y$ is computed by means of (4), as follows:

$$\Delta y = \tfrac{1}{2}(25.61 + 8.21 - 0.01) = 16.90.$$

Hence $y_1 = 25.16 + 16.90 = 42.06$, and the third line is complete.

Since the computation is now well started, we can double the time interval in this example without loss of accuracy. We therefore take $\Delta t = 1$ second and begin a new table, taking as the first line the initial values of $\dot{y}$ and $\ddot{y}$, and as the second line the values of these quantities already found for $t = 1$. The first differences for the longer interval are then entered in the second line. The third and succeeding lines are computed exactly as the third line was computed in the short table at the beginning.

| $t$ | $y$ | $\Delta y$ | $\dot{y}$ | $\Delta_1 \dot{y}$ | $\Delta_3 \dot{y}$ | $\Delta_5 \dot{y}$ | $\ddot{y}$ | $\Delta_1 \ddot{y}$ | $\Delta_3 \ddot{y}$ | $\Delta_5 \ddot{y}$ |
|---|---|---|---|---|---|---|---|---|---|---|
| 0 | 0 | | 58.61 | | | | −33.33 | | | |
| $\frac{1}{2}$ | | 25.16 | 41.95 | −16.66 | | | −33.00 | +0.33 | | |
| $\frac{1}{2}$ | 25.16 | | 42.03 | −16.58 | | | −33.00 | +0.33 | | |
| 1 | 42.06 | 16.90 | 25.61 | −16.42 | +0.16 | | −32.67 | +0.33 | 0.00 | |
| 0 | 0 | | 58.61 | | | | −33.33 | | | |
| 1 | 42.06 | | 25.61 | −33.00 | | | −32.67 | +0.66 | −0.02 | +0.02 |
| 2 | | | −6.73 | −32.34 | +0.66 | −0.02 | −32.03 | +0.64 | −0.02 | −0.02 |
| 2 | 51.45 | 9.39 | −6.74 | −32.35 | +0.65 | −0.01 | −32.03 | +0.64 | 0.00 | −0.02 |
| 3 | | | −38.46 | −31.72 | +0.63 | 0.00 | −31.39 | +0.64 | 0.00 | |
| 3 | 28.81 | −22.64 | −38.45 | −31.71 | +0.64 | −0.01 | −31.39 | +0.64 | 0.00 | |
| 4 | | | −69.52 | −31.07 | +0.64 | | −30.77 | +0.62 | −0.02 | |
| 4 | −25.22 | −54.03 | −69.53 | −31.08 | +0.63 | | −30.77 | +0.62 | −0.02 | |

To find the time of flight, assuming the ground to be level, we find the value of $t$ for $y = 0$. Since the relation between $y$ and $t$ is not supposed to be known, we assume that the part of the path through the points where $y$ has the values 51.45, 28.81, and $-25.22$ is the arc of a common parabola and that $y$ is therefore a quadratic function of $t$. Hence, using the first three terms of the interpolation formula (16: 2), we have

$$y = y_4 + \Delta_1 y_4(t - 4) + \frac{\Delta_2 y_4}{2}(t - 4)(t - 3).$$

To find the differences to be used in this formula we construct the small table

| $y$ | $\Delta_1 y$ | $\Delta_2 y$ |
|---|---|---|
| 51.45 | | |
| 28.81 | $-22.64$ | |
| $-25.22$ | $-54.03$ | $-31.39$ |

Hence

$$y = -25.22 - 54.03(t - 4) - \frac{31.39}{2}(t - 4)(t - 3).$$

Putting $y = 0$ and simplifying the terms on the right, we get

$$15.7\, t^2 - 55.87\, t = 2.5.$$

Solving this for $t$, we find $t = 3.60$ seconds as the time of flight.

The range is found by integrating the equation

(5) $$\ddot{x} = -0.02\dot{x}$$

from $t = 0$ to $t = 3.60$ seconds. The integration is carried out exactly as in the case for $y$, except that the value of $x$ is not computed for the separate intervals. The reason for not computing $x$ as we go along is that the values are not called for, only the range being desired. This is readily found by integrating the velocity by means of Simpson's rule. The following table gives the results of the numerical integration of (5).

| $t$ | $\dot{x}$ | $\Delta_1 \dot{x}$ | $\ddot{x}$ | $\Delta_1 \ddot{x}$ | $\Delta_2 \ddot{x}$ | $\Delta_3 \ddot{x}$ |
|---|---|---|---|---|---|---|
| 0 | 138.08 | | $-2.762$ | | | |
| $\frac{1}{3}$ | 136.70 | $-1.38$ | $-2.734$ | $+28$ | | |
| $\frac{2}{3}$ | 136.71 | $-1.37$ | $-2.734$ | $+28$ | | |
| 1 | 135.35 | $-1.36$ | $-2.707$ | $+27$ | $-1$ | |
| | | | | | | |
| 0 | 138.08 | | $-2.762$ | | | |
| 1 | 135.35 | $-2.73$ | $-2.707$ | $+0.055$ | | |
| 2 | 132.65 | $-2.70$ | $-2.653$ | $+0.054$ | $-1$ | |
| 2 | 132.67 | $-2.68$ | $-2.653$ | $0.054$ | $-1$ | |
| 3 | 130.04 | $-2.63$ | $-2.601$ | $0.052$ | $-2$ | $-1$ |
| 4 | 127.46 | $-2.58$ | $-2.549$ | $0.052$ | $0$ | $+2$ |

To find the range we have

$$x = \int_0^4 \dot{x}\, dt = \tfrac{1}{3}[138.08 + 4(135.35 + 130.04) + 2 \times 132.67 + 127.46]$$

$$= 530.81 \text{ ft.},$$

by Simpson's rule. But this result is too great, because the time of flight is only 3.6 seconds. Since the velocity decreased by 2.58 ft./sec. from $t=3$ to $t=4$, it is evident that it decreased about $2.58 \times 0.6 = 1.55$ ft./sec. from $t=3$ to $t=3.6$. Hence the velocity for $t=3.6$ is about $130.04 - 1.55 = 128.49$. The distance the ball would have traveled from $t=3.6$ to $t=4$ is therefore about

$$\frac{128.49 + 127.46}{2} \times 0.4 = 51.19 \text{ ft.}$$

Hence the range is about $530.81 - 51.19 = 479.6$ ft. $= 160$ yards, say.

*Remarks.* The given differential equations in this example can be integrated in analytical form. The results are

$$x = 6904(1 - e^{-0.02t}),$$

$$y = 83325(1 - e^{-0.02t}) - 1608\, t.$$

By putting $y=0$ in the second equation we find $t=3.60$, as before. When this value of $t$ is substituted in the first equation we find $x=479.6$ ft. for the range. The values for $y$ at the ends of the several time intervals are found to be

$$y_1 = 42.00, \quad y_2 = 51.22, \quad y_3 = 28.47, \quad y_4 = -25.67.$$

The discrepancies between these values and the corresponding values found by numerical integration are due quite as much to the inherent inaccuracy of the analytical formula for $y$ as to the method of numerical integration. The inaccuracy of the formula for $y$ lies in the fact that $y$ is equal to the difference of two quantities which are nearly equal (Art. 6).

If there had been no air resistance in this problem, the range of the ball would have been 503.3 feet.

*Example 2.* When a pendulum swings in a resisting medium its equation of motion is of the form

$$\frac{d^2\theta}{dt^2} + a\frac{d\theta}{dt} + b\sin\theta = 0,$$

where $a$ and $b$ are constants. Assuming $a=0.2$, $b=10$, tabulate the integral of the above equation for a complete period (double swing), taking as initial conditions $\theta=0.3$ radian and $d\theta/dt=0$ when $t=0$.

*Solution.*  Putting

$$\dot{\theta} = \frac{d\theta}{dt}, \qquad \ddot{\theta} = \frac{d\dot{\theta}}{dt} = \frac{d^2\theta}{dt^2},$$

we have the equations

$$\left\{ \begin{array}{l} \dfrac{d\theta}{dt} = \dot{\theta}, \\[3ex] \dfrac{d\dot{\theta}}{dt} = \ddot{\theta} = -0.2\dot{\theta} - 10\sin\theta. \end{array} \right.$$

Since the second equation involves the angle $\theta$ directly, it is necessary to compute this angle at every step throughout the computation. Also, since $\theta$ in this problem is always expressed in radians it is practically necessary to have at hand a table of circular functions in which the argument is given in radians* instead of degrees, minutes, and seconds.

The formulas used in the solution of this example are:

(1)     $\ddot{\theta} = -0.02\dot{\theta} - 10\sin\theta,$

given equation;

(2)   $\Delta\dot{\theta} = \displaystyle\int_{t_n}^{t_{n+1}} \ddot{\theta}\,dt = \Delta t \left( \ddot{\theta}_n + \frac{1}{2}\Delta_1\ddot{\theta}_n + \frac{5}{12}\Delta_2\ddot{\theta}_n + \frac{3}{8}\Delta_3\ddot{\theta}_n + \frac{1}{3}\Delta_4\ddot{\theta}_n \right),$

from starting a new line;

(3)   $\Delta\dot{\theta} = \displaystyle\int_{t_{n-1}}^{t_n} \ddot{\theta}\,dt = \Delta t \left( \ddot{\theta}_n - \frac{1}{2}\Delta_1\ddot{\theta}_n - \frac{1}{12}\Delta_2\ddot{\theta}_n - \frac{1}{24}\Delta_3\ddot{\theta}_n \right),$   for

checking and correcting the value of $\dot{\theta}$ found by (2);

(4)   $\Delta\theta = \displaystyle\int_{t_{n-1}}^{t_n} \dot{\theta}\,dt = \Delta t \left( \dot{\theta}_n - \frac{1}{2}\Delta_1\dot{\theta}_n - \frac{1}{12}\Delta_2\dot{\theta}_n - \frac{1}{24}\Delta_3\dot{\theta}_n \right),$

for finding $\theta$ in the new line; where $t_{n+1}$ in (2) denotes the same instant as $t_n$ in (3) and (4). After the computation is well started, these formulas are applied in the following order: (2), (4), (1); (3), (4), (1); (3), (4), (1), until the new line is finished.

The computation is started as follows: For the acceleration at the start we have

$$\ddot{\theta}_0 = -10\sin 0.3 = -2.955 \text{ rad./sec.}^2$$

We now have the values for the first line in the table. To start the next line we assume that the initial acceleration will continue unchanged

---

* An excellent table of this kind is contained in *Smithsonian Mathematical Tables. Hyperbolic Functions.* Washington, 1909.

for 0.05 second. Then the change in velocity for this interval is about

$$\Delta \dot{\theta} = 0.05(-2.955) = -0.1478 \text{ rad./sec.}$$

Hence the angular velocity at the *end* of 0.05 second is about

$$\dot{\theta}_1 = -0.1478 \text{ rad./sec.}$$

The decrease in the angle $\theta$ is then

$$\Delta \theta = \frac{\dot{\theta}_0 + \dot{\theta}_1}{2} \times 0.05 = -\frac{0.1478}{2} \times 0.05 = -0.0037 \text{ rad.}$$

Hence the value of $\theta$ at the end of the first time interval is

$$\theta_1 = 0.3 - 0.0037 = 0.2963 \text{ radian.}$$

These values of $\dot{\theta}_1$ and $\theta_1$ are now substituted in (1), and the corresponding value of $\ddot{\theta}_1$ is found to be

$$\ddot{\theta}_1 = -2.890 \text{ rad./sec}^2.$$

A better value of $\Delta \dot{\theta}$ is now computed by taking the *average* of $\ddot{\theta}_0$ and $\ddot{\theta}_1$, giving

$$\Delta \dot{\theta} = -\frac{2.955 + 2.890}{2} \times 0.05 = -0.1461.$$

The improved value of $\dot{\theta}$ is then $-0.1461$. As a second approximation for $\Delta \theta$ we have

$$\Delta \theta = \frac{-0.1461}{2} \times 0.05 = -0.0037,$$

and therefore $\theta_1 = 0.2963$. Substituting in (1) these improved values of $\dot{\theta}$ and $\theta$, we find

$$\ddot{\theta} = -2.891.$$

The cycle of computations is repeated once more, with the final results

$$\theta = 0.2963, \quad \dot{\theta} = -0.1462, \quad \ddot{\theta} = -2.891.$$

This completes the second line in the table, except for the differences, which are now entered.

Additional lines up to $t = 0.20$ are computed by means of formulas (2), (4), (1), (3), etc. Since the correct value of $\dot{\theta}$ for the lines $t = 0.15$ and $t = 0.20$ is given by a single application of (2) alone, it seems advisable to double the time interval before proceeding further with the computation. We therefore take $\Delta t = 0.1$ second and start a new table.

Before proceeding with the new table, however, we should check the values of $\Delta \dot{\theta}$ and $\Delta \theta$ in the short table already computed. We therefore apply formulas (75: 8), (75: 7), (75: 6) and find that $\Delta \dot{\theta}$ in the first interval should be $-0.1464$ instead of $-0.1462$. The short table is accordingly corrected from the second line onward, so as to get the correct values of the quantities in the lines for $t=0.1$ and $t=0.2$. The corrected table and not the original is given at the top of the main table.

The preliminary or trial lines are not given in the tabulated solution. Usually the correct values for $\theta$ and $\ddot{\theta}$ were found at the first trial, but the preliminary values of $\dot{\theta}$ had to be corrected in nearly all cases.

The student should notice that the time interval $\Delta t$ must be taken small in this example, because all the dependent quantities are changing rapidly. An interval longer than 0.1 second would be too inaccurate.

Fourth differences in the case of acceleration are used in (2) for starting a new line, but in no other case.

The computation for the line $t=1.2$ will now be given. Using the data of the line for $t=1.1$, we find $\Delta\dot{\theta}$ by means of (2). Thus,

$$\Delta\dot{\theta} = 0.1(2.497 - 0.091 - 0.106 + 0.001 + 0.009) = 0.2310.$$

Adding this to the previous $\dot{\theta}$, we get 0.4948 for $\dot{\theta}$ in the new line. We next compute $\Delta_2\theta$ and $\Delta_3\theta$ and then apply (4) to the data in the new line. We therefore have

$$\Delta\theta = 0.1(0.4948 - 0.1155 + 0.0025 + 0.0010) = 0.0383.$$

Adding this to the previous value of $\theta$, we get $-0.2195$ for the new $\theta$. On substituting in (1) these values of $\dot{\theta}$ and $\theta$ we find

$$\ddot{\theta} = 2.078.$$

The values of $\Delta_1\ddot{\theta}$, $\Delta_2\ddot{\theta}$, $\Delta_3\ddot{\theta}$ are next computed, and then the completed preliminary line is found to be

| $t$ | $\theta$ | $\Delta\theta$ | $\dot{\theta}$ | $\Delta_1\dot{\theta}$ | $\Delta_2\dot{\theta}$ | $\Delta_3\dot{\theta}$ | $\ddot{\theta}$ | $\Delta_1\ddot{\theta}$ | $\Delta_2\ddot{\theta}$ | $\Delta_3\ddot{\theta}$ |
|---|---|---|---|---|---|---|---|---|---|---|
| 1.2 | $-0.2195$ | 0.0383 | 0.4948 | 0.2310 | $-0.0299$ | $-0.0243$ | 2.078 | $-0.419$ | $-0.237$ | 0.018 |

Formula (3) is now applied to this line to check the value of $\Delta_1\dot{\theta}$ previously found by (2), giving

$$\Delta\dot{\theta} = 0.1(2.078 + 0.210 + 0.020 - 0.001) = 0.2307.$$

A better value for $\dot{\theta}$ is then $\dot{\theta}=0.2638+0.2307=0.4945$. The new differences $\Delta_2\theta$ and $\Delta_3\theta$ are next computed, and then formula (4) is applied again. The resulting $\Delta\theta$ is 0.0383, as previously found. These corrected values of $\dot{\theta}$ and $\theta$ are now substituted in (1), with the result that $\ddot{\theta}=2.078$, as before. The corrected differences $\Delta_1\ddot{\theta}$, $\Delta_2\ddot{\theta}$, $\Delta_3\ddot{\theta}$ will therefore be the same as previously found, and consequently a new application of (3) will give the same $\Delta\dot{\theta}$ as last found. The line for $t=1.2$ is therefore correct throughout.

The results in the table are shown graphically in Fig. 11.

| $t$ | $\theta$ | $\Delta\theta$ | $\dot\theta$ | $\Delta_1\dot\theta$ | $\Delta_2\dot\theta$ | $\Delta_3\dot\theta$ | $\ddot\theta$ | $\Delta_1\ddot\theta$ | $\Delta_2\ddot\theta$ | $\Delta_3\ddot\theta$ | $\Delta_4\ddot\theta$ |
|---|---|---|---|---|---|---|---|---|---|---|---|
| 0.00 | +0.3000 |  | 0.0000 |  |  |  | −2.955 |  |  |  |  |
| 0.05 | 0.2963 | −0.0037 | −0.1464 | −0.1464 |  |  | −2.891 | +0.064 |  |  |  |
| 0.10 | 0.2854 | −0.0109 | −0.2879 | −0.1415 | +0.0049 |  | −2.758 | +0.133 | +0.069 |  |  |
| 0.15 | 0.2676 | −0.0178 | −0.4211 | −0.1332 | +0.0083 | +0.0034 | −2.560 | +0.198 | 0.065 | −0.004 |  |
| 0.20 | 0.2434 | −0.0242 | −0.5429 | −0.1218 | 0.0114 | 0.0031 | −2.301 | 0.259 | 0.061 | −0.004 | 0.000 |
| 0.00 | +0.3000 |  | 0.0000 |  |  |  | −2.955 |  |  |  |  |
| 0.1 | 0.2854 | −0.0146 | −0.2879 | −0.2879 |  |  | −2.758 | +0.197 |  |  |  |
| 0.2 | 0.2434 | −0.0420 | −0.5429 | −0.2550 | +0.0329 |  | −2.301 | 0.457 | +0.260 |  |  |
| 0.3 | 0.1786 | −0.0648 | −0.7410 | −0.1981 | 0.0569 | +0.0240 | −1.629 | 0.672 | 0.215 | −0.045 |  |
| 0.4 | 0.0977 | −0.0809 | −0.8636 | −0.1226 | 0.0755 | 0.0186 | −0.803 | 0.826 | 0.154 | −0.061 | −0.016 |
| 0.5 | 0.0088 | −0.0889 | −0.8994 | −0.0358 | 0.0868 | 0.0113 | +0.092 | 0.895 | 0.069 | −0.085 | −0.024 |
| 0.6 | −0.0792 | −0.0880 | −0.8462 | +0.0532 | 0.0890 | 0.0022 | +0.960 | 0.868 | −0.027 | −0.096 | −0.011 |
| 0.7 | −0.1577 | −0.0785 | −0.7111 | +0.1351 | 0.0819 | −0.0071 | 1.713 | 0.753 | −0.115 | −0.088 | +0.008 |
| 0.8 | −0.2192 | −0.0615 | −0.5098 | 0.2013 | 0.0662 | −0.0157 | 2.276 | 0.563 | −0.190 | −0.075 | +0.013 |
| 0.9 | −0.2582 | −0.0390 | −0.2636 | 0.2462 | 0.0449 | −0.0213 | 2.606 | 0.330 | −0.233 | −0.043 | +0.032 |
| 1.0 | −0.2713 | −0.0131 | −0.0029 | 0.2665 | 0.0203 | −0.0246 | 2.679 | 0.073 | −0.257 | −0.024 | +0.019 |
| 1.1 | −0.2578 | +0.0135 | +0.2638 | 0.2609 | −0.0056 | −0.0257 | 2.497 | −0.182 | −0.255 | +0.002 | +0.026 |
| 1.2 | −0.2195 | +0.0383 | +0.4945 | 0.2307 | −0.0302 | −0.0246 | 2.078 | −0.419 | −0.237 | +0.018 | +0.016 |
| 1.3 | −0.1606 | 0.0589 | 0.6730 | 0.1785 | −0.0522 | −0.0220 | 1.464 | −0.614 | −0.195 | +0.042 | 0.024 |
| 1.4 | −0.0872 | 0.0734 | 0.7828 | 0.1098 | −0.0687 | −0.0165 | 0.714 | −0.750 | −0.136 | +0.059 | 0.017 |
| 1.5 | −0.0067 | 0.0805 | 0.8139 | 0.0311 | −0.0787 | −0.0100 | −0.096 | −0.810 | −0.060 | +0.076 | 0.017 |
| 1.6 | +0.0729 | 0.0796 | 0.7644 | −0.0495 | −0.0806 | −0.0019 | −0.881 | −0.785 | +0.025 | +0.085 | 0.009 |
| 1.7 | +0.1438 | 0.0709 | 0.6411 | −0.1233 | −0.0738 | +0.0068 | −1.561 | −0.680 | +0.105 | +0.080 | −0.005 |
| 1.8 | 0.1992 | 0.0554 | 0.4578 | −0.1833 | −0.0600 | +0.0138 | −2.071 | −0.510 | 0.170 | 0.065 | −0.015 |
| 1.9 | 0.2340 | 0.0348 | 0.2340 | −0.2238 | −0.0405 | 0.0195 | −2.366 | −0.295 | 0.215 | 0.045 | −0.020 |
| 2.0 | 0.2454 | 0.0114 | −0.0077 | −0.2417 | −0.0179 | 0.0226 | −2.428 | −0.062 | 0.233 | 0.018 | −0.027 |
| 2.1 | 0.2327 | −0.0127 | −0.2439 | −0.2362 | +0.0055 | 0.0234 | −2.257 | +0.171 | 0.233 | 0.000 | −0.018 |

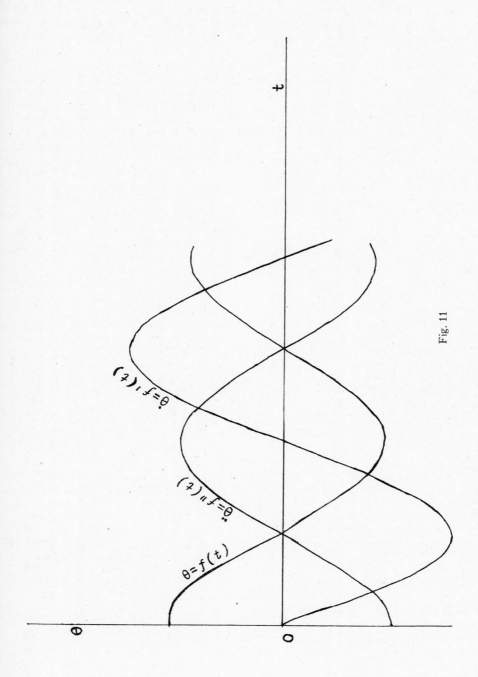

Fig. 11

*Example 3.* A bullet is fired at an angle of 38°30′ with the horizon and with an initial velocity of 780 feet per second. Assuming that the air resistance varies as the square of the velocity of the bullet and that the resistance coefficient is $-0.00005$, find the range, time of flight, and angle of fall of the bullet.

*Solution.* Let $\theta$ denote the angle which the velocity vector makes with the horizontal at any instant. Then the equations of motion are

$$\frac{d^2x}{dt^2} = -R\cos\theta = -0.00005v^2\cos\theta,$$

$$\frac{d^2y}{dt^2} = -R\sin\theta - g = -0.00005v^2\sin\theta - g,$$

where $R(=0.00005v^2)$ denotes the tangential retardation. Since $v\cos\theta = v_x = dx/dt$ and $v\sin\theta = v_y = dy/dt$, the equations of motion can be written in the form

$$\frac{d^2x}{dt^2} = -0.00005v\frac{dx}{dt},$$

$$\frac{d^2y}{dt^2} = -0.00005v\frac{dy}{dt} - g.$$

These can be reduced to a system of first order equations by putting

$$\dot{x} = \frac{dx}{dt}, \quad \dot{y} = \frac{dy}{dt}, \quad \ddot{x} = \frac{d\dot{x}}{dt} = \frac{d^2x}{dt^2}, \quad \ddot{y} = \frac{d\dot{y}}{dt} = \frac{d^2y}{dt^2}.$$

Taking $g = 32.16$ ft./sec.$^2$, we then have the system

$$\left\{ \begin{aligned} \frac{dx}{dt} &= \dot{x}, \\[1em] \frac{d\dot{x}}{dt} &= \ddot{x} = -0.00005v\dot{x}, \\[1em] \frac{dy}{dt} &= \dot{y}, \\[1em] \frac{d\dot{y}}{dt} &= \ddot{y} = -0.00005v\dot{y} - 32.16. \end{aligned} \right.$$

To start the numerical solution of this system of equations we first find the initial values of the velocities and accelerations. Thus,

$$v_0 = 780,$$

$$\dot{x}_0 = v_0 \cos 38°30' = 610.44,$$

$$\dot{y}_0 = v_0 \sin 38°30' = 485.56,$$

$$\ddot{x}_0 = -0.00005 v_0 \dot{x}_0 = -23.81,$$

$$\ddot{y}_0 = -0.00005 v_0 \dot{y}_0 - 32.16 = -51.10.$$

These quantities give the first line in the table to be computed.

To get the second line we assume that the initial accelerations will remain practically constant for a quarter of a second. Hence

$$\Delta\dot{y} = \tfrac{1}{4}(-51.10) = -12.78,$$

$$\Delta\dot{x} = \tfrac{1}{4}(-23.81) = -5.95;$$

and therefore

$$\overset{(1)}{\dot{y}_{1/4}} = \dot{y}_0 + \Delta\dot{y} = 485.56 - 12.78 = 472.78,$$

$$\overset{(1)}{\dot{x}_{1/4}} = \dot{x}_0 + \Delta\dot{x} = 610.44 - 5.95 = 604.49.$$

Since $v = \sqrt{\dot{x}^2 + \dot{y}^2}$, we have

$$\overset{(1)}{v_{1/4}} = \sqrt{(604.49)^2 + (472.78)^2} = 767.42.$$

Then

$$\overset{(2)}{\ddot{y}_{1/4}} = -0.00005 \times 767.42 \times 472.78 - 32.16 = -50.30,$$

$$\overset{(2)}{\ddot{x}_{1/4}} = -0.00005 \times 767.42 \times 604.49 = -23.20.$$

Better values for $\Delta\dot{y}$ and $\Delta\dot{x}$ are therefore

$$\Delta\dot{y} = \frac{1}{4}\left(\frac{-51.10 - 50.30}{2}\right) = -12.68,$$

$$\Delta\dot{x} = \frac{1}{4}\left(\frac{-23.81 - 23.20}{2}\right) = -5.88.$$

$$\therefore \quad \overset{(2)}{\dot{y}_{1/4}} = 485.56 - 12.68 = 472.88,$$

$$\overset{(2)}{\dot{x}_{1/4}} = 610.44 - 5.88 = 604.56,$$

$$\overset{(2)}{v_{1/4}} = \sqrt{(604.56)^2 + (472.88)^2} = 767.54.$$

The third approximations for the accelerations at the end of the interval are then

$$\overset{(3)}{\ddot{y}}_{1/4} = -50.31,$$
$$\overset{(3)}{\ddot{x}}_{1/4} = -23.20.$$

This value of $\ddot{x}_{1/4}$ is the same as that previously found, and the value of $\ddot{y}_{1/4}$ differs so little from the previous value that we get the same $\Delta y$ as before. We therefore take these values to be correct for the present.

To find the value of $y$ when $t = \frac{1}{4}$, we have

$$\Delta y = \frac{1}{4}\left(\frac{485.56 + 472.88}{2}\right) = 119.80 \text{ ft.}$$

$$\therefore \quad y_{1/4} = 0 + 119.80 = 119.80.$$

The values are now known for the second line in the table. To compute additional lines we apply the following formulas in the order in which they are written:

$$(1)\ \Delta\dot{y} = \int_{t_n}^{t_{n+1}} \ddot{y}\,dt = \Delta t\left[\ddot{y}_n + \frac{1}{2}\Delta_1\ddot{y}_n + \frac{5}{12}\Delta_2\ddot{y}_n + \frac{3}{8}\Delta_3\ddot{y}_n + \frac{1}{3}\Delta_4\ddot{y}_n\right],$$

for finding $\dot{y}$ in a new line;

$$(2)\ \Delta\dot{x} = \int_{t_n}^{t_{n+1}} \ddot{x}\,dt = \Delta t\left[\ddot{x}_n + \frac{1}{2}\Delta_1\ddot{x}_n + \frac{5}{12}\Delta_2\ddot{x}_n + \frac{3}{8}\Delta_3\ddot{x}_n + \frac{1}{3}\Delta_4\ddot{x}_n\right],$$

for finding $\dot{x}$ in the new line;

$$(3)\quad v = \sqrt{\dot{x}^2 + \dot{y}^2};$$

$$(4)\qquad \ddot{y} = -0.00005v\dot{y} - 32.16;$$

$$(5)\qquad \ddot{x} = -0.00005v\dot{x};$$

$$(6)\qquad \Delta\dot{y} = \int_{t_{n-1}}^{t_n} \ddot{y}\,dt = \Delta t\left[\ddot{y}_n - \frac{1}{2}\Delta_1\ddot{y}_n - \frac{1}{12}\Delta_2\ddot{y}_n - \frac{1}{24}\Delta_3\ddot{y}_n\right],$$

for checking and correcting the value of $\dot{y}$ found by (1);

$$(7)\qquad \Delta\dot{x} = \int_{t_{n-1}}^{t_n} \ddot{x}\,dt = \Delta t\left[\ddot{x}_n - \frac{1}{2}\Delta_1\ddot{x}_n - \frac{1}{12}\Delta_2\ddot{x}_n - \frac{1}{24}\Delta_3\ddot{x}_n\right],$$

for checking and correcting the value of $\dot{x}$ found by (2);

$$(8)\ \Delta y = \int_{t_{n-1}}^{t_n} \dot{y}\,dt = \Delta t\left[\dot{y}_n - \frac{1}{2}\Delta_1\dot{y}_n - \frac{1}{12}\Delta_2\dot{y}_n - \frac{1}{24}\Delta_3\dot{y}_n - \frac{1}{38}\Delta_4\dot{y}_n\right],$$

for finding the new $y$ after the correct value of $\dot{y}$ has been obtained. In these formulas the instant $t_{n+1}$ in (1) and (2) is the same as $t_n$ in (6), (7), and (8).

The increments in $x$ for the several intervals can be found by means of the formula

$$(9) \quad \Delta x = \int_{t_{n-1}}^{t_n} \dot{x}dt = \Delta t \left[ \dot{x}_n - \frac{1}{2}\Delta_1\dot{x}_n - \frac{1}{12}\Delta_2\dot{x}_n - \frac{1}{24}\Delta_3\dot{x}_n - \frac{1}{38}\Delta_4\dot{x}_n \right]$$

after the correct value of $\dot{x}$ has been found for the interval considered. Since only the range is called for in this problem, however, it is not necessary to find $x$ at the end of each interval. The range is more easily found by means of Simpson's rule, as follows:

$$x = \int_0^T \dot{x}dt = \frac{\Delta t}{3}[\dot{x}_0 + 4(\dot{x}_1 + \dot{x}_3 + \cdots + \dot{x}_{n-1})$$
$$+ 2(\dot{x}_2 + \dot{x}_4 + \cdots + \dot{x}_{n-2}) + \dot{x}_n],$$

where $T$ denotes the time of flight.

The table is continued with the time interval $\Delta t = \frac{1}{4}$ sec. until five lines have been computed. The computed values are then checked by means of formulas (75: 6), (75: 7), (75: 8). These formulas show that the value of $\Delta_1\dot{x}$ for $t = \frac{1}{4}$ should be $-5.87$ instead of $-5.88$. This value of $\dot{x}$ is therefore corrected, as well as the succeeding values which depend upon it.

Since the correct values are given at the first trial for $t = \frac{1}{2}$, $t = \frac{3}{4}$, and $t = 1$, we start a new table with $\Delta t = \frac{1}{2}$ sec., using the previously computed values of $\dot{x}$, $\dot{y}$, $\ddot{x}$, $\ddot{y}$, and $v$ for the lines $t = 0$, $t = \frac{1}{2}$, $t = 1$. Here, again, the correct values of the several quantities are given at the first trial in the fourth and fifth lines of the table. So we double the interval again and start a new table with $\Delta t = 1$ sec., using the previously computed values for lines $t = 0$, $t = 1$, $t = 2$. This new table is continued up to the line $t = 8$. Then the interval is doubled once more and a new table started. The computation is continued with this interval until the problem is finished. In most cases only one correction is necessary for $\dot{x}$, $\dot{y}$, and $v$, and none for $\ddot{y}$ and $\ddot{x}$.

In finding $v$ from the fomula $v = \sqrt{\dot{x}^2 + \dot{y}^2}$, the computation should be carried through to six significant figures and then the result rounded off to five figures. Also, when using formulas (1), (2), (6), (7), (8), with $\Delta t = 2$ the student should not round off the numbers within the brackets before multiplying through by the factor 2; for by so doing he would double the error due to rounding. He should also be careful not to discard fractional quantities of less than half a unit in the second decimal place until he is sure that the algebraic sum of these quantities is less than half a unit in the second decimal place. Attention to these matters, instead of being a waste of time, will frequently save the time and labor of recomputing a whole line in the table. For example, let us check the value of $\Delta y$ in the line for $t = 26$. We have

$$\Delta y = 2\left[-376.89 + \frac{1}{2}(47.27) - \frac{1}{12}(3.04) - \frac{1}{24}(0.15)\right]$$

$$= -753.78 + 47.27 - \frac{1}{6}(3.04) - \frac{1}{12}(0.15)$$

$$= -753.78 + 47.27 - 0.507 - 0.012 = -707.03.$$

By rounding off before multiplying by 2 we have

$$\Delta y = 2[-376.89 + 23.64 - 0.25 - 0.01] = -707.02,$$

which differs from the previous value by a unit in the last figure.

The preceding remarks apply with even greater force when $\Delta t = 4$.

The final results of the computation for this problem are given on the following page. The trial lines are not given, but the student when working a problem should always retain the trial lines in the computed schedule, so as to have a record of the computation at each step.

To find the time of flight we replace the terminal part of the trajectory by a parabola through the points corresponding to $t = 22$, $t = 24$, and $t = 26$. Hence $y$ is to be a quadratic function of $t$, and we find this function by constructing a table of differences and employing Newton's interpolation formula (II) of Art. 16.

| $t$ | $y$ | $\Delta_1 y$ | $\Delta_2 y$ |
|-----|-----|--------------|--------------|
| 22 | 1389.97 | | |
| 24 | 780.54 | $-609.43$ | |
| 26 | 73.51 | $-707.03$ | $-97.60$ |

Putting $y = 0$ in that formula, we have

$$y_n + \Delta_1 y_n u + \frac{\Delta_2 y_n}{2}(u^2 + u) = 0.$$

$$\therefore \quad 73.51 - 707.03u - 48.8(u^2 + u) = 0,$$

or

$$48.8u^2 + 755.83u = 73.51.$$

$$\therefore \quad u = \frac{-755.83 \pm 765.26}{97.6} = \frac{9.43}{9.76} = 0.0966,$$

and

$$\therefore \quad t = t_n + hu = 26 + 2 \times 0.0966 = 26.19 \text{ sec.}$$

| $t$ | $v$ | $y$ | $\Delta y$ | $\dot y$ | $\Delta\dot y$ | $\Delta^2\dot y$ | $\Delta^3\dot y$ | $\ddot y$ | $\Delta\ddot y$ | $\Delta^2\ddot y$ | $\Delta^3\ddot y$ | $\Delta^4\ddot y$ | $\dot x$ | $\Delta\dot x$ | $\ddot x$ | $\Delta\ddot x$ | $\Delta^2\ddot x$ | $\Delta^3\ddot x$ | $\Delta^4\ddot x$ |
|---|---|---|---|---|---|---|---|---|---|---|---|---|---|---|---|---|---|---|---|
| 0 | 780.00 | 0 | 119.80 | 485.56 | −12.68 | 0.20 | −0.02 | −51.10 | 0.79 | −0.03 | 0.00 | 0.01 | 610.44 | −5.87 | −23.81 | 0.61 | −0.03 | 0.02 | −0.04 |
| 1/4 | 767.54 | 119.80 | 116.64 | 472.88 | −12.48 | 0.18 | 0.00 | −50.31 | 0.76 | −0.03 | 0.01 |  | 604.57 | −5.73 | −23.20 | 0.58 | −0.01 | −0.02 |  |
| 1/2 | 755.35 | 236.44 | 113.56 | 460.40 | −12.30 | 0.18 |  | −49.55 | 0.73 | −0.02 |  |  | 598.84 | −5.58 | −22.62 | 0.57 | −0.03 |  |  |
| 3/4 | 743.47 | 350.00 | 110.50 | 448.10 | −12.12 |  |  | −48.82 | 0.71 |  |  |  | 593.26 | −5.44 | −22.05 | 0.54 |  |  |  |
| 1 | 731.85 | 460.50 |  | 435.98 |  |  |  | −48.11 |  |  |  |  | 587.82 |  | −21.51 |  |  |  |  |
| 0 | 780.00 | 0 | 236.44 | 485.56 | −25.16 | 0.74 | −0.04 | −51.10 | 1.55 | −0.11 | 0.00 | 0.01 | 610.44 | −11.60 | −23.81 | 1.19 | −0.08 | 0.00 | 0.01 |
| 1/2 | 755.35 | 236.44 | 224.06 | 460.40 | −24.42 | 0.70 | −0.06 | −49.55 | 1.44 | −0.11 | 0.01 |  | 598.84 | −11.02 | −22.62 | 1.11 | −0.08 | 0.01 |  |
| 1 | 731.85 | 460.50 | 212.03 | 435.98 | −23.72 | 0.64 |  | −48.11 | 1.33 | −0.10 |  |  | 587.82 | −10.50 | −21.51 | 1.03 | −0.07 |  |  |
| 1½ | 709.42 | 672.53 | 200.32 | 412.26 | −23.08 |  |  | −46.78 | 1.23 |  |  |  | 577.32 | −10.00 | −20.48 | 0.96 |  |  |  |
| 2 | 687.98 | 872.85 |  | 389.18 |  |  |  | −45.55 |  |  |  |  | 567.32 |  | −19.52 |  |  |  |  |
| 0 | 780.00 | 0 | 460.50 | 485.56 | −49.58 | 2.78 | −0.39 | −51.10 | 2.99 | −0.43 | 0.09 | −0.05 | 610.44 | −22.62 | −23.81 | 2.30 | −0.31 | 0.06 | −0.03 |
| 1 | 731.85 | 460.50 | 412.35 | 435.98 | −46.80 | 2.39 | −0.33 | −48.11 | 2.56 | −0.34 | 0.04 | +0.01 | 587.82 | −20.50 | −21.51 | 1.99 | −0.25 | 0.03 | 0.00 |
| 2 | 687.98 | 872.85 | 366.79 | 389.18 | −44.41 | 2.06 | −0.28 | −45.55 | 2.22 | −0.30 | 0.05 | −0.01 | 567.32 | −18.63 | −19.52 | 1.74 | −0.22 | 0.02 | −0.01 |
| 3 | 648.00 | 1239.64 | 323.44 | 344.77 | −42.35 | 1.78 | −0.20 | −43.33 | 1.92 | −0.25 | 0.04 | −0.01 | 548.69 | −17.00 | −17.78 | 1.52 | −0.19 | 0.02 | 0.00 |
| 4 | 611.67 | 1563.08 | 281.99 | 302.42 | −40.57 | 1.50 | −0.21 | −41.41 | 1.67 | −0.21 | 0.03 | 0.00 | 531.69 | −15.58 | −16.26 | 1.33 | −0.17 | 0.02 | 0.00 |
| 5 | 578.74 | 1845.07 | 242.24 | 261.85 | −38.99 | 1.37 | −0.17 | −39.74 | 1.46 | −0.18 | 0.03 |  | 516.11 | −14.34 | −14.93 | 1.16 | −0.15 | 0.02 |  |
| 6 | 549.04 | 2087.31 | 203.95 | 222.86 | −37.62 | 1.20 |  | −38.28 | 1.28 | −0.15 |  |  | 501.77 | −13.25 | −13.77 | 1.01 | −0.13 |  |  |
| 7 | 522.46 | 2291.26 | 166.94 | 185.24 | −36.42 |  |  | −37.00 | 1.13 |  |  |  | 488.52 | −12.31 | −12.76 | 0.88 |  |  |  |
| 8 | 498.93 | 2458.20 |  | 148.82 |  |  |  | −35.87 |  |  |  |  | 476.21 |  | −11.88 |  |  |  |  |
| 0 | 780.00 | 0 | 872.85 | 485.56 | −96.38 | 9.62 | −2.42 | −51.10 | 5.55 | −1.41 | 0.40 | −0.11 | 610.44 | −43.12 | −23.81 | 4.29 | −1.03 | 0.26 | −0.09 |
| 2 | 687.98 | 872.85 | 690.23 | 389.18 | −86.76 | 7.20 | −1.68 | −45.55 | 4.14 | −1.01 | 0.29 | −0.09 | 567.32 | −35.63 | −19.52 | 3.26 | −0.77 | 0.17 | −0.04 |
| 4 | 611.67 | 1563.08 | 524.23 | 302.42 | −79.56 | 5.52 | −1.26 | −41.41 | 3.13 | −0.72 | 0.20 | −0.02 | 531.69 | −29.92 | −16.26 | 2.49 | −0.60 | 0.13 | −0.05 |
| 6 | 549.04 | 2087.31 | 370.89 | 222.86 | −74.04 | 4.26 | −0.86 | −38.28 | 2.41 | −0.52 | 0.18 | −0.06 | 501.77 | −25.56 | −13.77 | 1.89 | −0.47 | 0.08 | −0.01 |
| 8 | 498.93 | 2458.20 | 227.22 | 148.82 | −69.78 | 3.40 | −0.51 | −35.87 | 1.89 | −0.34 | 0.12 | +0.03 | 476.21 | −22.28 | −11.88 | 1.42 | −0.39 | 0.07 | −0.01 |
| 10 | 460.77 | 2685.42 | 91.20 | 79.04 | −66.38 | 2.89 | −0.34 | −33.98 | 1.55 | −0.22 | 0.15 | −0.09 | 453.93 | −19.84 | −10.46 | 1.03 | −0.32 | 0.06 | 0.00 |
| 12 | 434.27 | 2776.62 | −38.63 | 12.66 | −63.49 | 2.55 | −0.05 | −32.43 | 1.33 | −0.07 | 0.06 | −0.01 | 434.09 | −18.09 | −9.43 | 0.71 | −0.26 | 0.06 | 0.00 |
| 14 | 419.05 | 2737.99 | −163.00 | −50.83 | −60.94 | 2.50 | 0.04 | −31.10 | 1.26 | −0.01 | 0.06 | −0.01 | 416.00 | −16.93 | −8.72 | 0.45 | −0.20 | 0.06 | 0.00 |
| 16 | 414.43 | 2574.99 | −282.39 | −111.77 | −58.44 | 2.54 | 0.16 | −29.84 | 1.25 | +0.05 | 0.05 | −0.07 | 399.07 | −16.26 | −8.27 | 0.25 | −0.14 | 0.05 | −0.01 |
| 18 | 418.95 | 2292.60 | −396.74 | −170.21 | −55.90 | 2.70 | 0.19 | −28.59 | 1.30 | 0.10 | −0.02 | 0.02 | 382.81 | −15.91 | −8.02 | 0.11 | −0.08 | 0.01 | −0.04 |
| 20 | 430.96 | 1895.86 | −505.89 | −226.11 | −53.20 | 2.89 | 0.15 | −27.29 | 1.40 | 0.08 | 0.00 |  | 366.90 | −15.78 | −7.91 | 0.03 | −0.03 |  |  |
| 22 | 448.66 | 1389.97 | −609.43 | −279.31 | −50.31 | 3.04 |  | −25.89 | 1.48 | 0.08 |  |  | 351.12 | −15.76 | −7.88 | 0.00 | −0.02 |  |  |
| 24 | 470.23 | 780.54 | −707.03 | −329.62 | −47.27 |  |  | −24.41 | 1.56 |  |  |  | 335.36 | −15.78 | −7.88 | −0.02 |  |  |  |
| 26 | 494.14 | 73.51 |  | −376.89 |  |  |  | −22.85 |  |  |  |  | 319.58 |  | −7.90 |  |  |  |  |

We next compute the range by means of Simpson's rule. The horizontal distance covered during the first two seconds is, taking $h = \Delta t = \frac{1}{2}$ sec.,

$$x = \tfrac{1}{6}[610.44 + 4(598.84 + 577.32) + 2 \times 587.82 + 567.32]$$
$$= 1176.3 \text{ ft.}$$

For the interval from $t = 2$ to $t = 26$, taking $h = 2$, we have

$$x = \tfrac{2}{3}[567.32 + 4(531.69 + 476.21 + 434.09 + 399.07$$
$$+ 366.90 + 335.36) + 2(501.77 + 453.93 + 416.00$$
$$+ 382.81 + 351.12) + 319.58] = 10181 \text{ ft.}$$

Hence the horizontal distance covered in the first 26 seconds is 10181 $+1176 = 11357$ ft.

To find the distance covered in the remaining 0.19 second we assume that the horizontal acceleration will remain at $-7.90$ for 0.19 sec. Then the change in velocity during this time will be $(-7.90) \times 0.19 = -1.5$. The horizontal velocity at the *end* of 26.19 seconds will therefore be $319.6 - 1.5$ or 318.1 ft./sec., and the average velocity during this fraction of a second is $(319.6 + 318.1)/2 = 318.8$ ft./sec. Hence the horizontal distance covered in the last 0.19 sec., is $318.8 \times 0.19 = 61$ ft. The total range is therefore

$$X = 11357 + 61 = \underline{11418 \text{ ft.}}$$

If we compute the increments in $x$ for the several time intervals and add them as we go along, as was done in the case of $y$, we shall find the same value for the range as found by Simpson's rule.

If $\omega$ denote the angle of fall, then

$$\tan \omega = \frac{\dot{y}}{\dot{x}}.$$

We have already found the value of $\dot{x}$ for $t = 26.19$. To find $\dot{y}$ we assume that the second difference in $\ddot{y}$ will be the same for the interval $t = 26$ to $t = 28$ as for the preceding interval. Then for the next two seconds we shall have $\Delta_1 \ddot{y} = 1.64$. Hence for one second the change in $\ddot{y}$ will be 0.82, and for 0.19 second it will be $0.82 \times 0.19 = 0.16$. The vertical acceleration when $t = 26.19$ will therefore be $-22.85 + 0.16 = -22.69$. The change in the vertical velocity during the last 0.19 second is then

$$\frac{-22.85 - 22.69}{2} \times 0.19 = -4.3.$$

Hence  $\dot{y} = -376.9 - 4.3 = -381.2$.

$$\therefore \quad \tan \omega = \frac{-381.2}{318.1} = -1.198,$$

and    $\omega = -50°9'$

The terminal velocity is

$$v = \sqrt{\dot{x}^2 + \dot{y}^2} = \sqrt{(318.1)^2 + (381.2)^2} = 496.5 \text{ ft./sec.}$$

The actual shape of the trajectory is shown in Fig. 12.

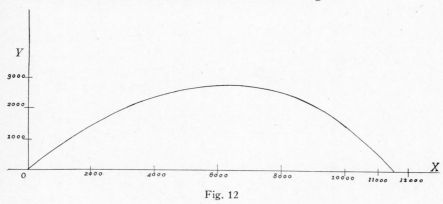

Fig. 12

*Note.* One of the most important applications of numerical integration as applied to differential equations is in the field of exterior ballistics—the science which deals with the motion of a projectile after it leaves the gun. The general problem of the flight of projectiles at high velocities can not be treated here, because of the lack of the necessary tables. The differential equations which hold for all velocities are

$$\ddot{x} = -E\dot{x},$$
$$\ddot{y} = -E\dot{y} - g,$$

where

$$E = \frac{G(v)H(y)}{C}.$$

Here $G(v)$ is a function of the velocity alone, $H(y)$ is a function of the altitude alone, and $C$ is a constant whose value depends on the weight and shape of the projectile. The function $H(y)$ has the form $H(y) = 10^{-ky}$, where $k$ has the value 0.000045  when $y$ is measured in meters.   The formula for $G(v)$ is much more complicated.*   These functions $G(v)$ and $H(y)$ have been tabulated for a wide range of values of $v$ and $y$†.

The application of numerical integration to exterior ballistics in this country is due to Professor F. R. Moulton.   The interested reader should consult the following literature:

1. *Exterior Ballistics*, by Lieutenant E. E. Hermann, U.S.N., Annapolis, 1926.

2. *The Method of Numerical Integration in Exterior Ballistics*, by Dunham Jackson, Washington, 1919.

3. The article "Ballistics" (Exterior), by W. H. Tschappat, in the *Encyclopaedia Britannica*, War Volumes (Vol. XXX), 1922.

4. *New Methods in Exterior Ballistics*, by F. R. Moulton, Chicago, 1926.

**77. Halving the Interval for $h$.**   Sometimes it may be desirable to decrease the interval $h$ at some stage of a computation.   Such a decrease should be made if the higher differences of a function should become large or if several trial computations should be required to obtain the correct result.   When decreasing the interval for $h$ we should always take it just half its previous value.   It is very necessary that the values of the functions to be computed should be accurately known for this mid-value of $h$, for whatever errors are committed in making the change of interval will be carried along throughout the remainder of the computation.

The best method for halving the interval is to apply Bessel's formula for interpolating to halves, namely:

$$(77:1) \quad y'_{1/2} = \frac{y'_0 + y'_1}{2} - \frac{1}{8} \frac{\Delta^2 y'_{-1} + \Delta^2 y'_0}{2} + \frac{3}{128} \frac{\Delta^4 y'_{-2} + \Delta^4 y'_{-1}}{2},$$

where $y'_{1/2}$ is the value of $y'$ halfway between $y'_0$ and $y'_1$.   Note that the differences used in this formula are ordinary diagonal differences.

It may be necessary to find the values of $y'$ at the mid-points of two or three consecutive intervals.   An example will make the matter clear.

---

* The formula for $G(v)$ is

$$G(v) = 0.001140v\left[\ 0.2550 + \frac{\sqrt[4]{1 + 0.0392\left(\dfrac{v-330}{500}\right)^8}}{27226 + 494\left(\dfrac{v-330}{50}\right)^2} \times \tan^{-1}\left(\dfrac{v-330}{50}\right)\ \right],$$

where $\tan^{-1}[(v-330)/50]$ is in minutes of arc and $v$ is in meters per second.

† See Tables Ia and Ic in *Exterior Ballistic Tables Based on Numerical Integration*, Vol. I, Washington, 1924.

*Example.* In Example 2 of Art. 76, find the value of $\theta$ when $t = 1.25$.
*Solution.* We first compute the following table of differences.

|     | $t$ | $\dot{\theta}$ | $\Delta\dot{\theta}$ | $\Delta^2\dot{\theta}$ | $\Delta_3\dot{\theta}$ | $\Delta_4\dot{\theta}$ |
|-----|-----|------|--------|--------|--------|--------|
| $-2$ | 1.0 | 0.0029 |        |        |        |        |
|      |     |        | 0.2609 |        |        |        |
| $-1$ | 1.1 | 0.2638 |        | $-302$ |        |        |
|      |     |        | 0.2307 |        | $-220$ |        |
| 0    | 1.2 | 0.4945 |        | $-522$ |        | 55     |
|      |     |        | 0.1785 |        | $-165$ |        |
| 1    | 1.3 | 0.6730 |        | $-687$ |        | 65     |
|      |     |        | 0.1098 |        | $-100$ |        |
| 2    | 1.4 | 0.7828 |        | $-787$ |        |        |
|      |     |        | 0.0311 |        |        |        |
| 3    | 1.5 | 0.8139 |        |        |        |        |

Substituting in the formula

$$\dot{\theta}_{1/2} = \frac{\dot{\theta}_0 + \dot{\theta}_1}{2} - \frac{1}{8}\frac{\Delta^2\dot{\theta}_{-1} + \Delta^2\dot{\theta}_0}{2} + \frac{3}{128}\frac{\Delta^4\dot{\theta}_{-2} + \Delta^4\dot{\theta}_{-1}}{2},$$

we have

$$\dot{\theta}_{1/2} = 0.58375 + 0.00755 + 0.0001 = 0.5914.$$

In a similar manner we could find the values of $\theta$ and $\ddot{\theta}$ for $t = 1.25$.
We could likewise find these quantities for $t = 1.35$, $1.45$, etc.

### EXAMPLES ON CHAPTER XI

1. Tabulate the solution of

$$\frac{dy}{dx} = 2x - y$$

from $x = 1$ to $x = 2.5$, given $x_0 = 1$, $y_0 = 3$.
2. Tabulate the solution of

$$\frac{dy}{dx} = \log_{10}\frac{x}{y}$$

from $x = 20$ to $x = 22.4$, given $x_0 = 20$, $y_0 = 5$.
3. Solve numerically the equation

$$\frac{dy}{dx} = \sin x + \cos y,$$

starting with $x = 30°$, $y = 45°$. Tabulate the solution to $x = 75°$.

4. Tabulate the solution of

$$\frac{d^2x}{dt^2} = \log_{10} \sin x$$

from $t=0$ to $t=4$, given $dx/dt=2$ and $x=30°$ when $t=0$.

5. Solve the equations

$$\frac{dx}{dt} = 2x + y, \quad \frac{dy}{dt} = x - 3y$$

subject to the conditions $x=0$, $y=0.5$ when $t=0$. Tabulate the solution from $t=0$ to $t=5$.

6. Solve

$$\frac{dy}{dx} = x^2 + y^2$$

with the initial conditions $x_0=1$, $y_0=0$. Tabulate the solution from $x=1$ to $x=3$.

7. Solve

$$\frac{dy}{dx} = -\frac{x}{2y} + \sqrt{\frac{x^2}{4y^2} - 1}$$

starting at $x_0=1$, $y_0=0.5$. Tabulate the solution from $x=1$ to $x=2.2$.

8. Tabulate the solution of

$$\frac{d^2\theta}{dt^2} + 0.9 \sin \theta = 0$$

from $t=0$ to $t=1$, given $\theta=5°$, $d\theta/dt=0$ when $t=0$.

9. Solve

$$\frac{d^2\theta}{dt^2} + 0.1\frac{d\theta}{dt} + \sin \theta = 0$$

with the initial conditions $\theta=30°$, $d\theta/dt=0$ when $t=0$. Tabulate the solution from $t=0$ to $t=1.2$.

10. Tabulate the solution of

$$\frac{d^2r}{dt^2} = -\frac{0.0002959}{r^2} + 0.01\left(\frac{dr}{dt}\right)^2,$$

given $r=1$, $dr/dt=0$ when $t=0$. Take $t=0$, 5, 10, etc. and compute the values of $r$ and $dr/dt$ from $t=0$ to $t=75$.

11. Tabulate the solution of the equations

$$\frac{d^2x}{dt^2} = -0.000035v\frac{dx}{dt},$$

$$\frac{d^2y}{dt^2} = -0.000035v\frac{dy}{dt} - 32.16,$$

from $t=0$ to $t=25$, given $v=800$, $dx/dt=692.8$, $dy/dt=400$ when $t=0$. Here

$$v = \sqrt{\left(\frac{dx}{dt}\right)^2 + \left(\frac{dy}{dt}\right)^2}.$$

12. Solve the equations

$$\frac{d^2x}{dt^2} = -\frac{0.0002959x}{r^3},$$

$$\frac{d^2y}{dt^2} = -\frac{0.0002959y}{r^3},$$

from $t=0$ to $t=10$, taking $t=0, 1, 2$, etc. and using the initial conditions $x=0.31$, $y=0$, $dx/dt=0$, $dy/dt=0.034$ when $t=0$. Here $r=\sqrt{x^2+y^2}$.

13. In the differential equation

(1) $$\frac{dy}{dx} = \frac{3(x^2 - 14400)}{2048000\sqrt{1 - \left[\dfrac{3(x^2 - 14400)}{2048000}\right]^2}}$$

compute the value of $dy/dx$ for $x=0, 5, 10, \cdots 120$. Then form a table of differences and compute the successive increments in $y$ by means of formula (75:5). Starting with the values $x=0$, $y=0$, find the values of $y$ corresponding to the several values of $x$ given above. Compare these values of $y$ with those computed from the equation

(2) $$y = \frac{3}{2048000}\left(\frac{x^3}{3} - 14400x\right).$$

*Note.* Equation (1) in the above example is the differential equation of the elastic curve of a simple beam loaded at the middle, when $(dy/dx)^2$ is not neglected in the formula for the radius of curvature. Equation (2) is the equation of the elastic curve of the same beam when $(dy/dx)^2$ is neglected as is usually done in beam theory.

# CHAPTER XII

## CONVERGENCE AND ACCURACY OF THE ITERATION PROCESS

**78. Proof of the Convergence of the Iteration Process.** Before starting on this chapter the student should go back and read Art. 73. We shall prove the convergence of the iteration process in the case of a single equation in two variables and in the case of a pair of simultaneous equations in three variables.

*78a). Equations in Two Variables.* The solution of the differential equation

$$\frac{dy}{dx} = f(x, y),$$

with inital conditions $x = x_0$, $y = y_0$, satisfies the integral equation

$$(78:1) \qquad y = y_0 + \int_{x_0}^{x} f(x, y)dx.$$

The first approximation to the solution is

$$(78:2) \qquad y^{(1)} = y_0 + \int_{x_0}^{x} f(x, y_0)dx.$$

Subtracting (78: 2) from (78: 1), we have

$$(78:3) \qquad y - y^{(1)} = \int_{x_0}^{x} \left[ f(x, y) - f(x, y_0) \right]dx.$$

The quantity within the brackets is the change in $f(x, y)$ due to a change in $y$ alone. Hence by the theorem of mean value we have

$$f(x, y) - f(x, y_0) = (y - y_0)\frac{\partial f(x, \bar{y})}{\partial y}, \quad y_0 \leqq \bar{y} \leqq y.$$

Then (78: 3) becomes

$$(78:4) \qquad y - y^{(1)} = \int_{x_0}^{x} (y - y_0)\frac{\partial f}{\partial y}dx.$$

Now let $M$ denote the maximum absolute value of $\partial f/\partial y$ in the interval $x - x_0$ and range $y - y_0$, and let $\epsilon_0, \epsilon_1, \epsilon_2, \cdots \epsilon_n$ denote the maximum absolute values of $y - y_0, y - y^{(1)}, y - y^{(2)}, \cdots y - y^{(n)}$, respectively, in the interval $x - x_0$. Then, considering only absolute values, $(78:4)$ can be written as

$$\epsilon_1 \leqq \epsilon_0 M \left| \int_{x_0}^{x} dx \right| = \epsilon_0 M \left| x - x_0 \right| .$$

A similar relation holds for succeeding approximations, so that

$$\epsilon_2 \leqq \epsilon_1 M \left| x - x_0 \right| ,$$

$$\epsilon_3 \leqq \epsilon_2 M \left| x - x_0 \right| ,$$

$$. \quad . \quad . \quad . \quad . \quad . \quad . \quad . \quad .$$

$$\epsilon_n \leqq \epsilon_{n-1} M \left| x - x_0 \right| .$$

Multiplying together all these inequalities, member for member, and then dividing the result through by the common factors $\epsilon_1, \epsilon_2, \cdots \epsilon_{n-1}$, we get

$$(78:5) \qquad \epsilon_n \leqq M^n \left| x - x_0 \right|^n \epsilon_0 = (M \left| x - x_0 \right|)^n \epsilon_0.$$

Now if $M|x - x_0| < 1$, it follows that $(M|x - x_0|)^n$ can be made as small as we please by taking $n$ sufficiently large   Hence $\epsilon_n$, or $|y - y^{(n)}|$, can be made as small as desired   Since the difference $|y - y^{(n)}|$ can be made arbitrarily small, it follows that $y^{(n)}$ approaches $y$ as a limit for all values of $x$ in the interval $(x, x_0)$.   The iteration process therefore converges to the true solution when

$$(78:6) \qquad \left| h \frac{\partial f}{\partial y} \right| < 1 \text{ or } h < \frac{1}{\left| \dfrac{\partial f}{\partial y} \right|},$$

where $h = x - x_0$.   This relation tells us that the larger the value of $\partial f / \partial y$ the smaller we must take $h$, and that the iteration process fails when $\partial f / \partial y = \infty$.

Before beginning the solution of a problem the student should examine the value of $\partial f / \partial y$ for all values of $x$ and $y$ in the proposed range of integration and then plan his work accordingly.   For example, the method would fail on the equation $dy/dx = \log_{10}(x/y)$ where $y = 0$.

*78b). Simultaneous Equations.*   Let us next consider two simultaneous equations of the first order:

$$(78:7) \qquad \begin{cases} \dfrac{dp}{dt} = f_1(p, q, t), \\[2mm] \dfrac{dq}{dt} = f_2(p, q, t), \end{cases}$$

where $p$ and $q$ are functions of $t$. If the initial conditions are $p = p_0$, $q = q_0$ when $t = t_0$, then the first approximations are

$$(78:8) \qquad p^{(1)} = p_0 + \int_{t_0}^{t} f_1(p_0, q_0, t) dt$$

and

$$(78:9) \qquad q^{(1)} = q_0 + \int_{t_0}^{t} f_2(p_0, q_0, t) dt.$$

The true values of $p$ and $q$ satisfy the integral equations

$$(78:10) \qquad p = p_0 + \int_{t_0}^{t} f_1(p, q, t) dt,$$

$$(78:11) \qquad q = q_0 + \int_{t_0}^{t} f_2(p, q, t) dt.$$

Subtracting (78:8) from (78:10), and (78:9) from (78:11), we get

$$(78:12) \qquad p - p^{(1)} = \int_{t_0}^{t} [f_1(p, q, t) - f_1(p_0, q_0, t)] dt,$$

$$(78:13) \qquad q - q^{(1)} = \int_{t_0}^{t} [f_2(p, q, t) - f_2(p_0, q_0, t)] dt.$$

Now applying to the differences within the brackets the theorem of mean value for a function of two independent variables, we have

$$f_1(p, q, t) - f_1(p_0, q_0, t) = (p - p_0)\frac{\partial \bar{f}_1}{\partial p} + (q - q_0)\frac{\partial \bar{f}_1}{\partial q},$$

$$f_2(p, q, t) - f_2(p_0, q_0, t) = (p - p_0)\frac{\partial \bar{f}_2}{\partial p} + (q - q_0)\frac{\partial \bar{f}_2}{\partial q},$$

where

$$\frac{\partial \bar{f}_1}{\partial p} = \frac{\partial f_1[p_0 + \theta(p - p_0), q_0 + \theta(q - q_0), t]}{\partial p}, 0 < \theta < 1,$$

and $\partial \bar{f}_1 / \partial q$ etc. have similar meanings. Replacing the bracketed expressions in (78:12) and (78:13) by their values as given above, we have

$$(78:14) \quad p - p^{(1)} = \int_{t_0}^{t} \left[(p - p_0)\frac{\partial \bar{f}_1}{\partial p} + (q - q_0)\frac{\partial \bar{f}_1}{\partial q}\right] dt,$$

$$(78\!:\!15) \quad q - q^{(1)} = \int_{t_0}^{t} \left[ (p - p_0)\frac{\partial \bar{f}_2}{\partial p} + (q - q_0)\frac{\partial \bar{f}_2}{\partial q} \right] dt.$$

Adding (78:14) and (78:15), we get

$$(78\!:\!16) \quad p - p^{(1)} + q - q^{(1)} = \int_{t_0}^{t} \left[ (p - p_0)\left( \frac{\partial \bar{f}_1}{\partial p} + \frac{\partial \bar{f}_2}{\partial p} \right) \right.$$
$$\left. + (q - q_0)\left( \frac{\partial \bar{f}_1}{\partial q} + \frac{\partial \bar{f}_2}{\partial q} \right) \right] dt.$$

Let $M$ denote the maximum value of either

$$\left| \frac{\partial f_1}{\partial p} \right| + \left| \frac{\partial f_2}{\partial p} \right| \quad \text{or} \quad \left| \frac{\partial f_1}{\partial q} \right| + \left| \frac{\partial f_2}{\partial q} \right|$$

in the interval $(t, t_0)$ and ranges $p - p_0$, $q - q_0$. Then (78:16) becomes

$$(78\!:\!17) \quad p - p^{(1)} + q - q^{(1)} \leqq M \int_{t_0}^{t} [(p - p_0) + (q - q_0)] dt.$$

Furthermore, let $\epsilon_0$, $\epsilon_1$ and $\delta_0$, $\delta_1$ denote the maximum values of $|p - p_0|$, $|p - p^{(1)}|$ and $|q - q_0|$, $|q - q^{(1)}|$, respectively. Then (78:17) may be written

$$\epsilon_1 + \delta_1 \leqq M(\epsilon_0 + \delta_0) \left| \int_{t_0}^{t} dt \right| = M(\epsilon_0 + \delta_0) \left| t - t_0 \right|.$$

This relation holds for the first application of the iteration process. Similar relations hold for the succeeding approximations, so that we may write

$$\epsilon_2 + \delta_2 \leqq M(\epsilon_1 + \delta_1) \left| t - t_0 \right|,$$
$$\epsilon_3 + \delta_3 \leqq M(\epsilon_2 + \delta_2) \left| t - t_0 \right|,$$
$$\cdot \quad \cdot \quad \cdot \quad \cdot \quad \cdot \quad \cdot \quad \cdot \quad \cdot \quad \cdot$$
$$\epsilon_n + \delta_n \leqq M(\epsilon_{n-1} + \delta_{n-1}) \left| t - t_0 \right|.$$

Multiplying together these $n$ inequalities, member for member, and dividing the result through by the common factors

$$(\epsilon_1 + \delta_1), (\epsilon_2 + \delta_2), \cdots (\epsilon_{n-1} + \delta_{n-1}),$$

we get

$$(78\!:\!18) \qquad \epsilon_n + \delta_n \leqq (M \left| t - t_0 \right|)^n (\epsilon_0 + \delta_0).$$

Now if $M|t - t_0| < 1$, the right-hand side of (78:18) can be made as small as we please. Hence $(\epsilon_n + \delta_n)$ can be made arbitrarily small; that is, the differences $|p - p^{(n)}|$ and $|q - q^{(n)}|$ can be made as small as we like. The iteration process therefore converges to the true values of $p$ and $q$. The condition for the convergence is therefore

$$M\Delta t < 1 \text{ or } \Delta t < \frac{1}{M}.$$

Stated otherwise, $\Delta t$ must be such that

$$\Delta t < \frac{1}{\left|\dfrac{\partial f_1}{\partial p}\right| + \left|\dfrac{\partial f_2}{\partial p}\right|}, \text{ or } \Delta t < \frac{1}{\left|\dfrac{\partial f_1}{\partial q}\right| + \left|\dfrac{\partial f_2}{\partial q}\right|}.$$

The iteration process will evidently fail wherever any one of the partial derivatives $\partial f_1/\partial p$, $\partial f_1/\partial q$, $\partial f_2/\partial p$, $\partial f_2/\partial q$ becomes infinite.

For the proof of the iteration process for systems of equations in any number of variables the reader is referred to F. R. Moulton's *New Methods in Exterior Ballistics*, Ch. V.

**79. Convergence in the Case of Substituted Polynomials.** The proofs given in the preceding article are based on the assumption that the iteration process is carried out as indicated in Art. 73. In that case no restrictions were placed on the *form* of the function $y$. In Arts. 75 and 76, however, the process was not carried out in this manner. In these articles a polynomial of definite degree was substituted for the *derivative* of the function, and this polynomial was then integrated over an interval of width $h$. Consequently the function itself was replaced in the given interval by a polynomial of a degree higher by one. Then at each repetition of the iteration process by means of formula (75:5), we always replaced the derivative by a polynomial of the *same degree* as the one previously used, but having different coefficients.* This amounted to replacing the unknown function by a polynomial of the fifth degree when fourth differences were used, by a polynomial of the fourth degree when third differences were used, etc. In particular, the unknown function was replaced by a straight line in the first interval and by a second-degree parabola in the second interval. This is why the intervals must be taken short at the start of a computation.

Now when the derivatives are thus replaced by polynomials, the iteration process converges rapidly to a definite limit, and the *conditions* for convergence are the same as those found in Art. 78. The *limit*, however, to which the process converges is not the true value of

---

* Since the coefficients in the substituted polynomial are functions of the differences $\Delta_1 y'$, $\Delta_2 y'$, etc., and since new differences are computed at each approximation, it is evident that the new polynomial will have coefficients different from the preceding.

the unknown function but is a definite *polynomial* of degree one higher than that substituted for the derivative in the successive approximations. This limiting polynomial can be made to approximate the true value of the function to any desired degree of accuracy in any one of three ways: (1) by decreasing the interval $h$, (2) by increasing the degree of the substituted polynomial, or (3) by decreasing $h$ and increasing the degree of the polynomial. Since the degree of the substituted polynomial can be increased only by using higher differences and since it is not desirable to use differences higher than the fourth, it is necessary to decrease $h$ in order to attain very high accuracy. If, for example, fourth differences are not used in formula (75: 5), the value of $h$ should be such that the fourth difference term in that formula, when multiplied by $h$, will not affect the last decimal place retained. The foregoing statements are illustrated in the following example.

The analytical solution of the differential equation

$$(79:1) \qquad \frac{dy}{dx} = x + y,$$

with initial conditions $x_0 = 0$, $y_0 = 1$, is

$$(79:2) \qquad y = 2e^x - x - 1.$$

By means of (79:2) the exact value of $y$ can be found for any value of $x$.

The entries in the first table below are true values computed from equations (79:2) and (79:1). The various orders of differences in these lines are therefore correct values. We shall now attempt to find the value of $y$ corresponding to $x = 1.0$, by starting with the exact values in the line for $x = 0.8$. The value of $h$ is therefore 0.2. Three separate computations will be made: (a) by using only first and second differences, (b) by utilizing third differences, and (c) by using fourth differences. The lines for the successive approximations are shown in each case. Also the absolute and percentage errors of the computed $y$ are given at the end of each computation.

The first preliminary line in each computation was found by integrating ahead by formula (75:4). The others were found by successive applications of formula (75:5).

| $x$ | $y$ | $\Delta y$ | $y'$ | $\Delta_1 y'$ | $\Delta_2 y'$ | $\Delta_3 y'$ | $\Delta_4 y'$ |
|---|---|---|---|---|---|---|---|
| 0.0 | 1.000000 | | 1.000000 | | | | |
| 0.2 | 1.242806 | | 1.442806 | 0.442806 | | | |
| 0.4 | 1.583650 | | 1.983650 | 0.540844 | 0.098038 | | |
| 0.6 | 2.044238 | | 2.644238 | 0.660588 | 0.119744 | 0.021706 | |
| 0.8 | 2.651082 | 0.606844 | 3.451082 | 0.806844 | 0.146256 | 0.026512 | 0.004806 |
| 1.0 | 3.436564 | 0.785482 | 4.436564 | 0.985482 | 0.178638 | 0.032382 | 0.005870 |

| | $x$ | $y$ | $\Delta y$ | $y'$ | $\Delta_1 y'$ | $\Delta_2 y'$ | $\Delta_3 y'$ | $\Delta_4 y'$ |
|---|---|---|---|---|---|---|---|---|
| | 0.8 | 2.651082 | | 3.451082 | 0.806844 | 0.146256 | | |
| | 1.0 | 3.434171 | 0.783089 | 4.434171 | 0.983089 | 0.176245 | | |
| (a) | 1.0 | 3.436670 | 0.785588 | 4.436670 | 0.985588 | 0.178944 | | |
| | 1.0 | 3.436878 | 0.785796 | 4.436878 | 0.985796 | 0.178952 | | |
| | 1.0 | 3.436895 | 0.785813 | 4.436895 | 0.985813 | 0.178969 | | |
| | 1.0 | 3.436897 | 0.785815 | 4.436897 | 0.985815 | 0.178971 | | |

Absolute error in $y_{1.0} = 0.000333$; percentage error $= 0.0097\%$.

| | $x$ | $y$ | $\Delta y$ | $y'$ | $\Delta_1 y'$ | $\Delta_2 y'$ | $\Delta_3 y'$ | $\Delta_4 y'$ |
|---|---|---|---|---|---|---|---|---|
| | 0.8 | 2.651082 | | 3.451082 | 0.806844 | 0.146256 | 0.026512 | |
| | 1.0 | 3.436159 | 0.785077 | 4.436159 | 0.985077 | 0.178233 | 0.031977 | |
| (b) | 1.0 | 3.436569 | 0.785487 | 4.436569 | 0.985487 | 0.178643 | 0.032387 | |
| | 1.0 | 3.436600 | 0.785518 | 4.436600 | 0.985518 | 0.178674 | 0.032418 | |
| | 1.0 | 3.436602 | 0.785520 | 4.436602 | 0.985520 | 0.178676 | 0.032420 | |

Absolute error in $y_{1.0} = 0.000038$; percentage error $= 0.0011\%$.

| | $x$ | $y$ | $\Delta y$ | $y'$ | $\Delta_1 y'$ | $\Delta_2 y'$ | $\Delta_3 y'$ | $\Delta_4 y'$ |
|---|---|---|---|---|---|---|---|---|
| | 0.8 | 2.651082 | | 3.451082 | 0.806844 | 0.146256 | 0.026512 | 0.004806 |
| | 1.0 | 3.436494 | 0.785412 | 4.436494 | 0.985412 | 0.178568 | 0.032312 | 0.005800 |
| (c) | 1.0 | 3.436564 | 0.785482 | 4.436564 | 0.985482 | 0.178638 | 0.032382 | 0.005870 |
| | 1.0 | 3.436568 | 0.785486 | 4.436568 | 0.985486 | 0.178642 | 0.032386 | 0.005874 |
| | 1.0 | 3.436569 | 0.785487 | 4.436569 | 0.985487 | 0.178643 | 0.032387 | 0.005875 |

Absolute error in $y_{1.0} = 0.000005$; percentage error $= 0.000145\%$.

It will be observed that the iteration process converges to a different value in each case, depending on whether we stop with second, third, or fourth differences. It should also be noted that for this value of $h$ the error is about 67 times as great when we stop with second differences as it is when fourth differences are used.

Even if we start with the correct values of all the quantities in the row for $x = 1.0$ and attempt to check them by repeated applications of formula (75:5), we shall find that the process, instead of checking the true values as one might suppose, actually converges to the same value for $y_{1.0}$ as was found by starting with the row for $x = 0.8$. The following table shows the results of such a computation.

| | $x$ | $y$ | $\Delta y$ | $y'$ | $\Delta_1 y'$ | $\Delta_2 y'$ |
|---|---|---|---|---|---|---|
| True | 0.8 | 2.651082 | | 3.451082 | 0.806844 | 0.146256 |
| values | 1.0 | 3.436564 | 0.785482 | 4.436564 | 0.985482 | 0.178638 |
| | 1.0 | 3.436869 | 0.785787 | 4.436869 | 0.985787 | 0.178943 |
| | 1.0 | 3.436895 | 0.785813 | 4.436895 | 0.985813 | 0.178969 |
| | 1.0 | 3.436897 | 0.785815 | 4.436897 | 0.985815 | 0.178971 |

It will be noticed that the last line in this table is the same as the last line of the corresponding computation (a) in the preceding table.

Of course we can get a more accurate result when stopping with second differences by using a smaller value for $h$. When only second differences are used, the attainable degree of accuracy is the same as that of Simpson's rule for the same value of $h$. Hence by taking $h$ half as large, we reduce the inherent error to one sixteenth of its previous value (Art. 49). Thus, if we take $h = 0.1$, start with the correct values for the line $x = 0.9$, and compute the value of $y_{1.0}$, we shall find $y_{1.0} = 3.436585$. The absolute error in this value is 0.000021, which is about one sixteenth of the error 0.000333 made by taking $h = 0.2$.

**80. Checks, Errors, and Accuracy.** Attention has already been called to the use of formulas (75:5), (75:6), (75:7), (75:8) for checking the computed change in a function over a single interval. Simpson's rule furnishes a convenient and reliable means of checking the summation of any function over an even number of intervals. For example, the decrease in the horizontal velocity of the bullet of Example 3, Art. 76, from $t = 2$ to $t = 26$, is

$$\Delta \dot{x} = \int_2^{26} \ddot{x} dt = \frac{\Delta t}{3} [\ddot{x}_2 + 4(\ddot{x}_4 + \ddot{x}_8 + \ddot{x}_{12} + \ddot{x}_{16} + \ddot{x}_{20} + \ddot{x}_{24})$$
$$+ 2(\ddot{x}_6 + \ddot{x}_{10} + \ddot{x}_{14} + \ddot{x}_{18} + \ddot{x}_{22}) + \ddot{x}_{26}],$$

or

$$\Delta \dot{x} = \tfrac{2}{3}[- 19.52 + 4(- 16.26 - 11.88 - 9.43 - 8.27 - 7.91 - 7.88)$$
$$+ 2(- 13.77 - 10.46 - 8.72 - 8.02 - 7.88) - 7.90] = -247.76.$$

Hence

$$\dot{x}_{26} = 567.32 - 247.76 = 319.56,$$

which differs from the value in the table by only two units in the last digit. The fifth figure in all these numbers is uncertain, probably worthless, but the two methods certainly check within a unit in the fourth figure. The values of $\dot{y}$ and $y$ may be checked in a similar manner.

A single error in any one of the quantities $\dot{x}$, $\dot{y}$, and $y$ will persist throughout the computation in the column in which it occurs, but its effect will usually not increase as the computation continues. An error in the acceleration will likewise persist and will affect in some degree all the other computed quantities, but the effect may not be serious. An error in the differences of the acceleration and in the second, third, and fourth differences of the other functions will soon disappear, and its effect on the final results will usually be negligible. If several errors are made, they will probably neutralize one another to a considerable extent, but it is possible that they may accumulate sufficiently to affect seriously some of the later results.

As an example of the effect of a single error near the beginning of a computation, it may be stated that Example 2 of Art. 76 was first computed throughout by starting with an error of two units in the last digit of $\dot{\theta}$ for $t = 0.05$ sec. The maximum error in any subsequent value of $\dot{\theta}$ was five units in the last digit, whereas the greatest error in any later value of $\theta$ and $\ddot{\theta}$ was only two units in the last figure.

An error of more than a unit in the last digit of a computed result can usually be detected by inspection of the second, third, and fourth differences of that result. If these higher differences run smoothly— that is, vary in a regular fashion without sudden changes in magnitude or sign—, it is quite certain that no error has been made; but if the third and fourth differences become grossly irregular, the student had better stop and look for an error at once. The error may be located approximately by the method explained in Art. 13. The computer should watch the behavior of the higher differences as he goes along, so as to detect an error as soon as possible after it appears.

The accuracy of the final results may be estimated in one or more ways. The safest plan to insure accuracy is to take $h$ so small that fourth differences will be negligible to the number of figures desired in the final results. When fourth differences are negligible, the application of formula (75: 5) as many times as it will effect improvement will usually insure that the error is less than half a unit in the last figure retained. Since these half-unit (or less) errors are as likely to be positive as negative and since the coefficients in Simpson's rule are all positive, it is evident that when these rounded numbers are summed by Simpson's rule the errors in the last digits are largely neutralized in the summation process. Hence it is not worth while to consider them in estimating the accuracy of a final result.

The computer should never forget that a result obtained by Simpson's rule (or by any other formula for that matter) can not be more accurate than the data to which it is applied. Hence if we compute the range of a projectile, for instance, by applying Simpson's rule to the column of horizontal velocities, the computed range can not be true to any more significant figures than are given in the velocity column. Occasionally it may happen that the numbers to be summed are more accurate than Simpson's rule, in which case we should compute the error due to the rule itself (Art. 48).

*80a). Formulas for the Maximum Error.* The error due to replacing the derivative of the given function by a polynomial can be calculated by integrating the remainder term in Newton's formula (II), since formulas (75:4) and (75:5) were obtained from this formula. In Art. 28 we found this remainder to be either

$$(80:1) \qquad R_n = \frac{h^{n+1}f^{(n+1)}(\xi)}{(n+1)!}u(u+1)(u+2)\cdots(u+n)$$

or

$$(80:2) \qquad R_n = \frac{\Delta_{n+1}y_n}{(n+1)!}u(u+1)(u+2)\cdots(u+n),$$

depending on whether we wish to use derivatives or differences.

Now if $y=f(x)$ denotes the solution of the given differential equation, we recall that our approximation to this solution was obtained by replacing $f'(x)$ by a polynomial. Hence the $f$ in (80:1) above must be replaced by $f'$ in our present problem. Likewise, the $y_n$ in (80:2) must be replaced by $y_n'$.

Furthermore, since we are integrating $f'(x)$, we get the required error by integrating $R_n(x)dx$. Since $dx=hdu$, we have from (80:1), on replacing $f$ by $f'$, or $f^{(n+1)}$ by $f^{(n+2)}$,*

$$E_{n-1}^n = \int_{x_{n-1}}^{x_n} R_n(x)dx = h\int_{-1}^{0} \frac{h^{n+1}f^{(n+2)}(\xi)}{(n+1)!}u(u+1)(u+2)\cdots(u+n)du.$$

Now since we usually stop with third differences in formula (75:5), we shall take $n=3$ in the formula above. Also, let $M_n$ denote the maximum value of $f^v(x)$ in the interval $x_{n-1}$ to $x_n$. Then we have

$$E_{n-1}^n \leqq \frac{M_n h^5}{24}\int_{-1}^{0} u(u+1)(u+2)(u+3)du = \frac{M_n h^5}{24}\left(\frac{19}{30}\right) = \frac{19M_n h^5}{720},$$

or

$$(80:3) \qquad\qquad\qquad E_{n-1}^n \leqq \frac{M_n h^5}{38},$$

practically.

If $M$ denote the maximum value of $f^v(x)$ in any interval $(a, b)$, then

$$(80:4) \qquad\qquad\qquad E_a^b \leqq \frac{nM h^5}{38}.$$

Or, since $b-a=nh$, this reduces to

$$(80:5) \qquad\qquad\qquad E_a^b \leqq \frac{M h^4}{38}(b - a).$$

* Here $f(x)$ stands for the solution of the given differential equation.

Formulas (80:3), (80:4), (80:5) are theoretically correct, but they are inconvenient to use in practice, because of the inconvenience of obtaining the fourth derivative of $f'(x)$. We shall therefore derive corresponding formulas in terms of differences.

Integrating (80:2) over the interval $x_{n-1}$ to $x_n$, we have

$$E_{n-1}^n = h \int_{-1}^{0} \frac{\Delta_4 y'_n}{4!} u(u+1)(u+2)(u+3)du = \frac{h\Delta_4 y'_n}{24}\left(\frac{19}{30}\right) = \frac{19h\Delta_4 y'_n}{720},$$

or, practically,

(80:6)
$$E_{n-1}^n = \frac{h}{38}\Delta_4 y'_n.$$

For an interval $(a, b)$ we thus have

(80:7)
$$E_a^b = \frac{h}{38}\sum\Delta_4 y',$$

provided $h$ has the same value in all the subintervals.

By bearing in mind the facts, principles, and formulas given in this article the computer should have no difficulty in estimating the reliability of his results.

### EXAMPLES ON CHAPTER XII

1. Using formula (80:7), estimate the error in the computed $y$'s in the example of Art. 75 and compare these computed errors with the actual errors.

2. Check the solutions of the examples in Art. 76 by Simpson's rule, Weddle's rule, or central-difference formula (41:3).

# CHAPTER XIII

## OTHER METHODS FOR THE NUMERICAL SOLUTION OF DIFFERENTIAL EQUATIONS

**81. Introduction.** Various methods have been devised for solving differential equations numerically, but some of them are of limited application. The method of successive approximations is doubtless the best general method, but in some problems the desired result can be obtained with less labor by some other method. In the present chapter we shall describe and illustrate the use of three additional methods which are of general application.

**82. The Method of J. C. Adams.** The method to be described in this article was devised by J. C. Adams,[*] the famous mathematical astronomer. Theoretically the method is applicable to equations of any order or to any system of equations, but practically it is of limited application, as will appear later.

Adams's method is somewhat similar to the method of successive approximations, but it differs from the latter in two respects: (1) the solution is started by computing the first four values of the function, after the initial values, by means of Taylor's series and (2) is continued by integrating ahead only—without repetitions.

To start a solution we write the ordinary Taylor series

$$f(x) = f(x_0) + f'(x_0)(x - x_0) + \frac{f''(x_0)}{2}(x - x_0)^2 + \frac{f'''(x_0)}{3!}(x - x_0)^3 + \cdots$$

in the equivalent form

**(82 : 1)** $y = y_0 + y_0'(x - x_0) + \dfrac{y_0''}{2}(x - x_0)^2 + \dfrac{y_0'''}{3!}(x - x_0)^3 + \cdots$

$$+ \frac{y_0^{(n)}}{n!}(x - x_0)^n + \cdots .$$

Then to find $y_1$, $y_2$, $y_3$, $y_4$ from this series we first calculate from the given differential equation the values of the derivatives $y'$, $y''$, $y'''$, etc.

[*] *Theories of Capillary Action*, by F. Bashforth and J. C. Adams, Cambridge, (England), 1883.

at the starting point $x = x_0$, $y = y_0$, and then put $x - x_0$ equal to $h$, $2h$, etc. in succession in formula (82:1). The method will be illustrated by showing how to apply it to the examples already solved by the iteration process.

*Example 1.* Start the solution of $dy/dx = x + y$ by Adams's method, the initial values being $x_0 = 0$, $y_0 = 1$.

*Solution.* We have

$$y' = x + y.$$

Hence

$$y'' = 1 + y', \ y''' = y'', \ y^{iv} = y''', \ y^{v} = y^{iv}, \ y^{vi} = y^{v}.$$

Then

$$y_0' = 1, \ y_0'' = 2, \ y_0''' = 2, \ y_0^{iv} = 2, \ y_0^{v} = 2, \ y_0^{v} = 2.$$

Substituting these in (82:1) and remembering that $x - x_0$ is simply $x$ (since $x_0 = 0$), we get

$$y = 1 + x + x^2 + \frac{x^3}{3} + \frac{x^4}{12} + \frac{x^5}{60} + \frac{x^6}{360} + \cdots.$$

If $h = 0.1$, so that $x_1 = 0.1$, $x_2 = 0.2$, etc., we have

$$y_1 = 1 + 0.1 + (0.1)^2 + \frac{(0.1)^3}{3} + \frac{(0.1)^4}{12} = 1.1103,$$

$$y_2 = 1 + 0.2 + (0.2)^2 + \frac{(0.2)^3}{3} + \frac{(0.2)^4}{12} = 1.2428,$$

$$y_3 = 1 + 0.3 + (0.3)^2 + \frac{(0.3)^3}{3} + \frac{(0.3)^4}{12} + \frac{(0.3)^5}{60} = 1.3997,$$

$$y_4 = 1 + 0.4 + (0.4)^3 + \frac{(0.4)^3}{3} + \frac{(0.4)^4}{12} + \frac{(0.4)^5}{60} = 1.5836.$$

These values are all correct to four decimal places.

Since $y' = x + y$, the values of $y_1'$, $y_2'$, etc. are found by adding the corresponding values of $x$ and $y$. The following table gives the results of the computation for the first five values of $y$ and $y'$.

| $x$ | $y$ | $y'$ | $\Delta_1 y'$ | $\Delta_2 y'$ | $\Delta_3 y'$ | $\Delta_4 y'$ |
|---|---|---|---|---|---|---|
| 0.0 | 1.0000 | 1.0000 | | | | |
| 0.1 | 1.1103 | 1.2103 | 0.2103 | | | |
| 0.2 | 1.2428 | 1.4428 | 0.2325 | 0.0222 | | |
| 0.3 | 1.3997 | 1.6997 | 0.2569 | 0.0244 | 0.0022 | |
| 0.4 | 1.5836 | 1.9836 | 0.2839 | 0.0270 | 0.0026 | 0.0004 |

The table is continued by integrating ahead, using formula (75:4).

Adams's method is evidently much shorter than the iteration method in this example.

*Example 2.* Work Example 1 of Art. 76 by the method of Adams.

*Solution.* The equations to be integrated are

$$\ddot{x} = -0.02\dot{x},$$

$$\ddot{y} = -0.02\dot{y} - 32.16,$$

with $x_0 = 0$, $y_0 = 0$, $t_0 = 0$. Since $t_0 = 0$, the Taylor series for $y$ is

$$y = y_0 + \dot{y}_0 t + \frac{\ddot{y}_0 t^2}{2} + \frac{\dddot{y}_0 t^3}{3!} + \frac{y_0^{iv} t^4}{4!} + \frac{y_0^{v} t^5}{5!} + \frac{y_0^{vi} t^6}{6!}.$$

Differentiating the equation $\ddot{y} = -0.02\dot{y} - 32.16$ with respect to $t$, we have

$$\dddot{y} = -0.02\ddot{y}, \quad y^{iv} = -0.02\dddot{y}, \quad y^{v} = -0.02y^{iv}, \quad y^{vi} = -0.02y^{v}.$$

Then since $\dot{y} = 150 \sin 23° = 58.61$, we get

$$\ddot{y} = -0.02 \times 58.61 - 32.16 = -33.33,$$

$$\dddot{y} = -0.02(-33.33) = 0.6666,$$

$$y^{iv} = -0.02(0.6666) = -0.01333,$$

$$y^{v} = -0.02(-0.01333) = 0.0002666,$$

$$y^{vi} = -0.02(0.0002666) = -0.000005332.$$

Hence

$$y = 58.61t - \frac{33.33}{2}t^2 + \frac{0.667}{6}t^3 - \frac{0.0133}{24}t^4$$

$$+ \frac{0.0003}{120}t^5 - \frac{0.000005}{720}t^6.$$

Putting $t = 1, 2, 3, 4$ in succession, we get

$$y_1 = 42.06, \quad y_2 = 51.44, \quad y_3 = 28.80, \quad y_4 = -25.22.$$

These values for $y_1$, $y_2$, $y_3$, $y_4$, are the same as those previously found by the method of successive approximations.

The time of flight of the ball in this problem is so short that the functions $x$ and $y$ can be represented by Taylor's series over the whole trajectory, so that integration ahead is unnecessary.

To find the range we represent $x$ by a Taylor series and substitute in this series the value of $t$ when $y=0$. This value of $t$ has already been found to be 3.6 seconds.

*Example 3.* Start the solution of Example 2, Art. 76, by Adams's method.

*Solution.* Here the equation to be integrated is

$$\ddot{\theta} = - 0.2\dot{\theta} - 10 \sin \theta,$$

with $\theta = 0.3$ and $\dot{\theta} = 0$ when $t = 0$.

The Taylor series for $\theta$ is

$$\theta = \theta_0 + \dot{\theta}_0 t + \frac{\ddot{\theta}_0 t^2}{2} + \frac{\dddot{\theta}_0 t^3}{3!} + \frac{\overset{iv}{\theta_0} t^4}{4!} + \frac{\overset{v}{\theta_0} t^5}{5!} + \frac{\overset{vi}{\theta_0} t^6}{6!} + \cdots .$$

From the given equation $\ddot{\theta} = -0.2\dot{\theta} - 10 \sin \theta$ we get

$$\dddot{\theta} = - 0.2\ddot{\theta} - 10\dot{\theta} \cos \theta,$$

$$\theta^{iv} = - 0.2\dddot{\theta} + 10(\dot{\theta}^2 \sin \theta - \ddot{\theta} \cos \theta),$$

$$\theta^{v} = - 0.2\theta^{iv} + 10[(\dot{\theta}^3 - \dddot{\theta}) \cos \theta + 3\dot{\theta}\ddot{\theta} \sin \theta],$$

$$\theta^{vi} = - 0.2\theta^{v} + 10[(3\dot{\theta}^2\ddot{\theta} - \theta^{iv}) \cos \theta - (\dot{\theta}^4 - \dot{\theta}\dddot{\theta}) \sin \theta$$

$$+ 3(\dot{\theta}^2\ddot{\theta} \cos \theta + \ddot{\theta}^2 \sin \theta + \dot{\theta}\ddot{\theta} \sin \theta)].$$

For $\theta = 0.3$ and $\dot{\theta} = 0$ these equations become

$$\ddot{\theta}_0 = - 10 \sin 0.3 = - 2.9552,$$

$$\dddot{\theta}_0 = - 0.2\ddot{\theta}_0 = 0.2 \times 2.9552 = 0.59104,$$

$$\overset{iv}{\theta_0} = - 0.2\dddot{\theta}_0 - 10\ddot{\theta}_0 \cos 0.3 = - 0.118 + 28.232 = 28.114,$$

$$\overset{v}{\theta_0} = - 0.2\overset{iv}{\theta_0} - 10\dddot{\theta}_0 \cos 0.3 = - 5.6228 - 5.6464 = - 11.269,$$

$$\overset{vi}{\theta_0} = - 0.2\overset{v}{\theta_0} - 10\overset{iv}{\theta_0} \cos 0.3 + 30\dot{\theta}^2 \sin 0.3$$

$$= 2.25 - 268.58 + 77.43 = - 188.90.$$

The Taylor expansion for $\theta$ at $t = 0$ is then

$$(1) \quad \theta = 0.3 - \frac{2.9552t^2}{2} + \frac{0.59104t^3}{6} + \frac{28.114t^4}{24} - \frac{11.269t^5}{120}$$

$$- \frac{188.90t^6}{720} \cdots .$$

Differentiating this equation with respect to $t$, we have

$$(2) \quad \dot{\theta} = -2.9552t + \frac{0.59104t^2}{2} + \frac{28.114t^3}{6} - \frac{11.269t^4}{24} - \frac{188.90t^5}{120} .$$

By means of equations (1) and (2) and the given differential equation the correct values of $\theta$, $\dot{\theta}$ and $\ddot{\theta}$ can be computed for sufficiently small values of $t$. Thus, for $t=0.1, 0.2, 0.3, 0.4$ the corresponding values of $\theta$ are found from (1) to be $\theta_1=0.2854$, $\theta_2=0.2435$, $\theta_3=0.1788$, $\theta_4=0.0978$; and from (2) the values of $\dot{\theta}$ are $\dot{\theta}_1=-0.2879$, $\dot{\theta}_2=-0.5430$, $\dot{\theta}_3=-0.7411$, $\dot{\theta}_4=-0.8631$. Reference to page 242 will show that these values, with the exception of $\dot{\theta}_4$, agree closely with those found by the iteration process. The value of $\dot{\theta}_4$ found above differs from that on page 242 by five units in its last figure and is probably incorrect by that amount.

Series (1) and (2) are not very satisfactory for purposes of computation, because they converge slowly even for small values of $t$. Moreover, the coefficients are so irregular that it would be a difficult matter to write down the general term. The interval of convergence is therefore not easy to determine.

*Example 4.* Apply Adams's method to Example 3 of Art. 76.

*Solution.* The equations to be integrated are

$$\ddot{x} = -0.00005\dot{x}\sqrt{\dot{x}^2 + \dot{y}^2},$$

$$\ddot{y} = -0.00005\dot{y}\sqrt{\dot{x}^2 + \dot{y}^2},$$

with the initial conditions $x_0=0$, $y_0=0$, $\dot{x}_0=780 \cos 38°30'$,

$$\dot{y}_0 = 780 \sin 38°30'$$

when $t=0$.

The Taylor expansion for $x$ is

$$x = x_0 + \dot{x}_0 t + \frac{\ddot{x}_0 t^2}{2} + \frac{\overset{\cdots}{x}_0 t^3}{3!} + \frac{\overset{iv}{x}_0 t^4}{4!} + \frac{\overset{v}{x}_0 t^5}{5!} + \frac{\overset{vi}{x}_0 t^6}{6!} + \cdots ,$$

and a similar series for $y$.

From the equation $\ddot{x} = -0.00005\dot{x}\sqrt{\dot{x}^2 + \dot{y}^2}$ we have

$$\dddot{x} = -0.00005\left[\ddot{x}\sqrt{\dot{x}^2 + \dot{y}^2} + \dot{x}\left(\frac{\dot{x}\ddot{x} + \dot{y}\ddot{y}}{\sqrt{\dot{x}^2 + \dot{y}^2}}\right)\right]$$

$$= -0.00005\left(\frac{\ddot{x}\dot{y}^2 + 2\ddot{x}\dot{x}^2 + \dot{x}\dot{y}\ddot{y}}{\sqrt{\dot{x}^2 + \dot{y}^2}}\right).$$

We shall not continue the differentiations further, as the student can see now that succeeding differentiations will become more and more laborious. Because of these laborious differentiations and the further labor involved in computing the numerical values of the complicated expressions, we make no further attempt to start the solution of this problem by Adams's method.

If we attempt to apply this method to the fundamental ballistic equations

$$\ddot{x} = -E\dot{x},$$

$$\ddot{y} = -E\dot{y} - g,$$

where

$$E = \frac{G(v)H(y)}{C},$$

we get into far greater difficulties; for here $E$ is a function of $t$ through $G(v)$ and this latter function is so complicated that the labor of finding even a single derivative directly would be practically prohibitive. The laborious direct differentiation can be avoided to some extent, however, by finding the derivatives numerically (by interpolation) from a table giving $G(v)$ for various values of $v$.*

*Remarks on the method of Adams.* The preceding examples serve to show some of the advantages and disadvantages of Adams's method. The success of the method in starting a solution evidently depends upon (1) the ease with which the successive derivatives of the unknown function can be calculated and (2) the rapidity with which the Taylor series converges. If the successive derivatives are easily calculated and the Taylor series converges rapidly, the method furnishes the best means of starting a solution and should be used in preference to any other. But if, on the other hand, the successive derivatives are not easily calculated, or if the Taylor series is such that the interval of convergence is not easily determined, the method should not be used. For continuing a computation after once started the method of Adams is inferior to the method of successive approximations when differences

* See Vahlen, *Ballistic* (1922) pp. 57 and 28.

of the same order and the same value of $h$ are used in both methods, but for the same value of $h$ the method of Adams (which consists merely in integrating ahead) will give a more accurate result by using fourth differences than will the method of successive approximations by using only second differences. A combination of the two methods—that is, starting the computation by Adams's method and continuing it by the iteration process—is frequently better than either alone.

Because of the difficulty of calculating the successive derivatives of the air-resistance function the method of Adams is not suitable for starting the computation of trajectories.

**83. The Runge-Kutta Method.** This method was devised by Runge* about the year 1894 and extended by Kutta† a few years later. It is unlike either of the methods explained in the preceding pages. Here the increments of the function (or functions) are calculated once for all by means of a definite set of formulas. The calculations for the first increment, for example, are exactly the same as for any other increment.

Let
$$\frac{dy}{dx} = f(x, y)$$

denote any first order differential equation connecting the variables $x$ and $y$, and let $h$ denote any increment $\Delta x$ in the independent variable $x$. Then if the initial values of the variables are $x_0$ and $y_0$ the first increment in $y$ is computed from the formulas

$$(83:1) \quad \begin{cases} k_1 = f(x_0,\, y_0)h, \\[2mm] k_2 = f\left(x_0 + \dfrac{h}{2},\ y_0 + \dfrac{k_1}{2}\right)h, \\[2mm] k_3 = f\left(x_0 + \dfrac{h}{2},\ y_0 + \dfrac{k_2}{2}\right)h, \\[2mm] k_4 = f(x_0 + h,\, y_0 + k_3)h, \\[2mm] \Delta y = \tfrac{1}{6}(k_1 + 2k_2 + 2k_3 + k_4), \end{cases}$$

taken in the order given. Then

$$x_1 = x_0 + h, \quad y_1 = y_0 + \Delta y.$$

The increment in $y$ for the second interval is computed in a similar manner by means of the formulas

---

* C. Runge, *Mathematisch Annalen*, Vol. 46 (1895).
† W. Kutta, *Zeitschrift für Math. und Phys.* Vol. 46 (1901).

$$k_1 = f(x_1, y_1)h,$$

$$k_2 = f\left(x_1 + \frac{h}{2}, \ y_1 + \frac{k_1}{2}\right)h,$$

$$k_3 = f\left(x_1 + \frac{h}{2}, \ y_1 + \frac{k_2}{2}\right)h,$$

$$k_4 = f(x_1 + h, \ y_1 + k_3)h,$$

$$\Delta y = \frac{1}{6}(k_1 + 2k_2 + 2k_3 + k_4),$$

and so on for the succeeding intervals.

It will be noticed that the only change in the formulas for the different intervals is in the values of $x$ and $y$ to be substituted. Thus, to find $\Delta y$ in the $n$th interval we should have to substitute $x_{n-1}$, $y_{n-1}$, in the expressions for $k_1$, $k_2$, etc.

In the special case where $dy/dx$ is a function of $x$ alone the Runge-Kutta method reduces to Simpson's rule. For if $dy/dx = f(x)$, then

$$k_1 = f(x_0)h,$$

$$k_2 = f\left(x_0 + \frac{h}{2}\right)h,$$

$$k_3 = f\left(x_0 + \frac{h}{2}\right)h,$$

$$k_4 = f(x_0 + h)h;$$

and therefore

$$\Delta y = \frac{h}{6}\left[f(x_0) + 2f\left(x_0 + \frac{h}{2}\right) + 2f\left(x_0 + \frac{h}{2}\right) + f(x_0 + h)\right]$$

$$= \frac{\left(\dfrac{h}{2}\right)}{3}\left[f(x_0) + 4f\left(x_0 + \frac{h}{2}\right) + f(x_0 + h)\right],$$

which is the same result as would be obtained by applying Simpson's rule to the interval from $x_0$ to $x_0 + h$ if we take two equal subintervals of width $h/2$.

To integrate a pair of simultaneous first-order equations such as

$$\frac{dx}{dt} = f_1(t, x, y),$$

$$\frac{dy}{dt} = f_2(t, x, y),$$

where $x$ and $y$ are functions of $t$, we compute the increments in $x$ and $y$ for the first interval by means of the formulas

$$
\begin{cases}
k_1 = f_1(t_0,\ x_0,\ y_0)\Delta t, \\[2mm]
k_2 = f_1\left(t_0 + \dfrac{\Delta t}{2},\ x_0 + \dfrac{k_1}{2},\ y_0 + \dfrac{l_1}{2}\right)\Delta t, \\[2mm]
k_3 = f_1\left(t_0 + \dfrac{\Delta t}{2},\ x_0 + \dfrac{k_2}{2},\ y_0 + \dfrac{l_2}{2}\right)\Delta t, \\[2mm]
k_4 = f_1(t_0 + \Delta t,\ x_0 + k_3,\ y_0 + l_3)\Delta t, \\[2mm]
\Delta x = \dfrac{1}{6}(k_1 + 2k_2 + 2k_3 + k_4).
\end{cases}
$$

(83:2)

$$
\begin{cases}
l_1 = f_2(t_0,\ x_0,\ y_0)\Delta t, \\[2mm]
l_2 = f_2\left(t_0 + \dfrac{\Delta t}{2},\ x_0 + \dfrac{k_1}{2},\ y_0 + \dfrac{l_1}{2}\right)\Delta t, \\[2mm]
l_3 = f_2\left(t_0 + \dfrac{\Delta t}{2},\ x_0 + \dfrac{k_2}{2},\ y_0 + \dfrac{l_2}{2}\right)\Delta t, \\[2mm]
l_4 = f_2(t_0 + \Delta t,\ x_0 + k_3,\ y_0 + l_3)\Delta t, \\[2mm]
\Delta y = \dfrac{1}{6}(l_1 + 2l_2 + 2l_3 + l_4).
\end{cases}
$$

The increments for the succeeding intervals are computed in exactly the same way except that $t_0$, $x_0$, $y_0$ are replaced by $t_1$, $x_1$, $y_1$, etc. as we proceed.

The derivation of the formulas used in the Runge-Kutta method is a somewhat lengthy process and will not be given here.*

The inherent error in the Runge-Kutta method is not easy to estimate, but is of the order $h^5$† and is therefore of the same order as that in Simpson's rule.

We shall illustrate the method by applying it to some of the examples to which the previous methods were applied.

*Example 1.* Solve the equation

$$\frac{dy}{dx} = x + y,$$

with the initial conditions $x_0 = 0$, $y_0 = 1$.

---

* See Kutta, *loc. cit.*, or *Numerisches Rechnen*, by C. Runge and H. König, pp. 287–294 and 311–313.

† See Kutta, *loc. cit.*, or *Numerische Integration*, by F. A. Willers, pp. 91–92.

*Solution.* Taking $h = 0.1$, we have

$$k_1 = 0.1 \times 1 = 0.1,$$

$$k_2 = 0.1[0.05 + 1.05] = 0.11,$$

$$k_3 = 0.1[0.05 + 1.055] = 0.1105,$$

$$k_4 = 0.1[0.1 + 1.1105] = 0.12105.$$

$$\therefore \quad \Delta y = \tfrac{1}{6}[0.1 + 0.22 + 0.221 + 0.12105] = 0.11034.$$

Hence $x_1 = x_0 + h = 0.1$, $y_1 = y_0 + \Delta y = 1 + 0.1103 = 1.1103$.

Then for the second interval we have

$$k_1 = 0.1(0.1 + 1.1103) = 0.12103,$$

$$k_2 = 0.1(0.1 + 0.05 + 1.1103 + 0.06051) = 0.13208,$$

$$k_3 = 0.1(0.1 + 0.05 + 1.1103 + 0.06604) = 0.13263,$$

$$k_4 = 0.1(0.1 + 0.1 + 1.1103 + 0.13262) = 0.14429.$$

$$\therefore \quad \Delta y = \tfrac{1}{6}(0.12103 + 0.26416 + 0.26526 + 0.14429) = 0.13246,$$

and $x_2 = 0.2$, $y_2 = 1.1103 + 0.1325 = 1.2428$. These values for $y_1$ and $y_2$ are correct to four decimal places. The computation can be continued in this manner as far as desired.

*Example 2.* Solve Example 2 of Art. 76 by the Runge-Kutta method.

*Solution.* Here the equations to be integrated are

$$\frac{d\theta}{dt} = \dot{\theta} = f_1(-, -, \dot{\theta}),$$

$$\frac{d\dot{\theta}}{dt} = -0.2\dot{\theta} - 10 \sin \theta = f_2(-, \theta, \dot{\theta}).$$

Since $t$ and $\theta$ are both absent in the first equation and $t$ is also absent in the second, the equations for computing the $k$'s and $l$'s in this example are as follows:

$$k_1 = f_1(\dot{\theta})\Delta t = \dot{\theta}\Delta t,$$

$$k_2 = f_1\left(\dot{\theta} + \frac{l_1}{2}\right)\Delta t = \left(\dot{\theta} + \frac{l_1}{2}\right)\Delta t,$$

$$k_3 = f_1\left(\dot{\theta} + \frac{l_2}{2}\right)\Delta t = \left(\dot{\theta} + \frac{l_2}{2}\right)\Delta t,$$

$$k_4 = f_1(\dot{\theta} + l_3)\Delta t = (\dot{\theta} + l_3)\Delta t.$$

$l_1 = f_2(\theta, \dot{\theta})\Delta t = - (0.2\dot{\theta} + 10 \sin \theta)\Delta t,$

$l_2 = f_2\left(\theta + \dfrac{k_1}{2}, \quad \dot{\theta} + \dfrac{l_1}{2}\right)\Delta t$

$\qquad = -\left[0.2\left(\dot{\theta} + \dfrac{l_1}{2}\right) + 10 \sin \left(\theta + \dfrac{k_1}{2}\right)\right]\Delta t,$

$l_3 = f_2\left(\theta + \dfrac{k_2}{2}, \quad \dot{\theta} + \dfrac{l_2}{2}\right)\Delta t$

$\qquad = -\left[0.2\left(\dot{\theta} + \dfrac{l_2}{2}\right) + 10 \sin \left(\theta + \dfrac{k_2}{2}\right)\right]\Delta t,$

$l_4 = f_2(\theta + k_3, \dot{\theta} + l_3)\Delta t = - [0.2(\dot{\theta} + l_3) + 10 \sin (\theta + k_3)]\Delta t.$

Taking $\Delta t = 0.1$ and remembering that the initial values of $\theta$ and $\dot{\theta}$ are $\theta_0 = 0.3$, $\dot{\theta}_0 = 0$, we have for the first interval

$k_1 = 0, \; l_1 = - 0.29552,$

$k_2 = - (0.14776) \times 0.1 = - 0.014776,$

$l_2 = - 0.1[0.2(- 0.14776) + 10 \times 0.29552] = - 0.29256,$

$k_3 = - 0.014628,$

$l_3 = - 0.1[0.2(- 0.14628) + 2.8729] = - 0.28436,$

$k_4 = - 0.028436,$

$l_4 = - 0.1[0.2(- 0.28436) + 2.8154] = - 0.27585.$

$\therefore \;\; \Delta\theta = \tfrac{1}{6}(0 - 0.029552 - 0.029256 - 0.028436) = - 0.014541.$

$\therefore \;\;\; \theta_1 = 0.3 - 0.014541 = 0.2855,$

and

$\qquad \Delta\dot{\theta} = \tfrac{1}{6}(- 0.29552 - 0.58512 - 0.56872 - 0.27585)$

$\qquad\qquad = - 0.2875.$

$\therefore \;\;\; \dot{\theta}_1 = - 0.2875.$

For the second interval we have

$$k_1 = -0.2875 \times 0.1 = -0.02875,$$

$$l_1 = -0.1[0.2(-0.2875) + 2.8164] = -0.27589,$$

$$k_2 = 0.1[-0.2875 - 0.1379] = -0.04254,$$

$$l_2 = -0.1[0.2(-0.4254) + 10(0.2678)] = -0.2593,$$

$$k_3 = 0.1[-0.2875 - 0.1296] = -0.04171,$$

$$l_3 = -0.1[0.2(-0.2875 - 0.1296) + 10(0.2611)] = -0.2528,$$

$$k_4 = 0.1[-0.2875 - 0.2528] = -0.05403,$$

$$l_4 = -0.1[0.2(-0.2875 - 0.2528 + 10(0.2414)] = -0.2306.$$

$$\therefore \quad \Delta\theta = \tfrac{1}{6}(-0.02875 - 0.08508 - 0.08342 - 0.05403) = -0.0419.$$

$$\therefore \quad \theta_2 = 0.2855 - 0.0419 = 0.2436;$$

and

$$\Delta\dot\theta = \tfrac{1}{6}(-0.27589 - 0.5186 - 0.5056 - 0.2306) = -0.2551,$$

$$\dot\theta_2 = -0.2875 - 0.2551 = -0.5426.$$

These values of $\theta_1$, $\theta_2$, $\dot\theta_1$, $\dot\theta_2$ are in close agreement with those found by the method of successive approximations.

Since the computations for the succeeding intervals are carried out in exactly the same manner as for the two intervals just computed, we shall not continue the computations in this example.

*Example 3.* Solve Example 3 of Art. 76 by the Runge-Kutta method.

*Solution*: The differential equations to be integrated are

$$\frac{d\dot x}{dt} = -0.00005v\dot x = -0.00005\dot x\sqrt{\dot x^2 + \dot y^2}$$

$$= f_1(-, \dot x, \dot y),$$

$$\frac{d\dot y}{dt} = -0.00005v\dot y - 32.16 = -0.00005\dot y\sqrt{\dot x^2 + \dot y^2} - 32.16$$

$$= f_2(-, \dot x, \dot y).$$

Since $t$ is absent in these equations, the equations for computing the $k$'s and $l$'s are

$$k_1 = f_1(\dot{x},\ \dot{y})\Delta t = -\ 0.00005\dot{x}\sqrt{\dot{x}^2 + \dot{y}^2}\ \Delta t,$$

$$k_2 = f_1\left(\dot{x} + \frac{k_1}{2},\ \dot{y} + \frac{l_1}{2}\right)\Delta t$$

$$= -\ 0.00005\left(\dot{x} + \frac{k_1}{2}\right)\sqrt{\left(\dot{x} + \frac{k_1}{2}\right)^2 + \left(\dot{y} + \frac{l_1}{2}\right)^2}\ \Delta t,$$

$$k_3 = f_1\left(\dot{x} + \frac{k_2}{2},\ \dot{y} + \frac{l_2}{2}\right)\Delta t$$

$$= -\ 0.00005\left(\dot{x} + \frac{k_2}{2}\right)\sqrt{\left(\dot{x} + \frac{k_2}{2}\right)^2 + \left(\dot{y} + \frac{l_2}{2}\right)^2}\ \Delta t,$$

$$k_4 = f_1(\dot{x} + k_3,\ \dot{y} + l_3)\Delta t$$

$$= -\ 0.00005(\dot{x} + k_3)\sqrt{(\dot{x} + k_3)^2 + (\dot{y} + l_3)^2}\ \Delta t;$$

$$l_1 = f_2(\dot{x},\ \dot{y})\Delta t = -\ (0.00005\dot{y}\sqrt{\dot{x}^2 + \dot{x}^2} + 32.16)\Delta t,$$

$$l_2 = f_2\left(\dot{x} + \frac{k_1}{2},\ \dot{y} + \frac{l_1}{2}\right)\Delta t$$

$$= -\left[0.00005\left(\dot{y} + \frac{l_1}{2}\right)\sqrt{\left(\dot{x} + \frac{k_1}{2}\right)^2 + \left(\dot{y} + \frac{l_1}{2}\right)^2} + 32.16\right]\Delta t,$$

$$l_3 = f_2\left(\dot{x} + \frac{k_2}{2},\ \dot{y} + \frac{l_2}{2}\right)\Delta t$$

$$= -\left[0.00005\left(\dot{y} + \frac{l_2}{2}\right)\sqrt{\left(\dot{x} + \frac{k_2}{2}\right)^2 + \left(\dot{y} + \frac{l_2}{2}\right)^2} + 32.16\right]\Delta t,$$

$$l_4 = f_2(\dot{x} + k_3,\ \dot{y} + l_3)\Delta t$$

$$= -\ [0.00005(\dot{y} + l_3)\sqrt{(\dot{x} + k_3)^2 + (\dot{y} + l_3)^2} + 32.16]\Delta t.$$

$$\Delta\dot{x} = \tfrac{1}{6}(k_1 + 2k_2 + 2k_3 + k_4), \quad \Delta\dot{y} = \tfrac{1}{6}(l_1 + 2l_2 + 2l_3 + l_4).$$

By means of these formulas we can compute corresponding values of $\dot{x}$ and $\dot{y}$ for various values of $t$. Then since $\dot{x}$ and $\dot{y}$ are now known for equal intervals of $t$, we can find $x$ and $y$ by computing the integrals $x = \int \dot{x}\,dt$ and $y = \int \dot{y}\,dt$ by Simpson's rule. The numerical work will not be carried out, as it consists merely in substituting the proper quantities in the formulas just given.

*Remarks on this method.* The chief advantage of the Runge-Kutta method is that the successive increments in the functions are computed with a high degree of accuracy from a definite set of formulas, the same set of formulas being used for computing all the increments. There are no trial values, no repetitions, and no expansions into series. The greatest disadvantage of the method is that, unless the functions to be integrated are very simple, the computation of the increments is apt to be a tedious and sometimes laborious process. The actual amount of labor involved in computing an increment by this method is probably greater than in the method of successive approximations. In some problems, however, the Runge-Kutta method, as in the case of Adams's method, may be used to advantage for starting a computation which is to be continued by the method of successive approximations.

**84. Milne's Method.** One of the latest and simplest methods for solving differential equations numerically is that devised by W. E. Milne.* We shall merely describe the method in its simplest form and show how to apply it to a simple example.

Let

$$(84:1) \qquad \frac{dy}{dx} = y' = f(x, y)$$

denote the differential equation to be solved. The first four values of $y$ and $y'$ are found by any method which happens to be the most applicable—the method of Adams, the Runge-Kutta method, the method of successive approximations, or some other method. The succeeding values are found as follows:

1. Find a first approximation to the next $y$ by means of the formula

$$(84:2) \qquad y_n^{(1)} = y_{n-4} + \frac{4h}{3}(2y_{n-1}' - y_{n-2}' + 2y_{n-3}').$$

2. Substitute this $y_n^{(1)}$ in (84: 1) to find the corresponding value of $y_n'$.

3. Substitute this $y_n'$ in the formula

$$(84:3) \qquad y_n^{(2)} = y_{n-2} + \frac{h}{3}(y_n' + 4y_{n-1}' + y_{n-2}').$$

If $y_2^{(1)}$ and $y_n^{(2)}$ agree to the desired number of significant figures, we take $y_n^{(2)}$ to be correct and then substitute it in (84: 1) to get the correct $y_n'$. We proceed then to the next interval and repeat the process.

If $y_n^{(1)}$ and $y_n^{(2)}$ as given by (84: 2) and (84: 3) do not agree very well and no error can be found in the computations, then compute the quantity

* "Numerical Integration of Ordinary Differential Equations." *The American Mathematical Monthly*, Vol. 33 (1926), pp. 455–460.

**(84 : 4)**
$$E = \frac{\left| \, y_n^{(2)} - y_n^{(1)} \, \right|}{29},$$

which is the error due to formula (84: 3). If this quantity is large enough to affect the last significant figure we desire to retain, then the only thing to do is to decrease the size of $h$.

Formulas (84: 2) and (84: 3) are derived by integrating Newton's formula (I), expressed in terms of $y'$. The first is obtained by integrating over an interval of width $4h$ from $x_{n-4}$ to $x_n$ and the second by integrating over an interval of width $2h$, from $x_{n-2}$ to $x_n$. Both formulas give correct results when fourth differences of $y'$ are negligible. It will be noted that (84: 3) is nothing but Simpson's rule applied to the $y''$'s. (84: 2) is essentially a formula for integrating ahead.

These two formulas (84: 2) and (84: 3) can be applied to systems of differential equations in exactly the same way as we applied formulas (75: 4) and (75: 5) in Art. 76. We shall now apply them to a simple differential equation of the first order.

*Example.* Solve by Milne's method the differential equation

$$\frac{dy}{dx} = x + y,$$

with initial values $x_0 = 0$, $y_0 = 1$.

*Solution.* Since we have already solved this problem several times in the preceding pages, we shall use the first four values of $y$ and $y'$ as already found. Hence we write down the following table of given values.

| $x$ | $y$ | $y'$ |
|-----|--------|--------|
| 0   | 1      | 1      |
| 0.1 | 1.1103 | 1.2103 |
| 0.2 | 1.2428 | 1.4428 |
| 0.3 | 1.3997 | 1.6997 |

To find a first approximation to $y_4$ we have by formula (84: 2)

$$y_4^{(1)} = y_0 + \frac{0.4}{3} \left[ 2(1.6997) - 1.4428 + 2(1.2103) \right]$$

$$= 1 + \frac{0.4}{3} (4.3772) = 1.5836.$$

Substituting this in the given equation, we get

$$y_4' = 0.4 + 1.5836 = 1.9836.$$

Now substituting this and the two preceding $y''$'s in (84: 3), we get

$$y_4^{(2)} = y_2 + \frac{0.1}{3}[1.9836 + 4(1.6997) + 1.4428]$$

$$= 1.2428 + \frac{1}{30}(10.2252) = 1.5836,$$

which is the same as $y_4^{(1)}$. We therefore take this value of $y_4$ to be correct.

Suppose, now, we take $h = 0.2$. The first four values of $y$ and $y'$ in this case have already been found to be as given in the table below.

| $x$ | $y$ | $y'$ |
|---|---|---|
| 0 | 1 | 1 |
| 0.2 | 1.2428 | 1.4428 |
| 0.4 | 1.5836 | 1.9836 |
| 0.6 | 2.0442 | 2.6442 |

To find $y_{0.8}$ we have

$$y_{0.8}^{(1)} = 1 + \frac{0.8}{3}[2(2.6442) - 1.9836 + 2(1.4428)$$

$$= 2.6508.$$

The corresponding value of $y'_{0.8}$ is therefore

$$y'_{0.8} = x + y = 0.8 + 2.6508 = 3.4508.$$

Substituting this and the two preceding $y''$'s in (84: 3), we get

$$y_{0.8}^{(2)} = 1.5836 + \frac{0.2}{3}[3.4508 + 4(2.6442) + 1.9836] = 2.6510.$$

This value of $y_{0.8}$ does not quite agree with that found by formula (84: 2), but the quantity $E = 0.0002/29 = 0.00001$ does not affect the fourth decimal place; so we take this value $y_{0.8}^{(2)}$ as correct. As a matter of fact, the correct value of $y_{0.8}$ is 2.65108. The value 0.2 for $h$ is slightly too large for obtaining results accurate to four decimals.

**85. A Final Remark.** In this book four general methods for solving differential equations numerically have been explained in some detail and illustrated by several types of examples. The student has observed that all four methods involve considerable labor. But the numerical methods also have certain redeeming features in their favor; for they provide a means of obtaining solutions to problems which could not be solved otherwise, and they also give a complete record of the behavior of the functions within the regions considered. In some problems the exact analytical solution may involve more labor than the numerical method if certain information is desired. The following example will illustrate this point.

Suppose the differential equation

$$\frac{dy}{dx} = \frac{y - x}{y + x}$$

is given, with initial conditions $x_0 = 0$, $y_0 = 1$, and it is required to find several corresponding values of $x$ and $y$. The given equation can be solved by putting $y = vx$, separating the variables, and integrating. The result, for the given initial conditions, is

$$\frac{1}{2} \log (x^2 + y^2) + \tan^{-1} \left( \frac{y}{x} \right) = \frac{\pi}{2}.$$

To find pairs of corresponding values of $x$ and $y$ from this equation we could substitute the desired values of $x$ and then solve the resulting equation for $y$. But this resulting equation will always be a complicated transcendental equation which can be solved only by trial—by Newton's method or otherwise. The labor of solving this equation for even a single value of $y$ would probably be as great as that of computing several tabular values by numerical integration. The numerical method might therefore be the easier in this example.

The numerical solution of a differential equation, however, will give no information concerning the function outside the range of computed values, whereas the exact analytical solution will enable us to predict the behavior of the function for any values whatever of the independent variable. For this reason the solutions of differential equations expressing natural phenomena should always be obtained in analytical form if possible.

### EXAMPLES ON CHAPTER XIII

1. Solve Ex. 1 of Chapter XI by the method of Adams and also by the method of Milne.

2. Solve Ex. 2, Ch. XI, by the Runge-Kutta method.

3. Solve Ex. 4, Ch. XI, by Adams's method.

4. Solve Ex. 6, Ch. XI, by the Runge-Kutta method and also by Milne's method.

5. Solve any of the remaining examples in Chapter XI by any of the methods of the present chapter.

# CHAPTER XIV

## THE NORMAL LAW OF ERROR AND THE PRINCIPLE OF LEAST SQUARES

**86. Errors of Observation and Measurement.** All measurements are subject to three kinds of errors: constant or systematic errors, mistakes, and accidental errors. *Systematic errors* are those which affect all measurements alike. They are mostly due to imperfections in the construction or adjustment of instruments, the "personal equation" of the observer, etc. Such errors are usually determinate and may be remedied by applying the proper corrections.

*Mistakes* or blunders are large errors due to careless reading of measuring instruments or faulty recording of the readings. They consist mostly in reading the wrong scale, reading a vernier backward, making a miscount in observations which involve counting, putting down the wrong number when recording the readings, etc. Mistakes do not follow any law and can be avoided or remedied only by constant vigilance and careful checking on the part of the observer.

*Accidental errors* are those whose causes are unknown and indeterminate. They are usually small, and they follow the laws of chance. The mathematical theory of errors deals with accidental errors only.

**87. The Law of Accidental Errors.** In order to get a better understanding of the behavior of accidental errors the reader should try the following experiment:

Take a sheet of ruled paper and draw with pen or pencil a line bisecting the space between two rulings near the middle of the sheet, as shown in Fig. 13. Lay the sheet flat on a table or floor, with the rulings upward. Now take a sharp-pointed pencil, hold it lightly by the top between the finger tips of both hands, and about two feet above the paper. Take good aim at the line on the paper and try to hit it by dropping the pencil on it. Drop the pencil in this way at least 100 times, making an honest effort to hit the line every time. The shots will be self-recorded as dots on the paper. Count the dots in the compartment (space between the rulings) containing the target line, and the number in each of the other compartments on each side of the central one. Plot a curve by using as abscissas the distances from the target line to the mid-points of the several compartments containing dots, and as ordinates the number of dots in the corresponding compartments.

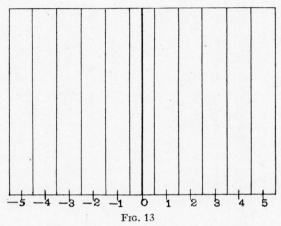

FIG. 13

An experiment of this kind gave the results recorded in the table below. The corresponding curve is shown in Fig. 14.

| Compartment | No. of dots |
|:-----------:|:-----------:|
| 3 | 1 |
| 2 | 6 |
| 1 | 31 |
| 0 | 53 |
| −1 | 32 |
| −2 | 6 |
| −3 | 1 |
| Total | 130 |

If the pencil had been dropped 10000 or more times instead of 130 and the width of the compartments correspondingly decreased, the plotted points would have followed the curve shown in Fig. 14. This

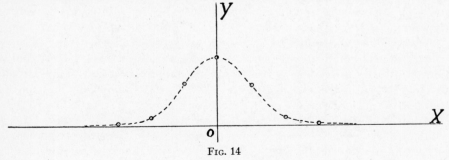

FIG. 14

curve is known as the *Normal Probability Curve*.  Its equation will be derived in Art. 89.

All kinds of accidental errors follow the same law as the pencil shots in this experiment.

**88. The Probability of Errors Lying between Given Limits.**  In many applications of the theory of probability it is necessary to find the chance that a given error will lie within certain specified limits.  In such cases we utilize the fact that *the probability that an error lies within given limits is equal to the area under the probability curve between those limits.* The following proof, while not altogether rigorous, is sufficient to show the truth of this statement.

Going back for a moment to the target experiment of Art. 87, we recall that in plotting the results we erected ordinates at equal distances apart along the $x$-axis.  The height of each ordinate was made proportional to the number of dots falling within the corresponding interval on the target.  If we imagine rectangles constructed with the equal intervals along the $x$-axis as bases and the corresponding ordinates as altitudes (see Fig. 15), we readily see that the area of each

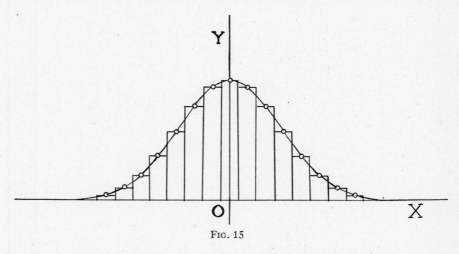

FIG. 15

rectangle is proportional to the number of dots falling within the corresponding compartment.  Thus, if $N_i$ is the number of dots in any compartment and $A_i$ is the area of the corresponding rectangle, we have

(88: 1)                          $A_i = k_1 N_i.$

Now if we make one more attempt to hit the target line in the experiment of Art. 87, the chance of hitting within the central compart-

ment is about 53/130, that of hitting within the next compartment to
the right is about 31/130, etc.  The chance of hitting within *some one*
of these compartments is therefore

$$\frac{53}{130} + \frac{31}{130} + \frac{6}{130} + \frac{1}{130} + \frac{32}{130} + \frac{6}{130} + \frac{1}{130} = \frac{130}{130} = 1.$$

Since the chance of hitting within any compartment is proportional to
the number of hits made in a large number of shots, we have for any
compartment

(88: 2)                       $$p_i = k_2 N_i,$$

where $p_i$ is the probability that a single additional shot will fall in any
compartment in which $N_i$ shots fell in a previous experiment.  Elimi-
nating $N_i$ between equations (88:1) and (88:2), we get

(88: 3)                       $$p_i = \frac{k_2}{k_1} A_i,$$

which shows that the chance of making a hit in any compartment is
proportional to the area of the corresponding rectangle.  The chance of
hitting within *some* compartment is therefore

(88:4) $$p = 1 = p_1 + p_2 + \cdots = \frac{k_2}{k_1}(A_1 + A_2 + \cdots) = \frac{k_2}{k_1} \sum A .$$

Now when the number of shots is increased indefinitely and the width
of each compartment on the target is correspondingly decreased, it is
plain that the bases of the corresponding rectangles will likewise decrease and that the sum of the areas of these rectangles will approach
the area under the probability curve as a limit.  The area under this
curve is always finite, and since it represents the probability that a
shot will fall *somewhere*, it (the area) represents certainty and therefore
may be taken as 1; or lim $\sum A = 1$.  Hence by (88:4) we have

$$1 = \frac{k_2}{k_1}(1), \quad \text{or} \quad k_2 = k_1.$$

Equation (88:3) now becomes

(88: 5)                       $$p_i = A_i,$$

which shows that the chance of making a hit in any compartment is
*equal* to the area of the corresponding rectangle.

From equation (88:5) we have the important result that the chance of making an error whose magnitude lies between $x$ and $x + \Delta x$ is*

$$(88:6) \qquad\qquad p = y\Delta x,$$

where $y$ is the ordinate to the probability curve. The chance of making an error whose magnitude is between $x_1$ and $x_2$ is therefore

$$(88:7) \qquad\qquad p = \lim_{\Delta x \to 0} \sum_{x=x_1}^{x=x_2} y\Delta x = \int_{x_1}^{x_2} y\,dx.$$

**89. The Probability Equation.** To derive the equation of the Probability Curve we make use of the following facts as to the distribution of accidental errors, as indicated by the table of Art. 87 and the corresponding curve:

1. Small errors are more frequent than large ones, showing that the probability of an error depends upon its size.

2. Positive and negative errors of the same size are about equal in number, thus making the probability curve symmetrical about the $y$-axis.

3. Very large accidental errors do not occur.

These three fundamental facts are so self-evident that they may be taken as axioms.

From axioms 1 and 2 it is plain that the ordinate to the probability curve must be a function of the square of the abscissa, or

$$y = f(x^2).$$

Here the function $f(x^2)$ is called the *error function*. Our problem now is to determine the form of this function.

Referring once more to the target experiment, we can readily see that if we had aimed at a particular *point* on the target line the distribution of shots *with respect to the line* would not have been different from that found in this experiment. Suppose, then, that we try another experiment of this kind and aim at some *point* $O$ in the plane of the paper. The shots will be distributed about $O$ in such a manner that if we draw *any* line through $O$ the probability that any shot hits at a distance $\epsilon$ *from this line* will be

$$p = f(\epsilon^2)d\epsilon.$$

Let us therefore draw through $O$ any two lines at right angles to each other. We shall take these as axes of coordinates for two variables

---

* Except for differentials of higher order.

$x$ and $y$. Let us consider any shot that falls at a point $P(x, y)$. The chance that $P$ lies in a strip of width $dx$ at distance $x$ from the $y$-axis is

$$p_x = f(x^2)dx;$$

and the chance that $P$ lies in a strip of width $dy$ at a distance $y$ from the $x$-axis is

$$p_y = f(y^2)dy.$$

The chance that $P$ lies in *both* of these strips and hence in the small rectangle $dxdy$ is therefore

(89: 1)                     $p = p_x p_y = f(x^2)f(y^2)dxdy.$

If we draw any other set of rectangular axes through $O$, so that the coordinates of $P$ referred to these axes are $x'$ and $y'$, we evidently have

$$p_{x'} = f(x'^2)dx',$$

$$p_{y'} = f(y'^2)dy'.$$

Hence the chance that $P$ lies in the rectangle $dx'dy'$ is

(89: 2)                     $p' = f(x'^2)f(y'^2)dx'dy'.$

But the chance that this particular shot falls within a small area $A$ is the same regardless of the orientation of the axes through $O$. Hence if we take $dx'$ and $dy'$ such that

$$dx'dy' = dxdy = A,$$

we have

$$p = f(x^2)f(y^2)A = f(x'^2)f(y'^2)A,$$

or

(89: 3)                     $f(x^2)f(y^2) = f(x'^2)f(y'^2).$

Suppose now that the axes $OX'$ and $OY'$ are oriented so that $OX'$ passes through $P$. Then

$$x' = \sqrt{x^2 + y^2}, \quad y' = 0.$$

Hence (89:3) becomes

(89: 4)        $f(x^2)f(y^2) = f(x^2 + y^2)f(0) = Cf(x^2 + y^2),$

since $f(0)$ is a constant.

Equation (89:4) is a *functional equation* and can be solved by first differentiating and then integrating.

Differentiating (89:4) partially with respect to $x^2$ and $y^2$ in turn, we have

$$f'(x^2)f(y^2) = C\frac{\partial f(x^2 + y^2)}{\partial(x^2)},$$

$$f'(y^2)f(x^2) = C\frac{\partial f(x^2 + y^2)}{\partial(y^2)}.$$

Now since $\partial(u+v)/\partial u = \partial(u+v)/\partial v$, the right-hand members of these equations are equal. Hence

$$f'(x^2)f(y^2) = f'(y^2)f(x^2),$$

or

$$\frac{f'(x^2)}{f(x^2)} = \frac{f'(y^2)}{f(y^2)} = k, \text{ say.}$$

Multiplying the equation $f'(x^2)/f(x^2) = k$ through by $d(x^2)$ and integrating with respect to $x^2$, we have

$$\log f(x^2) = kx^2 + \log c,$$

or

(89: 5)          $$f(x^2) = ce^{kx}.$$

Now since the probability of an error decreases as the size of the error increases, it is plain that $k$ must be negative. Putting $k = -h^2$, we have

(89: 6)          $$f(x^2) = ce^{-h^2x^2}.$$

Hence

(89: 7)          $$y = ce^{-h^2x^2}$$

is the equation of the probability curve.

To determine the constant $c$ we utilize the fact that the area under the probability curve is equal to 1. Hence we have

(89: 8)          $$1 = \int_{-\infty}^{\infty} ce^{-h^2x^2}dx = \frac{2c}{h} \int_0^{\infty} e^{-(hx)^2}d(hx).$$

This integral must be evaluated by an indirect method. To effect the evaluation let us consider the volume of the solid of revolution (Fig. 16) included between the $xy$-plane and the surface generated by revolving the curve $z = e^{-z^2}$ about the z-axis. Since this is a surface of revolution, its equation is

(89: 9) $$z = e^{-(x^2+y^2)}.$$

In cylindrical coordinates this equation becomes

(89: 10) $$z = e^{-r^2}, \quad \text{where} \quad x^2 + y^2 = r^2.$$

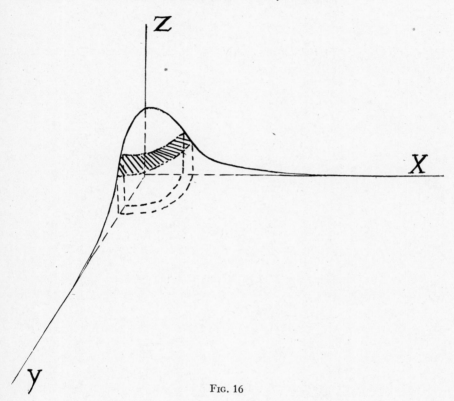

FIG. 16

Taking as the element of volume a cylindrical shell of radius $r$, thickness $dr$, and height $z$, we have

$$dV = 2\pi r \cdot dr \cdot z = 2\pi r e^{-r^2} dr.$$

(89: 11) $$\therefore V = 2\pi \int_0^\infty e^{-r^2} r \, dr = -\pi \int_0^\infty e^{-r^2}(-2r \, dr) = -\pi \left( e^{-r^2} \right]_0^\infty = \pi.$$

Using rectangular coordinates, we take as the element of volume a prism of base $dx dy$ and altitude $z$. Hence we have from (89:9)

$$(89:12) \qquad V = 4 \int zdxdy = 4 \int_0^\infty \int_0^\infty e^{-(x^2+v^2)}dxdy$$

$$= 4 \int_0^\infty e^{-x^2}dx \int_0^\infty e^{-v^2}dy.$$

Now since the value of a definite integral depends only on its limits and not on the variable of integration, we may replace $y$ by $x$ in the second integral. We then have

$$(89:13) \qquad V = 4 \int_0^\infty e^{-x^2}dx \int_0^\infty e^{-x^2}dx = \left[ 2 \int_0^\infty e^{-x^2}dx \right]^2.$$

Since we have already found $V = \pi$ above, we have

$$(89:14) \qquad \left[ 2 \int_0^\infty e^{-x^2}dx \right]^2 = \pi, \quad \text{or} \quad \int_0^\infty e^{-x^2}dx = \frac{\sqrt{\pi}}{2}.$$

Substituting this in (89:8), we get $c = h/\sqrt{\pi}$. Now putting this value of $c$ in (89:7), we have finally

$$(89:15) \qquad\qquad y = \frac{h}{\sqrt{\pi}}e^{-h^2x^2}$$

as the equation of the probability curve.

Equation (89:15) is of *fundamental importance;* for it is the foundation of the Theory of Errors, the Principle of Least Squares, and the Precision of Measurements. It is known as the Probability Equation, Error Equation, etc.; and its graph is known as the Normal Probability Curve, the Error Curve, Gaussian Curve, etc.

It will be observed that this important equation contains only one arbitrary constant. This constant $h$ is called the "index of precision." To see the reason for this name we notice that the larger $h$ is the higher the probability curve will rise in the middle and the more rapidly it will fall on each side of the "hump." This fact, when considered in connection with the target problem, means that a large percentage of the shots hit near the target and very few hit far from it. In other words, it means accurate shooting.

**90. The Law of Error of a Linear Function of Independent Quantities.** We shall next prove a fundamental theorem of great importance, namely:

If $M_1, M_2, \cdots M_n$ are *independent* observed quantities whose laws of error are

$$y = \frac{h_1}{\sqrt{\pi}}e^{-h_1^2x^2}, \quad y = \frac{h_2}{\sqrt{\pi}}e^{-h_2^2x^2}, \quad \cdots \quad y = \frac{h_n}{\sqrt{\pi}}e^{-h_n^2x^2},$$

then any linear function of these quantities obeys a similar law of error.

*Proof:* Let the linear function be

(90: 1)                 $$F = a_1 M_1 + a_2 M_2 + \cdots + a_n M_n,$$

where $a_1, a_2, \cdots a_n$ are arbitrary constants. If $x_1, x_2, \cdots x_n$ denote the errors of $M_1, M_2, \cdots M_n$, respectively, and $\xi$ denote the corresponding error in $F$, we have

$$F + \xi = a_1(M_1 + x_1) + a_2(M_2 + x_2) + \cdots + a_n(M_n + x_n)$$
$$= a_1 M_1 + a_1 x_1 + a_2 M_2 + a_2 x_2 + \cdots + a_n M_n + a_n x_n.$$

Subtracting (90:1),

(90: 2)                 $$\xi = a_1 x_1 + a_2 x_2 + \cdots a_n x_n.$$

The error $\xi$ in $F$ is thus a linear function of the errors in $M_1$, $M_2$, etc. We are now to show that the law of error for $\xi$ is the same as the laws for $x_1$, $x_2$, etc.

To simplify the proof we first take a linear function of two independent quantities,

$$F = a_1 M_1 + a_2 M_2.$$

Then

(90: 3)                 $$\xi = a_1 x_1 + a_2 x_2.$$

Hence

$$\xi + \Delta\xi = a_1(x_1 + \Delta x_1) + a_2(x_2 + \Delta x_2).$$

An error of magnitude $x_1$ to $x_1 + \Delta x_1$ in $M_1$ combined with an error of magnitude $x_2$ to $x_2 + \Delta x_2$ in $M_2$ will therefore produce an error of magnitude $\xi$ to $\xi + \Delta\xi$ in $F$.

The probability of the occurrence of an error lying between $x_1$ and $x_1 + \Delta x_1$ in $M_1$ is

$$p_1 = \frac{h_1}{\sqrt{\pi}} e^{-h_1{}^2 x_1{}^2} \Delta x_1,$$

and similarly the chance of an error lying between $x_2$ and $x_2 + \Delta x_2$ in $M_2$ is

$$p_2 = \frac{h_2}{\sqrt{\pi}} e^{-h_2{}^2 x_2{}^2} \Delta x_2.$$

The probability that these two independent errors will occur simultaneously and thereby cause an error lying between $\xi$ and $\xi + \Delta\xi$ in $F$ is therefore the product of their separate probabilities, or

(90: 4)         $$P = p_1 p_2 = \frac{h_1 h_2}{\pi} e^{-h_1{}^2 x_1{}^2 - h_2{}^2 x_2{}^2} \Delta x_1 \Delta x_2.$$

This is the probability that any single error in $M_1$ combined with any single error in $M_2$ will produce a single error in $F$. But equation (90:3) shows that an error in $F$ may be produced by combining any value of $x_2$ (that is, any error in $M_2$) with all possible values of $x_1$ from $-\infty$ to $+\infty$. Hence the total probability of an error between $\xi$ and $\xi + \Delta \xi$ is the sum of these mutually exclusive events, or

$$(90:5) \qquad \phi(\xi)\Delta\xi = \frac{h_1 h_2}{\pi} \Delta x_2 \int_{-\infty}^{\infty} e^{-h_1{}^2 x_1{}^2 - h_2{}^2 x_2{}^2} dx_1,$$

where $\phi(\xi)$ denotes the error function for $\xi$.

Let us now consider a single definite error $\xi$ in $F$. This means that $\xi$ in (90:3) is to be considered constant for the time being. Hence from (90:3) we have

$$x_2 = \frac{\xi - a_1 x_1}{a_2}.$$

Substituting this value of $x_2$ in (90:5), we get

$$(90:6) \qquad \phi(\xi)\Delta\xi = \frac{h_1 h_2}{\pi} \Delta x_2 \int_{-\infty}^{\infty} e^{-h_1{}^2 x_1{}^2 - h_2{}^2 [(\xi - a_1 x_1)/a_2]} dx_1 .$$

To simplify the integration we write the exponent of $e$ in the equivalent form

$$-\frac{h_1{}^2 h_2{}^2 \xi^2}{a_1{}^2 h_2{}^2 + a_2{}^2 h_1{}^2} - \frac{a_1{}^2 h_2{}^2 + a_2{}^2 h_1{}^2}{a_2{}^2} \left( x_1 - \frac{a_1 h_2{}^2 \xi}{a_1{}^2 h_2{}^2 + a_2{}^2 h_1{}^2} \right)^2.$$

This can be further simplified by putting $C^2 = a_1{}^2 h_2{}^2 + a_2{}^2 h_1{}^2$. Then the exponent of $e$ becomes

$$-\frac{h_1{}^2 h_2{}^2 \xi^2}{C^2} - \frac{C^2}{a_2{}^2} \left( x_1 - \frac{a_1 h_2{}^2 \xi}{C^2} \right)^2,$$

and (90:6) becomes

$$\phi(\xi)\Delta\xi = \frac{h_1 h_2}{\pi} \Delta x_2 \int_{-\infty}^{\infty} e^{-h_1{}^2 h_2{}^2 \xi^2 / C^2} \cdot e^{-(C^2/a_2{}^2)(x_1 - a_1 h_2{}^2 \xi/C^2)^2} dx_1$$

$$= \frac{h_1 h_2}{\pi} \Delta x_2 e^{-h_1{}^2 h_2{}^2 \xi^2 / C^2} \int_{-\infty}^{\infty} e^{-(C^2/a_2{}^2)(x_1 - a_1 h_2{}^2 \xi/C^2)^2} dx_1.$$

Now put

$$u = \frac{C}{a_2} \left( x_1 - \frac{a_1 h_2{}^2 \xi}{C^2} \right).$$

Then $du = (C/a_2)dx_1$, or $dx_1 = (a_2/C)du$, since $\xi$ is constant. Hence

$$\phi(\xi)\Delta\xi = \frac{h_1 h_2}{\pi} \Delta x_2 e^{-h_1{}^2 h_2{}^2 \xi^2 / C^2} \cdot \frac{a_2}{C} \int_{-\infty}^{\infty} e^{-u^2} du.$$

But

$$\int_{-\infty}^{\infty} e^{-u^2} du = 2 \int_{0}^{\infty} e^{-u^2} du = 2 \cdot \frac{\sqrt{\pi}}{2} = \sqrt{\pi},$$

by Art. 89.

(90: 7)   $$\therefore \quad \phi(\xi)\Delta\xi = \frac{h_1 h_2}{\sqrt{\pi}} \Delta x_2 e^{-h_1{}^2 h_2{}^2 \xi^2 / C^2} \cdot \frac{a_2}{C}.$$

We have now taken account of the effect of the errors $x_1$ in $M_1$ in causing a particular error $\xi$ in $F$, so that $\xi$ is now a function of $x_2$ alone. Hence from (90:3), regarding $x_1$ as a constant, we get $\Delta\xi = a_2\Delta x_2$. Substituting this value for $\Delta\xi$ in (90:7) and replacing $C$ by its value $\sqrt{a_1^2 h_2^2 + a_2^2 h_1^2}$, we get

(90: 8)   $$\phi(\xi) = \frac{\dfrac{h_1 h_2}{\sqrt{a_1^2 h_2^2 + a_2^2 h_1^2}}}{\sqrt{\pi}} e^{-[h_1{}^2 h_2{}^2 / (a_1{}^2 h_2{}^2 + a_2{}^2 h_1{}^2)]\xi^2},$$

or

(90: 9)   $$\phi(\xi) = \frac{H_1}{\sqrt{\pi}} e^{-H_1{}^2 \xi^2},$$

where

(90: 10)   $$H_1^2 = \frac{h_1^2 h_2^2}{a_1^2 h_2^2 + a_2^2 h_1^2}.$$

*The law of error for $\xi$, the error in $F$, is thus of the same form as the laws of error for $x_1$ and $x_2$, the errors in $M_1$ and $M_2$.*

From (90:10) we have

(90: 11)   $$\frac{1}{H_1^2} = \frac{a_1^2 h_2^2 + a_2^2 h_1^2}{h_1^2 h_2^2} = \frac{a_1^2}{h_1^2} + \frac{a_2^2}{h_2^2}.$$

To extend this relation to a linear function of any number of independent quantities take

$$F = a_1 M_1 + a_2 M_2 + a_3 M_3 = (a_1 M_1 + a_2 M_2) + a_3 M_3.$$

If $h_3$ denote the precision index of the errors in $M_3$, and $H_2$ the precision index for $F$, then by (90:11)

$$\frac{1}{H_2^2} = \frac{1}{H_1^2} + \frac{a_3^2}{h_3^2} = \frac{a_1^2}{h_1^2} + \frac{a_2^2}{h_2^2} + \frac{a_3^2}{h_3^2}.$$

In the same way, we can extend the formula to a linear function of

4, 5, or any number of quantities. We therefore arrive at the following result:

*If F be a linear function of n independent quantities which have been determined by observation, the function F follows an error law which is of the same form as the error laws of the independent unknowns.* If the function is

$$F = a_1 M_1 + a_2 M_2 + a_3 M_3 \cdots + a_n M_n,$$

the index of precision, $H$, of $F$ is given by

**(90: 12)**   $\dfrac{1}{H^2} = \dfrac{a_1^2}{h_1^2} + \dfrac{a_2^2}{h_2^2} + \dfrac{a_3^2}{h_3^2} + \cdots + \dfrac{a_n^2}{h_n^2} = \Sigma\left(\dfrac{a^2}{h^2}\right).$

Even when $F$ is not a linear function of the independent quantities $M_1, M_2, \cdots M_n$, the error $\xi$ in $F$ will follow the Normal Law approximately if the errors $x_1, x_2, \cdots x_n$ are relatively small. For let

(90: 13)            $F = f(M_1, M_2, \cdots M_n)$

represent any function of $M_1, M_2$, etc. Then errors in the $M$'s will cause an error in $F$ according to the relation

$$F + \xi = f(M_1 + x_1, M_2 + x_2, \cdots M_n + x_n).$$

Expanding the right-hand member by Taylor's theorem, as in Art. 5, we have

(90: 14) $F + \xi = f(M_1, M_2, \cdots M_n) + \dfrac{\partial f}{\partial M_1} x_1 + \dfrac{\partial f}{\partial M_2} x_2 + \cdots + \dfrac{\partial f}{\partial M_n} x_n$

$$+ \text{ terms in } x_1^2, x_1 x_2, \text{ etc.}$$

Now if $x_1, x_2$, etc. are so small that their squares, products, and higher powers may be neglected, we have after subtracting (90:13) from (90:14)

(90: 15)          $\xi = \dfrac{\partial F}{\partial M_1} x_1 + \dfrac{\partial F}{\partial M_2} x_2 + \cdots + \dfrac{\partial F}{\partial M_n} x_n,$

which is a linear function of $x_1, x_2$, etc. Hence by (90:12) we have

(90: 16)   $\dfrac{1}{H^2} = \dfrac{\left(\dfrac{\partial F}{\partial M_1}\right)^2}{h_1^2} + \dfrac{\left(\dfrac{\partial F}{\partial M_2}\right)^2}{h_2^2} + \cdots + \dfrac{\left(\dfrac{\partial F}{\partial M_n}\right)^2}{h_n^2},$

where $H$ denotes the index of precision for the errors $\xi$.

**91. The Probability Integral and Its Evaluation.** To find the probability that an error of a given series will lie between the limits $x_1$ and

$x_2$ we merely find the area under the probability curve from $x = x_1$ to $x = x_2$, as shown in Art. 88. This means that we must evaluate the integral

$$(91:1) \quad P = \frac{h}{\sqrt{\pi}} \int_{x_1}^{x_2} e^{-h^2 x^2} dx = \frac{h}{\sqrt{\pi}} \left\{ \int_0^{x_2} e^{-h^2 x^2} dx - \int_0^{x_1} e^{-h^2 x^2} dx \right\}.$$

The integral

$$I = h \int_0^x e^{-h^2 x^2} dx = \int_0^x e^{-(hx)^2} d(hx)$$

can not be evaluated in finite form, but we can expand the integrand into a power series and then integrate as many terms as we need. Since

$$e^x = 1 + x + \frac{x^2}{2!} + \frac{x^3}{3!} + \cdots + \frac{x^n}{n!} + \cdots,$$

we have

$$e^{-t^2} = 1 - t^2 + \frac{t^4}{2!} - \frac{t^6}{3!} + \frac{t^8}{4!} - \cdots.$$

Hence

$$(91:2) \quad I = \int_0^t e^{-t^2} dt = t - \frac{t^3}{3} + \frac{t^5}{5 \times 2!} - \frac{t^7}{7 \times 3!} + \frac{t^9}{9 \times 4!}.$$

This series converges rapidly for small values of $t$, and the error committed by stopping at any term is less than the first term omitted (Art. 10). For example, if $t = \frac{1}{2}$ we have

$$\int_0^{1/2} e^{-t^2} dt = \frac{1}{2} - \frac{1}{24} + \frac{1}{320} - \frac{1}{5376} + \frac{1}{110592}$$

$$= 0.5 - 0.04167 + 0.00313 - 0.00019 + 0.00001$$

$$= 0.46128.$$

This result is correct to the last figure, since the error is less than

$$\frac{(\frac{1}{2})^{11}}{11 \times 5!} = \frac{1}{2703360} = 0.00000037.$$

For large values of $t$ the series (91:2) is not convenient for purposes of computation, because too many terms are needed to give the desired degree of accuracy. We shall therefore derive an expansion in descending powers of $t$, which may be used when $t$ is large. Since

$$\int_0^\infty e^{-t^2} dt = \int_0^t e^{-t^2} dt + \int_t^\infty e^{-t^2} dt,$$

we have

$$(91:3) \qquad \int_0^t e^{-t^2}dt = \int_0^\infty e^{-t^2}dt - \int_t^\infty e^{-t^2}dt.$$

The value of the first integral on the right-hand side has already been found to be $\sqrt{\pi}/2$. Hence (91:3) becomes

$$(91:4) \qquad \int_0^t e^{-t^2}dt = \frac{\sqrt{\pi}}{2} - \int_t^\infty e^{-t^2}dt.$$

The remaining integral on the right-hand side can be written in the form

$$\int_t^\infty e^{-t^2}dt = -\frac{1}{2}\int_t^\infty \frac{1}{t}e^{-t^2}(-2tdt) = -\frac{1}{2}\int_t^\infty \frac{1}{t}d(e^{-t^2}).$$

Integrating this last expression by parts, by putting $u = 1/t$, $dv = d\,(e^{-t^2})$, we get

$$\int_t^\infty e^{-t^2}dt = -\frac{1}{2}\left[\frac{e^{-t^2}}{t}\right]_t^\infty + \frac{1}{2}\int_t^\infty \left(-\frac{1}{t^2}e^{-t^2}\right)dt$$

$$= \frac{1}{2}\frac{e^{-t^2}}{t} + \frac{1}{4}\int_t^\infty \frac{1}{t^3}e^{-t^2}(2tdt)$$

$$= \frac{1}{2}\frac{e^{-t^2}}{t} + \frac{1}{4}\int_t^\infty \frac{1}{t^3}d(e^{-t^2})$$

$$= \frac{1}{2}\frac{e^{-t^2}}{t} + \frac{1}{4}\left[\frac{e^{-t^2}}{t^3}\right]_t^\infty - \frac{1}{4}\int_t^\infty \left(-\frac{3}{t^4}e^{-t^2}\right)dt,$$

or

$$\int_t^\infty e^{-t^2}dt = \frac{1}{2}\frac{e^{-t^2}}{t} - \frac{1}{4}\frac{e^{-t^2}}{t^3} + \frac{3}{4}\int_t^\infty \frac{e^{-t^2}}{t^4}dt.$$

By continuing this process of integrating by parts and substituting limits, we get the following expansion:

$$(91:5) \qquad \int_t^\infty e^{-t^2}dt = \frac{e^{-t^2}}{2t}\left(1 - \frac{1}{2t^2} + \frac{1\cdot3}{(2t^2)^2} - \frac{1\cdot3\cdot5}{(2t^2)^3} + \cdots\right).$$

Substituting this in (91:4), we get

$$(91:6) \qquad \int_0^t e^{-t^2}dt = \frac{\sqrt{\pi}}{2} - \frac{e^{-t^2}}{2t}\left(1 - \frac{1}{2t^2} + \frac{1\cdot3}{(2t^2)^2} - \frac{1\cdot3\cdot5}{(2t^2)^3} + \cdots\right).$$

This series (91:6) is called an *asymptotic series*. It is divergent, but the terms within the parenthesis decrease in numerical value so long as the number of terms does not exceed $t^2+1$. This is the maximum number of terms ever used in computations with this series. The error committed in using (91:6) is less than the last term retained.*

As an example of the use of (91:6) we shall compute

$$\int_0^2 e^{-t^2} dt.$$

We have

$$\int_0^2 e^{-t^2} dt = \frac{\sqrt{\pi}}{2} - \frac{e^{-4}}{4}\left(1 - \frac{1}{8} + \frac{3}{64} - \frac{15}{512} + \cdots\right)$$

$$= 0.8862 - 0.004579(1 - 0.125 + 0.046875 - 0.029297)$$

$$= 0.8862 - 0.0041 = 0.8821.$$

The error committed is less than

$$0.004579 \times 0.029297 = 0.00013.$$

As a matter of fact, the number 0.8821 is correct to its last figure.

By means of formulas (91:2) and (91:6) one could compute a table giving the value of the probability integral for any value of $t$. Such tables were computed long ago, and a table of this kind is given at the end of this book. This table gives the probability of an error lying between $-t$ and $+t$, where $t = hx$. Since the probability curve is symmetrical with respect to the $y$-axis, the chance that an error lies between $-t$ and $+t$ is twice the chance that it lies between 0 and $+t$. Hence the probability of such an error is

$$P = \frac{1}{\sqrt{\pi}} \int_{-t}^t e^{-t^2} dt = \frac{2}{\sqrt{\pi}} \int_0^t e^{-t^2} dt,$$

where $t = hx$. The use of the table will be explained in working the examples in the next article.

**92. The Probability of Hitting a Target.** Suppose we take a rectangular target and draw through its geometric center two lines at right angles to each other and parallel to the sides of the target, as indicated in Fig. 17. Suppose, further, that we set up this target in a vertical plane at a convenient distance away and shoot at it 100 times with a good rifle. If the rifle is accurately aimed at the intersection of the dotted lines the hits will be distributed symmetrically above and below the horizontal dotted line and to the right and left of the vertical dotted line, just as in the case of the pencil hits described in Art. 87.

If we take the horizontal line as $x$-axis, the vertical line as $y$-axis, and

* See Chauvenet's *Spherical and Practical Astronomy*, Vol. I, p. 156.

a line through the intersection of these and perpendicular to the plane of the target as $z$-axis, the hits will be distributed on each side of the vertical line according to the formula

(92:1)
$$z = \frac{h_x}{\sqrt{\overline{\cdots}}} e^{-h_x^{\;2} x^2} :$$

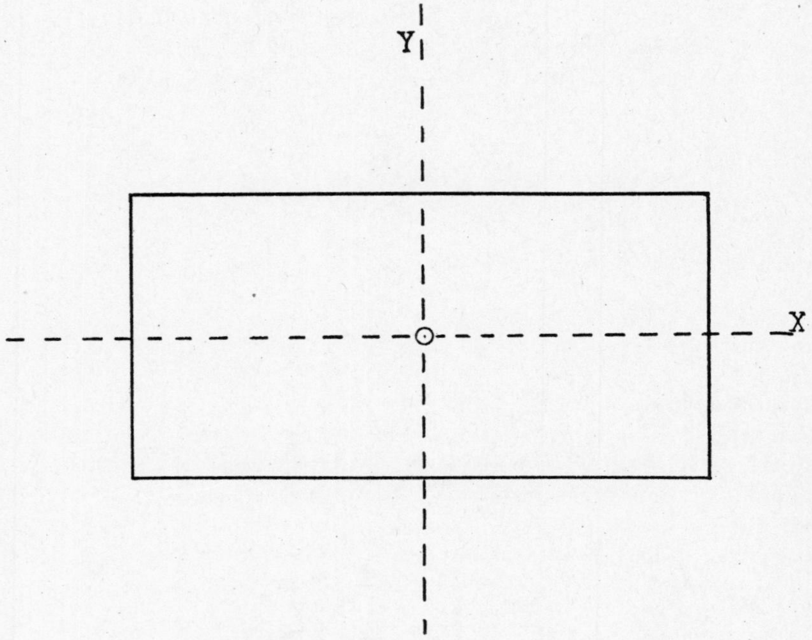

Fig. 17

and they will be distributed above and below the horizontal line according to the equation

(92:2)
$$z = \frac{h_y}{\sqrt{\pi}} e^{-h_y^{\;2} v^2} .$$

The indices of precision $h_x$ and $h_y$ in the two directions may or may not be equal.

Before we can apply formulas (92:1) and (92:2) to problems in target practice we must know the values of $h_x$ and $h_y$ for the particular gun at the given range. The precision of a gun is indicated by its probable error or its mean error (see Art. 101), and these are determined from firings at the proving grounds.

If $r$ and $\eta$ denote the probable error and the mean error, respectively, we have (see Art. 101)

$$h = \frac{0.4769}{r} = \frac{0.5642}{\eta} \, .$$

Hence

**(92: 3)**
$$hx = \frac{0.4769x}{r} = \frac{0.5642x}{\eta} \, .$$

*Note:* When using the probability table for the solution of target problems the student must keep in mind the fact that the argument for this table is $hx$, where $x$ is the given or allowable error; but since $hx = 0.4769x/r = 0.5642x/\eta$, it is evident that the proper argument for entering the table is

(a)
$$\frac{0.4769x}{r}$$

when the *probable* error of the gun is given, and

(b)
$$\frac{0.5642x}{\eta}$$

when the *mean* error of the gun is given.

*Example 1.* For a certain 3-inch gun at a range of 4000 yards the probable errors were $r_x = 10.4$ yards and $r_y = 5.8$ yards. Find the probability of hitting at the first shot a rectangular target 18 ft. high and 30 ft. long.

*Solution.* The probability that the shot will land in a vertical strip 10 yds. wide is

$$P_x = \frac{h_x}{\sqrt{\pi}} \int_{-5}^{5} e^{-h_x^2 x^2} dx = \frac{2}{\sqrt{\pi}} \int_{0}^{5} e^{-(h_x x)^2} d(h_x x);$$

and the probability that the same shot will land in a horizontal strip 6 yds. wide is

$$P_y = \frac{h_y}{\sqrt{\pi}} \int_{-3}^{3} e^{-h_y^2 y^2} dy = \frac{2}{\sqrt{\pi}} \int_{0}^{3} e^{-(h_y y)^2} d(h_y y).$$

The chance that the shot will land in both of these strips and therefore hit the target is

$$P = P_x P_y = \frac{2}{\sqrt{\pi}} \int_{0}^{5} e^{-(h_x x)^2} d(h_x x) \times \frac{2}{\sqrt{\pi}} \int_{0}^{3} e^{-(h_y y)^2} d(h_y y).$$

But

$$h_x x = \frac{0.4769x}{r_x} = \frac{0.4769 \times 5}{10.4} = 0.229,$$

by (92:3), and

$$h_y y = \frac{0.4769y}{r_y} = \frac{0.4769 \times 3}{5.8} = 0.247.$$

Entering the probability table with these values of $hx$ as arguments, we find

$$P_x = 0.254, \quad P_y = 0.273.$$

Hence

$$P = P_x P_y = 0.254 \times 0.273 = 0.0693.$$

It would therefore require on the average about $1/0.0693 = 15$ shots to get a single hit.

*Example* 2. The mean errors for a certain gun at a range of 3000 yards are

$$\eta_x = 8.3 \text{ yds.}, \quad \eta_y = 4.6 \text{ yds.}$$

If 30 shots are fired at the side of a house 12 yds. wide and 6 yds. high at a distance of 3000 yards,
(a) How many hits may be expected?
(b) What is the chance of hitting a door 6 ft. $\times$ 3 ft. in the lower right-hand corner of the side of the house?

*Solution.* (a) If the gun is accurately aimed at the geometric center of the side of the house, any shot will be a hit if it passes within 6 yards of the central vertical line and within 3 yards of the central horizontal line. Hence we have

$$x = 6 \text{ yds.}, \quad y = 3 \text{ yds.; and}$$

$$h_x x = \frac{0.5642x}{\eta_x} = \frac{0.5642 \times 6}{8.3} = 0.407,$$

$$h_y y = \frac{0.5642y}{\eta_y} = \frac{0.5642 \times 3}{4.6} = 0.368.$$

From the probability table we find

$$P_x = 0.435, \quad P_y = 0.397.$$

The chance of a hit for each shot is therefore

$$P = P_x P_y = 0.435 \times 0.397 = 0.173.$$

For 30 shots the number of hits would probably be $30 \times 0.173 = 5.2$ or 5, say.

(b) To find the probability that the door would be hit during the bombardment we assume that the gun is aimed at the geometric center of the side of the house, as in (a). Then the door will be hit if a shot strikes within the rectangle bounded by the lines $x = 5$, $x = 6$, $y = -1$, $y = -3$. The chance of hitting the door at each shot is therefore

$$P = P_x \cdot P_y = \frac{h_x}{\sqrt{\pi}} \int_5^6 e^{-h_x^2 x^2} dx \times \frac{h_y}{\sqrt{\pi}} \int_1^3 e^{-h_y^2 y^2} dy$$

$$= \left[ \frac{1}{\sqrt{\pi}} \int_0^6 e^{-(h_x x)^2} d(h_x x) - \frac{1}{\sqrt{\pi}} \int_0^5 e^{-(h_x x)^2} d(h_x x) \right] \left[ \frac{1}{\sqrt{\pi}} \int^3 e^{-(h_y y)^2} d(h_y y) \right.$$

$$\left. - \frac{1}{\sqrt{\pi}} \int_0^1 e^{-(h_y y)^2} d(h_y y) \right].$$

Hence the two values of $h_x x$ to be used in the probability table are

$$\frac{0.5642}{8.3} \times 6 = 0.407 \quad \text{and} \quad \frac{0.5642}{8.3} \times 5 = 0.340,$$

for which the probabilities are $P_{x6} = 0.435/2$, $P_{x5} = 0.369/2$. Therefore

$$P_x = \frac{0.435}{2} - \frac{0.369}{2} = \frac{0.066}{2}.$$

Likewise, the two values of $h_y y$ are

$$\frac{0.5642}{4.6} \times 3 = 0.368, \quad \frac{0.5642}{4.6} \times 1 = 0.1226.$$

The corresponding probabilities are found from the table to be

$$P_{y3} = \frac{0.397}{2}, \quad P_{y1} = \frac{0.138}{2}.$$

Hence $P_y = 0.397/2 - 0.138/2 = 0.159/2$, and we have finally

$$P = P_x \times P_y = \frac{0.066 \times 0.159}{4} = 0.0026.$$

The door will be hit unless every one of the 30 shots misses it. The chance that any shot will miss it is $1 - 0.0026 = 0.9974$. The chance that every one of the 30 shots misses is therefore $(0.9974)^{30} = 0.9249$. The chance of a hit is therefore $1 - 0.9249 = 0.0751$.

The door would probably be hit once out of the every $1/0.0026 = 380$ shots.

*Example 3.* Find the number of shots necessary to make the odds 10 to 1 in favor of at least one hit on the side of the house mentioned in Example 2.

*Solution.* The house will certainly be hit at least once unless every shot misses it. The chance that any shot will be a hit was found to be 0.173. The chance that any shot will miss it is therefore $1 - 0.173 = 0.827$. The chance that every one of $n$ shots will miss it is then $(0.827)^n$. The chance of at least one hit is therefore

$$P = 1 - (0.827)^n.$$

Since the odds are to be 10 to 1 in favor of a hit, we have $P = 10/11$. Hence

$$1 - (0.827)^n = \frac{10}{11}, \quad \text{or} \quad (0.827)^n = \frac{1}{11}.$$

$$\therefore \quad n \log (0.827) = - \log 11,$$

or

$$n = \frac{- \log 11}{\log 0.827} = \frac{- 1.0414}{9.9175 - 10} = \frac{- 1.0414}{- 0.0825} = 12.6 = 13, \text{ say.}$$

**93. The Principle of Least Squares.** Suppose we make a set of $n$ measurements $m_1, m_2, \cdots m_n$ of some object or quantity in an effort to determine as nearly as possible its true magnitude, using the same care, methods, and instruments in making each measurement. If we try to read the measuring instrument to the finest subdivision of its graduated scale and even estimate fractions of a subdivision, we shall find that the results of the several measurements do not agree exactly among themselves, however much care we may use; for each measurement is subject to unavoidable accidental errors. How, then, shall we decide upon the best result obtainable from any given set of measurements or observations?

This question is answered by the *Principle of Least Squares*, which says that the best or most probable value of the measured quantity is that value for which the sum of the squares of the errors is least. This answer is in accord with reason and common sense; for, since the accidental errors are real quantities their squares are positive quantities and the requirement that the sum of these positive quantities shall be as small as possible insures that the errors themselves shall be as small numerically as possible.

Furthermore, the requirement that the sum of the squares of the errors shall be a minimum leads to the result that the arithmetic mean or average of the measurements is the best value obtainable from any set of equally trustworthy direct measurements. This result is in accord with experience and common sense.

The principle of least squares also follows from the Normal Law of accidental errors, as we shall now show.

If we make a set of measurements all with equal care and use the same methods and instruments for each, the precision constant $h$ of the probability equation will be the same for all the measurements and the frequency of the accidental errors will be given by the same probability curve. If the accidental errors of the $n$ measurements $m_1, m_2, \cdots m_n$ be denoted by $x_1, x_2, \cdots x_n$, respectively, then the respective probabilities of these errors are

$$p_1 = \frac{h}{\sqrt{\pi}} e^{-h^2 x_1{}^2} dx_1, \quad p_2 = \frac{h}{\sqrt{\pi}} e^{-h^2 x_2{}^2} dx_2, \cdots p_n = \frac{h}{\sqrt{\pi}} e^{-h^2 x_n{}^2} dx_n.$$

Since the separate measurements are independent events, the probability that the set of errors $x_1, x_2, \cdots x_n$ will be made is the product of their separate probabilities, or

$$(93:1) \quad P = p_1 p_2 \cdots p_n = \left(\frac{h}{\sqrt{\pi}}\right)^n e^{-h^2 (x_1{}^2 + x_2{}^2 + \cdots + x_n{}^2)} dx_1 dx_2 \cdots dx_n.$$

Now since small errors occur more frequently than large ones, a set of small errors is a more probable event than a set of large ones in making any set of measurements. Hence the set which has the greatest probability will give us the best or most probable value of the quantity measured; and since the differentials $dx_1, dx_2$, etc. are perfectly arbitrary quantities (the smallest subdivisions of a graduated scale, for instance) it is evident from equation (93:1) that this probability $P$ is greatest when the exponent of $e$ is least, that is, when

$$x_1{}^2 + x_2{}^2 + \cdots + x_n{}^2 = \sum x^2 \text{ is a minimum.}$$

Thus, by the principles of probability we arrive at the *Principle of Least Squares*, namely:

*The best or most probable value obtainable from a set of measurements or observations of equal precision is that value for which the sum of the squares of the errors is a minimum.*

*Note.* Any measurable quantity has a definite, *true* magnitude; and the differences between this unknown magnitude and the several measurements made to determine it are the true errors of those measurements. However, when these errors are required to satisfy the condition that the sum of their squares shall be a minimum, for the purpose of arriving at the most probable magnitude of the quantity, they become residual errors, or simply *residuals* (see Art. 95). But it is shown in Art. 97 that the sum of the squares of the residuals is least when the sum of the squares of the errors is least.

**94. Weighted Observations.** If the measurements are not of equal precision, the values of $h$ will be different.  The probabilities of the errors will then be

$$p_1 = \frac{h_1}{\sqrt{\pi}} e^{-h_1^2 x_1^2} dx_1, \quad p_2 = \frac{h_2}{\sqrt{\pi}} e^{-h_2^2 x_2^2} dx_2, \cdots p_n = \frac{h_n}{\sqrt{\pi}} e^{-h_n^2 x_n^2} dx_n;$$

and the probability of their simultaneous occurrence will be

$$(94:1) \quad P = p_1 p_2 \cdots p_n = \frac{h_1 h_2 \cdots h_n}{(\sqrt{\pi})^n} e^{-(h_1^2 x_1^2 + h_2^2 x_2^2 + \cdots + h_n^2 x_n^2)} dx_1 dx_2 \cdots dx_n.$$

The best value obtainable from this set of measurements will therefore be that for which

$$(94:2) \quad \sum h^2 x^2 = h_1^2 x_1^2 + h_2^2 x_2^2 + \cdots + h_n^2 x_n^2 \text{ is a minimum.}$$

Since it is not customary in practice to make such an expression as (94:2) a minimum, it is necessary to introduce here the idea of *weighted* measurements or observations.  By the weight of an observation is meant its relative value or importance when compared with other observations of a set.  Thus, if we measure a line three times with the same care and accuracy, we regard the mean of the three measurements as more reliable than any one of the single measurements.  We express this by saying that the weight of the mean is three times that of a single measurement.  An observation of weight $w$ is therefore one which is equivalent in importance to $w$ observations of *unit* weight.

To find the relation between weight and precision index let

$h =$ precision index corresponding to weight 1,
$h_1 =$ precision index corresponding to weight $w_1$.

Then the probability of an error of magnitude $x$ in the observations of *unit* weight is given by

$$p = \frac{h}{\sqrt{\pi}} e^{-h^2 x^2} dx;$$

and the probability of an error of the *same magnitude* in a set of observations of weight $w_1$ is

$$p_1 = \frac{h_1}{\sqrt{\pi}} e^{-h_1^2 x^2} dx.$$

The probability of the same error (of magnitude $x$) in $w_1$ observations of *unit* weight is

$$P = p \cdot p \cdot p \cdots \text{ to } w_1 \text{ factors } = p^{w_1} = \left(\frac{h}{\sqrt{\pi}}\right)^{w_1} e^{-w_1 h^2 x^2} (dx)^{w_1}.$$

Now if the weighted observation (wt. $w_1$) is to be worth as much as the $w_1$ observations of unit weight, an error of magnitude $x$ must have the same probability in it as in the case of the $w_1$ observations. Hence we must have

$$p_1 \equiv P,$$

or

$$\frac{h_1}{\sqrt{\pi}} e^{-h_1^2 x^2} dx \equiv \left(\frac{h}{\sqrt{\pi}}\right)^{w_1} e^{-w_1 h^2 x^2} (dx)^{w_1}$$

for any $x$. Taking logarithms,

$$\log_e \frac{h_1}{\sqrt{\pi}} - h_1^2 x^2 \equiv w_1 \log_e \frac{h}{\sqrt{\pi}} - w_1 h^2 x^2 + (w_1 - 1) \log_e dx.$$

Equating coefficients of like powers of $x$,

$$h_1^2 = w_1 h^2, \quad \text{or} \quad w_1 = \frac{h_1^2}{h^2}.$$

Likewise, for observations of weights $w_2$, $w_3$, etc., we have

$$h_2^2 = w_2 h^2, \quad \text{or} \quad w_2 = \frac{h_2^2}{h^2};$$

$$h_3^2 = w_3 h^2, \quad \text{or} \quad w_3 = \frac{h_3^2}{h^2};$$

$$\text{etc.}$$

*The weights are therefore proportional to the squares of the precision indices.*
Substituting in (94:1) the values of $h_1^2$, $h_2^2$, etc. as given above, we get

$$P = \left(\frac{w_1 w_2 \cdots w_n}{\pi}\right)^{n/2} h^n e^{-h^2 (w_1 x_1^2 + w_2 x_2^2 + \cdots + w_n x_n^2)} dx_1 dx_2 \cdots dx_n.$$

In order that $P$ be a maximum we must have

**(94:3)**    $\sum wx^2 = w_1 x_1^2 + w_2 x_2^2 + \cdots + w_n x_n^2$ a minimum.

We can now state the Principle of Least Squares in its most general form:

*The best value of an unknown quantity that can be obtained from a set of measurements of unequal precision is that which makes the sum of the weighted squares of the errors a minimum.*

**95. Residuals.** In the preceding articles of the present chapter we have been discussing the *errors* of observations and measurements. The true or exact magnitude of a quantity can not be found by measurement; for the unit of measurement and the quantity to be measured are, in general, incommensurable. Moreover, all measurements are subject to errors of some kind. It is obvious, therefore, that the *error* of a measurement can never be determined, the error being defined as the true value minus the measured value. What we actually do, and all we can do, is to measure the quantity as many times as may be desirable or convenient and then find from these measurements the *most probable* value of the measured quantity. The difference between the most probable value and any particular measurement is called the *residual* for that measurement. For consistency in sign we always write

Error = True Value − Measured Value.

Residual = Most Probable Value − Measured Value.

Let $m_0$ denote the most probable value of a measured quantity and let $m_1$, $m_2$, $\cdots m_n$ denote the values of $n$ separate measurements. Then if $v_1$, $v_2$, $\cdots v_n$ denote the residuals of these measurements, we have by definition

$$v_1 = m_0 - m_1,$$

$$v_2 = m_0 - m_2,$$

$$\cdot \quad \cdot \quad \cdot \quad \cdot \quad \cdot \quad \cdot$$

$$v_n = m_0 - m_n.$$

**96. The Most Probable Value of a Set of Direct Measurements.** The definition of residuals leads us up to the problem of finding the most probable value of a set of measurements. Suppose we make $n$ direct measurements on some unknown magnitude, how shall we determine the best value of the magnitude, on the basis of the $n$ measurements? To give a general answer to this question we shall first assume that the measurements are of unequal weight.

Let $m_1$, $m_2$, $\cdots m_n$ denote the $n$ measurements and let $w_1$, $w_2$, $\cdots w_n$ denote their respective weights. Then if $m$ denote the true value of the unknown magnitude, the *errors* of the several measurements are

$$x_1 = m - m_1, \ x_2 = m - m_2, \cdots x_n = m - m_n.$$

Now the true value $m$ is unknown and can not be found, but we must adopt *some* value for it. The principle of least squares says that the best value is that which makes the sum of the weighted squares of the errors a minimum (Art. 94); that is,

$$(96\colon 1) \quad f(m) = w_1(m - m_1)^2 + w_2(m - m_2)^2 + \cdots + w_n(m - m_n)^2$$

must be a minimum.

Differentiating (96:1) with respect to $m$, putting the derivative equal to zero, and replacing $m$ by $m_0$, which is to be the adopted value of $m$, we have

$$w_1(m_0 - m_1) + w_2(m_0 - m_2) + \cdots + w_n(m_0 - m_n) = 0,$$

from which

**(96 : 2)**    $$m_0 = \frac{w_1 m_1 + w_2 m_2 + \cdots + w_n m_n}{w_1 + w_2 + \cdots + w_n} = \frac{\sum wm}{\sum w}.$$

This value $m_0$ is called the *weighted mean* of the several measurements.

If all the measurements are of equal weight, then $w_1 = w_2 = \cdots = w_n$, and (96:2) reduces to

**(96 : 3)**    $$m_0 = \frac{m_1 + m_2 + \cdots + m_n}{n},$$

which is simply the *average* of all the measurements. This result is in accord with experience and common sense.

Formulas (96:2) and (96:3) enable us to prove the following important theorem:

*In any set of measurements of equal weight the algebraic sum of the residuals is zero, and in a set of measurements of unequal weight the algebraic sum of the weighted residuals is zero.*

To prove this theorem let $m_0$ denote the most probable value of the $n$ measurements $m_1$, $m_2$, $\cdots m_n$; and let $v_1$, $v_2$, $\cdots v_n$ denote the residuals. Then

$$v_1 = m_0 - m_1,$$
$$v_2 = m_0 - m_2,$$
$$\cdot \quad \cdot \quad \cdot \quad \cdot \quad \cdot \quad \cdot$$
$$v_n = m_0 - m_n.$$

Adding these $n$ equations, we get

$$v_1 + v_2 + \cdots + v_n = nm_0 - (m_1 + m_2 + \cdots + m_n)$$
$$= nm_0 - nm_0 = 0, \text{ by } (96:3).$$

To prove the second part of the theorem let $w_1$, $w_2$, $\cdots w_n$ denote the weights of the several measurements. The weighted residuals are

$$w_1 v_1 = w_1 m_0 - w_1 m_1,$$
$$w_2 v_2 = w_2 m_0 - w_2 m_2,$$
$$\cdot \quad \cdot \quad \cdot \quad \cdot \quad \cdot \quad \cdot \quad \cdot$$
$$w_n v_n = w_n m_0 - w_n m_n.$$

Adding these $n$ equations, as before, we get

$$w_1 v_1 + w_2 v_2 + \cdots w_n v_n = m_0(w_1 + w_2 + \cdots w_n) - (w_1 m_1 + w_2 m_2 + \cdots)$$
$$= 0, \text{ by } (96:2).$$

This theorem provides us with a valuable check on the computed residuals in any set of measurements. However, since the residuals in such cases are rounded numbers their algebraic sum will rarely be exactly zero.

**97. Law of Error for Residuals.** We shall now show that when the errors of a set of measurements follow the Normal Law of error, the residuals likewise follow a similar law. To prove this let $m$ denote the true value of the measured quantity; $m_0$ the most probable value; $\epsilon_1, \epsilon_2, \cdots \epsilon_n$ the errors of measurement; $v_1, v_2, \cdots v_n$ the residuals; and $w_1, w_2, \cdots w_n$ the weights. Then

$$(v) \qquad\qquad\qquad (\epsilon)$$

$$v_1 = m_0 - m_1, \qquad\qquad \epsilon_1 = m - m_1,$$

$$v_2 = m_0 - m_2, \qquad\qquad \epsilon_2 = m - m_2,$$

$$\cdots\cdots\cdots \qquad\qquad \cdots\cdots\cdots$$

$$v_n = m_0 - m_n. \qquad\qquad \epsilon_n = m - m_n.$$

For the case of measurements of equal weight we have from column $(v)$

$$\sum v = nm_0 - \sum m = 0, \quad \text{or} \quad m_0 = \frac{\sum m}{n};$$

and from column $(\epsilon)$ we get in a similar manner

$$\sum \epsilon = nm - \sum m, \quad \text{or} \quad \sum m = nm - \sum \epsilon.$$

Substituting this value of $\sum m$ in the equation $m_0 = \sum m/n$, we get

$$(97:1) \qquad m_0 = \frac{nm - \sum \epsilon}{n} = m - \frac{\sum \epsilon}{n}.$$

Now substituting this value of $m_0$ in the equations of column $(v)$, we have

$$(97:2) \quad v_1 = m - \frac{1}{n}\sum \epsilon - m_1 = m - m_1 - \frac{1}{n}\sum \epsilon = \epsilon_1 - \frac{1}{n}\sum \epsilon$$

$$= \epsilon_1 - \frac{1}{n}\epsilon_1 - \frac{1}{n}\epsilon_2 - \cdots - \frac{1}{n}\epsilon_n,$$

or

$$v_1 = \left(\frac{n-1}{n}\right)\epsilon_1 - \frac{1}{n}\epsilon_2 - \frac{1}{n}\epsilon_3 - \cdots - \frac{1}{n}\epsilon_n.$$

Similarly,

$$v_2 = -\frac{1}{n}\epsilon_1 + \left(\frac{n-1}{n}\right)\epsilon_2 - \frac{1}{n}\epsilon_3 - \cdots - \frac{1}{n}\epsilon_n,$$

$$\cdots \cdots \cdots \cdots \cdots$$

$$v_n = -\frac{1}{n}\epsilon_1 - \frac{1}{n}\epsilon_2 - \cdots + \left(\frac{n-1}{n}\right)\epsilon_n.$$

We have thus proved that the residuals are linear functions of the errors. Hence by Art. 90 they follow the Normal Law.

If $h$ is the precision index for the $\epsilon$'s and $H$ that for the $v$'s, we have from (90:12)

$$\frac{1}{H^2} = \frac{\left(\frac{n-1}{n}\right)^2}{h^2} + \frac{\frac{1}{n^2}}{h^2} + \cdots + \frac{\frac{1}{n^2}}{h^2} = \frac{1}{n^2 h^2}[(n-1)^2 + n - 1],$$

or

$$\frac{1}{H^2} = \frac{n-1}{n}\frac{1}{h^2}.$$

Hence

(97:3)
$$H = h\sqrt{\frac{n}{n-1}}.$$

Since the residuals follow the Normal Law, the probability equation for them is

(97:4)
$$y = \frac{H}{\sqrt{\pi}}e^{-H^2 v^2}.$$

From (97:3) it is plain that the precision index for the residuals is a function of both $h$ and $n$, and that it is always larger than $h$. This means that the graph of (97:4) rises higher in the middle and falls off more rapidly on each side than does the graph of (89:15). As the number of measurements increases, the graph of (97:4) approaches that of (89:15) more and more closely, and would ultimately coincide with it if the number of measurements were increased indefinitely.

When the measurements are of unequal weight, the weighted residuals and weighted errors are as given in the columns $(wv)$ and $(w\epsilon)$ below.

|  $(wv)$  |  $(w\epsilon)$  |
|---|---|
| $w_1 v_1 = w_1 m_0 - w_1 m_1,$ | $w_1 \epsilon_1 = w_1 m - w_1 m_1,$ |
| $w_2 v_2 = w_2 m_0 - w_2 m_2,$ | $w_2 \epsilon_2 = w_2 m - w_2 m_2,$ |
| $\cdots \cdots \cdots \cdots$ | $\cdots \cdots \cdots \cdots$ |
| $w_n v_n = w_n m_0 - w_n m_n.$ | $w_n \epsilon_n = w_n m - w_n m_n.$ |

On adding the equations ($wv$) we get

$$\sum wv = m_0 \sum w - \sum wm = 0, \text{ by } (96:2).$$

$$\therefore \quad m_0 = \frac{\sum wm}{\sum w}.$$

By adding the equations in column ($w\epsilon$) we obtain

$$\sum w\epsilon = m \sum w - \sum wm, \quad \text{or} \quad \sum wm = m \sum w - \sum w\epsilon.$$

Substituting this value of $\Sigma wm$ in the expression for $m_0$ above, we get

$$(97:5) \qquad m_0 = \frac{m \sum w - \sum w\epsilon}{\sum w} = m - \frac{\sum w\epsilon}{\sum w}.$$

Hence

$$(97:6) \quad v_1 = m_0 - m_1 = m - m_1 - \frac{\sum w\epsilon}{\sum w} = \epsilon_1 - \frac{\sum w\epsilon}{\sum w}$$

$$= \epsilon_1 - \frac{w_1\epsilon_1}{\sum w} - \frac{w_2\epsilon_2}{\sum w} - \frac{w_3\epsilon_3}{\sum w} - \cdots - \frac{\sum w_n\epsilon_n}{\sum w},$$

or

$$v_1 = \left(1 - \frac{w_1}{\sum w}\right)\epsilon_1 - \frac{w_2}{\sum w}\epsilon_2 - \frac{w_3}{\sum w}\epsilon_3 - \cdots - \frac{w_n}{\sum w}\epsilon_n.$$

Similarly,

$$v_2 = -\frac{w_1}{\sum w}\epsilon_1 + \left(1 - \frac{w_2}{\sum w}\right)\epsilon_2 - \frac{w_3}{\sum w}\epsilon_3 - \cdots - \frac{w_n}{\sum w}\epsilon_n,$$

etc.

Hence in the case of measurements of unequal weight the residuals are linear functions of the errors and therefore follow the Normal Law. The residual $v_1$, for example, would follow the law

$$y = \frac{H_1}{\sqrt{\pi}} e^{-H_1{}^2 v_1{}^2},$$

where

$$\frac{1}{H_1{}^2} = \frac{1}{(\sum w)^2}\left[\frac{(\sum w - w_1)^2}{h_1{}^2} + \frac{w_2{}^2}{h_2{}^2} + \cdots + \frac{w_n{}^2}{h_n{}^2}\right].$$

And similarly for the other residuals.

On squaring and adding the $n$ equations $v_1 = \epsilon_1 - (1/n)\Sigma\epsilon$, $v_2 = \epsilon_2 - (1/n)\Sigma\epsilon$, etc., we obtain

$$(97:7) \qquad \sum v^2 = \sum \epsilon^2 - \frac{1}{n}(\sum \epsilon)^2,$$

which gives the relation between the sum of the squares of the residuals and the sum of the squares of the true errors in any set of measurements of equal weight.  Since both terms in the right member of (97:7) are positive quantities, it is evident that the sum of the squares of the residuals is always less than the sum of the squares of the errors, but that the difference is very slight.

Inasmuch as the quantity $\Sigma\epsilon$ is very nearly zero in any set of measurements, the square of this quantity is still smaller and $(1/n)(\Sigma\epsilon)^2$ is practically negligible in comparison with $\Sigma\epsilon^2$.  Hence any small shift in the values of the $\epsilon$'s would have very little effect on the already negligible quantity $(1/n)(\Sigma\epsilon)^2$.  We may therefore consider this quantity constant for small changes in the $\epsilon$'s, and then it is plain that $\Sigma v^2$ is least when $\Sigma\epsilon^2$ is least.

This can also be shown in a different way.  From equation (97:7) we have

$$\Sigma v^2 = \Sigma\epsilon^2 - \frac{(\epsilon_1 + \epsilon_2 + \cdots + \epsilon_n)^2}{n}$$

$$= \Sigma\epsilon^2 - \frac{(\epsilon_1^2 + \epsilon_2^2 + \cdots + \epsilon_n^2 + 2\epsilon_1\epsilon_2 + 2\epsilon_1\epsilon_3 + \cdots + 2\epsilon_{n-1}\epsilon_n)}{n}.$$

Now when the number of measurements is large, the product terms $2\epsilon_1\epsilon_2$, $2\epsilon_1\epsilon_3$, etc. will be about half positive and half negative; and they will average about the same size.  Hence they will cancel one another for the most part and then $\Sigma v^2$ reduces to

$$\Sigma v^2 = \Sigma\epsilon^2 - \frac{(\epsilon_1^2 + \epsilon_2^2 + \cdots + \epsilon_n^2)}{n}$$

$$= \Sigma\epsilon^2 - \frac{\Sigma\epsilon^2}{n} = \left(\frac{n-1}{n}\right)\Sigma\epsilon^2.$$

From the foregoing considerations we are justified in asserting that *The sum of the squares of the residuals is a minimum when the sum of the squares of the true errors is a minimum, and conversely.*

In a similar manner, on squaring the $n$ equations $v_1 = \epsilon_1 - \Sigma w\epsilon/\Sigma w$, $v_2 = \epsilon_2 - \Sigma w\epsilon/\Sigma w$, etc., then multiplying the squared equations by the corresponding weights $w_1$, $w_2$, etc. and adding the results, we get

$$(97:8) \qquad \Sigma wv^2 = \Sigma w\epsilon^2 - \frac{1}{\Sigma w}\left(\Sigma w\epsilon\right)^2.$$

Here, again, we see that the sum of the weighted squares of the residuals is a minimum when the sum of the weighted squares of the true errors is a minimum, and conversely, since the negligible quantity $(1/\Sigma w)(\Sigma w\epsilon)^2$ may be considered constant for small changes in the $\epsilon$'s.

*Remarks.*  Equation (97:1) shows that the arithmetic mean is equal to the true value of the quantity minus a very small quantity; for since the errors are as likely to be positive as negative the quantity $\Sigma\epsilon$ is not large, and $(1/n)\Sigma\epsilon$ is still smaller. Hence the larger the number of measurements the nearer does $m_0$ approach the true value of the quantity measured. Equation (97:5) shows a similar result in the case of weighted measurements.

Equations (97:2) and (97:6) show that any residual is equal to the corresponding error minus a very small quantity. Therefore when the number of measurements is large the residuals are practically equal to the true errors. Hence, although we can never determine the true magnitude of a measured quantity we can determine it as closely as we please by taking enough measurements.

**98. Agreement between Theory and Experience.** At the beginning of this chapter we described an experiment which was designed to show the behavior and distribution of accidental errors. In deriving the Probability Equation we made the assumptions that the probability of an error depended upon its size and that positive and negative errors of the same size were equally likely. These two assumptions were supported by the pencil experiment. The first is based upon experience, but the second is evident on purely *a priori* grounds and also supported by experience. No rigorous deduction of the Normal Law, based upon purely *a priori* considerations, has ever been given. The truth is that, for the kinds of errors considered in this book (errors of measurement and observation), the Normal Law is *proved by experience*. Several substitutes for this law have been proposed, but none fits the facts so well as it does.

To show how well the Normal Law agrees with experience when the number of measurements is large, we give in the table below the results of 470 observations made by Bradley on the right ascensions of the stars Sirius and Altair.

| Size of errors | Number computed from theory | Number actually found |
|---|---|---|
| 0″.0 to 0″.1 | 95 | 94 |
| 0″.1 to 0″.2 | 89 | 88 |
| 0″.2 to 0″.3 | 78 | 78 |
| 0″.3 to 0″.4 | 64 | 58 |
| 0″.4 to 0″.5 | 50 | 51 |
| 0″.5 to 0″.6 | 36 | 36 |
| 0″.6 to 0″.7 | 24 | 26 |
| 0″.7 to 0″.8 | 15 | 14 |
| 0″.8 to 0″.9 | 9 | 10 |
| 0″.9 to 1″.0 | 5 | 7 |
| over 1″.0 | 5 | 8 |

It will be seen that the agreement between theory and experience is remarkably close, with the exception of the number of errors of magnitude from $0''.3$ to $0''.4$.

## EXAMPLES ON CHAPTER XIV

1. Compute the value of the integral $\int_0^{1/3} e^{-t^2} dt$ correct to seven decimal places.

2. Compute the value of $\int_0^{2.2} e^{-t^2} dt$ correct to five decimal places.

3. Find the probability of hitting at the first shot a rectangular target 60 feet wide and 24 feet high at a distance of 4000 yards, the mean errors for the gun at this range being

$$n_x = 7.4 \text{ yds.}, \quad n_y = 5.2 \text{ yds.}$$

4. If 20 shots are fired at a cylindrical standpipe 120 feet high and 40 feet in diameter at a distance of three miles, find the chance that the standpipe will be hit if the probable errors of the gun for this range are

$$r_x = 14.2 \text{ feet}, \quad r_y = 10.6 \text{ feet.}$$

5. If the foretop of a battleship is a cylinder 12 feet in diameter and 8 feet high, find the chance that it will be hit by a shot aimed at a point 80 feet directly below, the mean errors for the gun in this case being

$$n_x = 42.6 \text{ feet}, \quad n_y = 36.5 \text{ feet.}$$

About how many shots would have to be fired at the ship (aimed at a point 80 feet below the foretop) before the foretop would be hit?

6. Twelve measurements of the length of a line are given below. Find the most probable length of the line.

| | | |
|---|---|---|
| 364.2 | 364.2 | 364.3 |
| 364.4 | 363.7 | 363.8 |
| 363.9 | 364.1 | 364.3 |
| 364.3 | 364.5 | 364.0 |

7. Seven measurements of an object by different methods are given in the following table. If the weights of the different measurements are as given in the table, find the most probable size of the object.

| Measurements | Weights |
|:---:|:---:|
| 369.2 | 2 |
| 368.3 | 1 |
| 371.1 | 3 |
| 370.2 | 5 |
| 369.1 | 2 |
| 370.6 | 4 |
| 372.2 | 1 |

Compute the residuals and weighted residuals. Find the algebraic sum of the weighted residuals and the sum of the weighted squares of the residuals.

# CHAPTER XV

# THE PRECISION OF MEASUREMENTS

**99. Measurements, Direct and Indirect.** Direct measurements are those made by methods and instruments whose indications give directly the quantity sought. Such measurements are usually made by reading a scale graduated in terms of the chosen unit. Yard sticks, clocks, voltmeters, chemical balances, etc. are instruments for making direct measurements.

*Indirect* measurements are those in which the quantity measured is not given directly by observation or readings taken, but must be calculated from them. Thus, in an indirect measurement the quantity sought is a function of one or more directly measured quantities. For example, if we measure two sides and the included angle of a plane triangle we can find the remaining side and the area by means of the formulas

$$a = \sqrt{b^2 + c^2 - 2bc \cos A}, \quad \text{Area} = \tfrac{1}{2}bc \sin A.$$

Here the directly measured quantities are $b$, $c$, $A$, and the indirectly measured (computed) ones are $a$ and the area.

The relation between observed and computed quantities may be expressed by the general formula

$$y = f(x_1, x_2, x_3, \cdots a, b, c, \cdots),$$

where $y$ and the $x$'s represent observed or computed quantities and $a$, $b$, $c$, etc. represent numerical constants.

**100. Precision and Accuracy.** The words "precision" and "accuracy", when used in the discussion of measurements, have quite different meanings. Precision has to do with *accidental* errors, and a precise measurement would be one free from accidental errors. An accurate measurement, on the other hand, would be one free from all kinds of errors—mistakes, systematic errors, and accidental errors. Barring mistakes, the systematic error is thus the difference between the precise value and the accurate or true value of the quantity measured. If the systematic error should happen to be large, a precise measurement might be very inaccurate. The accuracy of a measurement can be increased by using more refined instruments and methods, whereas the precision can be increased only by using more care in making the measurement.

### I. DIRECT MEASUREMENTS

**101. Measures of Precision.** The precision of a measurement can be estimated in several ways. The three *measures of precision* in common use are the following: the *mean square error* (M.S.E.), the *probable error* (P.E.), and the *average error*. These three measures are denoted by the letters $\mu$, $r$, $\eta$, respectively. We shall now derive expressions for them in terms of the precision index $h$.

*101a).* *The Mean Square Error* (M.S.E.). In discussing the error equation

$$y = \frac{h}{\sqrt{\pi}} e^{-h^2 x^2}$$

in Art. 89, we stated that $h$ is called the index of precision and indicated the reason for this name. Then in Art. 93 we found that the probability of the simultaneous occurrence of a set of errors $x_1$, $x_2$, $\cdots$ $x_n$ in a given measurement is

$$(101:1) \quad P = p_1 p_2 \cdots p_n = \left(\frac{h}{\sqrt{\pi}}\right)^n e^{-h^2(x_1^2 + x_2^2 + \cdots + x_n^2)} dx_1 dx_2 \cdots dx_n.$$

It was also shown in that article that the best or most probable result obtainable from a set of measurements is that corresponding to the maximum value of $P$.

Let us now assume that a given set of $n$ measurements has been made and let us try to find the best or most probable value of the precision index $h$ for this set of measurements. It is that value which makes $P$ a maximum and is found by differentiating $P$ with respect to $h$ and putting the derivative equal to zero. We thus get from (101:1)

$$\frac{dP}{dh} = \left(\frac{h}{\sqrt{\pi}}\right)^n e^{-h^2(x_1^2 + x_2^2 + \cdots)}\left[- 2h(x_1^2 + x_2^2 + \cdots + x_n^2)\right]$$

$$+ e^{-h^2(x_1^2 + x_2^2 + \cdots)} n\left(\frac{h}{\sqrt{\pi}}\right)^{n-1} \frac{1}{\sqrt{\pi}} = 0,$$

or

$$e^{-h^2(x_1^2 + x_2^2 + \cdots)}\left(\frac{h}{\sqrt{\pi}}\right)^{n-1} \frac{1}{\sqrt{\pi}}\left[- 2h^2(x_1^2 + x_2^2 + \cdots + x_n^2) + n\right] = 0.$$

$$\therefore \quad - 2h^2(x_1^2 + x_2^2 + \cdots + x_n^2) + n = 0,$$

or

$$\frac{1}{2h^2} = \frac{x_1^2 + x_2^2 + \cdots + x_n^2}{n},$$

from which

$$\frac{1}{h\sqrt{2}} = \sqrt{\frac{x_1^2 + x_2^2 + \cdots + x_n^2}{n}}.$$

The quantity on the right is usually called the *mean square error* (M.S.E.) of a single observation and is denoted by the Greek letter $\mu$. We therefore have

$$(101:2) \qquad \mu = \frac{1}{h\sqrt{2}} = \sqrt{\frac{x_1^2 + x_2^2 + \cdots + x_n^2}{n}}.$$

*101b). The Probable Error* (P.E.). The *probable error*, $r$, of a single measurement of a series is a quantity such that one half the errors of the series are greater than it and the other half less than it. In other words, the probability that the error of a single measurement will fall between $r$ and $-r$ is $\frac{1}{2}$, and the probability that it will fall outside these limits is $\frac{1}{2}$. Hence we must have

$$\int_{-r}^{+r} \frac{h}{\sqrt{\pi}} e^{-h^2 x^2} dx = \frac{1}{2}, \quad \text{or} \quad \frac{h}{\sqrt{\pi}} \int_0^r e^{-h^2 x^2} dx = \frac{1}{4},$$

since the probability that an error lies between any given limits is represented by the area under the probability curve between those limits.

To find the value of $r$ from the above equation we put

$$t = hx.$$

Then

$$dt = h\, dx,$$

and we have

$$\int_0^{hr} e^{-t^2} dt = \frac{\sqrt{\pi}}{4}, \quad \text{or} \quad \int_0^{\rho} e^{-t^2} dt = 0.4431135, \quad \text{where} \quad \rho = hr.$$

Now

$$e^{-t^2} = 1 - t^2 + \frac{t^4}{2} - \frac{t^6}{6} + \frac{t^8}{24} - \frac{t^{10}}{120} \cdots.$$

$$\therefore \int_0^{\rho} e^{-t^2} dt = \int_0^{\rho} \left( 1 - t^2 + \frac{t^4}{2} - \frac{t^6}{6} + \frac{t^8}{24} - \frac{t^{10}}{120} + \cdots \right) dt = 0.4431135,$$

or

$$(101:3) \quad \rho - \frac{\rho^3}{3} + \frac{\rho^5}{10} - \frac{\rho^7}{42} + \frac{\rho^9}{216} - \frac{\rho^{11}}{1320} - 0.4431135 = 0.$$

This is the equation which we have already solved in Art. 61 and found $\rho = 0.4769363$. The value of $\rho$ can also be found by interpolation, as we have already done in two ways in Exs. 2, Art. 21 and Ex. 1, Art. 24.

Using now the relation $\rho = hr$, we get

$$r = \frac{\rho}{h} = \frac{0.4769}{h} = 0.4769\left(\frac{1}{h}\right),$$

and from (101:2) we have

$$\frac{1}{h} = \sqrt{2}\sqrt{\frac{x_1^2 + x_2^2 + \cdots + x_n^2}{n}}.$$

Hence

$$r = 0.4769\sqrt{2}\sqrt{\frac{x_1^2 + x_2^2 + \cdots + x_n^2}{n}}$$

$$= 0.6745\sqrt{\frac{x_1^2 + x_2^2 + \cdots + x_n^2}{n}},$$

or

$$(101:4) \qquad r = 0.6745\sqrt{\frac{x_1^2 + x_2^2 + \cdots + x_n^2}{n}}.$$

*101c).* *The average error* is the arithmetic mean of all the errors of a set, without regard to signs. Thus,

$$(101:5) \qquad \eta = \frac{|x_1| + |x_2| + \cdots + |x_n|}{n}.$$

To find an expression for $\eta$ in terms of $h$ let us suppose that a set of $n$ measurements has been made, and that each measurement is affected with an error of some size. In the case of any single measurement the probability of an error of magnitude $x$ to $x+\Delta x$ is approximately $y\Delta x = (h/\sqrt{\pi})e^{-h^2x^2}\Delta x$ (Art. 88). Hence the probable *number* of errors of this size in the $n$ measurements is $n$ times this probability, or $(nh/\sqrt{\pi})e^{-h^2x^2}\Delta x$. The *sum* of these errors is therefore the number of errors times the size of a single error, or $(nhx/\sqrt{\pi})e^{-h^2x^2}\Delta x$. The sum of all the errors of all sizes is therefore

$$S = \int_{-\infty}^{\infty} \frac{nhx}{\sqrt{\pi}} e^{-h^2x^2} dx = \frac{2nh}{\sqrt{\pi}} \int_0^{\infty} e^{-h^2x^2} x\, dx$$

$$= -\frac{n}{h\sqrt{\pi}} \int_0^{\infty} e^{-h^2x^2}(-2h^2x\, dx) = -\frac{n}{h\sqrt{\pi}}\left[e^{-h^2x^2}\right]_0^{\infty},$$

or

$$S = \frac{n}{h\sqrt{\pi}}.$$

Hence

(101: 6)
$$\eta = \frac{S}{n} = \frac{1}{h\sqrt{\pi}} \cdot$$

**102. Relations between the Precision Measures.** From (101: 2) and (101:4) we have

(102: 1)    $r = 0.6745\mu = \frac{2}{3}\mu,$ roughly,

and

(102: 2)
$$\mu = \frac{r}{0.6745} = 1.4826r.$$

Also, since

$$\frac{1}{h} = \sqrt{2}\sqrt{\frac{x_1^2 + x_2^2 + \cdots + x_n^2}{n}} = \mu\sqrt{2},$$

we have

(102: 3)
$$\eta = \frac{1}{h}\cdot\frac{1}{\sqrt{\pi}} = \mu\sqrt{\frac{2}{\pi}} = 0.79788\mu$$

$$= 0.8\mu,\text{ approximately.}$$

Hence

(102: 4)
$$\mu = \frac{\eta}{0.79788} = 1.2533\eta.$$

Furthermore, from (102:2) and (102:4) we get

$$1.4826r = 1.2533\eta.$$

(102: 5)
$$\therefore \quad r = \frac{1.2533}{1.4826}\eta = 0.8453\eta,$$

and

(102: 6)
$$\eta = \frac{1.4826}{1.2533}r = 1.1829r.$$

All these relations are shown concisely in the following table:

|  | $\mu$ | $r$ | $\eta$ |
|---|---|---|---|
| $\mu =$ | 1.0000 | 1.4826 | 1.2533 |
| $r =$ | 0.6745 | 1.0000 | 0.8453 |
| $\eta =$ | 0.7979 | 1.1829 | 1.0000 |

**103. Geometric Significance of $\mu$, $r$, and $\eta$.** From the definition of $r$ it follows that its corresponding ordinate to the probability curve bisects the area under that curve on either side of the $y$-axis.

The quantity $\mu$ is the abscissa of the point of inflection of the probability curve, as we shall now show.

Taking the second derivative of

$$y = \frac{h}{\sqrt{\pi}} e^{-h^2 x^2}$$

and equating it to zero, we have

$$\frac{dy}{dx} = -\frac{2h^3}{\sqrt{\pi}} (x e^{-h^2 x^2}),$$

$$\frac{d^2y}{dx^2} = -\frac{2h^3}{\sqrt{\pi}} e^{-h^2 x^2}(1 - 2h^2 x^2) = 0.$$

Hence

$$1 - 2h^2 x^2 = 0,$$

or

$$x = \pm \frac{1}{h\sqrt{2}} = \pm \mu.$$

The precision measure $\eta$ is the abscissa of the center of gravity of the area (under the curve) on either side of the $y$-axis. To prove this we recall that if $x_0$ denote the abscissa of the center of gravity of that area we have

$$x_0 = \frac{\int xy\,dx}{\int y\,dx} = \frac{\int_0^\infty x\frac{h}{\sqrt{\pi}} e^{-h^2 x^2}dx}{\text{area}} = \frac{-\frac{1}{2h\sqrt{\pi}} \int_0^\infty e^{-h^2 x^2}(-2h^2 x)dx}{1/2}$$

$$= -\frac{1}{h\sqrt{\pi}} \left[ e^{-h^2 x^2} \right]_0^\infty = \frac{1}{h\sqrt{\pi}} = \eta.$$

The relative sizes of the precision measures and their geometric relations are shown in Fig. 18.

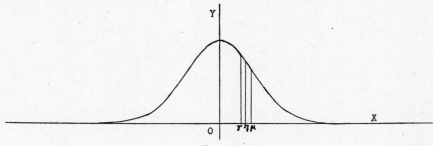

FIG. 18

The question naturally arises as to which precision measure is the best for practical use. On this point there is no universal agreement. In continental Europe the M.S.E. is used almost exclusively, but in England and America the P.E. is more often used. The average error is also used in America, but usually under the name *average deviation*.

The M.S.E. is quite generally used in Mathematical Statistics, where it is called the *standard deviation* and denoted by $\sigma$.

The average error is the easiest of all to compute, and the P.E. is the most laborious, because of the factor 0.6745. Nevertheless, in this book we shall conform to American practice and use the P.E. almost exclusively.

**104. Relation between Probable Error and Weight, and the Probable Error of the Arithmetic and Weighted Means.** In Art. 94 we derived the relation between the precision index $h$ and the weight $w$ of an observation, namely:

$$(104:1) \qquad \frac{h_1^2}{w_1} = \frac{h_2^2}{w_2} = \frac{h_3^2}{w_3} = \cdots = \frac{h_n^2}{w_n}.$$

Then in Art. 101 we found the relation

$$r = \frac{\rho}{h}, \quad \text{where} \quad \rho = 0.4769.$$

Hence

$$h = \frac{\rho}{r}.$$

Let $w_1, w_2, \cdots w_n$ be the weights of observations whose probable errors are $r_1, r_2, \cdots r_n$, respectively. Then

$$h_1 = \frac{\rho}{r_1}, \quad h_2 = \frac{\rho}{r_2}, \cdots h_n = \frac{\rho}{r_n}.$$

Substituting these values for $h_1, h_2, \cdots h_n$ in (104:1), we get

$$\frac{\rho^2}{r_1^2 w_1} = \frac{\rho^2}{r_2^2 w_2} = \cdots = \frac{\rho^2}{r_n^2 w_n},$$

or

$$\frac{1}{r_1^2 w_1} = \frac{1}{r_2^2 w_2} = \cdots = \frac{1}{r_n^2 w_n}.$$

Hence

$$(104:2) \qquad \frac{w_1}{w_2} = \frac{r_2^2}{r_1^2}, \quad \text{etc.}$$

*The weights are thus inversely proportional to the squares of the probable errors.*

This relation (104:2) enables us to find the P.E. of the arithmetic and weighted means of a set of $n$ direct measurements.

To find the P.E. of the arithmetic mean of $n$ direct measurements of *equal* weight, let the weight of each measurement be 1. Then the weight of the mean of all the measurements will be $n$. Denoting by $r$ the P.E. of any single measurement and by $r_0$ the P.E. of the mean of all the measurements, we have from (104:2)

$$\frac{1}{n} = \frac{r_0^2}{r^2}, \quad \text{or} \quad r_0^2 = \frac{r^2}{n}.$$

Hence the P.E. of the mean is

(104 : 3)
$$r_0 = \frac{r}{\sqrt{n}}.$$

If the measurements are not all of equal weight, let $w_1, w_2, \cdots w_n$ denote their weights. Then if $r$ denote the P.E. of a measurement of *unit* weight ($w = 1$) and $r_i$ the P.E. of a measurement of weight $w_i$, we have from (104:2)

$$\frac{1}{w_i} = \frac{r_i^2}{r^2}, \quad \text{or} \quad r_i^2 = \frac{r^2}{w_i}.$$

Hence

(104 : 4)
$$r_i = \frac{r}{\sqrt{w_i}}.$$

Now the weight of the weighted mean is $\Sigma w = w_1 + w_2 + \cdots + w_n$. Hence by (104:4) the P.E. of this mean is

(104 : 5)
$$r_0 = \frac{r}{\sqrt{\Sigma w}} = \frac{r}{\sqrt{w_1 + w_2 + \cdots + w_n}}.$$

Formula (104:3) shows that the P.E. of the arithmetic mean can be decreased by increasing the number of measurements. A glance at the graph of this equation shows, however, (see Fig. 19) that the decrease is very slight after several measurements have been made. Usually it does not pay to make more than ten measurements for the purpose of reducing the P.E. of the arithmetic mean.

## 105. Computation of the Precision Measures from the Residuals.
So far in our discussion of precision we have been considering the *errors*

of measurements. Since the true errors can not be found, it is necessary to derive formulas for the precision measures in terms of the residuals.

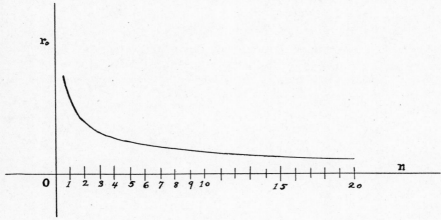

FIG. 19

In Art. 97 it was shown that when the errors of a set of measurements follow the Normal Law of error, the residuals likewise follow a similar law. The probability equation for any residual will therefore be of the form

$$(105:1) \qquad\qquad y = \frac{H}{\sqrt{\pi}} e^{-H^2 v^2}$$

for measurements of equal weight, where $H = h\sqrt{n/(n-1)}$. (See Art. 97.) For a set of $n$ direct measurements of equal weight we therefore have for the $n$ residuals the following probabilities:

$$p_1 = \frac{H}{\sqrt{\pi}} e^{-H^2 v_1^2} dv_1, \quad p_2 = \frac{H}{\sqrt{\pi}} e^{-H^2 v_2^2} dv_2, \cdots \quad p_n = \frac{H}{\sqrt{\pi}} e^{-H^2 v_n^2} dv_n.$$

The chance that this particular set of residuals will be made in any set of measurements is then

$$(105:2) \quad P = p_1 p_2 \cdots p_n = \left(\frac{H}{\sqrt{\pi}}\right)^n e^{-H^2 (v_1^2 + v_2^2 + \cdots + v_n^2)} dv_1 dv_2 \cdots dv_n.$$

Differentiating (105:2) with respect to $H$ and putting the derivative equal to zero, exactly as was done in Art. 101, we get

$$\frac{1}{H\sqrt{2}} = \sqrt{\frac{v_1^2 + v_2^2 + \cdots + v_n^2}{n}}.$$

But

$$\frac{1}{H} = \frac{1}{h}\sqrt{\frac{n-1}{n}}, \quad \text{and} \quad \frac{1}{h\sqrt{2}} = \mu.$$

Hence

$$\frac{1}{H\sqrt{2}} = \frac{1}{h\sqrt{2}}\sqrt{\frac{n-1}{n}} = \mu\sqrt{\frac{n-1}{n}}.$$

$$\therefore \quad \mu\sqrt{\frac{n-1}{n}} = \sqrt{\frac{v_1^2 + v_2^2 + \cdots + v_n^2}{n}},$$

or

(105: 3) $$\mu = \sqrt{\frac{v_1^2 + v_2^2 + \cdots + v_n^2}{n-1}} = \sqrt{\frac{\sum v^2}{n-1}}.$$

Therefore

(105: 4) $$r = 0.6745\mu = 0.6745\sqrt{\frac{\sum v^2}{n-1}}.$$

For the P.E. of the arithmetic mean we have

(105: 5) $$r_0 = \frac{r}{\sqrt{n}} = 0.6745\sqrt{\frac{\sum v^2}{n(n-1)}}.$$

If the measurements are not all of equal weight, the residuals will not have the same weight. They can all be reduced to unit weight, however, by multiplying each of them by the square root of its weight. This follows from (104:4), since $r_i\sqrt{w_i} = r$.

Let $v_1, v_2, \cdots v_n$ be the residuals of $n$ measurements of weights $w_1, w_2, \cdots w_n$. Then the residuals reduced to unit weight are

$$v_1' = v_1\sqrt{w_1},$$
$$v_2' = v_2\sqrt{w_2},$$
$$\cdots \cdots \cdots$$
$$v_n' = v_n\sqrt{w_n}.$$

Squaring these equations and adding, we get

(105: 6) $$\sum v'^2 = \sum wv^2.$$

Now for a set of measurements of equal weight we have from (105:4)

$$r = 0.6745\sqrt{\frac{\sum v'^2}{n-1}}.$$

Replacing $\Sigma v'^2$ by its equal from (105:6), we get

$$(105:7) \quad r = 0.6745 \sqrt{\frac{\sum wv^2}{n-1}} = 0.6745 \sqrt{\frac{w_1v_1^2 + w_2v_2^2 + \cdots + w_nv_n^2}{n-1}}.$$

This is the P.E. of a single measurement of *unit* weight.

To find the P.E. of a measurement of weight $w_i$ and the P.E. of the weighted mean we have from (104:4), (104:5), and (105:7)

$$(105:8) \qquad r_i = \frac{r}{\sqrt{w_i}} = 0.6745 \sqrt{\frac{\sum wv^2}{(n-1)w_i}}.$$

$$(105:9) \qquad r_0 = \frac{r}{\sqrt{\sum w}} = 0.6745 \sqrt{\frac{\sum wv^2}{(n-1)\sum w}}.$$

It will be observed that (105:9) reduces to (105:5) when all the weights are equal.

We now collect for easy reference the fundamental formulas for computing the P.E. of direct measurements.

(a) *Measurements of equal precision.* P.E. of a single measurement:

$$(105:4) \qquad r = 0.6745 \sqrt{\frac{v_1^2 + v_2^2 + \cdots + v_n^2}{n-1}}.$$

P.E. of arithmetic mean:

$$(105:5) \qquad r_0 = 0.6745 \sqrt{\frac{v_1^2 + v_2^2 + \cdots + v_n^2}{n(n-1)}}.$$

(b) *Weighted measurements.* P.E. of a single measurement of *unit* weight:

$$(105:7) \qquad r = 0.6745 \sqrt{\frac{w_1v_1^2 + w_2v_2^2 + \cdots + w_nv_n^2}{n-1}}.$$

P.E. of measurement of weight $w_i$:

$$(105:8) \qquad r_i = 0.6745 \sqrt{\frac{w_1v_2^2 + w_2v_2^2 + \cdots + w_nv_n^2}{(n-1)w_i}}.$$

P.E. of weighted mean:

$$(105:9) \qquad r_0 = 0.6745 \sqrt{\frac{w_1v_2^2 + w_2v_2^2 + \cdots w_nv_n^2}{(n-1)(w_1 + w_2 + \cdots + w_n)}}.$$

**106. The Combination of Sets of Measurements when the P.E.'s of the Sets are Given.** When several separate determinations of the magnitude of a quantity have been made by different observers or by different methods and the probable errors of the separate determinations are given, it is important to know just how to combine these several results so as to obtain from them the best value for the measured quantity and the probable error of this best value. For example, the results of five different determinations of the atomic weight of silver are given below. How can we obtain from them the best value for the atomic weight and how can we find the P.E. of this value?

$$107.9401 \pm 0.0058$$
$$107.9406 \pm 0.0049$$
$$107.9233 \pm 0.0140$$
$$107.9371 \pm 0.0045$$
$$107.9270 \pm 0.0090$$

This is really a problem in indirect measurements, but it can readily be solved by the methods already given. The proper method of procedure in a problem of this type is first to compute by the relation (104:2) the weights of the several determinations from their given probable errors and then find the weighted mean of the given values of the measured quantity. The P.E. of this weighted mean is to be computed by formula (104:5).

It would be incorrect to compute the P.E. of the weighted mean from the residuals by formula (105:9), because this formula can take no account of the *magnitudes* of the given probable errors. It takes account only of their ratios and would give the same result if all the given P.E.'s were ten times as great or only a hundredth part as great as they actually are in any given case. This statement will now be proved.[*]

Let $n$ sets of determinations of the magnitude of some quantity, with their corresponding probable errors, be denoted as follows:

$$M_1 \pm k\epsilon_1,$$
$$M_2 \pm k\epsilon_2,$$
$$\cdot \quad \cdot \quad \cdot \quad \cdot \quad \cdot$$
$$M_n \pm k\epsilon_n,$$

[*] See also a paper entitled "The Invalidity of a Commonly Used Method for Computing a Certain Probable Error," *Proc. Nat. Acad. Sci.*, Vol. 15, No. 8 (August, 1929), pp. 665–668.

where $k$ is a constant multiplier which we shall call the *magnitude factor* of the given P.E.'s, so that $r_1 = k\epsilon_1$, $r_2 = k\epsilon_2$, etc. From (104:2) we have $w_1 r_1^2 = w_2 r_2^2 = \cdots = w_n r_n^2 = c$, say. Hence

$$w_1 = \frac{c}{r_1^2} = \frac{c}{k^2 \epsilon_1^2}, \quad w_2 = \frac{c}{k^2 \epsilon_2^2}, \quad \cdots \quad w_n = \frac{c}{k^2 \epsilon_n^2}.$$

The weighted mean is

$$M_0 = \frac{w_1 M_1 + w_2 M_2 + \cdots + w_n M_n}{w_1 + w_2 + \cdots + w_n}$$

$$= \frac{\dfrac{c}{k^2 \epsilon_1^2} M_1 + \dfrac{c}{k^2 \epsilon_2^2} M_2 + \cdots + \dfrac{c}{k^2 \epsilon_n^2} M_n}{\dfrac{c}{k^2 \epsilon_1^2} + \dfrac{c}{k^2 \epsilon_2^2} + \cdots + \dfrac{c}{k^2 \epsilon_n^2}},$$

or

$$M_0 = \frac{\dfrac{1}{\epsilon_1^2} M_1 + \dfrac{1}{\epsilon_2^2} M_2 + \cdots + \dfrac{1}{\epsilon_n^2} M_n}{\dfrac{1}{\epsilon_1^2} + \dfrac{1}{\epsilon_2^2} + \cdots + \dfrac{1}{\epsilon_n^2}}$$

$$= \frac{M_1 + \left(\dfrac{\epsilon_1}{\epsilon_2}\right)^2 M_2 + \cdots + \left(\dfrac{\epsilon_1}{\epsilon_n}\right)^2 M_n}{1 + \left(\dfrac{\epsilon_1}{\epsilon_2}\right)^2 + \cdots + \left(\dfrac{\epsilon_1}{\epsilon_n}\right)^2}.$$

This result, be it noted, does not contain the magnitude factor $k$, but only the *ratios* of the given P.E.'s. Hence it is independent of the *size* of the P.E.'s of the $M$'s.

For the residuals of the $M$'s we have

$$v_1 = M_0 - M_1 = \frac{\dfrac{1}{\epsilon_2^2}(M_2 - M_1) + \dfrac{1}{\epsilon_3^2}(M_3 - M_1) + \cdots + \dfrac{1}{\epsilon_n^2}(M_n - M_1)}{\dfrac{1}{\epsilon_1^2} + \dfrac{1}{\epsilon_2^2} + \cdots + \dfrac{1}{\epsilon_n^2}}$$

$$= \frac{\left(\dfrac{\epsilon_1}{\epsilon_2}\right)^2(M_2 - M_1) + \left(\dfrac{\epsilon_1}{\epsilon_3}\right)^2(M_3 - M_1) + \cdots + \left(\dfrac{\epsilon_1}{\epsilon_n}\right)^2(M_n - M_1)}{1 + \left(\dfrac{\epsilon_1}{\epsilon_2}\right)^2 + \cdots + \left(\dfrac{\epsilon_1}{\epsilon_n}\right)^2},$$

$$v_2 = M_0 - M_2 = \frac{(M_1 - M_2) + \left(\dfrac{\epsilon_1}{\epsilon_3}\right)^2 (M_3 - M_2) + \cdots + \left(\dfrac{\epsilon_1}{\epsilon_n}\right)^2 (M_n - M_2)}{1 + \left(\dfrac{\epsilon_1}{\epsilon_2}\right)^2 + \cdots + \left(\dfrac{\epsilon_1}{\epsilon_n}\right)^2},$$

$$\cdots \cdots \cdots \cdots \cdots \cdots \cdots \cdots \cdots \cdots$$

$$v_n = M_0 - M_n = \frac{(M_1 - M_n) + \left(\dfrac{\epsilon_1}{\epsilon_2}\right)^2 (M_2 - M_n) + \cdots + \left(\dfrac{\epsilon_1}{\epsilon_{n-1}}\right)^2 (M_{n-1} - M_n)}{1 + \left(\dfrac{\epsilon_1}{\epsilon_2}\right)^2 + \cdots + \left(\dfrac{\epsilon_1}{\epsilon_n}\right)^2}.$$

Here, too, it is to be noted that the residuals do not contain the magnitude factor $k$, but only the ratios of the given P.E.'s.   Hence the residuals are independent of the *size* of the P.E.'s of the $M$'s.

Now substituting in formula (105:9) the values of the weights as given above, we have

$$r_0 = 0.6745 \left[ \frac{\dfrac{c}{k^2\epsilon_1^2} v_1^2 + \dfrac{c}{k^2\epsilon_2^2} v_2^2 + \cdots + \dfrac{c}{k^2\epsilon_n^2} v_n^2}{(n-1)\left(\dfrac{c}{k^2\epsilon_1^2} + \dfrac{c}{k^2\epsilon_2^2} + \cdots + \dfrac{c}{k^2\epsilon_n^2}\right)} \right]^{\frac{1}{2}}$$

$$= \frac{0.6745}{\sqrt{n-1}} \left[ \frac{\dfrac{1}{\epsilon_1^2} v_1^2 + \dfrac{1}{\epsilon_2^2} v_2^2 + \cdots + \dfrac{1}{\epsilon_n^2} v_n^2}{\dfrac{1}{\epsilon_1^2} + \dfrac{1}{\epsilon_2^2} + \cdots + \dfrac{1}{\epsilon_n^2}} \right]^{\frac{1}{2}},$$

or

$$(106:1) \quad r_0 = \frac{0.6745}{\sqrt{n-1}} \left[ \frac{{}_1^2 + \left(\dfrac{\epsilon_1}{\epsilon_2}\right)^2 v_2^2 + \cdots + \left(\dfrac{\epsilon_1}{\epsilon_n}\right)^2 v_n^2}{1 + \left(\dfrac{\epsilon_1}{\epsilon_2}\right)^2 + \cdots + \left(\dfrac{\epsilon_1}{\epsilon_n}\right)^2} \right]^{\frac{1}{2}}.$$

Since the $v$'s do not contain the magnitude factor $k$, it is evident that this expression for the P.E. of the weighted mean of the given $M$'s is absolutely independent of the *size* of the given P.E.'s of the $M$'s. Hence it can not be a measure of the true probable error of $M_0$. *It is a measure of the agreement of the $M$'s among themselves, and nothing more.*

The invalidity of the method of computing the P.E. of the weighted mean from the residuals in problems of the type considered in this article is brought out more strikingly if we assume that the given probable errors are all equal, so that $r_1 = r_2 = \cdots = r_n$ and therefore $\epsilon_1 = \epsilon_2 = \cdots = \epsilon_n$. Then we have

$$v_1 = \frac{M_2 - M_1 + M_3 - M_1 + \cdots + M_n - M_1}{n} = \frac{\sum M - nM_1}{n}$$

$$= \frac{\sum M}{n} - M_1,$$

$$v_2 = \frac{\sum M}{n} - M_2, \cdots v_n = \frac{\sum M}{n} - M_n;$$

and equation (106:1) reduces to

$$r_0 = \frac{0.6745}{\sqrt{n-1}} \sqrt{\frac{v_1^2 + v_2^2 + \cdots + v_n^2}{n}}$$

$$= \frac{0.6745}{\sqrt{n(n-1)}} \left[ \frac{(\sum M)^2}{n^2} - \frac{2M_1 \sum M}{n} + M_1^2 + \frac{(\sum M)^2}{n^2} - \frac{2M_2 \sum M}{n} \right.$$

$$\left. + M_2^2 + \cdots + \frac{(\sum M)^2}{n^2} - \frac{2M_n \sum M}{n} + M_n^2 \right]^{\frac{1}{2}},$$

or

(106:2)          $$r_0 = \frac{0.6745}{\sqrt{n(n-1)}} \sqrt{\sum M^2 - \frac{1}{n}(\sum M)^2}.$$

This expression for $r_0$ does not contain a trace of the probable errors of the given determinations and hence can take no account of them. This $r_0$ is therefore *not* the true P.E. of $M_0$ and is in no way related to it.

Even if we go back to the original direct measurements of which the given $M$'s are the means (or weighted means), as we can easily do by expressing the given $r$'s in terms of the original residuals by means of formula (105:9) (which is perfectly applicable to a set of direct measurements to which weights are assigned arbitrarily), we shall find that the P.E. of $M_0$ as computed from the residuals of the given $M$'s is still independent of the magnitudes of the original residuals but depends only on their ratios.

Let us next compute the P.E. of $M_0$ by formula (104:5) and examine the result. In the equations

$$w_1 r_1^2 = w_2 r_2^2 = \cdots = w_n r_n^2 = c$$

let us put $w_i = 1$, $(i = 1, 2, \cdots n)$. Then $c = r_i^2$, or $r_i = \sqrt{c} =$ P.E. of a measurement of unit weight. Formula (104:5) then becomes

$$r_0 = \frac{\sqrt{c}}{\sqrt{\sum w}} = \frac{\sqrt{c}}{\sqrt{\dfrac{c}{k^2\epsilon_1^2} + \dfrac{c}{k^2\epsilon_2^2} + \cdots + \dfrac{c}{k^2\epsilon_n^2}}},$$

or

$$(106:3) \quad r_0 = \frac{k}{\sqrt{\dfrac{1}{\epsilon_1^2} + \dfrac{1}{\epsilon_2^2} + \cdots + \dfrac{1}{\epsilon_n^2}}}$$

$$= \frac{k\epsilon_i}{\sqrt{\left(\dfrac{\epsilon_i}{\epsilon_1}\right)^2 + \left(\dfrac{\epsilon_i}{\epsilon_2}\right)^2 + \cdots + 1 + \cdots + \left(\dfrac{\epsilon_i}{\epsilon_n}\right)^2}},$$

or

$$(106:4) \quad r_0 = \frac{r_i}{\sqrt{\left(\dfrac{\epsilon_i}{\epsilon_1}\right)^2 + \left(\dfrac{\epsilon_i}{\epsilon_2}\right)^2 + \cdots + 1 + \cdots + \left(\dfrac{\epsilon_i}{\epsilon_n}\right)^2}},$$

$$(i = 1, 2, \cdots n).$$

This value of $r_0$ varies directly with the magnitudes of the given probable errors and is therefore a true measure of the P.E. of the weighted mean.

Considering now the case where all the P.E.'s of the given $M$'s are equal, we have $\epsilon_1 = \epsilon_2 = \cdots = \epsilon_n$. Hence (106:4) becomes

$$r_0 = \frac{r}{\sqrt{n}},$$

where $r$ denotes the P.E. of any $M$. Here, again, the P.E. of $M_0$ varies directly with the given P.E.'s as would naturally be expected.

The foregoing investigation shows that in problems of the type considered in this article the P.E. of the weighted mean can not be found from the residuals, because the P.E. computed in this manner bears little or no relation to the true P.E. of the weighted mean. The proper application of formula (105:9) is to a set of original measurements to which weights have been assigned arbitrarily.

In some instances, however, it may be advisable to compute the residuals in problems of the type considered in this article. If, for example, it were evident by inspection that the given $M$'s differed widely among themselves, the residuals should be computed and then substituted in formula (105:8) in order to find the P.E. of a single measurement of weight $w_i$. The several residuals should then be compared with the corresponding P.E.'s as found by (105:8) and if any residual be found too large the corresponding measurement should be rejected by the rule of Art. 109.

We shall now show the use of the formulas derived in the preceding sections.

*Example* 1. The following measurements were made to determine the length of a base line in a geodetic survey. Find the most probable length of the line, the P.E. of a single measurement, and the P.E. of the arithmetic mean.

*Solution.* The measurements, residuals, etc. are arranged in tabular form as shown below. The first step in the solution is to find the arithmetic mean of the given measurements. Then the residuals are found by subtracting each measurement from the arithmetic mean.

| | | |
|---|---|---|
| $M_1 = 455.35$ | $v_1 = -0.02$ | $v_1^2 = 0.0004$ |
| $M_2 = 455.35$ | $v_2 = -0.02$ | $v_2^2 = 0.0004$ |
| $M_3 = 455.20$ | $v_3 = +0.13$ | $v_3^2 = 0.0169$ |
| $M_4 = 455.05$ | $v_4 = +0.28$ | $v_4^2 = 0.0784$ |
| $M_5 = 455.75$ | $v_5 = -0.42$ | $v_5^2 = 0.1764$ |
| $M_6 = 455.40$ | $v_6 = -0.07$ | $v_6^2 = 0.0049$ |
| $M_7 = 455.10$ | $v_7 = +0.23$ | $v_7^2 = 0.0529$ |
| $M_8 = 455.30$ | $v_8 = +0.03$ | $v_8^2 = 0.0009$ |
| $M_9 = 455.50$ | $v_9 = -0.17$ | $v_9^2 = 0.0289$ |
| $M_{10} = 455.30$ | $v_{10} = +0.03$ | $v_{10}^2 = 0.0009$ |
| $\sum M = 10 \times 455 + 3.30$ | $\sum v = 0$ | $\sum v^2 = 0.3610$ |

$$M_0 = \frac{10 \times 455 + 3.30}{10} = 455.330.$$

$$r = 0.6745 \sqrt{\frac{0.3610}{9}} = 0.135, \quad \text{by (105:4)}.$$

$$r_0 = \frac{0.135}{\sqrt{10}} = 0.043, \quad \text{by (105:5)}.$$

The length of the line is therefore to be written

$$\underline{M = 455.330 \pm 0.043.}$$

*Note.* The number of significant figures to be recorded in the most probable value (arithmetic or general mean) is usually one more than the number given in the individual measurements (Art. 6). If the P.E. of the final result should be relatively large, however, we are not justified in recording this result to more figures than are contained in the separate measurements, and in such cases we record the final result to the same number of figures as given in the data.

The P.E. of the result is recorded to only one or two significant figures—just enough to extend to the last figure of the mean. Slide-rule accuracy is therefore amply sufficient in the computation of probable errors.

In finding the residuals we use only as many figures in the mean as are given in the individual measurements.

*Example* 2. The following measurements were made to determine a certain wave-length. Find the most probable wave-length and its P.E.

*Solution.* Here we first find the mean and then the residuals as before. The rounded mean is correct to its last figure as given, but since the last digit is slightly less than 5 the mean when rounded to three decimals is 4.505. From this number we subtract the individual measurements to find the residuals.

| $n$ | $M$ | $v$ | $v^2$ |
|---|---|---|---|
| 1 | 4.524 | −0.019 | 0.000361 |
| 2 | 4.500 | +0.005 | 0.000025 |
| 3 | 4.515 | −0.010 | 0.000100 |
| 4 | 4.508 | −0.003 | 0.000009 |
| 5 | 4.513 | −0.008 | 0.000064 |
| 6 | 4.511 | −0.006 | 0.000036 |
| 7 | 4.497 | +0.008 | 0.000064 |
| 8 | 4.507 | −0.002 | 0.000004 |
| 9 | 4.501 | +0.004 | 0.000016 |
| 10 | 4.502 | +0.003 | 0.000009 |
| 11 | 4.485 | +0.020 | 0.000400 |
| 12 | 4.519 | −0.014 | 0.000196 |
| 13 | 4.517 | −0.012 | 0.000144 |
| 14 | 4.504 | +0.001 | 0.000001 |
| 15 | 4.493 | +0.012 | 0.000144 |
| 16 | 4.492 | +0.013 | 0.000169 |
| 17 | 4.505 | 0.000 | 0.000000 |
| | $M_0 = 4.5055$ | $\sum V = -0.008$ | $\sum v^2 = 0.001742$ |

$$r_0 = 0.6745 \sqrt{\frac{0.001742}{17 \times 16}} = 0.0017, \text{ by } (105:5).$$

$$\therefore \quad \underline{M = 4.5055 \pm 0.0017.}$$

*Remark.* Theoretically the algebraic sum of the residuals should be zero, but this result is based on the assumption that these residuals are *algebraic* numbers. The residuals in any actual problem are necessarily *rounded* numbers, and their algebraic sum is rarely zero.

*Example* 3. Six measurements of the parallax of a star are given in the following table. Find the most probable value of the parallax and its P.E.

| $M$ | $w$ | $wM$ | $v$ | $v^2$ | $wv^2$ |
|---|---|---|---|---|---|
| $0''.507$ | 8 | 4.056 | $-0.104$ | 0.010816 | 0.086528 |
| $0''.438$ | 5 | 2.190 | $-0.035$ | 0.001225 | 0.006125 |
| $0''.381$ | 2 | 0.762 | 0.022 | 0.000484 | 0.000968 |
| $0''.371$ | 8 | 2.968 | 0.032 | 0.001024 | 0.008192 |
| $0''.350$ | 13 | 4.550 | 0.053 | 0.002809 | 0.036517 |
| $0''.402$ | 20 | 8.040 | 0.001 | 0.000001 | 0.000020 |
| | $\sum w = 56$ | $\sum wM$ $= 22.566$ | | | $\sum wv^2 = 0.13835$ |

$$M_0 = \frac{22.566}{56} = 0''.403.$$

$$r_0 = 0.6745 \sqrt{\frac{0.13835}{5 \times 56}} = 0.015.$$

Hence the final result is

$$\underline{M = 0''.403 \pm 0''.015.}$$

Here the P.E. of the weighted mean is so large (relatively) that we are not justified in recording the result to more figures than are given in the data.

*Example* 4. Seven separate determinations of the difference of longitude between two places gave the following results. Find the most probable value of the longitude difference and its P.E.

| 1 | $19^m\ 1^s.42 \pm 0^s.044$ |
|---|---|
| 2 | $19\quad 1.37 \pm 0.037$ |
| 3 | $19\quad 1.38 \pm 0.036$ |
| 4 | $19\quad 1.45 \pm 0.036$ |
| 5 | $19\quad 1.60 \pm 0.046$ |
| 6 | $19\quad 1.55 \pm 0.045$ |
| 7 | $19\quad 1.57 \pm 0.047$ |

*Solution.* The first step in the solution of this problem is to find the weights of the different determinations from their given probable errors. From Art. 104 we have

$$\frac{1}{r_1^2 w_1} = \frac{1}{r_2^2 w_2} = \cdots = \frac{1}{r_7^2 w_7} = \frac{1}{c}, \text{ say.}$$

Hence

$$r_1^2 w_1 = r_2^2 w_2 = \cdots = r_7^2 w_7 = c.$$

Let us take the weight of the last determination as unity, that is, let us put

$$w_7 = 1.$$

Then
$$c = r_7^2 = (0.047)^2.$$
Hence

$$w_1 = \frac{c}{r_1^2} = \left(\frac{0.047}{0.044}\right)^2 = \left(\frac{47}{44}\right)^2 = 1.14,$$

$$w_2 = \frac{c}{r_2^2} = \left(\frac{0.047}{0.037}\right)^2 = \left(\frac{47}{37}\right)^2 = 1.61.$$

In like manner we find

$$w_3 = 1.70, \quad w_4 = 1.70, \quad w_5 = 1.04, \quad w_6 = 1.09.$$

To save labor in the computation of the weighted mean let us denote by $d_1, d_2, \cdots d_7$ the differences between the various determinations and an assumed approximate value of the weighted mean, say $19^m1^s.40$. Then the various determinations are $19^m1^s.40 + d_1$, $19^m1^s.40 + d_2$, etc.; and their weighted mean is

$$
\begin{aligned}
M_0 &= \frac{(19^m1^s.40 + d_1)w_1 + (19^m1^s.40 + d_2)w_2 + \cdots + (19^m1^s.40 + d_7)w_7}{w_1 + w_2 + \cdots + w_7} \\[2mm]
&= \frac{(w_1 + w_2 + \cdots + w_7)(19^m1^s.40) + w_1d_1 + w_2d_2 + \cdots + w_7d_7}{w_1 + w_2 + \cdots + w_7} \\[2mm]
&= 19^m1^s.40 + \frac{w_1d_1 + w_2d_2 + \cdots + w_7d_7}{w_1 + w_2 + \cdots + w_7}.
\end{aligned}
$$

This equation shows that it is necessary to multiply only the $d$'s by the weights. We therefore complete the solution by making out the table shown below and then using (104:5).

| $M$ | $d$ | $w$ | $wd$ |
|---|---|---|---|
| $19^m1^s.42$ | 0.02 | 1.14 | 0.023 |
| 19 1 .37 | −0.03 | 1.61 | −0.048 |
| 19 1 .38 | −0.02 | 1.70 | −0.034 |
| 19 1 .45 | 0.05 | 1.70 | 0.085 |
| 19 1 .60 | 0.20 | 1.04 | 0.208 |
| 19 1 .55 | 0.15 | 1.09 | 0.164 |
| 19 1 .57 | 0.17 | 1.00 | 0.170 |
| | | $\sum w = 9.28$ | $\sum wd = 0.568$ |

Hence

$$M_0 = 19^m1^s.40 + \frac{0.568}{9.28} = 19^m1^s.40 + 0.061 = 19^m1^s.461.$$

Then since the weight of $M_7$ is assumed to be 1, we substitute the value of $r_7$ in the formula (104: 5) and get

$$r_0 = \frac{0.047}{\sqrt{9.28}} = 0^s.015.$$

$$\therefore \quad \underline{M = 19^m1^s.461 \pm 0^s.015.}$$

*Note.* The reader is reminded that the expression $M = M_0 \pm r$ *does not* mean that the true value of $M$ is somewhere between $M_0 + r$ and $M_0 - r$; nor does it mean that $M$ is probably in error by the amount $r$. It means that, so far as accidental errors are concerned, the true value of $M$ is just as likely to lie between $M_0 + r$ and $M_0 - r$ as it is to lie outside of these limits.

## II. INDIRECT MEASUREMENTS

**107. The Probable Error of any Function of Independent Quantities whose P. E.'s are known.**

Let

(107: 1) $$Q = f(q_1, q_2, q_3, \cdots q_n)$$

represent any function of directly measured quantities $q_1, q_2, \cdots q_n$. Then errors $\Delta q_1, \Delta q_2, \cdots \Delta q_n$ in the $q$'s will cause an error $\Delta Q$ in the function $Q$, so that

$$Q + \Delta Q = f(q_1 + \Delta q_1, \ q_2 + \Delta q_2, \cdots q_n + \Delta q_n).$$

Expanding the right-hand member by Taylor's theorem and proceeding exactly as in Art. 5, we get

(107: 2) $$\Delta Q = \frac{\partial Q}{\partial q_1} \Delta q_1 + \frac{\partial Q}{\partial q_2} \Delta q_2 + \cdots + \frac{\partial Q}{\partial q_n} \Delta q_n.$$

This expression for $\Delta Q$ holds for any kind of errors whatever. If $\Delta q_1, \Delta q_2, \cdots \Delta q_n$ are *accidental* errors, so that they obey the Normal Law of error, then $\Delta Q$ is likewise an accidental error which obeys the Normal Law, as proved in Art. 90. In this case equation (107:2) is exactly like equation (90:2), and all the results of that article apply to it. Hence if $H, h_1, h_2, \cdots h_n$ denote the precision indices of $Q_1, q_1, q_2, \cdots q_n$, respectively, we have from (90:16)

$$(107:3) \quad \frac{1}{H^2} = \frac{\left(\frac{\partial Q}{\partial q_1}\right)^2}{h_1^2} + \frac{\left(\frac{\partial Q}{\partial q_2}\right)^2}{h_2^2} + \frac{\left(\frac{\partial Q}{\partial q_3}\right)^2}{h_3^2} + \cdots + \frac{\left(\frac{\partial Q}{\partial q_n}\right)^2}{h_n^2}.$$

Let us denote the probable errors of $Q$, $q_1$, $q_2$, $\cdots q_n$ by $R$, $r_1$, $r_2$, $\cdots$ $r_n$, respectively. Then from the relation $\rho = hr$ found in Art. 101 we have

$$\frac{1}{H^2} = \frac{R^2}{\rho^2}, \quad \frac{1}{h_1^2} = \frac{r_1^2}{\rho^2}, \quad \frac{1}{h_2^2} = \frac{r_2^2}{\rho^2}, \quad \cdots \quad \frac{1}{h_n^2} = \frac{r_n^2}{\rho^2}, \text{ where } \rho = 0.4769.$$

Substituting these values of $1/H^2$, $1/h_1^2$, etc. in (107:3) and reducing, we get

$$(107:4) \quad R = \sqrt{\left(\frac{\partial Q}{\partial q_1}\right)^2 r_1^2 + \left(\frac{\partial Q}{\partial q_2}\right)^2 r_2^2 + \cdots + \left(\frac{\partial Q}{\partial q_n}\right)^2 r_n^2}.$$

This formula is of *great importance*, for it includes all possible cases of a function of directly measured quantities. It expresses the law of the *propagation of errors* and is the foundation of the whole subject of indirect measurements.

The terms relative error and percentage error may also be applied to probable errors. The fundamental formula for the relative error in indirect measurements is obtained by dividing (107:4) throughout by $Q$. We then have

$$(107:5) \quad \frac{R}{Q} = \sqrt{\left(\frac{\partial Q}{\partial q_1}\right)^2 \frac{r_1^2}{Q^2} + \left(\frac{\partial Q}{\partial q_2}\right)^2 \frac{r_2^2}{Q^2} + \cdots + \left(\frac{\partial Q}{\partial q_n}\right)^2 \frac{r_n^2}{Q^2}}$$

for the probable relative error. The probable percentage error is 100 times this.

Formula (107:5) assumes a very simple form when $Q$ happens to be a product of several functions or a logarithm of a single function. Suppose, for instance, that

$$(107:6) \qquad\qquad Q = K x^m y^n z^p.$$

Then

$$\frac{\partial Q}{\partial x} = \frac{Qm}{x}, \quad \frac{\partial Q}{\partial y} = \frac{Qn}{y}, \quad \frac{\partial Q}{\partial z} = \frac{Qp}{z};$$

and when these are substituted in (107:5) we get

$$(107:7) \qquad \frac{R}{Q} = \sqrt{m^2 \left(\frac{r_1}{x}\right)^2 + n^2 \left(\frac{r_2}{y}\right)^2 + p^2 \left(\frac{r_3}{z}\right)^2}$$

for the probable relative error of $Q$.

It is worth while to notice here that the P.E. of the weighted mean of several sets of measurements whose P.E.'s are given (Art. 106) can be found by the methods of the present article; for the weighted mean may be written in the form

$$M_0 = \frac{w_1}{\sum w}M_1 + \frac{w_2}{\sum w}M_2 + \cdots + \frac{w_n}{\sum w}M_n,$$

which is a linear function of the $M$'s. Hence on substituting in (107:4) the partial derivatives $\partial M_0/\partial M_1 = w_1/\Sigma w$, $\partial M_0/\partial M_2 = w_2/\Sigma w$, etc., we get

$$(107:8) \quad R = \sqrt{\frac{w_1^2}{(\sum w)^2}r_1^2 + \frac{w_2^2}{(\sum w)^2}r_2^2 + \cdots + \frac{w_n^2}{(\sum w)^2}r_n^2}.$$

But since $r_1^2 = c/w_1$, $r_2^2 = c/w_2$, etc., we have

$$R = \sqrt{\frac{w_1^2}{(\sum w)^2}\frac{c}{w_1} + \frac{w_2^2}{(\sum w)^2}\frac{c}{w_2} + \cdots + \frac{w_n^2}{(\sum w)^2}\frac{c}{w_n}}$$

$$= \frac{\sqrt{c}}{\sum w}\sqrt{w_1 + w_2 + \cdots + w_n} = \frac{\sqrt{c}}{\sum w}\sqrt{\sum w} = \frac{\sqrt{c}}{\sqrt{\sum w}}.$$

Now if we take $w_i = 1$ $(i = 1, 2, \cdots n)$, we get $\sqrt{c} = r_i$ and therefore

$$R = \frac{r_i}{\sqrt{\sum w}},$$

which is formula (104:5).

On putting $w_1 = w_2 = \cdots = w_n$ we get $r_1 = r_2 = \cdots = r_n$, by (104:2). Then (107:8) reduces to

$$R = \frac{r}{\sqrt{n}},$$

which is formula (104:3).

## 108. The Two Fundamental Problems of Indirect Measurements.

The two main problems of indirect measurements are the following:

1. Given the P.E.'s of a number of directly measured quantities, to find the P.E. of any function of these quantities.

2. Given a prescribed P.E. of the function to find the allowable P.E.'s of the directly measured quantities.

The first of these problems is solved by substituting the data directly in formula (107:4) or (107:5), according as the given P.E.'s are absolute or relative.

The second problem is mathematically indeterminate when the number of directly observed quantities is greater than one. For a function of a single quantity, say

$$Q = f(x),$$

we have by (107:4)

$$R = \sqrt{\left(\frac{\partial Q}{\partial x}\right)^2 r_1^2} = \frac{\partial Q}{\partial x} r_1, \text{ or } r_1 = \frac{R}{\dfrac{\partial Q}{\partial x}}.$$

*108a). The Method of Equal Effects.* If, on the other hand, $Q$ is a function of several directly measured quantities, we obtain the definite solution by using the *method of equal effects*, as explained in Art. 8. This method assumes that all the components (directly measured independent quantities) contribute the same amount to the resultant error in $Q$. Under these conditions all the terms under the radical in (107: 4) are equal to one another, so that

$$R = \sqrt{n\left(\frac{\partial Q}{\partial q_1}\right)^2 r_1^2} = \sqrt{n}\frac{\partial Q}{\partial q_1}r_1 = \sqrt{n}\frac{\partial Q}{\partial q_2}r_2 = \cdots = \sqrt{n}\frac{\partial Q}{\partial q_n}r_n.$$

Hence

(108: 1)     $$r_1 = \frac{R}{\sqrt{n}\dfrac{\partial Q}{\partial q_1}}, \quad r_2 = \frac{R}{\sqrt{n}\dfrac{\partial Q}{\partial q_2}}, \cdots r_n = \frac{R}{\sqrt{n}\dfrac{\partial Q}{\partial q_n}}.$$

In some problems the P.E.'s of some of the components are so small in comparison with the others that we may neglect them entirely when applying the method of equal effects, thereby simplifying the problem. Thus, if we wished to find the local time at any place on the earth's surface, we could compute it from the formula

$$\cos t = \frac{\sin h}{\cos L \cos d} - \tan L \tan d$$

as soon as we knew the altitude ($h$) and declination ($d$) of a heavenly body and the latitude ($L$) of the place. The declination can be found from the *Nautical Almanac* to a hundredth part of a second of arc, but the altitude and latitude have to be measured at the place where the local time is wanted. If these are measured with a sextant or an engineers' transit, they can not be measured much closer than to the nearest *minute* of arc. Hence the declination is known so much more accurately than the altitude and latitude can be measured that we may treat the declination as free from error, so that the error in $t$ will be due entirely to the errors in $h$ and $L$. If, therefore, we desired the local time to the nearest second, we would treat $t$ as a function of $h$ and $L$ alone, take $n = 2$, and find the allowable P.E.'s of $h$ and $L$ by means of formulas (108:1).

To find out whether the error in any particular component has a negligible effect in producing an error in the function $Q$ we apply the following criterion:

*108b). Criterion for Negligible Effects:* If any component $q_k$ has a negligible effect in causing an error in $Q$, then we must have*

$$(108: 2) \qquad \frac{\partial Q}{\partial q_k} r_k \leqq \frac{1}{3} R,$$

where $R$ is the stipulated P.E. of $Q$. If several components $q_1, q_2, \cdots q_m$ should each satisfy (108:2), they may all be neglected provided

$$(108: 3) \quad \sqrt{\left(\frac{\partial Q}{\partial q_1}\right)^2 r_1^2 + \left(\frac{\partial Q}{\partial q_2}\right)^2 r_2^2 + \cdots + \left(\frac{\partial Q}{\partial q_m}\right)^2 r_m^2} \leqq \frac{1}{3} R.$$

When applying the criteria (108:2) and (108:3) to any particular problem, we are supposed to know in advance the size of the P.E.'s of the components we contemplate neglecting, as in the case of the declination $d$ in the astronomical problem mentioned above. If we know nothing concerning the size of the P.E.'s whose effect we contemplate neglecting, then the best we can do is to apply the method of equal effects to the terms under the radical in (108:3), thereby obtaining

$$\sqrt{m\left(\frac{\partial Q}{\partial q_1}\right)^2 r_1^2} = \sqrt{m}\frac{\partial Q}{\partial q_1} r_1 = \sqrt{m}\frac{\partial Q}{\partial q_2} r_2 = \sqrt{m}\frac{\partial Q}{\partial q_m} r_m \leqq \frac{1}{3} R,$$

from which

$$r_1 \leqq \frac{R}{3\sqrt{m}\dfrac{\partial Q}{\partial q_1}}, \quad r_2 \leqq \frac{R}{3\sqrt{m}\dfrac{\partial Q}{\partial q_2}}, \quad \cdots \ r_m \leqq \frac{R}{3\sqrt{m}\dfrac{\partial Q}{\partial q_m}}.$$

We may therefore neglect the effect of $m$ components $q_1, q_2, \cdots q_m$ if each satisfies the condition

$$(108: 4) \qquad r_k \leqq \frac{R}{3\sqrt{m}\dfrac{\partial Q}{\partial q_k}}, \qquad (k = 1, 2, 3, \cdots m).$$

* See Palmer's *Theory of Measurements*, p. 151.

The proofs of criteria (108:2) and (108:3) are simple and easy, but they will not be given here.*

We shall now apply the preceding formulas to some examples.

*Example* 1. From the simple pendulum formula

$$T = \pi \sqrt{\frac{l}{g}}$$

we get

$$g = \frac{\pi^2 l}{T^2} = f(l, T).$$

If $l = 100$ cm. and $T = 1$ sec., find the error in $g$ due to errors of 0.10 cm. in $l$ and 0.0020 sec. in $T$, respectively.

*Solution.* Differentiating $g$ with respect to $l$ and $T$ separately, we have

$$\frac{\partial g}{\partial l} = \frac{\pi^2}{T^2}, \quad \frac{\partial g}{\partial T} = -\frac{2\pi^2 l}{T^3}.$$

From this point onward we proceed in one of two ways, depending on the meaning of the errors in $l$ and $T$.

(a) If the errors in $l$ and $T$ are actual, definite errors of the magnitudes given, then we compute the error in $g$ by the formula

$$\Delta g = \frac{\partial g}{\partial l} \Delta l + \frac{\partial g}{\partial T} \Delta T. \qquad \text{[See (5:4)]}$$

Hence

$$\Delta g = \frac{\pi^2}{T^2} \Delta l - \frac{2\pi^2 l}{T^3} \Delta T$$

$$= 9.8696(0.10 + 200 \times 0.002) = 4.935 \text{ cm./sec.}^2 = \underline{4.9}, \text{ say.}$$

Since we do not know the signs of $\Delta T$ and $\Delta l$, we disregard the negative sign on the right and take the arithmetic sum of the terms. This gives the maximum numerical value of $\Delta g$.

(b) If the given values of $l$ and $T$ are the means of several measurements and their given errors are the P.E.'s of these arithmetic means, then we compute the P.E. of $g$ by formula (107:4). Hence we have

$$R = \sqrt{\frac{\pi^4}{T^4}(\Delta l)^2 + \frac{4\pi^4}{T^6}l^2(\Delta T)^2} = 9.8696\sqrt{0.01 + 0.16}$$

$$= 9.8696 \times 0.4123 = 4.068 \text{ cm./sec.}^2 = \underline{4.1}, \text{ say.}$$

* See Palmer's *Theory of Measurements*, p. 151.

To find the relative and percentage errors under the two suppositions (a) and (b), we have

(a)     Relative error $= \dfrac{\Delta g}{g} = \dfrac{\Delta l}{l} + 2\dfrac{\Delta T}{T} = \dfrac{0.1}{100} + \dfrac{2(0.002)}{1}$

$= 0.001 + 0.004 = \underline{0.005}.$

Percentage error $= 100 \ (\Delta g/g) = 100 \times 0.005 = \underline{0.5}$ per cent.

(b) Since we are here dealing with a product of several quantities, we use formula (107:7). Hence

$$\dfrac{R}{g} = \sqrt{\left(\dfrac{\Delta l}{l}\right)^2 + 4\left(\dfrac{\Delta T}{T}\right)^2} = \sqrt{(0.001)^2 + 4(0.002)^2}$$

$= 0.00412 = \underline{0.004}$, say.

Percentage P.E. $= 100 \ (R/g) = 100 \times 0.004 = \underline{0.4}$ per cent.

*Example* 2.  Two sides and the included angle of a triangle were measured with the following results:

$$a = 252.52 \pm 0.06 \text{ feet},$$
$$b = 300.01 \pm 0.06 \text{ feet},$$
$$C = 42°13'00'' \pm 30''.$$

Find the area of the triangle and its P.E.

*Solution.* The formula for the area is

$$A = \tfrac{1}{2}ab \sin C.$$

Hence

$$\dfrac{\partial A}{\partial a} = \dfrac{b \sin C}{2}, \quad \dfrac{\partial A}{\partial b} = \dfrac{a \sin C}{2}, \quad \dfrac{\partial A}{\partial C} = \dfrac{ab \cos C}{2}.$$

Since the errors given in this problem are the probable errors of the given measurements, we should use formula (107:4). The use of that formula in this example, however, would call for a considerable amount of numerical work. To avoid this we calculate the relative error by formula (107:5) and then get the P.E. from the relative error. Hence we have (107:5)

$$\dfrac{R}{A} = \sqrt{\left(\dfrac{\Delta a}{a}\right)^2 + \left(\dfrac{\Delta b}{b}\right)^2 + (\Delta C \cot C)^2}.$$

The error in $C$ must be expressed in radians. Hence

$$\Delta C = 30 \times \dfrac{\pi}{180} \times \dfrac{1}{3600} = 0.0001454.$$

Also cot $C =$ cot $42°\ 13' = 1.1022$.

$$\therefore\quad \frac{R}{A} = \sqrt{\left(\frac{0.06}{252.52}\right)^2 + \left(\frac{0.06}{300.01}\right)^2 + (0.0001454 \times 1.1022)^2}$$

$$= 0.00035.$$

The area is

$$A = \frac{252.52 \times 300.01 \times \sin 42°13'}{2} = 25452 \text{ sq. ft.}$$

$$\therefore\quad R = 0.00035 \times A = 0.00035 \times 25452 = 8.9 = 9, \text{ say.}$$

The required result is therefore

$$\underline{A = 25452 \pm 9 \text{ sq. ft.}}$$

*Example* 3. The distance between two inaccessible points $A$ and $B$ is desired to $\pm 0.1$ foot. The required distance can not be measured directly but must be calculated from the measurements of $CA$, $CB$, and $\angle ACB$. If $a$, $b$, and $\theta$ (see Fig. 20) are approximately equal to 200 ft., 150 ft., and 45°, respectively, find the allowable errors in these directly measured quantities.

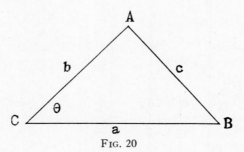

Fig. 20

*Solution.* Here

$$c = \sqrt{a^2 + b^2 - 2ab\ \cos\theta},$$

and

$$R = 0.1.$$

The best way to solve this problem is by the method of equal effects, and we therefore use formulas (108:1). Differentiating $c$ with respect to $a$, $b$, and $\theta$ in turn, we have

$$\frac{\partial c}{\partial a} = \frac{a - b\ \cos\theta}{c}, \quad \frac{\partial c}{\partial b} = \frac{b - a\ \cos\theta}{c}, \quad \frac{\partial c}{\partial \theta} = \frac{ab\ \sin\theta}{c}.$$

But $c = \sqrt{40000 + 22500 - 30000\sqrt{2}} = 141.7$.

$$\therefore \quad \frac{\partial c}{\partial a} = \frac{200 - 75\sqrt{2}}{141.7} = \frac{93.93}{141.7} = 0.66,$$

$$\frac{\partial c}{\partial b} = \frac{150 - 100\sqrt{2}}{141.7} = \frac{8.58}{141.7} = 0.060,$$

$$\frac{\partial c}{\partial \theta} = \frac{200 \times 150 \times \dfrac{\sqrt{2}}{2}}{141.7} = \frac{21213}{141.7} = 149.7;$$

and $n = 3$.

Then by (108:1) we have

$$r_a = \frac{0.1}{\sqrt{3}\dfrac{\partial c}{\partial a}} = \frac{0.1}{\sqrt{3} \times 0.66} = \frac{0.1732}{1.98} = 0.087 = \underline{0.09 \text{ ft.}}$$

$$r_b = \frac{0.1}{\sqrt{3} \times 0.06} = \frac{0.1732}{0.18} = \underline{0.96 \text{ ft.}}$$

$$r_\theta = \frac{0.1}{\sqrt{3} \times 149.7} = \frac{0.1732}{449.1} = 0.000386 \text{ rad.} = \underline{1'20''.}$$

The large allowable error in $b$ is due to the fact that $b$ is nearly perpendicular to $c$, so that a considerable change in the former has little effect on the latter.

*Example 4.* The modulus of elasticity of a beam of length $l$, breadth $b$, and depth $d$, supported at the ends and loaded at the center by a weight $W$, is given by the formula

$$E = \frac{Wl^3}{4ab\,d^3},$$

where $a$ is the deflection produced at the center. If it is desired to measure $E$ to 1 per cent, and the error in $W$ may be neglected, compute the allowable errors in $a$, $b$, $d$, and $l$.

*Solution.* The formula for $E$ may be written

$$E = \tfrac{1}{4}Wl^3 a^{-1}b^{-1}d^{-3}.$$

This is of the form (107:6), where $K = W/4$. Then since $R/E = 1\%$ $= 0.01$, we have from 107:7)

$$0.01 = \sqrt{9\left(\frac{\Delta l}{l}\right)^2 + \left(\frac{\Delta a}{a}\right)^2 + \left(\frac{\Delta b}{b}\right)^2 + 9\left(\frac{\Delta d}{d}\right)^2}.$$

Now using the method of equal effects, we have

$$\sqrt{4 \times 9\left(\frac{\Delta l}{l}\right)^2} = 0.01, \quad \text{or} \quad 6\left(\frac{\Delta l}{l}\right) = 0.01.$$

$$\therefore \quad \frac{\Delta l}{l} = \frac{0.01}{6}, \quad \text{and} \quad 100\frac{\Delta l}{l} = \frac{1}{6} = \underline{0.167} \text{ per cent.}$$

$$\sqrt{4\left(\frac{\Delta a}{a}\right)^2} = 0.01, \quad \text{or} \quad \frac{\Delta a}{a} = 0.005.$$

$$\therefore \quad 100\frac{\Delta a}{a} = \underline{0.5} \text{ per cent.}$$

Likewise,

$$100\frac{\Delta b}{b} = \underline{0.5} \text{ per cent.}$$

$$100\frac{\Delta d}{d} = \frac{1}{6} = \underline{0.167} \text{ per cent.}$$

Hence if the percentage P.E. of $E$ is to be 1 per cent, the percentage P.E.'s of $a$, $b$, $d$, $l$, must not exceed $\frac{1}{2}$, $\frac{1}{2}$, $\frac{1}{6}$, $\frac{1}{6}$ of one per cent, respectively.

**109. Rejection of Observations and Measurements.** Occasionally some individual measurement may differ so widely from the others of the same set that we may suspect the discrepancy to be due to a mistake. In such a case it may be well to reject this measurement entirely. To decide what to do about it we apply the following rule:

*Find the mean of all the measurements (including the "wild" one) and find the residual for each. Compute the P.E. of a single measurement by formula (105:4). Reject any measurement whose residual exceeds 5 times the P.E. of a single measurement.*

This rule rests on the following considerations:

Suppose the chance of an error of magnitude $x$ is 1 in 1000. Then its probability is $p = 1/1000 = 0.001$. The chance that an error of this size will *not* occur is therefore $1 - 0.001 = 0.999$. From the probability table we find the corresponding $hx$ to be 2.326.

Now from Art. 101 we have

$$hr = \rho = 0.4769,$$

from which

$$h = \frac{0.4769}{r}.$$

Hence

$$hx = \frac{0.4769}{r}x = 2.326.$$

$$\therefore \quad x = \frac{2.326}{0.4769}r = 4.9r,$$

to two figures.

The chance of making an error as great as five times the P.E. of a single measurement is therefore less than one in a thousand. An error of such a magnitude is therefore so improbable that we may safely neglect it.

*Example.* A quantity $M$ was measured with the results given below. Should any of the measurements be rejected?

$M = 236, 251, 249, 252, 248, 254, 246, 257, 243, 274.$

*Solution.* The average of these measurements is

$$M_0 = 251.$$

Hence the residuals are

$$v_1 = + 15, \ v_2 = 0, \ v_3 = + 2, \ v_4 = - 1, \ v_5 = + 3, \ v_6 = - 3, \ v_7 = + 5,$$
$$v_8 = - 6, \ v_9 = + 8, \ v_{10} = - 23.$$

The P.E. of a single measurement is

$$r = 0.6745\sqrt{\frac{225 + 4 + 1 + 9 + 9 + 25 + 36 + 64 + 529}{9}}$$

$$= 0.6745 \times 10.01 = 6.75.$$

Five times this P.E. is 33.75, and since all the residuals are less than this we retain all the measurements.

## EXAMPLES ON CHAPTER XV

### I.  DIRECT MEASUREMENTS

1. Ten measurements of equal precision were made to determine the density of a body, the results of the measurements being as follows: 9.662, 9.673, 9.664, 9.659, 9.677, 9.662, 9.663, 9.680, 9.645, 9.654. Find the probable error of a single measurement, the most probable value of the density, and its P.E.

2. Twelve measurements of an angle in a primary triangulation gave

the following results.   Find the P.E. of a single measurement, the most probable value of the angle, and its P.E.

| | |
|---|---|
| 116 43′ 44″.45 | 116 43′ 51″.75 |
| 50 .95 | 52 .35 |
| 49 .20 | 51 .05 |
| 47 .40 | 49 .05 |
| 51 .05 | 49 .25 |
| 50 .60 | 49 .25 |

3. Ten measurements of the coefficient of expansion of dry air gave the following results.  Find the most probable value of the coefficient and its P.E.

| | |
|---|---|
| $3.643 \times 10^{-3}$ | $3.636 \times 10^{-3}$ |
| 54 | 51 |
| 44 | 43 |
| 50 | 43 |
| 53 | 45 |

4. A certain coefficient of expansion was measured with different apparatus with the following results.  Find the best value for the coefficient and its P.E.

| Measurement | Weight | Measurement | Weight |
|---|---|---|---|
| 0.0045 | 3 | 0.0036 | 2 |
| 0.0039 | 2 | 0.0026 | 2 |
| 0.0034 | 5 | 0.0027 | 1 |
| 0.0030 | 4 | 0.0043 | 3 |

5. An angle was measured several times with a transit and then several times with a theodolite, with the following results:

Transit.........................36° 41′ 28″±11″
Theodolite....................36° 41′ 23″.8±2″.7

Find the most probable value of the angle and its P.E.

6. Six determinations of the velocity of light by different observers at different times gave the following results, with their probable errors:

$$298000 \pm 1000$$
$$298500 \pm 1000$$
$$299930 \pm \ 100$$
$$299990 \pm \ 200$$
$$300100 \pm 1000$$
$$299944 \pm \ \ 50$$

Find the most probable value obtainable from these determinations and its P.E.

7. Find the best value of the atomic weight of silver and its P.E. from the following determinations:

$$107.9401 \pm 0.0058$$
$$107.9406 \pm 0.0049$$
$$107.9233 \pm 0.0140$$
$$107.9371 \pm 0.0045$$
$$107.9270 \pm 0.0090$$

## II.  INDIRECT MEASUREMENTS

8. The side $b$ and the angles $B$ and $C$ of a plane triangle were measured with the following results:

$$b = 106 \pm 0.06 \text{ ft.}, \ B = 28°36' \pm 1', \ C = 120°12' \pm 1'.5.$$

Find the angle $A$, the side $a$, and their P.E.'s.

9. Two sides $a$ and $b$ and the included angle $C$ of a town lot were measured to be

$$a = 104.86 \pm 0.02 \text{ ft.}, \ b = 214.24 \pm 0.03 \text{ ft.},$$
$$C = 47°13' \pm 1'.$$

Find the side $c$ and its absolute and percentage error.

10. The index of refraction of prism is given by the formula

$$n = \frac{\sin \frac{1}{2}(a + D)}{\sin \frac{1}{2}a}.$$

If $D = 28°34' \pm 0'.5$ and $a = 62°48' \pm 0'.7$, find $n$ and its P.E.

11. The current in a tangent galvanometer is given by the formula

$$I = K \tan \theta.$$

Find $I$ and its P.E. when $K = 1.963 \pm 0.002$ and $\theta = 35° \pm 0°.1$.

12. The volume of a right circular cylinder is given by the formula

$$V = \frac{\pi}{4} d^2 h.$$

Find $V$ and its P.E. when $h = 116.85 \pm 0.28$ mm. and $d = 82.54 \pm 0.28$ mm.

13. How accurately should the length and time of vibration of a seconds pendulum be measured in order that the computed value of $g$ may be reliable to 0.05 per cent?

14. If in the formula

$$R = \frac{r^2}{2h} + \frac{h}{2}$$

the percentage error in $R$ is not to exceed 0.3%, find the allowable percentage errors in $r$ and $h$ when $r = 48$ mm. and $h = 56$ mm.

15. When the index of refraction of a liquid is determined by means of a refractometer, the index $n$ is given by the formula

$$n = \sqrt{N^2 - \sin^2 \theta}.$$

If $N = 1.62200 \pm 0.00004$ and $\theta = 38°$ approximately, find $\Delta\theta$ in order that $n$ may be reliable to 0.02 per cent.

16. The diameter of a rod was measured several times with the following results:

1.034, 1.031, 1.029, 1.032, 1.034, 1.030, 1.034, 1.033, 1.032, 1.031.

Find the P.E. of a single measurement, the P.E. of the mean, the most probable diameter of the rod, its cross sectional area, and the P.E. of this area.

17. The area of the cross section of a rod is desired to 0.2 per cent. How precisely should the diameter be measured?

18. The diameter of a polished steel rod was measured ten times with the following results:

0.5003, 0.5002, 0.4999, 0.4998, 0.4999, 0.5003, 0.5001, 0.5004, 0.5001,

0.4999.

Find the cross sectional area and its P.E.

19. Explain how you would decide in any given problem whether to use formula (5:4) or formula (107:4). What is the fundamental difference between these two formulas?

# CHAPTER XVI

## EMPIRICAL FORMULAS

**110. Introduction.** An empirical formula, or empirical equation, is one whose *form* is inferred from the results of experiment or observation and in which the *constants* are determined from experimental or observational data. Thus, it is known that the speed of a ship varies with the horse power according to the formula

$$P = a + bV^3.$$

The constants to be determined in this formula are $a$ and $b$, and for the purpose of determining them we should take several sets of readings of the speed and corresponding horse power. These sets of simultaneous values of $V$ and $P$ would, when substituted in the given formula, give several equations in the two unknowns $a$ and $b$. The next thing to be done would be to find the best values for $a$ and $b$ from the several equations. For the solution of this part of the problem three methods are available: the *graphic method* or *method of selected points*, the *method of averages, and the method of Least Squares.* We shall now consider these methods in the order named and illustrate each by several examples.

**111. The Graphic Method or Method of Selected Points.** This method can be used whenever the given formula can be plotted as a straight line either directly or after a suitable transformation. The equation given above, for example, can be reduced to a straight line form by putting $V^3 = t$, thereby reducing the equation to the form

$$P = a + bt,$$

which is the linear in the variables $t$ and $P$.

To apply the graphic method to this problem we plot on coordinate paper the corresponding values of $t(=V^3)$ and $P$. The plotted points should lie nearly on a straight line. We then draw a straight line which will be a good compromise for all the plotted points and pass as near as possible to each of them. The slope of this line will be the value of $b$ and its $P$-intercept will be $a$. If the line happens to pass through two of the plotted points, or through any other two points whose coordinates are easily determined (points at the corners of squares, for instance), we can substitute their coordinates in the given equation and solve the two resulting equations for $a$ and $b$, but the points so used should be as far apart as possible. The drawing of the best representative straight line is a matter of good judgment.

This method will give fairly good results when finely divided coordinate paper is used, but in general it is not recommended except for obtaining approximate values of the constants or in cases where the results obtainable by the method are as accurate as the data used.

*Example* 1. The electrical resistance of a copper wire varies with the temperature according to the equation

$$R = a + bT.$$

For the purpose of determining the constants $a$ and $b$ the measurements of temperature and corresponding resistance given in the following table were made. Find the values of $a$ and $b$.

| $T$ | 19.1 | 25.0 | 30.1 | 36.0 | 40.0 | 45.1 | 50.0 |
|---|---|---|---|---|---|---|---|
| $R$ | 76.30 | 77.80 | 79.75 | 80.80 | 82.35 | 83.90 | 85.10 |

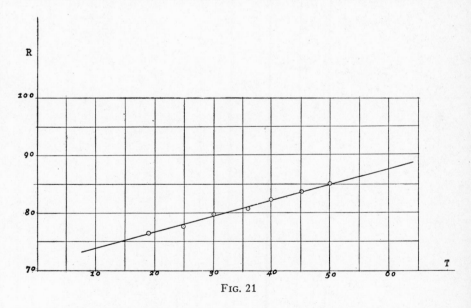

Fig. 21

*Solution.* Plotting these pairs of values and drawing what seems to be a good compromise line (Fig. 21), we find that this line passes through the points (21, 77) and (64, 89). Substituting in the given equation the coordinates of these points, we have

$$a + 21b = 77$$
$$\underline{a + 64b = 89}$$
$$43b = 12 \quad \therefore \quad b = \frac{12}{43} = 0.2790,$$

and

$$a = 77 - 21 \times 0.2790 = 71.14.$$

Hence the required relation between $R$ and $T$ is

$$\underline{R = 71.14 + 0.2790T.}$$

To see how well this formula fits the data in the table we compute the *residuals* of the several measurements. Writing

$$v = 0.2790T + 71.14 - R,$$

we have

$$v_1 = 0.2790 \times 19.1 + 71.14 - 76.30 = 0.15$$
$$v_2 = 0.2790 \times 25.0 + 71.14 - 77.80 = 0.32$$
$$v_3 = -0.21$$
$$v_4 = \quad 0.39$$
$$v_5 = -0.05$$
$$v_6 = -0.19$$
$$v_7 = -0.01$$

$$\therefore \quad \sum v = 0.40, \quad \sum v^2 = 0.36.$$

*Example* 2. The data in the following table fit a formula of the type

(111: 1)                           $$y = ax^n.$$

Find the values of $a$ and $n$ and thence the required formula.

| $x$ | 10 | 20 | 30 | 40 | 50 | 60 | 70 | 80 |
|-----|------|------|------|------|------|------|------|------|
| $y$ | 1.06 | 1.33 | 1.52 | 1.68 | 1.81 | 1.91 | 2.01 | 2.11 |

*Solution.* Taking the logarithm of each side of the given equation, we have

(111: 2) $$\log y = \log a + n \log x.$$

Putting

$$y' = \log y, \quad x' = \log x,$$

we get

$$y' = \log a + nx' = a' + nx',$$

where $a' = \log a$.

This is the equation of a straight line in the new variables $x'$ and $y'$. To plot this line the most conveniently we use logarithmic paper. Plotting the given points on such paper, we find that they lie almost

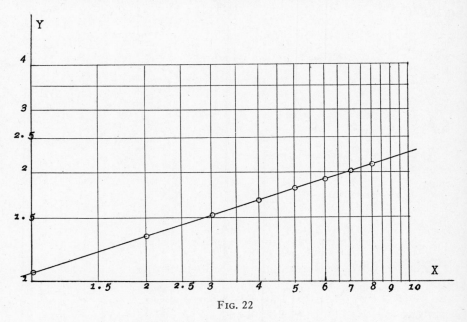

Fig. 22

exactly on a straight line (Fig. 22). Hence we substitute in (111:2) the coordinates of the first and last of the given points and get

$$\log 1.06 = \log a + n,$$

$$\log 2.11 = \log a + n \log 80 ;$$

or

$$n + \log a = 0.0253,$$

$$1.9031n + \log a = 0.3243.$$

$$\therefore \quad \overline{\phantom{0.9031n = }0.9031n = 0.2990,}$$

or
$$n = 0.3311.$$
Also
$$\log a = 0.0253 - n$$
$$= 0.0253 - 0.3311$$
$$= 9.6942 - 10.$$
$$\therefore \quad a = 0.4945.$$

The required formula is therefore

$$y = 0.4945 \, x^{0.3311}.$$

*Example 3.* Find a formula of the form
$$(111:3) \qquad\qquad y = ke^{mx}$$
which will fit the data in the table below.

| $x$ | 1 | 2 | 3 | 4 | 5 | 6 | 7 | 8 |
|---|---|---|---|---|---|---|---|---|
| $y$ | 15.3 | 20.5 | 27.4 | 36.6 | 49.1 | 65.6 | 87.8 | 117.6 |

*Solution.* Taking the common logarithm of each side of the given equation, we have

$$(111:4) \qquad \log y = \log k + mx \log e = \log k + (m \log e)x,$$
or
$$y' = \log k + (m \log e)x, \text{ where } y' = \log y.$$

This is the equation of a straight line in the variables $x$ and $y'$. To plot it we use semilogarithmic paper. Plotting the given values of $x$ and $y$ on semilogarithmic paper, we find that the points lie nearly on a straight line (Fig. 23). Drawing what seems to be a good representative line, we notice that it passes through the points (0.4, 13) and (8.6, 140). Substituting these values in (111:4), we have

$$\log 13 = \log k + 0.43429m(0.4) = \log k + 0.1737m,$$
$$\log 140 = \log k + 0.43429m(8.6) = \log k + 3.7349m.$$

Solving these equations for $m$ and $k$, we get

$$m = 0.2898,$$
$$k = 11.58.$$

The required equation is therefore

$$y = 11.58e^{0 \cdot 2898x}.$$

*Note.* In logarithmic coordinate paper the origin is the point $(1, 1)$. Hence the equations of the axes are $x = 1$, $y = 1$. Putting $x = 1$ in the equation $y = ax^n$, we get $y = a$. Hence *in the straight-line graph of the equation $y = ax^n$ on logarithmic paper the constant $a$ is the y-intercept.*

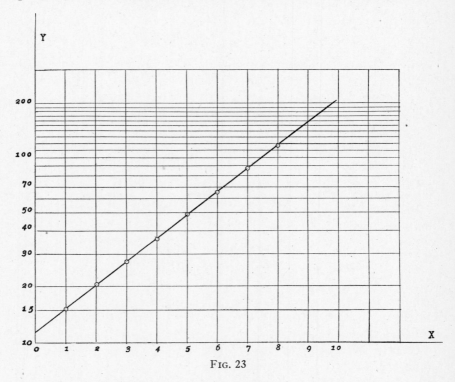

FIG. 23

To find a formula for the exponent $n$ let $(x_1, y_1)$ and $(x_2, y_2)$ be any two pairs of corresponding values of $x$ and $y$. Then from (111:2)

$$\log y_2 = \log a + n \log x_2,$$

$$\log y_1 = \log a + n \log x_1.$$

$$\therefore \quad \log y_2 - \log y_1 = n(\log x_2 - \log x_1),$$

or

(111: 5)
$$n = \frac{\log y_2 - \log y_1}{\log x_2 - \log x_1}.$$

The origin of coordinates in semilogarithmic paper is the point $(0, 1)$. The equation of the $y$-axis is therefore $x = 0$, and that of the $x$-axis is $y = 1$. Putting $x = 0$ in (111:3), we get $y = k$. Hence in the straight-line graph of the equation $y = ke^{mx}$ on semilogarithmic paper the constant $k$ is the $y$-intercept.

To find a formula for the exponent $m$ we substitute in (111:4) two pairs of corresponding values of $x$ and $y$, obtaining the two equations

$$\log y_2 = \log k + (m \log e) x_2,$$

$$\log y_1 = \log k + (m \log e) x_1.$$

$$\therefore \quad \log y_2 - \log y_1 = (x_2 - x_1) m \log e,$$

or

$$(111: 6) \qquad m = \frac{\log y_2 - \log y_1}{(x_2 - x_1) \log e} = 2.3026 \frac{(\log y_2 - \log y_1)}{x_2 - x_1}.$$

If the given points are so plotted that the equations of the axes are not as stated above, the $y$-intercept will *not* be the value of the constant $a$ or $k$. For instance, in Example 2 we plotted the point $(10, 1.06)$ *on the y-axis*. This is really equivalent to making the substitution $x = 10\,x'$, so that the given equation is transformed into the equivalent equation

$$y = a(10x')^n = a \times 10^n x'^n.$$

Putting $x' = 1$, we get $y = a \times 10^n = 0.4945 \times 10^{0.3311} = 1.06$, and this is the actual plotted value of the $y$-intercept. The student should have no difficulty in deciding whether or not the $y$-intercept of the plotted straight line gives the true value of the coefficients $a$ and $k$ in any given example.

**112. The Method of Averages.** The *residuals* of a series of plotted points are the vertical distances of these points from the best representative curve. Some of the residuals will be positive and others negative. The method of averages assumes that the best representative curve is that for which the algebraic sum of the residuals is zero. To find the unknown constants in an empirical formula by this method we first substitute in the given formula the several pairs of observed or measured values of $x$ and $y$. We thus get as many residuals as there are pairs of observed values. Then we divide the residuals, or residual equations, into as many groups as there are constants in the assumed formula. Each group should contain as nearly as possible the same number of residuals. By placing the sum of the residuals in the first group equal to zero we get a single equation in the unknown constants.

Placing the sum of the residuals in the second group equal to zero, we get a second equation in the constants, and so on. Since the sum of the residuals in each group is zero, the sum of all the residuals is necessarily zero. On solving simultaneously the equations obtained from the several groups, we obtain the values of the unknown constants in the original formula. A few examples will make the method clear.

*Example* 1. The data in the following table will fit a formula of the type

$$(1) \qquad\qquad y = a + bx + cx^2.$$

Find the formula.

| $x$ | 87.5 | 84.0 | 77.8 | 63.7 | 46.7 | 36.9 |
|---|---|---|---|---|---|---|
| $y$ | 292 | 283 | 270 | 235 | 197 | 181 |

*Solution.* Substituting in (1) the several pairs of corresponding values of $x$ and $y$, we get

$$
\begin{aligned}
&\text{I} \begin{cases} v_1 = a + 87.5b + 7656c - 292 \\ v_2 = a + 84.0b + 7056c - 283 \end{cases} \\[4pt]
&\text{II} \begin{cases} v_3 = a + 77.8b + 6053c - 270 \\ v_4 = a + 63.7b + 4058c - 235 \end{cases} \quad \begin{array}{l}\text{Residual}\\ \text{equations.}\end{array} \\[4pt]
&\text{III} \begin{cases} v_5 = a + 46.7b + 2181c - 197 \\ v_6 = a + 36.9b + 1362c - 181 \end{cases}
\end{aligned}
$$

Dividing these equations into three groups (since there are three constants to be determined), as indicated by the braces at the left, adding the equations of each group, and placing the sums equal to zero, we get the three equations

$$
\begin{aligned}
2a + 171.5b + 14712c &= 575 \\
2a + 141.5b + 10111c &= 505 \\
2a + \phantom{0}83.6b + \phantom{0}3543c &= 378
\end{aligned}
$$

Solving these three equations simultaneously for $a$, $b$, and $c$, we get

$$a = 111.7,\ b = 1.663,\ c = 0.00437.$$

Hence the required formula is

$$y = 111.7 + 1.663x + 0.00437x^2.$$

This method of averages requires no graph and can be applied to any formula which is *linear* (of the first degree) in the unknown constants or to any formula which is reducible to a form linear in the constants.

*Example* 2. Solve Example 2, Art. 111, by the method of averages.

*Solution.* Strictly speaking, the residuals are, by definition,

$$v_1 = ax_1{}^n - y_1, \quad v_2 = ax_2{}^n - y_2, \text{ etc.}$$

But if we divide these equations into groups, add, and attempt to solve the resulting equations for $a$ and $n$, we get into trouble at once; for the unknown $n$ occurs as an exponent in several terms of a sum.

We can avoid this trouble without much loss in accuracy by proceeding as follows: Instead of equating to zero the sum of the residuals of the $y$'s, we equate to zero the sum of the residuals of the *logarithms* of the $y$'s. For any residual we have from (111:2)

$$v' = \log a + n \log x - \log y.$$

Hence the several residuals are

$$\text{I}\begin{cases} v_1' = \log a + 1.0000n - 0.0253 \\ v_2' = \log a + 1.3010n - 0.1239 \\ v_3' = \log a + 1.4771n - 0.1818 \\ v_4' = \log a + 1.6021n - 0.2253 \end{cases}$$

$$\text{II}\begin{cases} v_5' = \log a + 1.6990n - 0.2577 \\ v_6' = \log a + 1.7782n - 0.2810 \\ v_7' = \log a + 1.8451n - 0.3032 \\ v_8' = \log a + 1.9031n - 0.3243. \end{cases}$$

In actual practice we do not write down these equations in this form, but in the form given below:

$$\log a + 1.0000n = 0.0253 \qquad \log a + 1.6990n = 0.2577$$

$$\log a + 1.3010n = 0.1239 \qquad \log a + 1.7782n = 0.2810$$

$$\log a + 1.4771n = 0.1818 \qquad \log a + 1.8451n = 0.3032$$

$$\underline{\log a + 1.6021n = 0.2253} \qquad \underline{\log a + 1.9031n = 0.3243}$$

(1)  $4 \log a + 5.3802n = 0.5563.$  (2) $4 \log a + 7.2254n = 1.1662.$

Solving (1) and (2) simultaneously, we get

$$n = 0.3305, \log a = -0.3055 = 9.6945 - 10 \therefore a = 0.4949.$$

The required formula is therefore

$$\underline{y = 0.4949x^{0.3305}}.$$

*Note.* The method of averages is the shortest and easiest method for finding the constants in an empirical formula, but it must not be used blindly. The residual equations can be grouped in several ways,* and each different grouping will give different values for the unknown constants, even though the algebraic sum of the residuals be zero in every case. The resulting formulas will thus be different, and some of them will fit the data much better than the others.

There is no way to determine in advance just what grouping will give the best result. As a general rule the best formula is obtained by grouping the residual equations in consecutive order, as was done in Examples 1 and 2. The following example will serve to clear up the matter of grouping.

*Example* 3. Find by the method of averages a formula of the type

$$y = a + bx^3$$

which will fit the following data:

| $x$ | 5 | 7 | 9 | 11 | 12 |
|-----|-----|-----|------|------|------|
| $y$ | 290 | 560 | 1044 | 1810 | 2300 |

* The number of possible groupings is given by the following formulas:

*a) Two groups.* The number of different ways in which $p+q$ different things can be divided into *two* groups of $p$ things and $q$ things, respectively, is

$$\frac{(p+q)!}{p!q!}.$$

*b) Three groups.* The number of different ways in which $p+q+r$ different things can be divided into *three* groups of $p$ things, $q$ things, and $r$ things, respectively, is

$$\frac{(p+q+r)!}{p!q!r!}.$$

*c) Four or more groups.* The number of ways in which we can divide $p+q+r+s$ different things into *four* groups of $p$ things, $q$ things, $r$ things, and $s$ things, respectively, is

$$\frac{(p+q+r+s)!}{p!q!r!s!}.$$

And so on for any other case. For the proof of these formulas see Wentworth's *College Algebra*, pp. 263–264; or Whitworth's *Choice and Chance*, pp. 63–64.

*Solution.*  The residual equations are

$$v_1 = a + \phantom{0}125b - \phantom{00}290$$

$$v_2 = a + \phantom{0}343b - \phantom{00}560$$

$$v_3 = a + \phantom{0}729b - 1044$$

$$v_4 = a + 1331b - 1810$$

$$v_5 = a + 1728b - 2300.$$

The number of possible groupings of these equations is $5!/(3!2!) = 10$. The ten different groupings and the resulting formulas corresponding to them are given below.

1.
$$\begin{cases} v_1 \\ v_2 \end{cases} \quad y = 130.9 + 1.257x^3.$$

$$\begin{cases} v_3 \\ v_4 \\ v_5 \end{cases} \quad \sum v = 0, \quad \sum v^2 = 80.$$

2.
$$\begin{cases} v_1 \\ v_2 \\ v_3 \end{cases} \quad y = 128.9 + 1.259x^3.$$

$$\begin{cases} v_4 \\ v_5 \end{cases} \quad \sum v = 0, \quad \sum v^2 = 76.$$

3.
$$\begin{cases} v_1 \\ v_3 \end{cases} \quad y = 129.7 + 1.258x^3.$$

$$\begin{cases} v_2 \\ v_4 \\ v_5 \end{cases} \quad \sum v = 0, \quad \sum v^2 = 74.$$

4.
$$\begin{cases} v_1 \\ v_4 \end{cases} \quad y = 158.9 + 1.224x^3.$$

$$\begin{cases} v_2 \\ v_3 \\ v_5 \end{cases} \quad \sum v = 0, \quad \sum v^2 = 2054.$$

5.
$$\begin{cases} v_1 \\ v_5 \end{cases} \quad y = 135.9 + 1.251x^3.$$

$$\begin{cases} v_2 \\ v_3 \\ v_4 \end{cases} \quad \sum v = 0, \quad \sum v^2 = 130.$$

6.
$$\begin{cases} v_2 \\ v_4 \end{cases} \quad y = 253.7 + 1.113x^3.$$

$$\begin{cases} v_1 \\ v_3 \\ v_5 \end{cases} \quad \sum v = 0, \quad \sum v^2 = 37676.$$

7.
$$\begin{cases} v_1 \\ v_2 \\ v_4 \end{cases} \quad y = 137.6 + 1.249x^3.$$

$$\begin{cases} v_3 \\ v_5 \end{cases} \quad \sum v = 0, \quad \sum v^2 = 184.$$

8.
$$\begin{cases} v_1 \\ v_2 \\ v_5 \end{cases} \quad y = 123.9 + 1.2651x^3.$$

$$\begin{cases} v_3 \\ v_4 \end{cases} \quad \sum v = 0, \quad \sum v^2 = 176.$$

9.
$$\begin{cases} v_2 \\ v_3 \end{cases} \quad y = 123.9 + 1.2652x^3.$$

$$\begin{cases} v_1 \\ v_4 \\ v_5 \end{cases} \quad \sum v = 0, \quad \sum v^2 = 176.$$

10.
$$\begin{cases} v_2 \\ v_5 \end{cases} \quad y = 142.2 + 1.244x^3.$$

$$\begin{cases} v_1 \\ v_3 \\ v_4 \end{cases} \quad \sum v = 0, \quad \sum v^2 = 420.$$

The best formulas are those for which $\sum v^2$ is least and are evidently 1, 2, 3. The poorest are 4 and 6.

The best formula obtainable is found by the method of Least Squares to be

$$y = 130.8 + 1.257x^3,$$

for which $\sum v = 0$ and $\sum v^2 = 62$.

A carefully constructed graph, obtained by putting $x^3 = u$ and plotting the straight line $y = a + bu$ on a large sheet of finely squared paper, gave

$$y = 125 + 1.33x^3,$$

for which $\sum v = 281$, $\sum v^2 = 25397$. This formula obtained from a good graph is far inferior to nine of the ten formulas obtained by the method of averages.

When the number of residual equations is large enough to allow three or more to each group, the method of averages can be depended upon to give good results. If we have only a few sets of data (readings or measurements) and can not easily obtain more, we should always use the method of Least Squares. This method gives only one formula and that is always the best possible one.

Every empirical formula, however obtained, should always be tested by computing the residuals and seeing whether they are within allowable limits.

**113. The Method of Least Squares.** This method says that the best representative curve is that for which the sum of the squares of the residuals is a minimum. Since the squares of the residuals are positive quantities, the requirement that their sum shall be as small as possible insures that the numerical values of the residuals will be small; and this means that in the case of a series of plotted points the best representative curve will pass as closely as possible to all the points. Before applying this method to empirical formulas we shall first derive a fundamental rule which reduces the method to a simple procedure.

For simplicity let us consider the formula

$$(113: 1) \qquad\qquad y = a + bx + cx^2$$

and find the values of $a$, $b$, and $c$ which will make the graph of $(113:1)$ pass as near as possible to each of the $n$ points $(x_1, y_1)$, $(x_2, y_2)$, $\cdots$ $(x_n, y_n)$; or, stated otherwise, let us find an equation of the form $(113:1)$ which will be satisfied as nearly as possible by *each* of the $n$ pairs of observed values $(x_1, y_1)$, $(x_2, y_2)$, $\cdots$ $(x_n, y_n)$. The equation will not, in general, be satisfied exactly by any of the $n$ pairs. Substituting in $(113:1)$ each of the $n$ pairs of values in turn, we get the following *residual equations*:

$$v_1 = a + bx_1 + cx_1^2 - y_1,$$

$$v_2 = a + bx_2 + cx_2^2 - y_2,$$

$(113: 2)$

$$\cdots \cdots \cdots \cdots \cdots$$

$$v_n = a + bx_n + cx_n^2 - y_n.$$

The principle of least squares says that the best values of the unknown constants $a$, $b$, and $c$ are those which make the sum of the squares of the residuals a minimum, or

$$\sum v^2 = v_1^2 + v_2^2 + \cdots + v_n^2$$

must be a minimum. Hence

$$\sum(a + bx + cx^2 - y)^2 = (a + bx_1 + cx_1^2 - y_1)^2 + (a + bx_2 + cx_2^2 - y_2)^2$$
$$+ \cdots + (a + bx_n + cx_n^2 - y_n)^2 = f(a, b, c)$$

is to be a minimum.

The condition that $f(a, b, c)$ be a maximum or a minimum is that its partial derivatives with respect to $a$, $b$, and $c$ shall each be zero. We therefore have

$$\frac{\partial f}{\partial a} = 2(a + bx_1 + cx_1^2 - y_1) + 2(a + bx_2 + cx_2^2 - y_2) + \cdots = 0,$$

$$\frac{\partial f}{\partial b} = 2(a + bx_1 + cx_1^2 - y_1)x_1 + 2(a + bx_2 + cx_2^2 - y_2)x_2 + \cdots = 0,$$

$$\frac{\partial f}{\partial c} = 2(a + bx_1 + cx_1^2 - y_1)x_1^2 + 2(a + bx_2 + cx_2^2 - y_2)x_2^2 + \cdots = 0.$$

Dividing through by 2, we get the following three *normal equations*:

$$(113\!:\!3) \quad \begin{cases} (a + bx_1 + cx_1^2 - y_1) + (a + bx_2 + cx_2^2 - y_2) \\ \qquad + \cdots + (a + bx_n + cx_n^2 - y_n) = 0, \\ x_1(a + bx_1 + cx_1^2 - y_1) + x_2(a + bx_2 + cx_2^2 - y_2) \\ \qquad + \cdots + x_n(a + bx_n + cx_n^2 - y_n) = 0, \\ x_1^2(a + bx_1 + cx_1^2 - y_1) + x_2^2(a + bx_2 + cx_2^2 - y_2) \\ \qquad + \cdots + x_n^2(a + bx_n + cx_n^2 - y_n) = 0. \end{cases}$$

It will be observed that these normal equations can be written down immediately by applying the following

*Rule*: To find the *first* normal equation multiply the right-hand member of each residual equation by the coefficient of the *first unknown* in that member, add the products thus obtained, and equate their sum to zero; to get the *second* normal equation multiply the right-hand member of each residual equation by the coefficient of the *second unknown* in that member, add the products so obtained, and place their sum equal to zero; and so on for the remaining normal equations.

The normal equations are solved by the ordinary methods of algebra for solving simultaneous equations of the first degree in two or more unknowns. It is usually best to solve by determinants when the coefficients are large.

The number of normal equations is always the same as the number of unknown constants to be determined, whereas the number of residual equations is equal to the number of observations. The number of observations must always be *greater* than the number of undetermined constants if the method of least squares is to be of any benefit in the solution.

The rule stated above is applicable to any formula which is *linear in the constants* or to any formula which can be reduced to a form linear in the constants.

*Example* 1. Find the equation of the straight line which comes nearest to passing through the following points:

| $x$ | 0.5 | 1.0 | 1.5 | 2.0 | 2.5 | 3.0 |
|---|---|---|---|---|---|---|
| $y$ | 0.31 | 0.82 | 1.29 | 1.85 | 2.51 | 3.02 |

*Solution.* Let the equation of the line be

$$y = a + bx.$$

Substituting in this equation the several pairs of values of $x$ and $y$, we get the following *residual equations*:

$$\left.\begin{aligned}
v_1 &= a + 0.5b - 0.31 \\
v_2 &= a + \phantom{0.5}b - 0.82 \\
v_3 &= a + 1.5b - 1.29 \\
v_4 &= a + \phantom{0.5}2b - 1.85 \\
v_5 &= a + 2.5b - 2.51 \\
v_6 &= a + \phantom{0.5}3b - 3.02
\end{aligned}\right\} \text{Residual equations.}$$

Adding the right-hand members and equating their sum to zero, we get

$$6a + 10.5b - 9.80 = 0.$$

Multiplying the right-hand member of the first residual equation by 0.5, the second by 1, the third by 1.5, etc., adding the products, and equating their sum to zero, we get

$$10.5a + 22.75b - 21.945 = 0.$$

Hence the normal equations are

$$\left.\begin{aligned}
6a + 10.5b &= 9.80 \\
10.5a + 22.75b &= 21.945
\end{aligned}\right\} \text{Normal equations.}$$

Solving these by determinants, we have

$$a = \frac{\begin{vmatrix} 9.80 & 10.5 \\ 21.945 & 22.75 \end{vmatrix}}{\begin{vmatrix} 6 & 10.5 \\ 10.5 & 22.75 \end{vmatrix}} = \frac{222.950 - 230.422}{136.50 - 110.25} = -\frac{7.472}{26.25} = -0.285.$$

$$b = \frac{\begin{vmatrix} 6 & 9.80 \\ 10.5 & 21.945 \end{vmatrix}}{26.25} = \frac{131.670 - 102.900}{26.25} = \frac{28.770}{26.25} = 1.096$$

$$= 1.10, \text{ say.}$$

The required equation is therefore

$$y = -0.285 + 1.10x.$$

Computing the residuals by substituting the given points in this formula, we have

$$v_1 = -0.045, \quad v_2 = -0.005, \quad v_3 = 0.075,$$
$$v_4 = 0.065, \quad v_5 = -0.045, \quad v_6 = -0.005.$$
$$\therefore \quad \sum v = 0.04, \quad \sum v^2 = 0.014.$$

*Example 2.* Find a formula of the form

$$y = a + bx + cx^2$$

which will fit the following data:

| $x$ | 0 | 0.1 | 0.2 | 0.3 | 0.4 | 0.5 | 0.6 | 0.7 | 0.8 | 0.9 |
|---|---|---|---|---|---|---|---|---|---|---|
| $y$ | 3.1950 | 3.2299 | 3.2532 | 3.2611 | 2.2516 | 3.2282 | 3.1807 | 3.1266 | 3.0594 | 2.9759 |

*Solution.* Substituting in the assumed formula the corresponding values of $x$ and $y$ as given in the table, we get

$$v_1 = a + 0b + 0c - 3.1950$$
$$v_2 = a + 0.1b + 0.01c - 3.2299$$
$$v_3 = a + 0.2b + 0.04c - 3.2532$$
$$v_4 = a + 0.3b + 0.09c - 3.2611$$
$$v_5 = a + 0.4b + 0.16c - 3.2516$$
$$v_6 = a + 0.5b + 0.25c - 3.2282 \quad \} \text{ Residual equations.}$$
$$v_7 = a + 0.6b + 0.36c - 3.1807$$
$$v_8 = a + 0.7b + 0.49c - 3.1266$$
$$v_9 = a + 0.8b + 0.64c - 3.0594$$
$$v_{10} = a + 0.9b + 0.81c - 2.9759$$

Applying the rule of page 364 to these equations, we get

$$10a + 4.5b + 2.85c = 31.7616$$
$$4.5a + 2.85b + 2.025c = 14.0896$$
$$2.85a + 2.025b + 1.5333c = 8.82881$$

Normal equations.

Solving these for $a$, $b$, $c$, we find

$$a = 3.1951,$$
$$b = 0.44254,$$
$$c = -0.76531.$$

Hence the required equation is

$$y = 3.1951 + 0.44254x - 0.76531x^2.$$

If we compute the residuals by substituting in this formula the values of $x$ and $y$ given in the table, we find

$$\sum v = 0.0001, \quad \sum v^2 = 0.0000549.$$

The following example is given to call attention to a pitfall against which the computer should ever be on his guard.

*Example* 3.  The indicated horse power, $I$, required to drive a ship of displacement $D$ tons at a ten-knot speed is given by the following data.  Find a formula of the form $I = aD^n$ which will fit the data.

| $D$ | 1720 | 2300 | 3200 | 4100 |
|---|---|---|---|---|
| $I$ | 655 | 789 | 1000 | 1164 |

*Solution.*  We have

$$I = aD^n.$$
$$\therefore \quad \log I = \log a + n \log D.$$

The residuals are really

$$v_1 = aD_1{}^n - I_1, \quad v_2 = aD_2{}^n - I_2, \text{ etc.},$$

but we save a great deal of labor and commit very little error by writing

$$v_1' = \log a + n \log D_1 - \log I_1,$$
$$v_2' = \log a + n \log D_2 - \log I_2,$$

$$\text{etc.,}$$

and making the sum of the squares of the $v''$'s a minimum. Substituting in these equations the corresponding values of $D$ and $I$, we get

$$
\left.
\begin{aligned}
v_1' &= \log a + 3.236n - 2.816 \\
v_2' &= \log a + 3.362n - 2.897 \\
v_3' &= \log a + 3.505n - 3.000 \\
v_4' &= \log a + 3.613n - 3.066
\end{aligned}
\right\} \text{Residual equations.}
$$

Since these equations are *linear* in the constants $n$ and $\log a$, we can apply the rule stated on page 364. Adding the right-hand members and equating their sum to zero, we find the first normal equation to be

$$4 \log a + 13.716n = 11.779.$$

Multiplying the right-hand member of the first residual equation by 3.236, the second by 3.362, etc., adding the products, and equating their sum to zero, we get

$$13.716 \log a + 47.11n = 40.445$$

for the second normal equation. Rounding off these numbers to four figures, we have

$$
\left.
\begin{aligned}
47.11n + 13.72 \log a &= 40.44 \\
13.72n + 4 \log a &= 11.78
\end{aligned}
\right\} \text{Normal equations.}
$$

Solving these equations by determinants, we have

$$
n = \frac{\begin{vmatrix} 40.44 & 13.72 \\ 11.78 & 4 \end{vmatrix}}{\begin{vmatrix} 47.11 & 13.72 \\ 13.72 & 4 \end{vmatrix}} = \frac{161.76 - 161.62}{188.44 - 188.24} = \frac{0.14}{0.20} = 0.700,
$$

$$
\log a = \frac{\begin{vmatrix} 47.11 & 40.44 \\ 13.72 & 11.78 \end{vmatrix}}{0.20} = \frac{554.96 - 554.84}{0.20} = \frac{0.12}{0.20} = 0.600.
$$

$$\therefore \quad a = 3.981.$$

The resulting formula is therefore

$$I = 3.98 D^{0.700}.$$

Computing the residuals by substituting the data in this formula, we get

$$v_1 = -77, \quad v_2 = -108, \quad v_3 = -131, \quad v_4 = -182.$$

Hence

$$\sum v^2 = 67,878.$$

The formula which we have found is evidently so poor as to be worthless; for the residuals are large, all of the same sign, and the sum of their squares is exceedingly large. The correct formula is known to be

$$I = 4.56D^{2/3},$$

for which the residuals are

$$v_1 = -0.6, \quad v_2 = 5.4, \quad v_3 = -9.1, \quad v_4 = 4.7;$$

and therefore

$$\sum v^2 = 134.4.$$

The poor result obtained above is due primarily to the fact that in the process of solving the normal equations three of the most important significant figures *disappeared by subtraction* (see Art. 6); for $n$ and log $a$ were determined from the simple fractions $0.14/0.20$ and $0.12/0.20$, respectively, in each of which the second figure in both numerator and denominator is doubtful. This loss of significant figures did not seriously affect $n$, but in the case of $a$ the effect was disastrous. The reason for the greater effect on $a$ is this: An error $\epsilon$ in log $N$ will cause an error $2.3026\ N\epsilon$ in the antilog (Art. 6).

The only way in which we can hope to get the required constants correct to four significant figures in this example is to solve the problem anew and carry all computations to *eight significant figures*, so that we shall have five left after the first three disappear by subtraction. We therefore make a new computation, using 7-place logs. The results are as follows:

$$n = \frac{161.55494 - 161.77315}{188.10644 - 188.43257} = \frac{0.21821}{0.32613} = 0.6691,$$

$$\log a = \frac{554.68739 - 554.89978}{-0.32613} = \frac{0.21239}{0.32613} = 0.65725.$$

and

$$\therefore \quad a = 4.4797 = 4.480, \text{ say.}$$

Hence the final formula is

$$I = 4.480D^{0.6691}.$$

The residuals are found to be

$$v_1 = -0.1, \quad v_2 = 6.4, \quad v_3 = -7.8, \quad v_4 = 7.1;$$

and

$$\therefore \quad \sum v^2 = 152.2.$$

*Note.* This example serves to bring out an important point which must be kept in mind when determining the constants in empirical formulas. The point is this: The data used in determining the constants should be treated as *exact* numbers, and the computer must be careful about rounding off and dropping seemingly superflous digits at any stage of the computation. The final values of the constants should be given to as many significant figures as are given in the original data.

When it happens that some of the most important significant figures disappear by subtraction, as in the example above, the computation must be carried through with enough significant figures at all stages to give a reliable result. As a general rule it may be stated that if the constants are desired to $m$ significant figures and if a preliminary calculation shows that the first $p$ figures will disappear by subtraction, the calculation must be performed with $m+p+1$ significant figures throughout from beginning to end.

**114. Weighted Residuals.** It sometimes happens that the residuals are not all of the same weight. This is the case when we use the residuals of a *function* of $y$ instead of those of $y$ itself. In Ex. 2, Art. 111, and Ex. 3, Art. 113, for example, we found it necessary to use the residuals of log $y$ instead of those of $y$. In these cases the residuals were no longer of equal weight, as we shall now show.

Using the notation of Art. 107, let

$$Q = f(y).$$

Then

$$\frac{\partial Q}{\partial y} = f'(y).$$

Substituting this in (107:4), we get

$$R = f'(y)r,$$

where $r$ denotes the P. E. of $y$ and $R$ the P. E. of $f(y)$. Hence

$$\frac{R}{r} = f'(y).$$

Since the same relations hold between residuals as between probable errors, we may write

$$\frac{R}{r} = \frac{V}{v},$$

where $v$ and $V$ denote the residuals of $y$ and $f(y)$, respectively. Hence

$$\frac{V}{v} = f'(y).$$

Denoting by $w_y$ and $w_f$ the weights of $y$ and $f(y)$, respectively, we have from (104:2)

$$\frac{w_f}{w_y} = \frac{r^2}{R^2} = \frac{v^2}{V^2} = \frac{1}{[f'(y)]^2}.$$

**(114 : 1)**    $$\therefore \quad w_f = \frac{w_y}{[f'(y)]^2}.$$

Now if $f(y) = \log_{10} y = M \log_e y$, where $M = 0.43429$, we have

$$f'(y) = \frac{M}{y}.$$

Hence from (114:1)

$$w_f = \frac{y^2 w_y}{M^2};$$

and if all the $y$'s are of equal weight, then $w_y = 1$ and we have

(114: 2)    $$w_f = \frac{y^2}{M^2}.$$

We shall next derive the fundamental rule for writing down the normal equations when the residuals have different weights.

By Art. 94 the best result obtainable from measurements of unequal weight is that for which the sum of the weighted squares of the residuals is a minimum. Hence we must have

$$\sum wv^2 = w_1 v_1^2 + w_2 v_2^2 + \cdots + w_n v_n^2 \text{ a minimum.}$$

In the case of the equation $y = a + bx + cx^2$ (Art. 113) we therefore have

$$w_1(a + bx_1 + cx_1^2 - y_1)^2 + w_2(a + bx_2 + cx_2^2 - y_2)^2 + \cdots \text{ a minimum.}$$

Calling this expression $f(a, b, c)$, taking the partial derivatives with respect to $a, b, c$ in turn, and equating each to zero, we have

$$\frac{\partial f}{\partial a} = 2w_1(a + bx_1 + cx_1^2 - y_1) + 2w_2(a + bx_2 + cx_2^2 - y_2) + \cdots = 0,$$

$$\frac{\partial f}{\partial b} = 2w_1x_1(a + bx_1 + cx_1^2 - y_1) + 2w_2x_2(a + bx_2 + cx_2^2 - y_2) + \cdots = 0,$$

$$\frac{\partial f}{\partial c} = 2w_1x_1^2(a + bx_1 + cx_1^2 - y_1) + 2w_2x_2^2(a + bx_2 + cx_2^2 - y_2) + \cdots = 0.$$

Hence on dividing through by 2 we get

$$
\left.
\begin{aligned}
&w_1(a + bx_1 + cx_1^2 - y_1) + w_2(a + bx_2 + cx_2^2 - y_2) \\
&\qquad + \cdots + w_n(a + bx_n + cx_n^2 - y_n) = 0 \\
&w_1x_1(a + bx_1 + cx_1^2 - y_1) + w_2x_2(a + bx_2 + cx_2^2 - y_2) \\
&\qquad + \cdots + w_nx_n(a + bx_n + cx_n^2 - y_n) = 0 \\
&w_1x_1^2(a + bx_1 + cx_1^2 - y_1) + w_2x_2^2(a + bx_2 + cx_2^2 - y_2) \\
&\qquad + \cdots + w_nx_n^2(a + bx_n + cx_n^2 - y_n) = 0
\end{aligned}
\right\}
\begin{aligned}
&\text{Weighted} \\
&\text{normal} \\
&\text{equations.}
\end{aligned}
$$

In the case of *weighted* residuals we can therefore write down the normal equations according to the following

*Rule*: To get the *first* normal equation multiply the right-hand side of each residual equation by its weight and by the coefficient of the *first unknown* in that equation, add the products thus obtained, and equate their sum to zero; to find the *second* normal equation multiply the right-hand member of each residual equation by its weight and by the coefficient of the *second unknown* in that member, add the products, and equate their sum to zero; and so on for the others.

We shall now work Ex. 3 of the preceding article by the method of weights. The weights of the residuals are $I_1^2/M^2$, $I_2^2/M^2$, $I_3^2/M^2$, and $I_4^2/M^2$; but since the factor $1/M^2$ will divide out in the normal equations we do not write it down at all. The solution given below should be self-explanatory.

$$I = aD^n.$$

$$\therefore \quad \log I = \log a + n \log D.$$

| $D$ | 1720 | 2300 | 3200 | 4100 |
|---|---|---|---|---|
| $I$ | 655 | 789 | 1000 | 1164 |
| $I^2$ | 429025 | 622521 | 1000000 | 1354896 |

Weights

$$v_1 = \log a + 3.2355284n - 2.8162413 \qquad 429025$$
$$v_2 = \log a + 3.3617278n - 2.8970770 \qquad 622521$$
$$v_3 = \log a + 3.5051500n - 3.0000000 \qquad 1000000$$
$$v_4 = \log a + 3.6127839n - 3.0659530 \qquad 1354896$$

Residual equations.

Now applying the rule for writing down the weighted normal equations, we find them to be

$$11880965.2n + 3406442 \log a = 10165776.6$$
$$41497013.1n + 11880965.2 \log a = 35495260.6$$

Weighted normal equations.

Solving these by determinants, we find

$$n = 0.6671, \quad a = 4.546.$$

The required formula is therefore

$$I = 4.546D^{0.6671}.$$

The residuals are found to be

$$v_1 = -0.3, \quad v_2 = 5.8, \quad v_3 = -9.4, \quad v_4 = 4.8.$$

$$\therefore \quad \sum V = 0.9, \quad \sum v^2 = 145.1.$$

The value of $\sum v$ is now much less than in the previous solution, but $\sum v^2$ is only slightly less. The formula obtained by the method of weighted residuals thus fits the data slightly better than the one derived by leaving weights out of consideration, but the improvement is not marked. After applying this weighting method to several simple examples of different types and comparing the results with those obtained by ignoring differences in weight, the author is of the opinion that ordinarily it is not worth while to bother about the weights of the residuals; but problems sometimes arise in which the weights must be considered.*

*Remark.* Since the weights in the preceding example are approximately as the numbers 43, 62, 100, and 135, the student may wonder why it is not sufficient to multiply the residuals by these smaller numbers instead of by the actual weights 429025, 622521, etc. The answer is that if we did this the corresponding products would be true to only two or three significant figures and these would disappear in this prob-

---

* For a striking example of the effect of weighting in some problems see an important paper by C. E. Van Orstrand: "On the Empirical Representation of Certain Production Curves," *Journal of the Washington Academy of Sciences,* Vol. 15 (1925), No. 2.

lem by subtraction in solving the normal equations, so that the results found would be very uncertain. We can state as a general rule that the number of significant figures used in the weights must not be less than the number of significant figures which are to be retained throughout the computation, unless the exact values of the weights happen to contain fewer figures than the number retained throughout the computation.

**115. Non-Linear Formulas.—The General Case.** Not all empirical formulas can be handled by the methods thus far considered. For example, the relation between the pressure $p$ and temperature $t$ of saturated steam can be expressed by a formula of the type

$$p = a(10)^{bt/(c+t)},$$

where $a$, $b$, $c$, are unknown constants. These constants do not enter the formula linearly, and no transformation of the formula will give a linear relation among them. Consequently they can not be determined by the methods previously given. We are now going to develop a method which will apply to any type of formula, however complicated it may be.

Let us consider a formula involving two variables, $x$ and $y$, and three undetermined constants, $a$, $b$, $c$. Such a formula may be written in the symbolic form

(115: 1) $$y = f(x, a, b, c).$$

Let $a_0$, $b_0$, $c_0$ be approximate values of $a$, $b$, $c$, obtained from a graph or by any other means, and let $\alpha$, $\beta$, $\gamma$ denote corrections which are to be applied to $a_0$, $b_0$, $c_0$, respectively, so that

(115: 2) $$\begin{cases} a = a_0 + \alpha, \\ b = b_0 + \beta, \\ c = c_0 + \gamma. \end{cases}$$

Then

(115: 3) $$y' = f(x, a_0, b_0, c_0)$$

will be a function whose graph approximates the graph of (115:1) more or less closely. The values of this approximating function corresponding to $x_1$, $x_2$, $\cdots x_n$ will be

(115: 4) $$\begin{cases} y_1' = f(x_1, a_0, b_0, c_0), \\ y_2' = f(x_2, a_0, b_0, c_0), \\ \cdots \cdots \cdots \cdots \cdots \\ y_n' = f(x_n, a_0, b_0, c_0). \end{cases}$$

If we take (115:1) to be the best or most probable function and its graph to be the best representative curve, then the residuals will be

(115: 5)

$$\begin{cases} v_1 = f(x_1, a, b, c) - y_1 \\ v_2 = f(x_2, a, b, c) - y_2 \\ \cdots \cdots \cdots \cdots \\ v_n = f(x_n, a, b, c) - y_n, \end{cases}$$

where $y_1, y_2, \cdots y_n$ are the *observed* $y$'s corresponding to $x_1, x_2, \cdots x_n$, respectively. Substituting in (115:5) the values of $a$, $b$, $c$ as given by (115:2), we have for the first residual

$$v_1 = f(x_1, a_0 + \alpha, b_0 + \beta, c_0 + \gamma) - y_1,$$

or

(115: 6)　　　　$v_1 + y_1 = f(x_1, a_0 + \alpha, b_0 + \beta, c_0 + \gamma).$

Considering the right-hand member of (115:6) as a function of $a$, $b$, $c$ and expanding it by Taylor's theorem for a function of several variables, we have

(115: 7)　$v_1 + y_1 = f(x_1, a_0, b_0, c_0)$

$$+ \alpha \left( \frac{\partial f_1}{\partial a} \right)_0 + \beta \left( \frac{\partial f_1}{\partial b} \right)_0 + \gamma \left( \frac{\partial f_1}{\partial c} \right)_0 + \cdots ,$$

where $(\partial f_1/\partial a)_0$ means

$$\left( \frac{\partial f}{\partial a} \right)_{\substack{x=x_1 \\ a=a_0 \\ b=b_0 \\ c=c_0}}, \quad \text{etc.}$$

Then since $y_1' = f(x_1, a_0, b_0, c_0)$, (115:7) becomes

$$v_1 + y_1 = y_1' + \alpha \left( \frac{\partial f_1}{\partial a} \right)_0 + \beta \left( \frac{\partial f_1}{\partial b} \right)_0 + \gamma \left( \frac{\partial f_1}{\partial c} \right)_0 + \cdots ,$$

or

$$v_1 = \alpha \left( \frac{\partial f_1}{\partial a} \right)_0 + \beta \left( \frac{\partial f_1}{\partial b} \right)_0 + \gamma \left( \frac{\partial f_1}{\partial c} \right)_0 + y_1' - y_1.$$

Let

$$r_1 = y_1' - y_1, \ r_2 = y_2' - y_2, \cdots r_n = y_n' - y_n.$$

Then the residuals become

$$v_1 = \alpha\left(\frac{\partial f_1}{\partial a}\right)_0 + \beta\left(\frac{\partial f_1}{\partial b}\right)_0 + \gamma\left(\frac{\partial f_1}{\partial c}\right)_0 + r_1$$

(115:8)    $$v_2 = \alpha\left(\frac{\partial f_2}{\partial a}\right)_0 + \beta\left(\frac{\partial f_2}{\partial b}\right)_0 + \gamma\left(\frac{\partial f_2}{\partial c}\right)_0 + r_2$$    Residual

$$\cdots \cdots \cdots \cdots \cdots \cdots \cdots \cdots$$    equations.

$$v_n = \alpha\left(\frac{\partial f_n}{\partial a}\right)_0 + \beta\left(\frac{\partial f_n}{\partial b}\right)_0 + \gamma\left(\frac{\partial f_n}{\partial c}\right)_0 + r_n$$

These equations are *linear* (of the first degree) *in the corrections* $\alpha$, $\beta$, $\gamma$, and we may therefore deal with the problem from this point onward either by the method of averages or by the method of least squares. If we use the latter method, we write down the normal equations by the rule stated on page 364.

The quantities $r_1$, $r_2$, $\cdots r_n$ are the residuals for the approximation curve $y' = f(x, a_0, b_0, c_0)$, since they are the differences between the observed ordinates and the ordinates to this curve.

We shall now apply this general method to two examples.

*Example* 1. Find a formula of the form

$$y = mx + b$$

which will fit the following data:

| $x$ | 27 | 33 | 40 | 55 | 68 |
|---|---|---|---|---|---|
| $y$ | 109.9 | 112.0 | 114.7 | 120.1 | 125.0 |

*Solution.* When these values are plotted on ordinary coordinate paper, the points are found to lie nearly on a straight line (Fig. 24). The line which seems (to the eye) to fit them best has a slope of 0.37 and a $y$-intercept of 99.7. Hence we take

$$m_0 = 0.37, \quad b_0 = 99.7.$$

The approximation curve is therefore the line

$$y' = 0.37x + 99.7.$$

Substituting in this equation the observed values of $x$, we get

$$y_1' = 0.37 \times 27 + 99.7 = 109.7,$$

$$y_2' = 0.37 \times 33 + 99.7 = 111.9,$$

$$y_3' = 114.7, \quad y_4' = 120.0, \quad y_5' = 124.9.$$

Hence

$$r_1 = 109.7 - 109.9 = -0.2,$$

$$r_2 = 111.9 - 112.0 = -0.1,$$

$$r_3 = 0.0, \quad r_4 = -0.1, \quad r_5 = -0.1.$$

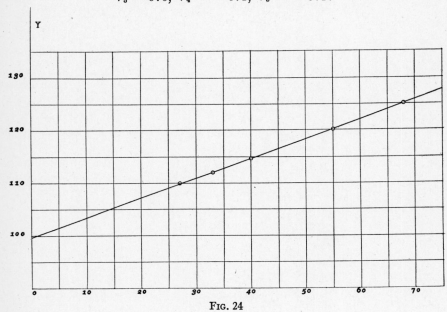

FIG. 24

Also, since

$$f(x, m, b) = mx + b.$$

we have

$$\frac{\partial f}{\partial m} = x, \quad \frac{\partial f}{\partial b} = 1.$$

$$\therefore \quad \frac{\partial f_1}{\partial m} = x_1 = 27,$$

$$\frac{\partial f_2}{\partial m} = x_2 = 33,$$

$$\frac{\partial f_3}{\partial m} = 40, \quad \frac{\partial f_4}{\partial m} = 55, \quad \frac{\partial f_5}{\partial m} = 68;$$

and

$$\frac{\partial f_1}{\partial b} = 1 = \frac{\partial f_2}{\partial b} = \frac{\partial f_3}{\partial b} = \frac{\partial f_4}{\partial b} = \frac{\partial f_5}{\partial b}.$$

Substituting in (115:8) these values of the $r$'s and partial derivatives, we get

$$
\left.
\begin{aligned}
v_1 &= 27\alpha + \beta - 0.2 \\
v_2 &= 33\alpha + \beta - 0.1 \\
v_3 &= 40\alpha + \beta + 0.0 \\
v_4 &= 55\alpha + \beta - 0.1 \\
v_5 &= 68\alpha + \beta - 0.1
\end{aligned}
\right\}
\begin{aligned}
&\text{Residual} \\
&\text{equations.}
\end{aligned}
$$

We shall complete the problem by finding the best values of $\alpha$ and $\beta$ by the method of least squares. Forming the normal equations according to the rule on page 364, we get

$$
\left.
\begin{aligned}
11068\alpha + 223\beta &= 21.0 \\
223\alpha + \quad 5\beta &= \;\;0.5
\end{aligned}
\right\}
\begin{aligned}
&\text{Normal} \\
&\text{equations.}
\end{aligned}
$$

Solving these for $\alpha$ and $\beta$, we find

$$\alpha = -\,0.0012, \quad \beta = 0.152.$$

Hence

$$m = 0.37 - 0.0012 = 0.3688,$$

$$b = 99.7 + 0.15 = 99.85.$$

The required formula is therefore

$$y = 0.3688x + 99.85.$$

*Example 2.* Find more accurate values for the constants $a$, $b$, $c$, in the formula

$$p = a(10)^{bt/(c+t)},$$

given the approximate values

$$a_0 = 4.53, \quad b_0 = 7.45, \quad c_0 = 234.7.$$

*Solution:* For the partial derivatives $(\partial p/\partial a)_0$, $(\partial p/\partial b)_0$, $(\partial p/\partial c)_0$ we have

$$\left(\frac{\partial p}{\partial a}\right)_0 = (10)^{b_0 t/(c_0+t)}, \quad \left(\frac{\partial p}{\partial b}\right)_0 = a_0(10)^{b_0 t/(c_0+t)} \cdot \frac{t}{c_0+t} \cdot \log_e 10,$$

$$\left(\frac{\partial p}{\partial c}\right)_0 = -\,a_0(10)^{b_0 t/(c_0+t)} \cdot \frac{b_0 t}{(c_0+t)^2}\, \log_e 10.$$

Also

$$p_1' = a_0(10)^{b_0 t_1/(c_0+t_1)}, \quad p_2' = a_0(10)^{b_0 t_2/(c_0+t_2)}, \quad \text{etc.};$$

and

$$r_1 = p_1' - p_1, \quad r_2 = p_2' - p_2, \quad \text{etc.}$$

In the following table are given the observed values of $t$ and $p$, the corresponding values of the partial derivatives, and the corresponding $r$'s.

| No. | $t°\ C$ | $p$ | $\left(\dfrac{\partial p}{\partial a}\right)_0$ | $\left(\dfrac{\partial p}{\partial b}\right)_0$ | $\left(\dfrac{\partial p}{\partial c}\right)_0$ | $r$ | Group |
|---|---|---|---|---|---|---|---|
| 1 | −5.31 | 2.95 | 0.672 | −0.161 | +0.005 | +0.095 | |
| 2 | −3.64 | 3.45 | 0.763 | −0.124 | +0.005 | +0.007 | |
| 3 | 0.00 | 4.52 | 1.000 | 0.000 | 0.000 | +0.005 | |
| 4 | 8.01 | 7.93 | 1.761 | 0.605 | −0.018 | +0.049 | I |
| 5 | 11.98 | 9.88 | 2.300 | 1.165 | −0.035 | +0.541 | |
| 6 | 16.82 | 13.52 | 3.149 | 2.196 | −0.064 | +0.746 | |
| 7 | 23.85 | 22.24 | 4.867 | 4.681 | −0.136 | −0.194 | |
| 8 | 35.95 | 43.96 | 9.763 | 13.523 | −0.373 | +0.265 | |
| 9 | 44.90 | 71.20 | 15.717 | 26.326 | −0.726 | −0.002 | |
| 10 | 52.12 | 101.40 | 22.583 | 42.806 | −1.112 | +0.903 | |
| 11 | 58.68 | 139.72 | 30.910 | 64.490 | −1.636 | +0.893 | II |
| 12 | 74.47 | 281.55 | 62.300 | 156.520 | −3.723 | +0.649 | |
| 13 | 78.83 | 330.58 | 73.152 | 190.924 | −4.543 | +1.248 | |
| 14 | 82.25 | 387.56 | 85.765 | 232.136 | −5.455 | +1.365 | |
| 15 | 86.21 | 453.31 | 100.319 | 281.098 | −6.528 | +3.807 | |
| 16 | 91.34 | 552.20 | 122.213 | 357.103 | −8.160 | +0.592 | |
| 17 | 93.66 | 602.53 | 133.354 | 396.752 | −9.003 | +2.314 | |
| 18 | 99.39 | 743.49 | 164.564 | 510.637 | −11.381 | +1.916 | III |
| 19 | 100.87 | 784.07 | 173.547 | 544.065 | −12.079 | +6.439 | |
| 20 | 104.64 | 895.83 | 198.293 | 637.758 | −13.999 | −3.435 | |

Denoting the corrections to $a$, $b$, $c$ by $\alpha$, $\beta$, $\gamma$, respectively, and substituting in (115: 8) the values of the $r$'s and partial derivatives given in the table, we get 20 residual equations for determining $\alpha$, $\beta$, $\gamma$. In this problem we are going to use the method of averages; so it is not necessary to write down the residual equations. We simply divide the coefficients into three groups, as indicated in the table, and add the coefficients in each group. We thus get the following three equations:

$$\begin{cases} 14.512\alpha + \quad\ 8.362\beta - \quad 0.243\gamma = -\quad 1.249, \\ 300.190\alpha + \quad 726.725\beta - 17.568\gamma = -\quad 5.321, \\ 892.290\alpha + 2727.413\beta - 61.150\gamma = - 11.633. \end{cases}$$

Solving these equations for $\alpha$, $\beta$, $\gamma$, we get

$$\alpha = -\ 0.131, \quad \beta = -\ 0.0603, \quad \gamma = -\ 4.437,$$

so that the corrected values of the constants are

$$a = \quad 4.53 - 0.131 \quad = \ 4.399,$$

$$b = \quad 7.45 - 0.0603 = 7.390,$$

$$c = 234.70 - 4.44 \quad = 230.26.$$

The final equation is therefore

$$p = 4.399(10)^{7.390t/(230.26+t)}.$$

**116. Determination of the Constants when Both Variables are Subject to Error.** In Arts. 112–115 it was tacitly assumed that the given values of the independent variable were absolutely correct and free from all error; the values of the function alone were supposed to be subject to error. This assumption is legitimate in most cases, for it is usually possible and practicable to obtain the values of one variable more accurately than the other.

If both variables are subject to errors of the same order of magnitude, the problem of finding the best values of the empirical constants is more complicated and has never been solved except for those cases in which the data can be plotted as a straight-line graph, either directly or after a suitable change of one or both variables. This special case for straight-line formulas was first solved by Mansfield Merriman,* but the most general and complete solution has been given by H. S. Uhler.† In the present article we shall treat only the simple case in which both variables are of equal weight. This is sufficient for most problems; for, as was seen in Art. 114, it is not often necessary to take account of differences in weight. When differences in weight must be considered, the reader is referred to Uhler's paper for the proper formulas to use.

Let us consider $n$ pairs of values $(x_1, y_1)$, $(x_2, y_2)$, $\cdots$ $(x_n, y_n)$, and let these be plotted as points on a straight-line graph. The line which best fits these points will evidently be that for which the sum of the squares of the *perpendicular distances* from the points to it is a minimum. The equation of any straight line may be written in the form

(116: 1)                    $$ax + by + 1 = 0,$$

this symmetrical form being used because both $x$ and $y$ are equally subject to error. The perpendicular distance from any point $(x', y')$ to the line (116: 1) is given by the formula

(116: 2)                    $$d = \frac{ax' + by' + 1}{\sqrt{a^2 + b^2}}.$$

---

* Report of the U. S. Coast and Geodetic Survey, 1890, p. 687.

† "Method of Least Squares and Curve Fitting," *Journal of the Optical Society of America and Review of Scientific Instruments.* Vol. 7 (1923), pp. 1043–1066.

The sum of the squares of the perpendicular distances from the points $(x_1, y_1)$, $(x_2, y_2)$, etc. to the line (116:1) is therefore

$$(116:3)\quad F(a, b) = \sum d^2 = \frac{1}{a^2 + b^2}[(ax_1 + by_1 + 1)^2$$
$$+ (ax_2 + by_2 + 1)^2 + \cdots + (ax_n + by_n + 1)^2].$$

Since this is to be a minimum, its partial derivatives with respect to $a$ and $b$ must each be zero.

Taking the partial derivative of (116:3) with respect to $a$, we have

$$\frac{\partial F}{\partial a} = -\frac{2a}{(a^2 + b^2)^2}[(ax_1 + by_1 + 1)^2 + (ax_2 + by_2 + 1)^2$$
$$+ \cdots + (ax_n + by_n + 1)^2]$$
$$+ \frac{2}{a^2 + b^2}[x_1(ax_1 + by_1 + 1) + x_2(ax_2 + by_2 + 1)$$
$$+ \cdots + x_n(ax_n + by_n + 1)].$$

Expanding the terms within the brackets, reducing to a common denominator, and collecting terms, we get

$$(116:4)\quad \frac{\partial F}{\partial a} = \frac{2}{(a^2 + b^2)^2}[b(b^2 - a^2)\sum xy + (b^2 - a^2)\sum x$$
$$+ ab^2(\sum x^2 - \sum y^2) - 2ab\sum y - an].$$

Likewise, by symmetry,

$$(116:5)\quad \frac{\partial F}{\partial b} = \frac{2}{(a^2 + b^2)^2}[a(a^2 - b^2)\sum xy + (a^2 - b^2)\sum y$$
$$+ a^2b(\sum y^2 - \sum x^2) - 2ab\sum x - bn].$$

Multiplying (116:4) by $a$, (116:5) by $b$, adding the results, and simplifying, we get

$$(116:6)\quad a\frac{\partial F}{\partial a} + b\frac{\partial F}{\partial b} = -\frac{2}{a^2 + b^2}[a\sum x + b\sum y + n].$$

But since $\partial F/\partial a = 0$ and $\partial F/\partial b = 0$ for a minimum, (116:6) reduces to

$$a\sum x + b\sum y + n = 0,$$

or

$$(116:7)\qquad a\left(\frac{\sum x}{n}\right) + b\left(\frac{\sum y}{n}\right) + 1 = 0,$$

which shows that equation (116:1) is satisfied by the values

$$x = \frac{\sum x}{n} = \bar{x}, \quad y = \frac{\sum y}{n} = \bar{y}.$$

In other words, *the best representative line always passes through the centroid of the given points.*

Since $\partial F/\partial a$ and $\partial F/\partial b$ must be zero for a minimum, we have from (116:4) and (116:5), respectively,

(116:8) $\quad b(b^2 - a^2) \sum xy + (b^2 - a^2) \sum x - 2ab \sum y$

$$+ ab^2(\sum x^2 - \sum y^2) - an = 0,$$

(116:9) $\quad a(a^2 - b^2) \sum xy + (a^2 - b^2) \sum y - 2ab \sum x$

$$- a^2 b(\sum x^2 - \sum y^2) - bn = 0.$$

Problems of the type treated in this article are to be solved by means of formulas (116:7) and (116:8) or (116:7) and (116:9), always using (116:7) first. We shall apply this method to Example 1 of Art. 113.

*Example.*

| $x$ | $y$ | $xy$ | $x^2$ | $y^2$ |
|---|---|---|---|---|
| 0.5 | 0.31 | 0.155 | 0.25 | 0.0961 |
| 1.0 | 0.82 | 0.820 | 1.00 | 0.6724 |
| 1.5 | 1.29 | 1.935 | 2.25 | 1.6641 |
| 2.0 | 1.85 | 3.700 | 4.00 | 3.4225 |
| 2.5 | 2.51 | 6.275 | 6.25 | 6.3001 |
| 3.0 | 3.02 | 9.060 | 9.00 | 9.1204 |
| Sums 10.5 | 9.80 | 21.945 | 22.75 | 21.2756 |

To facilitate the computation the several known quantities are arranged in tabular form as shown above.

Since

$$\frac{\sum x}{n} = \frac{10.5}{6} = 1.75, \quad \frac{\sum y}{n} = \frac{9.80}{6} = \frac{4.90}{3},$$

we have by (116:7)

$$1.75a + \frac{4.90}{3} b + 1 = 0,$$

or

$$b = -\frac{5.25a + 3}{4.9}.$$

Substituting this value of $b$ in (116:9) and reducing, we get

$$5.7187a^3 + 23.4548a^2 + 6.165a = 0.$$

Solving for $a$, we find

$$a = 0, \quad -3.8191, \quad -0.28227.$$

The corresponding values of $b$ are found from the equation $b = -(5.25a + 3)/4.9$ to be

$$b = -0.61224, \quad 3.4796, \quad -0.30981.$$

Since the slope of the line (116: 1) is $-a/b$, it is obvious that the values $a = -3.8191$, $b = 3.4796$ are the only ones which will fit the data of this example. The required line is therefore

$$-3.8191x + 3.4796y + 1 = 0,$$

or

$$3.819x - 3.480y = 1,$$

or

$$y = -0.2874 + 1.097x.$$

This last equation agrees closely with that found by the ordinary method in Art. 113.

If we compute the sum of the squares of the perpendicular distances from the several points to this line, we find

$$\sum d^2 = 0.00618.$$

For the line found in Ex. 1, Art. 113, we find

$$\sum d^2 = 0.00619.$$

the two results are thus practically identical.

*Remark.* The reader will observe that the determination of the best representative line by the method of the present article involves but little, if any, more labor than the ordinary method of Art. 113.

**117. Finding the Best Type of Formula.** There exists no general method for finding the best type of formula to fit any given set of data. Probably the best one can do is to proceed as follows:

1. Plot the data on rectangular coordinate paper, taking care to choose the proper scales along the two axes so as to make the graph show up to the best advantage.

2. If the graph is a straight line, or nearly so, assume a formula of the type

$$y = a + bx.$$

3. If the graph is not a straight line but is a fairly smooth curve without sharp turns or bends, it is likely that the data can be fitted by some one of the following formulas:

*Remarks* and *Suggestions*.

(a)     $y = a + bx + cx^2 + dx^3$.     Linear in the constants.

(b)     $y = a + \dfrac{b}{x}$.     Linear in constants. Put $1/x = t$ to plot.

(c)     $y = \dfrac{1}{a + bx}$, or $\dfrac{1}{y} = a + bx$.     Put $1/y = u$ and plot the straight line $u = a + bx$.

(d)     $y^2 = a + bx + cx^2 + dx^3$.     Linear in constants.

(e)     $y = ab^x$,     or $\log y = \log a + x \log b$.

(f)     $y = ae^{bx}$,     or $\log y = \log a + bx \log e$.

(g) $\log y = a + bx + cx^2$.     Linear in constants.

(h)     $y = \dfrac{x}{a + bx + cx^2}$,

or

    $\dfrac{x}{y} = a + bx + cx^2$.     Linear in constants.

(i)     $y = ax^n$,     or $\log y = \log a + n \log x$.

(j)     $y = ax^n + b$.     Use general method of Art. 115.

(k)     $y = ae^{bx} + c$.     "    "     "    "    "    "

(l)     $y = \dfrac{x}{a + bx} + c$.     "    "     "    "    "    "

(m)     $y = ae^{bx} + ce^{dx}$.     "    "     "    "    "    "

(n)     $y = ax^m + bx^n$.     "    "     "    "    "    "

4. As aids in determining which of the formulas (a)–(n) to use in any given problem, the following suggestions are offered:

(a) If the observed data give a straight-line graph when plotted on *logarithmic* paper, use the formula

$$y = ax^n.$$

(b) If the data give a straight line when plotted on *semi*logarithmic paper, the proper formula is

$$y = ae^{bx}, \text{ or } y = ab^x.$$

(c) If the points $(1/x, y)$ or $(x, 1/y)$ lie on a straight line when plotted on ordinary coordinate paper, the proper formula is $y = a + b/x$ in the first case and $y = 1/(a+bx)$ or $1/y = a + bx$ in the second case.

5. The polynomial formula

$$y = a + bx + cx^2 + dx^3 + \cdots + qx^n$$

can be used to fit any set of data by taking a sufficient number of terms. The requisite number of terms is given by the following

*Theorem: If the values of x are in arithmetic progression and the nth differences of the y's are constant, the last term in the required polynomial is $x^n$.*

This theorem is simply a corollary of the theorem proved in Art. 14. For example, the third differences in the following data are nearly constant; so the required polynomial is

$$y = a + bx + cx^2 + dx^3.$$

| $x$ | $y$ | $\Delta_1 y$ | $\Delta_2 y$ | $\Delta_3 y$ |
|-----|-----|------|------|------|
| 0 | 0 | | | |
| 0.1 | 0.212 | 0.212 | | |
| 0.2 | 0.463 | 0.251 | 0.039 | |
| 0.3 | 0.772 | 0.309 | 0.058 | 0.019 |
| 0.4 | 1.153 | 0.381 | 0.072 | 0.014 |
| 0.5 | 1.625 | 0.472 | 0.091 | 0.019 |
| 0.6 | 2.207 | 0.582 | 0.110 | 0.019 |
| 0.7 | 2.917 | 0.710 | 0.128 | 0.018 |
| 0.8 | 3.776 | 0.859 | 0.149 | 0.021 |
| 0.9 | 4.798 | 1.022 | 0.163 | 0.014 |
| 1.0 | 6.001 | 1.203 | 0.181 | 0.018 |

This theorem applies *only* when the $x$'s are taken at *equal intervals* apart. It rarely pays to take more than three or four terms in a polynomial formula, on account of the labor involved in determining the constants.

### EXAMPLES ON CHAPTER XVI

1. Find by the method of averages a formula of the form $y = ax^n$ which will fit the following data:

| $x$ | 273 | 283 | 288 | 293 | 313 | 333 | 353 | 373 |
|---|---|---|---|---|---|---|---|---|
| $y$ | 29.4 | 33.3 | 35.2 | 37.2 | 45.8 | 55.2 | 65.6 | 77.3 |

2. Plot on logarithmic paper the data of the above example and find $a$ and $n$ graphically or from selected points.

3. Find by the method of least squares a formula of the form $y = a + bx^2$ which will fit the following data:

| $x$ | 19 | 25 | 31 | 38 | 44 |
|---|---|---|---|---|---|
| $y$ | 1900 | 3230 | 4900 | 7330 | 9780 |

4. The data in the following table can be fitted by a formula of the type $y = ax^n$. Find the formula by the method of averages.

| $x$ | 53.92 | 26.36 | 14.00 | 6.992 | 4.280 | 2.748 | 1.853 |
|---|---|---|---|---|---|---|---|
| $y$ | 6.86 | 14.70 | 28.83 | 60.40 | 101.9 | 163.3 | 250.3 |

5. The data given below can be fitted by an exponential formula of the type $y = ae^{bx}$. Plot the data on semilogarithmic paper and find values for $a$ and $b$.

| $x$ | 2 | 5 | 8 | 11 | 14 | 17 | 27 | 31 | 35 | 44 |
|---|---|---|---|---|---|---|---|---|---|---|
| $y$ | 94.8 | 89.7 | 81.3 | 74.9 | 68.7 | 64.0 | 49.3 | 44.0 | 39.1 | 31.6 |

6. Solve the preceding example by the method of averages.

7. Find by the method of least squares a formula of the type $y = a + bx^2$ which will fit the following data:

| $x$ | 7.87 | 11.50 | 16.40 | 22.60 | 32.80 |
|---|---|---|---|---|---|
| $y$ | 0.2 | 0.4 | 0.8 | 1.6 | 3.2 |

8. The data in the table below can be fitted by a formula of the type $x/y = a + bx$. Find the formula by the method of averages.

| $x$ | 3.8 | 7.0 | 9.5 | 11.3 | 17.5 | 31.5 | 45.0 | 64.0 | 95.0 |
|---|---|---|---|---|---|---|---|---|---|
| $y$ | 10.0 | 12.5 | 13.5 | 14.0 | 15.0 | 16.0 | 16.5 | 17.0 | 17.5 |

9. Work the preceding example by plotting the points $(x, x/y)$ on ordinary coordinate paper and finding the values of $a$ and $b$.

*Hint*: Put $x/y = u$. Then the equation becomes $u = a + bx$, the graph of which is a straight line.

10. In Example 3 put $x^2 = t$ and plot the equation $y = a + bt$. Find from the graph the approximate values of $a$ and $b$ and then find corrections to these values by the general method of Art. 115.

11. The data in the table below can be fitted by a formula of the form $y = a + b/(x + c)$. Approximate values for $a$, $b$, and $c$ are $a_0 = 0.18$, $b_0 = -0.13$, $c_0 = -0.50$. Find corrections to these values.

| $x$ | 0.65 | 0.87 | 0.88 | 0.90 | 0.93 | 1.16 | 1.80 | 2.12 | 3.00 |
|---|---|---|---|---|---|---|---|---|---|
| $y$ | 0.129 | 0.217 | 0.228 | 0.234 | 0.275 | 0.318 | 0.400 | 0.410 | 0.435 |

12. Find by the method of averages a polynomial formula which will fit the data in the following table:

| $x$ | 8.5 | 9.5 | 10.5 | 11.5 | 12.5 | 13.5 | 14.5 | 15.5 | 16.5 | 17.5 |
|---|---|---|---|---|---|---|---|---|---|---|
| $y$ | 1260 | 1660 | 2150 | 2850 | 3670 | 4730 | 6050 | 7750 | 10000 | 13050 |

13. The data in the table below are to be fitted by a formula having $y = 20$ as an asymptote  Find the formula by any method.

| $x$ | 0 | 1 | 2 | 3 | 4 | 5 | 6 | 7 | 8 | 9 | 10 |
|---|---|---|---|---|---|---|---|---|---|---|---|
| $y$ | 84.9 | 79.9 | 75.0 | 70.7 | 67.2 | 64.3 | 61.9 | 59.9 | 57.6 | 55.6 | 53.4 |

14. The table below gives the atmospheric refraction for a star at various altitudes above the horizon. Assume that $R'' = a/(b + \tan h)$, omit the first and last values in the table, and find $a$ and $b$ by the method of least squares.

| $h$ | 0° | 2° | 4° | 6° | 8° | 10° | 20° | 40° | 60° | 90° |
|---|---|---|---|---|---|---|---|---|---|---|
| $R$ | 34′50″ | 18′06″ | 11′37″ | 8′23″ | 6′29″ | 5′16″ | 2′37″ | 1′09″ | 0′33″ | 0 |

## CHAPTER XVII

## HARMONIC ANALYSIS OF EMPIRICAL FUNCTIONS

**118. Introduction.** Any periodic function can be represented by a trigonometric series of the form

$$(118:1) \quad y = a_0 + a_1 \cos x + a_2 \cos 2x + \cdots + a_n \cos nx$$
$$+ b_1 \sin x + b_2 \sin 2x + \cdots + b_n \sin nx.$$

This function is periodic and has the period $2\pi$. A periodic function having a period different from $2\pi$ can be reduced to the form (118: 1) by a suitable change of the independent variable (Art. 121).

When we wish to find an empirical formula to represent a phenomenon that is known to be periodic—such, for example, as the tides, alternating currents and voltages, mean monthly temperatures, etc.—, we should always assume a formula of the type (118: 1). If the values of the function are known for certain equidistant values of the independent variable—from readings of an instrument, measurements of a graph, or otherwise—, it is an easy matter to find the unknown constants $a_0, a_1, \cdots a_n, b_1, b_2, \cdots b_n$. In the present chapter we shall give explicit formulas for computng these coefficients when the number of equally spaced ordinates is either 12 or 24. We shall also give schemes for reducing the numerical work to a minimum.

**119. Case of 12 Ordinates.** We assume that the period of the unknown function is $2\pi$ and that the value of the function is known for 12 equidistant values of the independent variable. The appropriate formula is then

$$(119:1) \quad y = a_0 + a_1 \cos x + a_2 \cos 2x + a_3 \cos 3x + a_4 \cos 4x$$
$$+ a_5 \cos 5x + a_6 \cos 6x + b_1 \sin x + b_2 \sin 2x$$
$$+ b_3 \sin 3x + b_4 \sin 4x + b_5 \sin 5x.$$

Let the corresponding values of $x$ and $y$ be as given in the table below.

| $x$ | 0° | 30° | 60° | 90° | 120° | 150° | 180° | 210° | 240° | 270° | 300° | 330° |
|---|---|---|---|---|---|---|---|---|---|---|---|---|
| $y$ | $y_0$ | $y_1$ | $y_2$ | $y_3$ | $y_4$ | $y_5$ | $y_6$ | $y_7$ | $y_8$ | $y_9$ | $y_{10}$ | $y_{11}$ |

Then on substituting in (119: 1) each of these corresponding sets of values we obtain the following conditional equations:

$$y_0 = a_0 + a_1 + a_2 + a_3 + a_4 + a_5 + a_6 + 0 \cdot b_1 + 0 \cdot b_2 + 0 \cdot b_3 + 0 \cdot b_4 + 0 \cdot b_5,$$

$$y_1 = a_0 + \frac{\sqrt{3}}{2}a_1 + \frac{1}{2}a_2 + 0 \cdot a_3 - \frac{1}{2}a_4 - \frac{\sqrt{3}}{2}a_5 - a_6 + \frac{1}{2}b_1 + \frac{\sqrt{3}}{2}b_2$$
$$+ b_3 + \frac{\sqrt{3}}{2}b_4 + \frac{1}{2}b_5,$$

$$y_2 = a_0 + \frac{1}{2}a_1 - \frac{1}{2}a_2 - a_3 - \frac{1}{2}a_4 + \frac{1}{2}a_5 + a_6 + \frac{\sqrt{3}}{2}b_1 + \frac{\sqrt{3}}{2}b_2$$
$$+ 0 \cdot b_3 - \frac{\sqrt{3}}{2}b_4 - \frac{\sqrt{3}}{2}b_5,$$

$$y_3 = a_0 + 0 \cdot a_1 - a_2 + 0 \cdot a_3 + a_4 + 0 \cdot a_5 - a_6 + b_1 + 0 \cdot b_2$$
$$- b_3 + 0 \cdot b_4 + b_5,$$

$$y_4 = a_0 - \frac{1}{2}a_1 - \frac{1}{2}a_2 + a_3 - \frac{1}{2}a_4 - \frac{1}{2}a_5 + a_6 + \frac{\sqrt{3}}{2}b_1$$
$$- \frac{\sqrt{3}}{2}b_2 + 0 \cdot b_3 + \frac{\sqrt{3}}{2}b_4 - \frac{\sqrt{3}}{2}b_5,$$

$$y_5 = a_0 - \frac{\sqrt{3}}{2}a_1 + \frac{1}{2}a_2 + 0 \cdot a_3 - \frac{1}{2}a_4 + \frac{\sqrt{3}}{2}a_5 - a_6 + \frac{1}{2}b_1$$
$$- \frac{\sqrt{3}}{2}b_2 + b_3 - \frac{\sqrt{3}}{2}b_4 + \frac{1}{2}b_5,$$

$$y_6 = a_0 - a_1 + a_2 - a_3 + a_4 - a_5 + a_6 + 0 \cdot b_1 + 0 \cdot b_2 + 0 \cdot b_3 + 0 \cdot b_4 + 0 \cdot b_5,$$

$$y_7 = a_0 - \frac{\sqrt{3}}{2}a_1 + \frac{1}{2}a_2 + 0 \cdot a_3 - \frac{1}{2}a_4 + \frac{\sqrt{3}}{2}a_5 - a_6 - \frac{1}{2}b_1$$
$$+ \frac{\sqrt{3}}{2}b_2 - b_3 + \frac{\sqrt{3}}{2}b_4 - \frac{1}{2}b_5,$$

$$y_8 = a_0 - \frac{1}{2}a_1 - \frac{1}{2}a_2 + a_3 - \frac{1}{2}a_4 - \frac{1}{2}a_5 + a_6 - \frac{\sqrt{3}}{2}b_1$$
$$+ \frac{\sqrt{3}}{2}b_2 + 0 \cdot b_3 - \frac{\sqrt{3}}{2}b_4 + \frac{\sqrt{3}}{2}b_5,$$

$$y_9 = a_0 + 0 \cdot a_1 - a_2 + 0 \cdot a_3 + a_4 + 0 \cdot a_5 - a_6 - b_1 + 0 \cdot b_2 + b_3 + 0 \cdot b_4 - b_5,$$

$$y_{10} = a_0 + \frac{1}{2}a_1 - \frac{1}{2}a_2 - a_3 - \frac{1}{2}a_4 + \frac{1}{2}a_5 + a_6 - \frac{\sqrt{3}}{2}b_1 - \frac{\sqrt{3}}{2}b_2$$

$$+ \, 0 \cdot b_3 + \frac{\sqrt{3}}{2}b_4 + \frac{\sqrt{3}}{2}b_5,$$

$$y_{11} = a_0 + \frac{\sqrt{3}}{2}a_1 + \frac{1}{2}a_2 + 0 \cdot a_3 - \frac{1}{2}a_4 - \frac{\sqrt{3}}{2}a_5 - a_6 - \frac{1}{2}b_1 - \frac{\sqrt{3}}{2}b_2$$

$$- \, b_3 - \frac{\sqrt{3}}{2}b_4 - \frac{1}{2}b_5.$$

To solve these equations for the $a$'s and $b$'s we apply the rule of Art. 113 for writing down normal equations. Thus, to find $a_0$ we multiply each equation by the coefficient of $a_0$ in that equation and add the results. We then get

$$12a_0 = y_0 + y_1 + y_2 + y_3 + y_4 + y_5 + y_6 + y_7 + y_8 + y_9 + y_{10} + y_{11},$$

which gives $a_0$ explicitly in terms of the known quantities $y_0, y_1, \cdots y_{11}$.

To find $a_1$ we multiply each equation by the coefficient of $a_1$ in that equation and add the results. This gives*

$$6a_1 = y_0 + \frac{\sqrt{3}}{2}y_1 + \frac{1}{2}y_2 - \frac{1}{2}y_4 - \frac{\sqrt{3}}{2}y_5 - y_6 - \frac{\sqrt{3}}{2}y_7 - \frac{1}{2}y_8$$

$$+ \frac{1}{2}y_{10} + \frac{\sqrt{3}}{2}y_{11}.$$

* The reason for the disappearance of all the $a$'s and $b$'s except one in the normal equations is as follows:

Since the multipliers used in obtaining the normal equations are sines and cosines, the coefficients of the $a$'s and $b$'s in the resulting normal equations are all of some one of the forms

$$\sum_r \sin px_r, \quad \sum_r \cos qx_r, \quad \sum_r \sin px_r \sin qx_r, \quad \sum_r \sin px_r \cos qx_r, \quad \sum_r \cos px_r \cos qx_r,$$

$$\sum_r \sin^2 px_r, \qquad \sum_r \cos^2 qx_r,$$

where $r$ takes the values $0, 1, 2, \cdots (m-1)$, and $m$ is the number of equidistant ordinates. But

$$\sum_r \sin px_r = 0, \quad \sum_r \cos qx_r = 0, \quad \sum_r \sin px_r \cos qx_r = 0,$$

$$\left.\begin{array}{l} \sum_r \sin px_r \sin qx_r = 0 \\ \sum_r \cos px_r \cos qx_r = 0 \end{array}\right\} \text{ if } p \neq q,$$

$$\sum_r \sin^2 px_r = \frac{m}{2}, \quad \sum_r \cos^2 qx_r = \frac{m}{2}.$$

Since only one of the $a$'s or $b$'s in each normal equation has a coefficient of the form $\sum_r \sin^2 px_r$ or $\sum_r \cos^2 qx_r$, it is evident that all but one must disappear.

For a simple and elegant proof of the relations given above the reader is referred to Runge and König's *Numerisches Rechnen*, page 212.

Continuing in this manner, we get the following equations for finding the remaining $a$'s and $b$'s:

$$6a_2 = y_0 + \frac{1}{2}y_1 - \frac{1}{2}y_2 - y_3 - \frac{1}{2}y_4 + \frac{1}{2}y_5 + y_6 + \frac{1}{2}y_7 - \frac{1}{2}y_8 - y_9$$
$$- \frac{1}{2}y_{10} + \frac{1}{2}y_{11},$$

$$6a_3 = y_0 - y_2 + y_4 - y_6 + y_8 - y_{10},$$

$$6a_4 = y_0 - \frac{1}{2}y_1 - \frac{1}{2}y_2 + y_3 - \frac{1}{2}y_4 - \frac{1}{2}y_5 + y_6 - \frac{1}{2}y_7 - \frac{1}{2}y_8$$
$$+ y_9 - \frac{1}{2}y_{10} - \frac{1}{2}y_{11},$$

$$6a_5 = y_0 - \frac{\sqrt{3}}{2}y_1 + \frac{1}{2}y_2 - \frac{1}{2}y_4 + \frac{\sqrt{3}}{2}y_5 - y_6 + \frac{\sqrt{3}}{2}y_7 - \frac{1}{2}y_8$$
$$+ \frac{1}{2}y_{10} - \frac{\sqrt{3}}{2}y_{11},$$

$$12a_6 = y_0 - y_1 + y_2 - y_3 + y_4 - y_5 + y_6 - y_7 + y_8 - y_9 + y_{10} - \boldsymbol{y_{11}},$$

$$6b_1 = \frac{1}{2}y_1 + \frac{\sqrt{3}}{2}y_2 + y_3 + \frac{\sqrt{3}}{2}y_4 + \frac{1}{2}y_5 - \frac{1}{2}y_7 - \frac{\sqrt{3}}{2}y_8$$
$$- y_9 - \frac{\sqrt{3}}{2}y_{10} - \frac{1}{2}y_{11},$$

$$6b_2 = \frac{\sqrt{3}}{2}(y_1 + y_2 - y_4 - y_5 + y_7 + y_8 - y_{10} - y_{11}),$$

$$6b_3 = y_1 - y_3 + y_5 - y_7 + y_9 - y_{11},$$

$$6b_4 = \frac{\sqrt{3}}{2}(y_1 - y_2 + y_4 - y_5 + y_7 - y_8 + y_{10} - y_{11}),$$

$$6b_5 = \frac{1}{2}y_1 - \frac{\sqrt{3}}{2}y_2 + y_3 - \frac{\sqrt{3}}{2}y_4 + \frac{1}{2}y_5 - \frac{1}{2}y_7 + \frac{\sqrt{3}}{2}y_8 - y_9$$
$$+ \frac{\sqrt{3}}{2}y_{10} - \frac{1}{2}y_{11}.$$

We could find the values of the $a$'s and $b$'s directly from these equations, but it would be a tedious process on account of the large number of terms in the right-hand members. We therefore reduce the number of terms on the right by grouping terms and substituting new variables for the different groups. The first grouping gives

$$12a_0 = (y_0 + y_6) + (y_1 + y_{11}) + (y_2 + y_{10}) + (y_3 + y_9) + (y_4 + y_8)$$
$$+ (y_5 + y_7),$$

$$6a_1 = (y_0 - y_6) + \frac{\sqrt{3}}{2}(y_1 + y_{11}) + \frac{1}{2}(y_2 + y_{10}) - \frac{1}{2}(y_4 + y_8)$$
$$- \frac{\sqrt{3}}{2}(y_5 + y_7),$$

$$6a_2 = (y_0 + y_6) + \frac{1}{2}(y_1 + y_{11}) - \frac{1}{2}(y_2 + y_{10}) - (y_3 + y_9)$$
$$- \frac{1}{2}(y_4 + y_8) + \frac{1}{2}(y_5 + y_7),$$

$$6a_3 = (y_0 - y_6) - (y_2 + y_{10}) + (y_4 + y_8),$$

$$6a_4 = (y_0 + y_6) - \frac{1}{2}(y_1 + y_{11}) - \frac{1}{2}(y_2 + y_{10}) + (y_3 + y_9)$$
$$- \frac{1}{2}(y_4 + y_8) - \frac{1}{2}(y_5 + y_7),$$

$$6a_5 = (y_0 - y_6) - \frac{\sqrt{3}}{2}(y_1 + y_{11}) + \frac{1}{2}(y_2 + y_{10}) - \frac{1}{2}(y_4 + y_8)$$
$$+ \frac{\sqrt{3}}{2}(y_5 + y_7),$$

$$12a_6 = (y_0 + y_6) - (y_1 + y_{11}) + (y_2 + y_{10}) - (y_3 + y_9) + (y_4 + y_8)$$
$$- (y_5 + y_7),$$

$$6b_1 = \frac{1}{2}(y_1 - y_{11}) + \frac{\sqrt{3}}{2}(y_2 - y_{10}) + (y_3 - y_9) + \frac{\sqrt{3}}{2}(y_4 - y_8)$$
$$+ \frac{1}{2}(y_5 - y_7),$$

$$6b_2 = \frac{\sqrt{3}}{2}[(y_1 - y_{11}) + (y_2 - y_{10}) - (y_4 - y_8) - (y_5 - y_7)],$$

$$6b_3 = (y_1 - y_{11}) - (y_3 - y_9) + (y_5 - y_7),$$

$$6b_4 = \frac{\sqrt{3}}{2}[(y_1 - y_{11}) - (y_2 - y_{10}) + (y_4 - y_8) - (y_5 - y_7)],$$

$$6b_5 = \frac{1}{2}(y_1 - y_{11}) - \frac{\sqrt{3}}{2}(y_2 - y_{10}) + (y_3 - y_9) - \frac{\sqrt{3}}{2}(y_4 - y_8)$$
$$+ \frac{1}{2}(y_5 - y_7).$$

Let us now put

$$y_0 + y_6 = u_0 \qquad\qquad y_0 - y_6 = v_0$$
$$y_1 + y_{11} = u_1 \qquad\qquad y_1 - y_{11} = v_1$$
$$y_2 + y_{10} = u_2 \qquad\qquad y_2 - y_{10} = v_2$$
$$y_3 + y_9 = u_3 \qquad\qquad y_3 - y_9 = v_3$$
$$y_4 + y_8 = u_4 \qquad\qquad y_4 - y_8 = v_4$$
$$y_5 + y_7 = u_5 \qquad\qquad y_5 - y_7 = v_5.$$

Then the normal equations become

$$12a_0 = u_0 + u_1 + u_2 + u_3 + u_4 + u_5 = (u_0 + u_3) + (u_1 + u_5) + (u_2 + u_4),$$

$$6a_1 = v_0 + \frac{\sqrt{3}}{2}u_1 + \frac{1}{2}u_2 - \frac{1}{2}u_4 - \frac{\sqrt{3}}{2}u_5 = v_0 + \frac{\sqrt{3}}{2}(u_1 - u_5)$$
$$+ \frac{1}{2}(u_2 - u_4),$$

$$6a_2 = u_0 + \frac{1}{2}u_1 - \frac{1}{2}u_2 - u_3 - \frac{1}{2}u_4 + \frac{1}{2}u_5 = (u_0 - u_3)$$
$$+ \frac{1}{2}(u_1 + u_5) - \frac{1}{2}(u_2 + u_4),$$

$$6a_3 = v_0 - u_2 + u_4 = v_0 - (u_2 - u_4),$$

$$6a_4 = u_0 - \frac{1}{2}u_1 - \frac{1}{2}u_2 + u_3 - \frac{1}{2}u_4 - \frac{1}{2}u_5 = (u_0 + u_3) - \frac{1}{2}(u_1 + u_5)$$
$$- \frac{1}{2}(u_2 + u_4),$$

$$6a_5 = v_0 - \frac{\sqrt{3}}{2}u_1 + \frac{1}{?}u_2 - \frac{1}{2}u_4 + \frac{\sqrt{3}}{2}u_5 = v_0 - \frac{\sqrt{3}}{2}(u_1 - u_5)$$
$$+ \frac{1}{2}(u_2 - u_4),$$

$$12a_6 = u_0 - u_1 + u_2 - u_3 + u_4 - u_5 = (u_0 - u_3) - (u_1 + u_5) + (u_2 + u_4),$$

$$6b_1 = \frac{1}{2}v_1 + \frac{\sqrt{3}}{2}v_2 + v_3 + \frac{\sqrt{3}}{2}v_4 + \frac{1}{2}v_5 = \frac{1}{2}(v_1 + v_5)$$
$$+ \frac{\sqrt{3}}{2}(v_2 + v_4) + v_3,$$

$$6b_2 = \frac{\sqrt{3}}{2}(v_1 + v_2 - v_4 - v_5) = \frac{\sqrt{3}}{2}[(v_1 - v_5) + (v_2 - v_4)],$$

$$6b_3 = v_1 - v_3 + v_5 = (v_1 + v_5) - v_3,$$

$$6b_4 = \frac{\sqrt{3}}{2}(v_1 - v_2 + v_4 - v_5) = \frac{\sqrt{3}}{2}[(v_1 - v_5) - (v_2 - v_4)],$$

$$6b_5 = \frac{1}{2}v_1 - \frac{\sqrt{3}}{2}v_2 + v_3 - \frac{\sqrt{3}}{2}v_4 + \frac{1}{2}v_5 = \frac{1}{2}(v_1 + v_5)$$
$$- \frac{\sqrt{3}}{2}(v_2 + v_4) + v_3.$$

If we make the further substitutions

$$u_0 + u_3 = r_0 \qquad u_0 - u_3 = s_0 \qquad v_1 + v_5 = p_1 \qquad v_1 - v_5 = q_1$$

$$u_1 + u_5 = r_1 \qquad u_1 - u_5 = s_1 \qquad v_2 + v_4 = p_2 \qquad v_2 - v_4 = q_2,$$

$$u_2 + u_4 = r_2 \qquad u_2 - u_4 = s_2$$

the normal equations take the simpler forms

$$12a_0 = r_0 + r_1 + r_2 = r_0 + (r_1 + r_2),$$

$$6a_1 = v_0 + \frac{\sqrt{3}}{2}s_1 + \frac{1}{2}s_2,$$

$$6a_2 = s_0 + \frac{1}{2}r_1 - \frac{1}{2}r_2 = s_0 + \frac{1}{2}(r_1 - r_2),$$

$$6a_3 = v_0 - s_2,$$

$$6a_4 = r_0 - \frac{1}{2}r_1 - \frac{1}{2}r_2 = r_0 - \frac{1}{2}(r_1 + r_2),$$

$$6a_5 = v_0 - \frac{\sqrt{3}}{2}s_1 + \frac{1}{2}s_2,$$

$$12a_6 = s_0 - r_1 + r_2 = s_0 - (r_1 - r_2),$$

$$6b_1 = \frac{1}{2}p_1 + \frac{\sqrt{3}}{2}p_2 + v_3 = v_3 + \frac{1}{2}p_1 + \frac{\sqrt{3}}{2}p_2,$$

$$6b_2 = \frac{\sqrt{3}}{2}(q_1 + q_2),$$

$$6b_3 = p_1 - v_3,$$

$$6b_4 = \frac{\sqrt{3}}{2}(q_1 - q_2),$$

$$6b_5 = \frac{1}{2}p_1 - \frac{\sqrt{3}}{2}p_2 + v_3 = v_3 + \frac{1}{2}p_1 - \frac{\sqrt{3}}{2}p_2.$$

Finally, we write

$$r_1 + r_2 = l \qquad\qquad q_1 + q_2 = g$$
$$r_1 - r_2 = m \qquad\qquad q_1 - q_2 = h.$$

Then the equations for finding the coefficients in the trigonometric series are

$$a_0 = \frac{1}{12}(r_0 + l),$$

$$a_1 = \frac{1}{6}\left(v_0 + \frac{\sqrt{3}}{2}s_1 + \frac{1}{2}s_2\right),$$

$$a_2 = \frac{1}{6}\left(s_0 + \frac{1}{2}m\right),$$

$$a_3 = \frac{1}{6}(v_0 - s_2),$$

$$a_4 = \frac{1}{6}\left(r_0 - \frac{1}{2}l\right),$$

$$a_5 = \frac{1}{6}\left(v_0 - \frac{\sqrt{3}}{2}s_1 + \frac{1}{2}s_2\right),$$

(119:2)

$$a_6 = \frac{1}{12}(s_0 - m),$$

$$b_1 = \frac{1}{6}\left(v_3 + \frac{1}{2}p_1 + \frac{\sqrt{3}}{2}p_2\right),$$

$$b_2 = \frac{\sqrt{3}}{12}g,$$

$$b_3 = \frac{1}{6}(p_1 - v_3),$$

$$b_4 = \frac{\sqrt{3}}{12}h,$$

$$b_5 = \frac{1}{6}\left(v_3 + \frac{1}{2}p_1 - \frac{\sqrt{3}}{2}p_2\right).$$

The several substitutions made above can be accomplished very simply by the addition and subtraction scheme given below,* starting with the given $y$'s.

|  |  |  |  |  |  |  |
|---|---|---|---|---|---|---|
|  | $y_0$ | $y_1$ | $y_2$ | $y_3$ | $y_4$ | $y_5$ |
|  | $y_6$ | $y_{11}$ | $y_{10}$ | $y_9$ | $y_8$ | $v_7$ |
| Sum | $u_0$ | $u_1$ | $u_2$ | $u_3$ | $u_4$ | $u_5$ |
| Diff. | $\mathbf{v_0}$ | $v_1$ | $v_2$ | $\mathbf{v_3}$ | $v_4$ | $v_5$ |

|  |  |  |  |  |  |
|---|---|---|---|---|---|
|  | $u_0$ | $u_1$ | $u_2$ | $v_1$ | $v_2$ |
|  | $u_3$ | $u_5$ | $u_4$ | $v_5$ | $v_4$ |
| Sum | $\mathbf{r_0}$ | $r_1$ | $r_2$ | $p_1$ | $p_2$ |
| Diff. | $s_0$ | $s_1$ | $s_2$ | $q_1$ | $q_2$ |

|  |  |  |
|---|---|---|
|  | $r_1$ | $q_1$ |
|  | $r_2$ | $q_2$ |
| Sum | $l$ | $g$ |
| Diff. | $m$ | $h$ |

The quantities $v_0$, $v_3$, and $r_0$ are printed in heavy type because they are somewhat isolated from the other quantities which appear in the final formulas for the coefficients.

*Check formulas.* Since the chances of making an error in the additions and subtractions are considerable, it is important to have a reliable check on the computed $a$'s and $b$'s. As a check on the $a$'s we have from the first conditional equation

$$y_0 = a_0 + a_1 + a_2 + a_3 + a_4 + a_5 + a_6.$$

To find a check for the $b$'s we subtract the twelfth conditional equation from the second, giving

$$y_1 - y_{11} = b_1 + \sqrt{3}b_2 + 2b_3 + \sqrt{3}b_4 + b_5;$$

or, since

$$v_1 = y_1 - y_{11},$$

$$v_1 = b_1 + b_5 + 2b_3 + \sqrt{3}(b_2 + b_4).$$

The check formulas are therefore

---

* Such schemes for computing the $a$'s and $b$'s were first devised by Professor Carl Runge about the year 1903. See *Zeitschrift für Math. und Physik.*, XLVIII (1903), p. 443, and LII (1905), p. 117.

$$(119:3) \qquad \begin{cases} \sum a = y_0, \\ (b_1 + b_5) + 2b_3 + \sqrt{3}(b_2 + b_4) = v_1. \end{cases}$$

We shall now work an example to show the application of the above scheme.

*Example 1.* Find an empirical formula to fit the following data:

| $x$ | 0° | 30° | 60° | 90° | 120° | 150° | 180° | 210° | 240° | 270° | 300° | 330° |
|---|---|---|---|---|---|---|---|---|---|---|---|---|
| $y$ | 9.3 | 15.0 | 17.4 | 23.0 | 37.0 | 31.0 | 15.3 | 4.0 | −8.0 | −13.2 | −14.2 | −6.0 |

*Solution.* The first part of the computation is carried out according to the scheme above and should be self-explanatory.

|  | 0 | 1 | 2 | 3 | 4 | 5 |
|---|---|---|---|---|---|---|
| $y$'s | 9.3 | 15.0 | 17.4 | 23.0 | 37.0 | 31.0 |
|  | 15.3 | − 6.0 | −14.2 | −13.2 | −8.0 | 4.0 |
| Sum ($u$) | 24.6 | 9.0 | 3.2 | 9.8 | 29.0 | 35.0 |
| Diff. ($v$) | − 6.0 | 21.0 | 31.6 | 36.2 | 45.0 | 27.0 |

|  | 0 | 1 | 2 |  |  | 1 | 2 |
|---|---|---|---|---|---|---|---|
| $u$'s | 24.6 | 9.0 | 3.2 |  | $v$'s | 21.0 | 31.6 |
|  | 9.8 | 35.0 | 29.0 |  |  | 27.0 | 45.0 |
| Sum ($r$) | 34.4 | 44.0 | 32.2 |  | Sum ($p$) | 48.0 | 76.6 |
| Diff. ($s$) | 14.8 | −26.0 | −25.8 |  | Diff. ($q$) | − 6.0 | −13.4 |

|  |  |  |  |
|---|---|---|---|
| $r$'s | 44.0 | $q$'s | − 6.0 |
|  | 32.2 |  | −13.4 |
| $l$ | = 76.2 | $g$ | = −19.4 |
| $m$ | = 11.8 | $h$ | = 7.4 |

Now substituting these quantities in equations (119:2), we get

$$a_0 = \frac{1}{12}(34.4 + 76.2) = 9.22,$$

$$a_1 = \frac{1}{6}\left(- 6.0 - 26\frac{\sqrt{3}}{2} - 12.9\right) = - 6.90,$$

$$a_2 = \frac{1}{6}(14.8 + 5.9) = 3.45,$$

$$a_3 = \frac{1}{6}(-6.0 + 25.8) = 3.30,$$

$$a_4 = \frac{1}{6}(34.4 - 38.1) = -0.62,$$

$$a_5 = \frac{1}{6}\left(-6.0 + 26\frac{\sqrt{3}}{2} - 12.9\right) = 0.60,$$

$$a_6 = \frac{1}{12}(14.8 - 11.8) = 0.25,$$

$$b_1 = \frac{1}{6}(36.2 + 24.0 + 66.3) = 21.09,$$

$$b_2 = \frac{\sqrt{3}}{12}(-19.4) = -2.80,$$

$$b_3 = \frac{1}{6}(48.0 - 36.2) = 1.97,$$

$$b_4 = \frac{\sqrt{3}}{12}(7.4) = 1.07,$$

$$b_5 = \frac{1}{6}(36.2 + 24.0 - 66.3) = -1.02.$$

Applying the check formulas (119: 3), we have

$$\sum a = 9.30 = y_0,$$

$$(b_1 + b_5) + 2b_3 + \sqrt{3}(b_2 + b_4) = 24.01 = v_1.$$

The coefficients are therefore correct and the final formula is

$$y = 9.22 - 6.90 \cos x + 3.45 \cos 2x + 3.30 \cos 3x - 0.62 \cos 4x$$
$$+ 0.60 \cos 5x + 0.25 \cos 6x + 21.09 \sin x - 2.80 \sin 2x$$
$$+ 1.97 \sin 3x + 1.07 \sin 4x - 1.02 \sin 5x.$$

*Note.* Since the terms of a trigonometric series are *additive*, it is necessary that the coefficients all be computed to the same number of *decimal places* (Art. 6).

**120. Case of 24 Ordinates.** For 24 equally spaced ordinates the values of $x$ are taken at equal intervals of 15° apart from 0° to 345° inclusive. The appropriate formula for this case is

**(120:1)** $y = a_0 + a_1 \cos x + a_2 \cos 2x + a_3 \cos 3x + a_4 \cos 4x + a_5 \cos 5x$

$\qquad + a_6 \cos 6x + a_7 \cos 7x + a_8 \cos 8x + a_9 \cos 9x + a_{10} \cos 10x$

$\qquad + a_{11} \cos 11x + a_{12} \cos 12x + b_1 \sin x + b_2 \sin 2x + b_3 \sin 3x$

$\qquad + b_4 \sin 4x + b_5 \sin 5x + b_6 \sin 6x + b_7 \sin 7x + b_8 \sin 8x$

$\qquad + b_9 \sin 9x + b_{10} \sin 10 + b_{11} \sin 11x.$

| $x$ | 0° | 15° | 30° | 45° | 60° | 75° | 90° | 105° | 120° | 135° | 150° | 165° | 180° |
|---|---|---|---|---|---|---|---|---|---|---|---|---|---|
| $y$ | $y_0$ | $y_1$ | $y_2$ | $y_3$ | $y_4$ | $y_5$ | $y_6$ | $y_7$ | $y_8$ | $y_9$ | $y_{10}$ | $y_{11}$ | $y_{12}$ |

| $x$ | 195° | 210° | 225° | 240° | 255° | 270° | 285° | 300° | 315° | 330° | 345° |
|---|---|---|---|---|---|---|---|---|---|---|---|
| $y$ | $y_{13}$ | $y_{14}$ | $y_{15}$ | $y_{16}$ | $y_{17}$ | $y_{18}$ | $y_{19}$ | $y_{20}$ | $y_{21}$ | $y_{22}$ | $y_{23}$ |

Let the corresponding values of $x$ and $y$ be as given in the table above. Then on substituting in (120: 1) these corresponding values of $x$ and $y$ we get 24 conditional equations. Applying to these the rule for obtaining normal equatons, we get 24 equations in which the $a$'s and $b$'s are given explicitly in terms of the $y$'s. Then we group the terms in the right-hand members, substitute new variabes for the different groups, group again, etc., just as in the case of 12 ordinates. The final formulas for computing the $a$'s and $b$'s are found to be as follows:

$$a_0 = \frac{1}{24}(l_0 + e),$$

$$a_1 = \frac{1}{12}\left(v_0 + Cs_1 + \frac{\sqrt{3}}{2}s_2 + \frac{1}{\sqrt{2}}s_3 + \frac{1}{2}s_4 + Ss_5\right),$$

$$a_2 = \frac{1}{12}\left(s_0 + \frac{\sqrt{3}}{2}m_1 + \frac{1}{2}m_2\right),$$

$$a_3 = \frac{1}{12}\left(v_0 + \frac{1}{\sqrt{2}}(s_1 - s_3 - s_5) - s_4\right),$$

$$a_4 = \frac{1}{12}\left(m_0 + \frac{1}{2}f\right),$$

$$a_5 = \frac{1}{12}\left(v_0 + Ss_1 - \frac{\sqrt{3}}{2}s_2 - \frac{1}{\sqrt{2}}s_3 + \frac{1}{2}s_4 + Cs_5\right),$$

$$a_6 = \frac{1}{12}(s_0 - m_2).$$

$$a_7 = \frac{1}{12}\left(v_0 - Ss_1 - \frac{\sqrt{3}}{2}s_2 + \frac{1}{\sqrt{2}}s_3 + \frac{1}{2}s_4 - Cs_5\right),$$

$$a_8 = \frac{1}{12}\left(l_0 - \frac{1}{2}e\right),$$

$$a_9 = \frac{1}{12}\left(v_0 - \frac{1}{\sqrt{2}}(s_1 - s_3 - s_5) - s_4\right),$$

$$a_{10} = \frac{1}{12}\left(s_0 - \frac{\sqrt{3}}{2}m_1 + \frac{1}{2}m_2\right),$$

$$a_{11} = \frac{1}{12}\left(v_0 - Cs_1 + \frac{\sqrt{3}}{2}s_2 - \frac{1}{\sqrt{2}}s_3 + \frac{1}{2}s_4 - Ss_5\right),$$

$$a_{12} = \frac{1}{24}(m_0 - f),$$

(120 : 2)

$$b_1 = \frac{1}{12}\left(Sp_1 + \frac{1}{2}p_2 + \frac{1}{\sqrt{2}}p_3 + \frac{\sqrt{3}}{2}p_4 + Cp_5 + v_6\right),$$

$$b_2 = \frac{1}{12}\left(\frac{1}{2}g_1 + \frac{\sqrt{3}}{2}g_2 + q_3\right),$$

$$b_3 = \frac{1}{12}\left(p_2 - v_6 + \frac{1}{\sqrt{2}}(p_1 + p_3 - p_5)\right),$$

$$b_4 = \frac{\sqrt{3}}{24}c,$$

$$b_5 = \frac{1}{12}\left(Cp_1 + \frac{1}{2}p_2 - \frac{1}{\sqrt{2}}p_3 - \frac{\sqrt{3}}{2}p_4 + Sp_5 + v_6\right),$$

$$b_6 = \frac{1}{12}(g_1 - q_3),$$

$$b_7 = \frac{1}{12}\left(Cp_1 - \frac{1}{2}p_2 - \frac{1}{\sqrt{2}}p_3 + \frac{\sqrt{3}}{2}p_4 + Sp_5 - v_6\right),$$

$$b_8 = \frac{\sqrt{3}}{24}d,$$

$$b_9 = \frac{1}{12}\left(v_6 - p_2 + \frac{1}{\sqrt{2}}(p_1 + p_3 - p_5)\right),$$

$$b_{10} = \frac{1}{12}\left(\frac{1}{2}g_1 - \frac{\sqrt{3}}{2}g_2 + q_3\right),$$

$$b_{11} = \frac{1}{12}\left(Sp_1 - \frac{1}{2}p_2 + \frac{1}{\sqrt{2}}p_3 - \frac{\sqrt{3}}{2}p_4 + Cp_5 - v_6\right),$$

where $C = \cos 15° = 0.9659258$, $S = \sin 15° = 0.2588190$, and the other quantities are obtained from the given $y$'s according to the following scheme:

| | $y_0$ | $y_1$ | $y_2$ | $y_3$ | $y_4$ | $y_5$ | $y_6$ | $y_7$ | $y_8$ | $y_9$ | $y_{10}$ | $y_{11}$ |
|---|---|---|---|---|---|---|---|---|---|---|---|---|
| | $y_{12}$ | $y_{23}$ | $y_{22}$ | $y_{21}$ | $y_{20}$ | $y_{19}$ | $y_{18}$ | $y_{17}$ | $y_{16}$ | $y_{15}$ | $y_{14}$ | $y_{13}$ |
| Sum | $u_0$ | $u_1$ | $u_2$ | $u_3$ | $u_4$ | $u_5$ | $u_6$ | $u_7$ | $u_8$ | $u_9$ | $u_{10}$ | $u_{11}$ |
| Diff. | $\mathbf{v_0}$ | $v_1$ | $v_2$ | $v_3$ | $v_4$ | $v_5$ | $\mathbf{v_6}$ | $v_7$ | $v_8$ | $v_9$ | $v_{10}$ | $v_{11}$ |

| | $u_0$ | $u_1$ | $u_2$ | $u_3$ | $u_4$ | $u_5$ | | $v_1$ | $v_2$ | $v_3$ | $v_4$ | $v_5$ |
|---|---|---|---|---|---|---|---|---|---|---|---|---|
| | $u_6$ | $u_{11}$ | $u_{10}$ | $u_9$ | $u_8$ | $u_7$ | | $v_{11}$ | $v_{10}$ | $v_9$ | $v_8$ | $v_7$ |
| Sum | $r_0$ | $r_1$ | $r_2$ | $r_3$ | $r_4$ | $r_5$ | Sum | $p_1$ | $p_2$ | $p_3$ | $p_4$ | $p_5$ |
| Diff. | $s_0$ | $s_1$ | $s_2$ | $s_3$ | $s_4$ | $s_5$ | Diff. | $q_1$ | $q_2$ | $\mathbf{q_3}$ | $q_4$ | $q_5$ |

| | $r_0$ | $r_1$ | $r_2$ | | $q_1$ | $q_2$ | | $l_1$ | | $h_1$ |
|---|---|---|---|---|---|---|---|---|---|---|
| | $r_3$ | $r_5$ | $r_4$ | | $q_5$ | $q_4$ | | $l_2$ | | $h_2$ |
| Sum | $l_0$ | $l_1$ | $l_2$ | Sum | $g_1$ | $g_2$ | Sum | $e$ | Sum | $c$ |
| Diff. | $m_0$ | $m_1$ | $m_2$ | Diff. | $h_1$ | $h_2$ | Diff. | $f$ | Diff. | $d$ |

Here the quantities $v_0$, $v_6$, and $q_3$ are printed in heavy type because they are somewhat isolated from the other quantities which appear in the final formulas for the coefficients.

A check formula for the $a$'s is given by the first conditional equation, and is

$$\sum a = y_0.$$

To find a check formula for the $b$'s we subtract the 23d conditional equation from the second and obtain

$$y_1 - y_{23} = v_1 = 2S(b_1 + b_{11}) + (b_2 + b_{10}) + \sqrt{2}(b_3 + b_9)$$
$$+ \sqrt{3}(b_4 + b_8) + 2C(b_5 + b_7) + 2b_6.$$

The check formulas are therefore

$$(120:3) \quad \begin{cases} \sum a = y_0, \\ 2S(b_1 + b_{11}) + (b_2 + b_{10}) + \sqrt{2}(b_3 + b_9) + \sqrt{3}(b_4 + b_8) \\ \qquad + 2C(b_5 + b_7) + 2b_6 = v_1. \end{cases}$$

*Example 2.* Find an empirical formula to fit the data in the following table:

| $x$ | 0° | 15° | 30° | 45° | 60° | 75° | 90° | 105° | 120° | 135° | 150° | 165° | 180° |
|---|---|---|---|---|---|---|---|---|---|---|---|---|---|
| $y$ | 149 | 137 | 128 | 126 | 128 | 135 | 159 | 178 | 189 | 191 | 189 | 187 | 178 |

| $x$ | 195° | 210° | 225° | 240° | 255° | 270° | 285° | 300° | 315° | 330° | 345° |
|---|---|---|---|---|---|---|---|---|---|---|---|
| $y$ | 170 | 177 | 183 | 181 | 179 | 179 | 185 | 182 | 176 | 166 | 160 |

*Solution.* The preliminary quantities are found by the scheme below:

|  |  | 0 | 1 | 2 | 3 | 4 | 5 | 6 | 7 | 8 | 9 | 10 | 11 |
|---|---|---|---|---|---|---|---|---|---|---|---|---|---|
|  | $y$'s | 149 | 137 | 128 | 126 | 128 | 135 | 159 | 178 | 189 | 191 | 189 | 187 |
|  |  | 178 | 160 | 166 | 176 | 182 | 185 | 179 | 179 | 181 | 183 | 177 | 170 |
| Sum | $(u)$ | 327 | 297 | 294 | 302 | 310 | 320 | 338 | 357 | 370 | 374 | 366 | 357 |
| Diff. | $(v)$ | −29 | −23 | −38 | −50 | −54 | −50 | −20 | −1 | 8 | 8 | 12 | 17 |

|  |  | 0 | 1 | 2 | 3 | 4 | 5 |
|---|---|---|---|---|---|---|---|
|  | $u$'s | 327 | 297 | 294 | 302 | 310 | 320 |
|  |  | 338 | 357 | 366 | 374 | 370 | 357 |
| Sum | $(r)$ | 665 | 654 | 660 | 676 | 680 | 677 |
| Diff. | $(s)$ | − 11 | − 60 | − 72 | − 72 | − 60 | − 37 |

|  |  | 1 | 2 | 3 | 4 | 5 |
|---|---|---|---|---|---|---|
|  | $v$'s | −23 | −38 | −50 | −54 | −50 |
|  |  | 17 | 12 | 8 | 8 | − 1 |
| Sum | $(p)$ | − 6 | −26 | −42 | −46 | −51 |
| Diff. | $(q)$ | −40 | −50 | −58 | −62 | −49 |

|  |  | 0 | 1 | 2 |  |  | 1 | 2 |
|---|---|---|---|---|---|---|---|---|
|  | $r$'s | 665 | 654 | 660 |  | $q$'s | −40 | −50 |
|  |  | 676 | 677 | 680 |  |  | −49 | −62 |
| Sum | $(l)$ | 1341 | 1331 | 1340 | Sum | $(g)$ | −89 | −112 |
| Diff. | $(m)$ | −11 | −23 | −20 | Diff. | $(h)$ | 9 | 12 |

|  |  |  |  |  |
|---|---|---|---|---|
| $l$'s | 1331 |  | $h$'s | 9 |
|  | 1340 |  |  | 12 |
| $e =$ | 2671 |  | $c =$ | 21 |
| $f =$ | −9 |  | $d =$ | −3 |

Now substituting these quantities in (120: 2), we find

$a_0 = 167.167, \quad a_1 = -19.983, \quad a_2 = -3.410, \quad a_3 = 5.471,$

$a_4 = -1.292, \; a_5 = 0.250, \quad\quad a_6 = 0.750, \quad\quad a_7 = 0.309,$

$a_8 = 0.458, \quad\quad a_9 = -0.304, \quad a_{10} = -0.090, \; a_{11} = -0.243,$

$a_{12} = -0.083.$

$b_1 = -12.779, \; b_2 = -16.625, \quad b_3 = -0.323, \; b_4 = 1.516,$

$b_5 = 1.462, \quad\quad b_6 = -2.583, \quad\quad b_7 = 0.322, \quad\quad b_8 = -0.216,$

$b_9 = 0.677, \quad\quad b_{10} = -0.459, \quad b_{11} = -0.640.$

The check formulas (120: 3) give

$$\sum a = 149.000 = y_0,$$

$$2S(b_1 + b_{11}) + (b_2 + b_{10}) + \sqrt{2}(b_3 + b_9) + \sqrt{3}(b_4 + b_8) + 2C(b_5 + b_7)$$
$$+ 2b_6 = -22.997 = v_1,$$

practically.

Hence the required formula is

$$y = 167.167 - 19.983 \cos x - 3.410 \cos 2x + 5.471 \cos 3x$$
$$- 1.292 \cos 4x + 0.250 \cos 5x + 0.750 \cos 6x + 0.309 \cos 7x$$
$$+ 0.458 \cos 8x - 0.304 \cos 9x - 0.090 \cos 10x - 0.243 \cos 11x$$
$$- 0.083 \cos 12x - 12.779 \sin x - 16.625 \sin 2x - 0.323 \sin 3x$$
$$+ 1.516 \sin 4x + 1.462 \sin 5x - 2.583 \sin 6x + 0.322 \sin 7x$$
$$- 0.216 \sin 8x + 0.677 \sin 9x - 0.459 \sin 10x - 0.640 \sin 11x.$$

The graph of this equation is shown in Fig. 25.

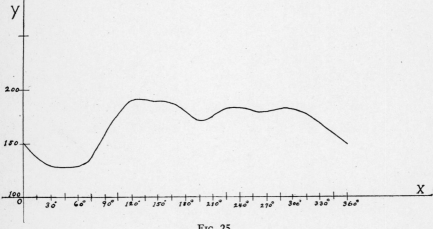

FIG. 25

### 121. Miscellaneous Matters.

*121a). Computation of the Coefficients for any Number of Equidistant Ordinates.* In this chapter we have considered only the cases where the number of given ordinates is 12 or 24, because these are the most important cases from a practical standpoint. It is possible, however, to derive formulas for the $a$'s and $b$'s in the case of any number of equidistant ordinates, such as 6, 8, 10, 16, 20, etc. The method of procedure in all these cases is exactly the same as that in the case of 12 ordinates. Computing schemes for the cases just mentioned are given in Running's *Empirical Formulas*, pp. 76–85.

Pollak's *Rechentafeln zur Harmonischen Analyse* enable one to find the $a$'s and $b$'s directly from the normal equations for any number of equidistant ordinates from 3 to 40 inclusive. The tables are accompanied by full directions for their use.

*121b). Periods other than $2\pi$.* When a function is periodic and has a period different from $2\pi$, we change the independent variable by a linear substitution. Thus, if $x$ is the independent variable and the given function is $y = f(x)$, we write

$$(121:1) \qquad\qquad x = k + m\theta.$$

If the limits for $x$ are 0 and $p$ and we wish the limits of $\theta$ to be 0 and $2\pi$, we have only to substitute in (121:1) these corresponding values of $x$ and $\theta$ and then solve the resulting equations for $k$ and $m$. Hence in this case we have from (121:1)

$$0 = k + 0, \quad \text{or} \quad k = 0;$$

$$p = k + 2\pi m = 2\pi m.$$

$$\therefore \quad m = \frac{p}{2\pi}.$$

The required formula is therefore

$$(121:2) \qquad\qquad x = \frac{p\theta}{2\pi}, \quad \text{or} \quad \theta = \frac{2\pi x}{p}.$$

Let us now consider the general case in which the lower and upper limits for $x$ are $g$ and $h$, respectively. If the corresponding limits for $\theta$ are 0 and $2\pi$, we have from (121:1)

$$g = k + 0, \quad \text{or} \quad k = g;$$

and

$$h = k + 2\pi m = g + 2\pi m.$$

Hence $m = (h - g)/2\pi$, and the desired formula of transformation is

**(121 : 3)**    $$x = g + \frac{(h - g)}{2\pi}\theta, \text{ or } \theta = \frac{2\pi(x - g)}{h - g}.$$

In all these cases the proper formula to assume for $y$ is

(121 : 4)    $y = a_0 + a_1 \cos \theta + a_2 \cos 2\theta + \cdots + a_n \cos n\theta$

$$+ b_1 \sin \theta + b_2 \sin 2\theta + \cdots + b_{n-1} \sin (n - 1)\theta.$$

For example, if the period of a phenomenon is known to be 18.3 days and we wish to use 12 equidistant ordinates, the values of $x$ corresponding to these ordinates would be $x_0 = 0$, $x_1 = 18.3/12 = 1.525$, $x_2 = 3.050$, etc. The corresponding values of $\theta$ would be $0°$, $30°$, $60°$, etc. The values of the $a$'s and $b$'s in (121 : 4) would be found by substituting in (121 : 4) these values of $\theta$ and the corresponding $y$'s, or simply applying the 12-ordinate scheme to the given $y$'s. The resulting formula in terms of $x$ would then be, by (121 : 2) and (121 : 4),

(120 : 5)    $y = a_0 + a_1 \cos \left(\dfrac{2\pi x}{18 \cdot 3}\right) + a_2 \cos 2 \left(\dfrac{2\pi x}{18 \cdot 3}\right) + \cdots$

$$+ b_1 \sin \left(\dfrac{2\pi x}{18 \cdot 3}\right) + b_2 \sin 2 \left(\dfrac{2\pi x}{18 \cdot 3}\right) + \cdots.$$

*121c). Caution in the Use of Empirical Formulas.* Empirical formulas are really interpolation formulas of particular forms, and are therefore subject to all the limitations of interpolation formulas. They can be relied upon for all values of the independent variable within the range of values used in determining the coefficients, but should not be trusted outside of these limits, except possibly for very short distances outside the range of values used. Stated otherwise, empirical formulas may be used for interpolation but not for extrapolation.

If, however, the given function is known to have a certain form for *all* values of the independent variable, we may use the formula for computing *rough* values of the function outside the range of values used in determining the coefficients.

### EXAMPLES ON CHAPTER XVII

1. Find a periodic function that will fit the following data:

| $x$ | 0° | 30° | 60° | 90° | 120° | 150° | 180° | 210° | 240° | 270° | 300° | 330° |
|---|---|---|---|---|---|---|---|---|---|---|---|---|
| $y$ | 38.4 | 11.8 | 4.3 | 13.8 | 3.9 | −18.1 | −22.9 | −27.2 | −23.8 | 8.2 | 31.7 | 34.2 |

2. Do the same for the following:

| $x$ | 0° | 15° | 30° | 45° | 60° | 75° | 90° | 105° | 120° | 135° | 150° | 165° | 180° |
|---|---|---|---|---|---|---|---|---|---|---|---|---|---|
| $y$ | 45 | 110 | 142 | 128 | 138 | 88 | −2 | −12 | −25 | −39 | −21 | −38 | −69 |

| 195° | 210° | 225° | 240° | 255° | 270° | 285° | 300° | 315° | 330° | 345° |
|---|---|---|---|---|---|---|---|---|---|---|---|
| −78 | −90 | −112 | −92 | −70 | −45 | 25 | 68 | 59 | 40 | 54 |

3. The equation of time for twelve equidistant intervals in a certain year is given in the following table. Taking the period of this phenomenon to be 365.2 days, find an empirical formula that will give its value at any instant in that year.

$$3^m 10^s.9,\ 13^m 30^s.4,\ 12^m 20^s.6,\ 3^m 53^s.6,\ -\ 3^m 2^s.7,\ -\ 2^m 22^s.6,\ 3^m 42^s.0,$$

$$9^m 10^s.0,\ 0^m 9^s.3,\ -\ 10^m 13^s.8,\ -\ 16^m.18^s.2,\ -\ 10^m 59^s.6.$$

4. The period of a certain phenomenon is 14.4 days. Twenty-four values for equal time intervals are given below. Find an empirical formula to represent this phenomenon.

2.4, 5.6, 6.7, 7.4, 8.8, 9.9, 10.4, 12.0, 13.8, 14.9, 16.4, 16.8, 17.5, 18.4, 19.2, 20.8, 21.4, 20.5, 18.5, 16.0, 15.1, 14.8, 12.2, 6.4.

# APPENDIX
## VALUES OF THE PROBABILITY INTEGRAL

$$P = \frac{2}{\sqrt{\pi}} \int_0^t e^{-t^2}dt, \quad \text{where } t = hx.$$

| hx | 0 | 1 | 2 | 3 | 4 | 5 | 6 | 7 | 8 | 9 |
|------|---|---|---|---|---|---|---|---|---|---|
| 0.00 | 0.00000 | 00113 | 00226 | 00339 | 00451 | 00564 | 00677 | 00790 | 00903 | 01016 |
| 0.01 | 0.01128 | 01241 | 01354 | 01467 | 01580 | 01792 | 01805 | 01918 | 02031 | 02144 |
| 0.02 | 0.02256 | 02369 | 02482 | 02595 | 02708 | 02820 | 02933 | 03046 | 03159 | 03271 |
| 0.03 | 0.03384 | 03497 | 03610 | 03722 | 03835 | 03948 | 04060 | 04173 | 04286 | 04398 |
| 0.04 | 0.04511 | 04624 | 04736 | 04849 | 04962 | 05074 | 05187 | 05299 | 05412 | 05525 |
| 0.05 | 0.05637 | 05750 | 05862 | 05975 | 06087 | 06200 | 06312 | 06425 | 06537 | 06650 |
| 0.06 | 0.06762 | 06875 | 06987 | 07099 | 07212 | 07324 | 07437 | 07549 | 07661 | 07773 |
| 0.07 | 0.07886 | 07998 | 08110 | 08223 | 08335 | 08447 | 08559 | 08671 | 08784 | 08896 |
| 0.08 | 0.09008 | 09120 | 09232 | 09344 | 09456 | 09568 | 09680 | 09792 | 09904 | 10016 |
| 0.09 | 0.10128 | 10240 | 10352 | 10464 | 10576 | 10687 | 10799 | 10911 | 11023 | 11135 |
| 0.10 | 0.11246 | 11358 | 11470 | 11581 | 11693 | 11805 | 11916 | 12028 | 12139 | 12251 |
| 0.11 | 0.12362 | 12474 | 12585 | 12697 | 12808 | 12919 | 13031 | 13142 | 13253 | 13365 |
| 0.12 | 0.13476 | 13587 | 13698 | 13809 | 13921 | 14032 | 14143 | 14254 | 14365 | 14476 |
| 0.13 | 0.14587 | 14698 | 14809 | 14919 | 15030 | 15141 | 15252 | 15363 | 15473 | 15584 |
| 0.14 | 0.15695 | 15805 | 15916 | 16027 | 16137 | 16248 | 16358 | 16468 | 16579 | 16689 |
| 0.15 | 0.16800 | 16910 | 17020 | 17130 | 17241 | 17351 | 17461 | 17571 | 17681 | 17791 |
| 0.16 | 0.17901 | 18011 | 18121 | 18231 | 18341 | 18451 | 18560 | 18670 | 18780 | 18890 |
| 0.17 | 0.18999 | 19109 | 19218 | 19328 | 19437 | 19547 | 19656 | 19766 | 19875 | 19984 |
| 0.18 | 0.20094 | 20203 | 20312 | 20421 | 20530 | 20639 | 20748 | 20857 | 20966 | 21075 |
| 0.19 | 0.21184 | 21293 | 21402 | 21510 | 21619 | 21728 | 21836 | 21945 | 22053 | 22162 |
| 0.20 | 0.22270 | 22379 | 22487 | 22595 | 22704 | 22812 | 22920 | 23028 | 23136 | 23244 |
| 0.21 | 0.23352 | 23460 | 23568 | 23676 | 23784 | 23891 | 23999 | 24107 | 24214 | 24322 |
| 0.22 | 0.24430 | 24537 | 24645 | 24752 | 24859 | 24967 | 25074 | 25181 | 25288 | 25395 |
| 0.23 | 0.25502 | 25609 | 25716 | 25823 | 25930 | 26037 | 26144 | 26250 | 26357 | 26463 |
| 0.24 | 0.26570 | 26677 | 26783 | 26889 | 26996 | 27102 | 27208 | 27314 | 27421 | 27527 |
| 0.25 | 0.27633 | 27739 | 27845 | 27950 | 28056 | 28162 | 28268 | 28373 | 28479 | 28584 |
| 0.26 | 0.28690 | 28795 | 28901 | 29006 | 29111 | 29217 | 29322 | 29427 | 29532 | 29637 |
| 0.27 | 0.29742 | 29847 | 29952 | 30056 | 30161 | 30266 | 30370 | 30475 | 30579 | 30684 |
| 0.28 | 0.30788 | 30892 | 30997 | 31101 | 31205 | 31309 | 31413 | 31517 | 31621 | 31725 |
| 0.29 | 0.31828 | 31922 | 32036 | 32139 | 32243 | 32346 | 32450 | 32553 | 32656 | 32760 |
| 0.30 | 0.32863 | 32966 | 33069 | 33172 | 33275 | 33378 | 33480 | 33583 | 33686 | 33788 |
| 0.31 | 0.33891 | 33993 | 34096 | 34198 | 34300 | 34403 | 34505 | 34607 | 34709 | 34811 |
| 0.32 | 0.34913 | 35014 | 35116 | 35218 | 35319 | 35421 | 35523 | 35624 | 35725 | 35827 |
| 0.33 | 0.35928 | 36029 | 36130 | 36231 | 36332 | 36433 | 36534 | 36635 | 36735 | 36836 |
| 0.34 | 0.36936 | 37037 | 37137 | 37238 | 37338 | 37438 | 37538 | 37638 | 37738 | 37838 |
| 0.35 | 0.37938 | 38038 | 38138 | 38237 | 38337 | 38436 | 38536 | 38635 | 38735 | 38834 |
| 0.36 | 0.38933 | 39032 | 39131 | 39230 | 39329 | 39428 | 39526 | 39625 | 39724 | 39822 |
| 0.37 | 0.39921 | 40019 | 40117 | 40215 | 40314 | 40412 | 40510 | 40608 | 40705 | 40803 |
| 0.38 | 0.40901 | 40999 | 41096 | 41194 | 41291 | 41388 | 41486 | 41583 | 41680 | 41777 |
| 0.39 | 0.41874 | 41971 | 42068 | 42164 | 42261 | 42358 | 42454 | 42550 | 42647 | 42743 |
| 0.40 | 0.42839 | 42935 | 43031 | 43127 | 43223 | 43319 | 43415 | 43510 | 43606 | 43701 |
| 0.41 | 0.43797 | 43892 | 43988 | 44083 | 44178 | 44273 | 44368 | 44463 | 44557 | 44652 |
| 0.42 | 0.44747 | 44841 | 44936 | 45030 | 45124 | 45219 | 45313 | 45407 | 45501 | 45595 |
| 0.43 | 0.45689 | 45782 | 45876 | 45970 | 46063 | 46157 | 46250 | 46343 | 46436 | 46529 |
| 0.44 | 0.46623 | 46715 | 46808 | 46901 | 46994 | 47086 | 47179 | 47271 | 47364 | 47456 |
| 0.45 | 0.47548 | 47640 | 47732 | 47824 | 47916 | 48008 | 48100 | 48191 | 48283 | 48374 |
| 0.46 | 0.48466 | 48557 | 48648 | 48739 | 48830 | 48921 | 49012 | 49103 | 49193 | 49284 |
| 0.47 | 0.49375 | 49465 | 49555 | 49646 | 49736 | 49826 | 49916 | 50006 | 50096 | 50185 |
| 0.48 | 0.50275 | 50365 | 50454 | 50543 | 50633 | 50722 | 50811 | 50900 | 50989 | 51078 |
| 0.49 | 0.51167 | 51256 | 51344 | 51433 | 51521 | 51609 | 51698 | 51786 | 51874 | 51962 |

# VALUES OF THE PROBABILITY INTEGRAL

$$P = \frac{2}{\sqrt{\pi}} \int_0^t e^{-t^2}dt, \quad \text{where } t = hx.$$

| $hx$ | 0 | 1 | 2 | 3 | 4 | 5 | 6 | 7 | 8 | 9 |
|------|---|---|---|---|---|---|---|---|---|---|
| 0.50 | 0.52050 | 52138 | 52226 | 52313 | 52401 | 52488 | 52576 | 52663 | 52750 | 52837 |
| 0.51 | 0.52924 | 53011 | 53098 | 53185 | 53272 | 53358 | 53445 | 53531 | 53617 | 53704 |
| 0.52 | 0.53790 | 53876 | 53962 | 54048 | 54134 | 54219 | 54305 | 54390 | 54476 | 54561 |
| 0.53 | 0.54646 | 54732 | 54817 | 54902 | 54987 | 55071 | 55156 | 55241 | 55325 | 55410 |
| 0.54 | 0.55494 | 55578 | 55662 | 55746 | 55830 | 55914 | 55998 | 56082 | 56165 | 56249 |
| 0.55 | 0.56332 | 56416 | 56499 | 56582 | 56665 | 56748 | 56831 | 56914 | 56996 | 57079 |
| 0.56 | 0.57162 | 57244 | 57326 | 57409 | 57491 | 57573 | 57655 | 57737 | 57818 | 57900 |
| 0.57 | 0.57982 | 58063 | 58144 | 58226 | 58307 | 58388 | 58469 | 58550 | 58631 | 58712 |
| 0.58 | 0.58792 | 58873 | 58953 | 59034 | 59114 | 59194 | 59274 | 59354 | 59434 | 59514 |
| 0.59 | 0.59594 | 59673 | 59753 | 59832 | 59912 | 59991 | 60070 | 60149 | 60228 | 60307 |
| 0.60 | 0.60386 | 60464 | 60543 | 60621 | 60700 | 60778 | 60856 | 60934 | 61012 | 61090 |
| 0.61 | 0.61168 | 61246 | 61323 | 61401 | 61478 | 61556 | 61633 | 61710 | 61787 | 61864 |
| 0.62 | 0.61941 | 62018 | 62095 | 62171 | 62248 | 62324 | 62400 | 62477 | 62553 | 62629 |
| 0.63 | 0.62705 | 62780 | 62856 | 62932 | 63007 | 63083 | 63158 | 63233 | 63309 | 63384 |
| 0.64 | 0.63459 | 63533 | 63608 | 63683 | 63757 | 63832 | 63906 | 63981 | 64055 | 64129 |
| 0.65 | 0.64203 | 64277 | 64351 | 64424 | 64498 | 64572 | 64645 | 64718 | 64791 | 64865 |
| 0.66 | 0.64938 | 65011 | 65083 | 65156 | 65229 | 65301 | 65374 | 65446 | 65519 | 65591 |
| 0.67 | 0.65663 | 65735 | 65807 | 65878 | 65950 | 66022 | 66093 | 66165 | 66236 | 66307 |
| 0.68 | 0.66378 | 66449 | 66520 | 66591 | 66662 | 66732 | 66803 | 66873 | 66944 | 67014 |
| 0.69 | 0.67084 | 67154 | 67224 | 67294 | 67364 | 67433 | 67503 | 67572 | 67642 | 67711 |
| 0.70 | 0.67780 | 67849 | 67918 | 67987 | 68056 | 68125 | 68193 | 68262 | 68330 | 68398 |
| 0.71 | 0.68467 | 68535 | 68603 | 68671 | 68738 | 68806 | 68874 | 68941 | 69009 | 69076 |
| 0.72 | 0.69143 | 69210 | 69278 | 69344 | 69411 | 69478 | 69545 | 69611 | 69678 | 69744 |
| 0.73 | 0.69810 | 69877 | 69943 | 70009 | 70075 | 70140 | 70206 | 70272 | 70337 | 70403 |
| 0.74 | 0.70468 | 70533 | 70598 | 70663 | 70728 | 70793 | 70858 | 70922 | 70987 | 71051 |
| 0.75 | 0.71116 | 71180 | 71244 | 71308 | 71372 | 71436 | 71500 | 71563 | 71627 | 71690 |
| 0.76 | 0.71754 | 71817 | 71880 | 71943 | 72006 | 72069 | 72132 | 72195 | 72257 | 72320 |
| 0.77 | 0.72382 | 72444 | 72507 | 72569 | 72631 | 72693 | 72755 | 72816 | 72878 | 72940 |
| 0.78 | 0.73001 | 73062 | 73124 | 73185 | 73246 | 73307 | 73368 | 73429 | 73489 | 73550 |
| 0.79 | 0.73610 | 73671 | 73731 | 73791 | 73851 | 73911 | 73971 | 74031 | 74091 | 74151 |
| 0.80 | 0.74210 | 74270 | 74329 | 74388 | 74447 | 74506 | 74565 | 74624 | 74683 | 74742 |
| 0.81 | 0.74800 | 74859 | 74917 | 74976 | 75034 | 75092 | 75150 | 75208 | 75266 | 75323 |
| 0.82 | 0.75381 | 75439 | 75496 | 75553 | 75611 | 75668 | 75725 | 75782 | 75839 | 75896 |
| 0.83 | 0.75952 | 76009 | 76066 | 76122 | 76178 | 76234 | 76291 | 76347 | 76403 | 76459 |
| 0.84 | 0.76514 | 76570 | 76626 | 76681 | 76736 | 76792 | 76847 | 76902 | 76957 | 77012 |
| 0.85 | 0.77067 | 77122 | 77176 | 77231 | 77285 | 77340 | 77394 | 77448 | 77502 | 77556 |
| 0.86 | 0.77610 | 77664 | 77718 | 77771 | 77825 | 77878 | 77932 | 77985 | 78038 | 78091 |
| 0.87 | 0.78144 | 78197 | 78250 | 78302 | 78355 | 78408 | 78460 | 78512 | 78565 | 78617 |
| 0.88 | 0.78669 | 78721 | 78773 | 78824 | 78876 | 78928 | 78979 | 79031 | 79082 | 79133 |
| 0.89 | 0.79184 | 79235 | 79286 | 79337 | 79388 | 79439 | 79489 | 79540 | 79590 | 79641 |
| 0.90 | 0.79691 | 79741 | 79791 | 79841 | 79891 | 79941 | 79990 | 80040 | 80090 | 80139 |
| 0.91 | 0.80188 | 80238 | 80287 | 80336 | 80385 | 80434 | 80482 | 80531 | 80580 | 80628 |
| 0.92 | 0.80677 | 80725 | 80773 | 80822 | 80870 | 80918 | 80966 | 81013 | 81061 | 81109 |
| 0.93 | 0.81156 | 81204 | 81251 | 81299 | 81346 | 81393 | 81440 | 81487 | 81534 | 81580 |
| 0.94 | 0.81627 | 81674 | 81720 | 81767 | 81813 | 81859 | 81905 | 81951 | 81997 | 82043 |
| 0.95 | 0.82089 | 82135 | 82180 | 82226 | 82271 | 82317 | 82362 | 82407 | 82452 | 82497 |
| 0.96 | 0.82542 | 82587 | 82632 | 82677 | 82721 | 82766 | 82810 | 82855 | 82899 | 82943 |
| 0.97 | 0.82987 | 83031 | 83075 | 83119 | 83162 | 83206 | 83250 | 83293 | 83337 | 83380 |
| 0.98 | 0.83423 | 83466 | 83509 | 83552 | 83595 | 83638 | 83681 | 83723 | 83766 | 83808 |
| 0.99 | 0.83851 | 83893 | 83935 | 83977 | 84020 | 84061 | 84103 | 84145 | 84187 | 84229 |

# VALUES OF THE PROBABILITY INTEGRAL

$$P = \frac{2}{\sqrt{\pi}} \int_0^t e^{-t^2}dt, \quad \text{where } t = hx.$$

| hx | 0 | 1 | 2 | 3 | 4 | 5 | 6 | 7 | 8 | 9 |
|------|---|---|---|---|---|---|---|---|---|---|
| 1.00 | 0.84270 | 84312 | 84353 | 84394 | 84435 | 84477 | 84518 | 84559 | 84600 | 84640 |
| 1.01 | 0.84681 | 84722 | 84762 | 84803 | 84843 | 84883 | 84924 | 84964 | 85004 | 85044 |
| 1.02 | 0.85084 | 85124 | 85163 | 85203 | 85243 | 85282 | 85322 | 85361 | 85400 | 85439 |
| 1.03 | 0.85478 | 85517 | 85556 | 85595 | 85634 | 85673 | 85711 | 85750 | 85788 | 85827 |
| 1.04 | 0.85865 | 85903 | 85941 | 85979 | 86017 | 86055 | 86093 | 86131 | 86169 | 86206 |
| 1.05 | 0.86244 | 86281 | 86318 | 86356 | 86393 | 86430 | 86467 | 86504 | 86541 | 86578 |
| 1.06 | 0.86614 | 86651 | 86688 | 86724 | 86760 | 86797 | 86833 | 86869 | 86905 | 86941 |
| 1.07 | 0.86977 | 87013 | 87049 | 87085 | 87120 | 87156 | 87191 | 87227 | 87262 | 87297 |
| 1.08 | 0.87333 | 87368 | 87403 | 87438 | 87473 | 87507 | 87542 | 87577 | 87611 | 87646 |
| 1.09 | 0.87680 | 87715 | 87749 | 87783 | 87817 | 87851 | 87885 | 87919 | 87953 | 87987 |
| 1.10 | 0.88021 | 88054 | 88088 | 88121 | 88155 | 88188 | 88221 | 88254 | 88287 | 88320 |
| 1.11 | 0.88353 | 88386 | 88419 | 88452 | 88484 | 88517 | 88549 | 88582 | 88614 | 88647 |
| 1.12 | 0.88679 | 88711 | 88743 | 88775 | 88807 | 88839 | 88871 | 88902 | 88934 | 88966 |
| 1.13 | 0.88997 | 89029 | 89060 | 89091 | 89122 | 89154 | 89185 | 89216 | 89247 | 89277 |
| 1.14 | 0.89308 | 89339 | 89370 | 89400 | 89431 | 89461 | 89492 | 89522 | 89552 | 89582 |
| 1.15 | 0.89612 | 89642 | 89672 | 89702 | 89732 | 89762 | 89792 | 89821 | 89851 | 89880 |
| 1.16 | 0.89910 | 89939 | 89968 | 89997 | 90027 | 90056 | 90085 | 90114 | 90142 | 90171 |
| 1.17 | 0.90200 | 90229 | 90257 | 90286 | 90314 | 90343 | 90371 | 90399 | 90428 | 90456 |
| 1.18 | 0.90484 | 90512 | 90540 | 90568 | 90595 | 90623 | 90651 | 90678 | 90706 | 90733 |
| 1.19 | 0.90761 | 90788 | 90815 | 90843 | 90870 | 90897 | 90924 | 90951 | 90978 | 91005 |
| 1.20 | 0.91031 | 91058 | 91085 | 91111 | 91138 | 91164 | 91191 | 91217 | 91243 | 91269 |
| 1.21 | 0.91296 | 91322 | 91348 | 91374 | 91399 | 91425 | 91451 | 91477 | 91502 | 91528 |
| 1.22 | 0.91553 | 91579 | 91604 | 91630 | 91655 | 91680 | 91705 | 91730 | 91755 | 91780 |
| 1.23 | 0.91805 | 91830 | 91855 | 91879 | 91904 | 91929 | 91953 | 91978 | 92002 | 92026 |
| 1.24 | 0.92051 | 92075 | 92099 | 92123 | 92147 | 92171 | 92195 | 92219 | 92243 | 92266 |
| 1.25 | 0.92290 | 92314 | 92337 | 92361 | 92384 | 92408 | 92431 | 92454 | 92477 | 92500 |
| 1.26 | 0.92524 | 92547 | 92570 | 92593 | 92615 | 92638 | 92661 | 92684 | 92706 | 92729 |
| 1.27 | 0.92751 | 92774 | 92796 | 92819 | 92841 | 92863 | 92885 | 92907 | 92929 | 92951 |
| 1.28 | 0.92973 | 92995 | 93017 | 93039 | 93061 | 93082 | 93104 | 93126 | 93147 | 93168 |
| 1.29 | 0.93190 | 93211 | 93232 | 93254 | 93275 | 93296 | 93317 | 93338 | 93359 | 93380 |
| 1.30 | 0.93401 | 93422 | 93442 | 93463 | 93484 | 93504 | 93525 | 93545 | 93566 | 93586 |
| 1.31 | 0.93606 | 93627 | 93647 | 93667 | 93687 | 93707 | 93727 | 93747 | 93767 | 93787 |
| 1.32 | 0.93807 | 93826 | 93846 | 93866 | 93885 | 93905 | 93924 | 93944 | 93963 | 93982 |
| 1.33 | 0.94002 | 94021 | 94040 | 94059 | 94078 | 94097 | 94116 | 94135 | 94154 | 94173 |
| 1.34 | 0.94191 | 94210 | 94229 | 94247 | 94266 | 94284 | 94303 | 94321 | 94340 | 94358 |
| 1.35 | 0.94376 | 94394 | 94413 | 94431 | 94449 | 94467 | 94485 | 94503 | 94521 | 94538 |
| 1.36 | 0.94556 | 94574 | 94592 | 94609 | 94627 | 94644 | 94662 | 94679 | 94697 | 94714 |
| 1.37 | 0.94731 | 94748 | 94766 | 94783 | 94800 | 94817 | 94834 | 94851 | 94868 | 94885 |
| 1.38 | 0.94902 | 94918 | 94935 | 94952 | 94968 | 94985 | 95002 | 95018 | 95035 | 95051 |
| 1.39 | 0.95067 | 95084 | 95100 | 95116 | 95132 | 95148 | 95165 | 95181 | 95197 | 95213 |
| 1.40 | 0.95229 | 95244 | 95260 | 95276 | 95292 | 95307 | 95323 | 95339 | 95354 | 95370 |
| 1.41 | 0.95385 | 95401 | 95416 | 95431 | 95447 | 95462 | 95477 | 95492 | 95507 | 95523 |
| 1.42 | 0.95538 | 95553 | 95568 | 95582 | 95597 | 95612 | 95627 | 95642 | 95656 | 95671 |
| 1.43 | 0.95686 | 95700 | 95715 | 95729 | 95744 | 95758 | 95773 | 95787 | 95801 | 95815 |
| 1.44 | 0.95830 | 95844 | 95858 | 95872 | 95886 | 95900 | 95914 | 95928 | 95942 | 95956 |
| 1.45 | 0.95970 | 95983 | 95997 | 96011 | 96024 | 96038 | 96051 | 96065 | 96078 | 96092 |
| 1.46 | 0.96105 | 96119 | 96132 | 96145 | 96159 | 96172 | 96185 | 96198 | 96211 | 96224 |
| 1.47 | 0.96237 | 96250 | 96263 | 96276 | 96289 | 96302 | 96315 | 96327 | 96340 | 96353 |
| 1.48 | 0.96365 | 96378 | 96391 | 96403 | 96416 | 96428 | 96440 | 96453 | 96465 | 96478 |
| 1.49 | 0.96490 | 96502 | 96514 | 96526 | 96539 | 96551 | 96563 | 96575 | 96587 | 96599 |

# VALUES OF THE PROBABILITY INTEGRAL

$$P = \frac{2}{\sqrt{\pi}} \int_0^t e^{-t^2}dt, \text{ where } t = hx.$$

| hx | 0 | 2 | 4 | 6 | 8 | hx | 0 | 2 | 4 | 6 | 8 |
|---|---|---|---|---|---|---|---|---|---|---|---|
| 1.50 | 0.96611 | 96634 | 96658 | 96681 | 96705 | 2.00 | 0.99532 | 99536 | 99540 | 99544 | 99548 |
| 1.51 | 0.96728 | 96751 | 96774 | 96796 | 96819 | 2.01 | 0.99552 | 99556 | 99560 | 99564 | 99568 |
| 1.52 | 0.96841 | 96864 | 96886 | 96908 | 96930 | 2.02 | 0.99572 | 99576 | 99580 | 99583 | 99587 |
| 1.53 | 0.96952 | 96973 | 96995 | 97016 | 97037 | 2.03 | 0.99591 | 99594 | 99598 | 99601 | 99605 |
| 1.54 | 0.97059 | 97080 | 97100 | 97121 | 97142 | 2.04 | 0.99609 | 99612 | 99616 | 99619 | 99622 |
| 1.55 | 0.97162 | 97183 | 97203 | 97223 | 97243 | 2.05 | 0.99626 | 99629 | 99633 | 99636 | 99639 |
| 1.56 | 0.97263 | 97283 | 97302 | 97322 | 97341 | 2.06 | 0.99642 | 99646 | 99649 | 99652 | 99655 |
| 1.57 | 0.97360 | 97379 | 97398 | 97417 | 97436 | 2.07 | 0.99658 | 99661 | 99664 | 99667 | 99670 |
| 1.58 | 0.97455 | 97473 | 97492 | 97510 | 97528 | 2.08 | 0.99673 | 99676 | 99679 | 99682 | 99685 |
| 1.59 | 0.97546 | 97564 | 97582 | 97600 | 97617 | 2.09 | 0.99688 | 99691 | 99694 | 99697 | 99699 |
| 1.60 | 0.97635 | 97652 | 97670 | 97687 | 97704 | 2.10 | 0.99702 | 99705 | 99707 | 99710 | 99713 |
| 1.61 | 0.97721 | 97738 | 97754 | 97771 | 97787 | 2.11 | 0.99715 | 99718 | 99721 | 99723 | 99726 |
| 1.62 | 0.97804 | 97820 | 97836 | 97852 | 97868 | 2.12 | 0.99728 | 99731 | 99733 | 99736 | 99738 |
| 1.63 | 0.97884 | 97900 | 97916 | 97931 | 97947 | 2.13 | 0.99741 | 99743 | 99745 | 99748 | 99750 |
| 1.64 | 0.97962 | 97977 | 97993 | 98008 | 98023 | 2.14 | 0.99753 | 99755 | 99757 | 99759 | 99762 |
| 1.65 | 0.98038 | 98052 | 98067 | 98082 | 98096 | 2.15 | 0.99764 | 99766 | 99768 | 99770 | 99773 |
| 1.66 | 0.98110 | 98125 | 98139 | 98153 | 98167 | 2.16 | 0.99775 | 99777 | 99779 | 99781 | 99783 |
| 1.67 | 0.98181 | 98195 | 98209 | 98222 | 98236 | 2.17 | 0.99785 | 99787 | 99789 | 99791 | 99793 |
| 1.68 | 0.98249 | 98263 | 98276 | 98289 | 98302 | 2.18 | 0.99795 | 99797 | 99799 | 99801 | 99803 |
| 1.69 | 0.98315 | 98328 | 98341 | 98354 | 98366 | 2.19 | 0.99805 | 99806 | 99808 | 99810 | 99812 |
| 1.70 | 0.98379 | 98392 | 98404 | 98416 | 98429 | 2.20 | 0.99814 | 99815 | 99817 | 99819 | 99821 |
| 1.71 | 0.98441 | 98453 | 98465 | 98477 | 98489 | 2.21 | 0.99822 | 99824 | 99826 | 99827 | 99829 |
| 1.72 | 0.98500 | 98512 | 98524 | 98535 | 98546 | 2.22 | 0.99831 | 99832 | 99834 | 99836 | 99837 |
| 1.73 | 0.98558 | 98569 | 98580 | 98591 | 98602 | 2.23 | 0.99839 | 99840 | 99842 | 99843 | 99845 |
| 1.74 | 0.98613 | 98624 | 98635 | 98646 | 98657 | 2.24 | 0.99846 | 99848 | 99849 | 99851 | 99852 |
| 1.75 | 0.98667 | 98678 | 98688 | 98699 | 98709 | 2.25 | 0.99854 | 99855 | 99857 | 99858 | 99859 |
| 1.76 | 0.98719 | 98729 | 98739 | 98749 | 98759 | 2.26 | 0.99861 | 99862 | 99863 | 99865 | 99866 |
| 1.77 | 0.98769 | 98779 | 98789 | 98798 | 98808 | 2.27 | 0.99867 | 99869 | 99870 | 99871 | 99873 |
| 1.78 | 0.98817 | 98827 | 98836 | 98846 | 98855 | 2.28 | 0.99874 | 99875 | 99876 | 99877 | 99879 |
| 1.79 | 0.98864 | 98873 | 98882 | 98891 | 98900 | 2.29 | 0.99880 | 99881 | 99882 | 99883 | 99885 |
| 1.80 | 0.98909 | 98918 | 98927 | 98935 | 98944 | 2.30 | 0.99886 | 99887 | 99888 | 99889 | 99890 |
| 1.81 | 0.98952 | 98961 | 98969 | 98978 | 98986 | 2.31 | 0.99891 | 99892 | 99893 | 99894 | 99896 |
| 1.82 | 0.98994 | 99003 | 99011 | 99019 | 99027 | 2.32 | 0.99897 | 99898 | 99899 | 99900 | 99901 |
| 1.83 | 0.99035 | 99043 | 99050 | 99058 | 99066 | 2.33 | 0.99902 | 99903 | 99904 | 99905 | 99906 |
| 1.84 | 0.99074 | 99081 | 99089 | 99096 | 99104 | 2.34 | 0.99906 | 99907 | 99908 | 99909 | 99910 |
| 1.85 | 0.99111 | 99118 | 99126 | 99133 | 99140 | 2.35 | 0.99911 | 99912 | 99913 | 99914 | 99915 |
| 1.86 | 0.99147 | 99154 | 99161 | 99168 | 99175 | 2.36 | 0.99915 | 99916 | 99917 | 99918 | 99919 |
| 1.87 | 0.99182 | 99189 | 99196 | 99202 | 99209 | 2.37 | 0.99920 | 99920 | 99921 | 99922 | 99923 |
| 1.88 | 0.99216 | 99222 | 99229 | 99235 | 99242 | 2.38 | 0.99924 | 99924 | 99925 | 99926 | 99927 |
| 1.89 | 0.99248 | 99254 | 99261 | 99267 | 99273 | 2.39 | 0.99928 | 99928 | 99929 | 99930 | 99930 |
| 1.90 | 0.99279 | 99285 | 99291 | 99297 | 99303 | 2.40 | 0.99931 | 99932 | 99933 | 99933 | 99934 |
| 1.91 | 0.99309 | 99315 | 99321 | 99326 | 99332 | 2.41 | 0.99935 | 99935 | 99936 | 99937 | 99937 |
| 1.92 | 0.99338 | 99343 | 99349 | 99355 | 99360 | 2.42 | 0.99938 | 99939 | 99939 | 99940 | 99940 |
| 1.93 | 0.99366 | 99371 | 99376 | 99382 | 99387 | 2.43 | 0.99941 | 99942 | 99942 | 99943 | 99943 |
| 1.94 | 0.99392 | 99397 | 99403 | 99408 | 99413 | 2.44 | 0.99944 | 99945 | 99945 | 99946 | 99946 |
| 1.95 | 0.99418 | 99423 | 99428 | 99433 | 99438 | 2.45 | 0.99947 | 99947 | 99948 | 99949 | 99949 |
| 1.96 | 0.99443 | 99447 | 99452 | 99457 | 99462 | 2.46 | 0.99950 | 99950 | 99951 | 99951 | 99952 |
| 1.97 | 0.99466 | 99471 | 99476 | 99480 | 99485 | 2.47 | 0.99952 | 99953 | 99953 | 99954 | 99954 |
| 1.98 | 0.99489 | 99494 | 99498 | 99502 | 99507 | 2.48 | 0.99955 | 99955 | 99956 | 99956 | 99957 |
| 1.99 | 0.99511 | 99515 | 99520 | 99524 | 99528 | 2.49 | 0.99957 | 99958 | 99958 | 99958 | 99959 |
| 2.00 | 0.99532 | 99536 | 99540 | 99544 | 99548 | 2.50 | 0.99959 | 99960 | 99960 | 99961 | 99961 |

# VALUES OF THE PROBABILITY INTEGRAL

$$P = \frac{2}{\sqrt{\pi}} \int_0^t e^{-t^2} dt, \quad \text{where } t = hx.$$

| $hx$ | 0 | 1 | 2 | 3 | 4 | 5 | 6 | 7 | 8 | 9 |
|------|-----|-----|-----|-----|-----|-----|-----|-----|-----|-----|
| 2.5 | 0.99959 | 99961 | 99963 | 99965 | 99967 | 99969 | 99971 | 99972 | 99974 | 99975 |
| 2.6 | 0.99976 | 99978 | 99979 | 99980 | 99981 | 99982 | 99983 | 99984 | 99985 | 99986 |
| 2.7 | 0.99987 | 99987 | 99988 | 99989 | 99989 | 99990 | 99991 | 99991 | 99992 | 99992 |
| 2.8 | 0.99992 | 99993 | 99993 | 99994 | 99994 | 99994 | 99995 | 99995 | 99995 | 99996 |
| 2.9 | 0.99996 | 99996 | 99996 | 99997 | 99997 | 99997 | 99997 | 99997 | 99997 | 99998 |
| 3.0 | 0.99998 | 99998 | 99998 | 99998 | 99998 | 99998 | 99998 | 99998 | 99999 | 99999 |

# INDEX

(The numbers refer to pages)